Understanding Distributed Processor Systems for Control

By Samuel M. Herb, P.E.

67 Alexander Drive
P.O. Box 12277
Research Triangle Park, NC 27709

Printed in the United States of America.
10 9 8 7 6 5 4 3 2 1

ISBN 1-55617-645-7

Library of Congress Cataloging-in-Publication Data

Herb, S. M. (Samuel M.)
Understanding distributed processor systems for control / by Sam Herb.
p. cm.
Includes bibliographical references and index.
ISBN 1-55617-645-7
1. Process control–Data processing. 2. Electronic data Processing–distributed processing. I. Title.
TS156.8H47 1999
670.4275–dc21 98-38912

Dedication

I dedicate this book to my family, Sam, Corinne, David, Beth, and especially my long suffering young wife, Judy! No stranger to ISA work, at my suggestion she became the editor of the Philadelphia section's Transducer, transforming it from a meeting notice into a sixteen-page journal that was sustained by the advertising. In that role she became something of a den mother to the section, which had to happen to keep the darn thing on schedule. (Den mother is the title on the clock the section gave her, but also the official job she had with our sons in Scouts same function, different age group.) At the suggestion of Ross Forman and other members of the section, she has also been the registrar of the education program certification system since its inception, two and a half decades ago.

Judy kept me on track through the very difficult process of starting and staying with this project which lasted over four years. Her gentle prodding and patient listening gave this project substance and form. More directly, she suggested that I dictate into a tape recorder the copious stray notes from over fifteen years of developing and teaching the course this book is intended to accompany. She then translated all of that spoken text into something written ("spoken" and "written" are quite different, you know). Using our trusty old Macintosh, Judy transformed well over 140,000 words into a document that could actually be read. My computer tells me this took nearly a million characters in over 15,000 single-spaced lines clustered into 4,800 paragraphs on 450 pages of draft. Tell me if that isn't more than just moral support!

Because of her blood, sweat, and tears and ability to be a tremendous sounding board and consultant for me, I think of Judy as the co-author. Though she was not trained as an engineer, her way of thinking would have made her a good one. In performing all these activities, Judy picked up quite a bit about the essence of process control. That helped her critique this work from the audience's viewpoint and provide some excellent inspiration for creative explanations. She watched the draft go painfully out on review, knowing it still needed grammatical work but understood it could be improved later. I apologize to her for the appearance of that final effort, because I unexpectedly had to do this last part alone. Judy was really the one who was good at editing, assuring good flow and proper sense. More than a mother, wife, lover and dynamic teammate, she was my very best friend. I wish she could have lived to see this book in her hands. I believe, however, that she feels my relief that it actually made it into print. Thank you for everything, Judy.

"Pari Passu"
(Done together)

Sam

Preface

Why the Title of This Book?

I struggled with the title for this book and created something of a controversy among my reviewers as well as several others with whom I consulted. My first book was called *Understanding Distributed Process Control* written with Scotty Moore. It went with a course created with the same name, back in 1980. I would have liked to have given this book the same name, except for a peculiar marketing event that occurred in the mid 1990s. A major vendor tried to make a "product distinction" from another major vendor and claimed that its own distributed control system (DCS) was no longer a DCS, that all DCSs were obsolete! Now, all of the processors were still distributed within that system, and it still was used to control. Furthermore, most of the major vendors of DCSs by that time could also do much more than process control with their respective systems.

Nevertheless, so as not to look obsolete, everyone else jumped on the bandwagon and declared that they also no longer sold DCSs, but rather some vast plant management system. I am reminded of the old story about the emperor's new clothes. Meanwhile, people stopped signing up for my DCS course, some stating that such a topic was obsolete. After renaming the course to coincide with the current title of this book, sign-ups were as high as ever! Sigh! Who says that engineers and managers are never swayed by a marketing blitz? By the way, I had an opportunity to talk to the product manager of the advertised "non-DCS" and asked him what he did call their system? He candidly told me he didn't know, and was not happy with that.

I reasoned that, if anything, given the advances in microprocessors, small processing modules now permeated the entire system in ways never envisioned when the idea of DCS first started. They are in the sensors, and throughout the business side (*enterprise* is the current buzzword). This book primarily addresses the challenges of the process control effort, but we can no longer speak of this in isolation from factory automation systems. The systems and their functions are indeed merging. Discrete, continuous and batch can be performed together, or certainly by the same system used in diverse applications. What is said in this book can easily apply to factory automation systems as well as process. In fact, it applies to any system that has multiple processors within one system. Hence this book's much broader implied title, *Understanding Distributed Processor Systems for (as applied to) Control*.

What about the Rapidly Changing Technology?

It is impossible to put anything on paper about any high technology subject without becoming obsolete before the ink is dry. The concepts, however, are still the same, they have just grown to encompass new and exciting nuances. In reality, however, this book must also cover all of the past technologies because students also come to the course this book is based on to learn about the system already in their plant. This has to be true of the readers of this book as well.

As a guess, there are well over two hundred thousand "old" systems in the marketplace that are operating just fine but have a new generation of people looking after them. These people want to learn why those systems work as they do. It is far easier to understand them if you know their evolution, and how the limits of technology over the years have forced some unique improvisations, which established a "tradition." Learning which traditions reflect those technology limits and which traditions are still valid because of the fundamental characteristics of process control is essential to good operating strategy.

It is also necessary to understand the existing system to gain the proper perspective when deciding to purchase the latest system. Many "stupid" requests for bids have emerged when people with mainframe computer experience would merely ask for "the same, but distributed." Understanding the new differences is necessary so you can make logical requests. You do not want to ask for something that causes unnecessary expense any more than you want to *fail* to ask for something that is now easy to do but was once costly.

Who Is the Intended Reader?

The reason I use the word *understanding* in the book title is because I believe you (the reader, and perhaps the student in the course) are already experienced and knowledgeable, perhaps even a Ph.D., but you have not necessarily been exposed to the technologies and issues I talk about in this book. Perhaps you are a biologist, or a purchasing agent, but do not have an instrumentation background. Many additional people come into the field of instrumentation who do not have engineering degrees, and even have little knowledge of computers. I know this from the many attendees of the course for which this was written.

In teaching this course, I have had many cultures as an audience: nationalistic, geographic, professional discipline-specific, industry-specific, corporate-specific, and beyond. Some of the same words mean different things to different backgrounds. The topics as well as the descriptions used in the content are a pragmatic response to the many questions that actually occurred, and often reoccur in the classroom over the years. Some of the information and explanations may not be new to those readers who have been around the industry for many years. That same information and explanations, however, have been very useful to the many who have just begun their exposure to the outburst of technology in the venerable measurements and control field. For this reason, the approach of this book is an effort to try to assume *nothing*, and describe even basic concepts, but hopefully in a way that those who already know such things can easily skip past those parts, or be amused by our simplistic explanations. Remember, NO ONE knows *everything* about instrumentation or process control, certainly including the author. Anyone who tells you otherwise is either a fool or a liar!

Sam Herb
New Britain, PA
April, 1998

Illustrations in this book are intended to be consistent to the ISA course by the same name. Many of the illustrations are based upon the slides from that course. The sequence of the course is intended to follow the same order as the book.

About The Author

Samuel M. Herb, P.E. is currently with Moore Process Automation Solutions, Spring House, Pennsylvania. He previously worked with Leeds & Northrup (North Wales, Pennsylvania) and Honeywell (Ft. Washington, Pennsylvania), and has been in the utility and process controls industries for nearly four decades. He has performed various roles in marketing, business development, control applications, product management, systems engineering, project management, product evaluation, technical publications, and education.

Background ranges from design and testing of components within instrumentation, to responsibility for overall product line viability. Experience includes sensors, transmitters, pneumatic and electric controllers, final control elements, indicators and recorders, each as individual products as well as their combined use within systems. For over two decades, he has been primarily involved with microprocessor-based distributed process control systems.

Mr. Herb holds a bachelor's of science degree in electrical engineering from Drexel University, and is a member of the Industrial Computing Society as well as ISA. He served six years on the faculty of Spring Garden College, Pennsylvania and has served as a consultant to several companies. The author of dozens of journal articles and technical papers, both domestically and internationally, for a variety of professional societies and technical publications. Mr. Herb has developed and presented internationally seminars and courses in instrumentation for over two decades. He is a member of the ISA SP95 committee, a consultant on several ISA videotape series, and coauthored the textbook *Understanding Distributed Process Control*.

Acknowledgments

The material used for this book has accumulated over three decades. I truly do not know where it all came from. It reflects what I have learned from so many coworkers and especially from students. I apologize if I overlooked anyone, and if anyone finds something they feel they should have been given credit for, please let me know and I assure you it will be in the next edition.

Lynn Craig of MAA Inc. and Kevin Chance of Moore Process Automation Solutions provided me with information about batch control. My understanding of the IEC 61131 languages was taught to me by John Robinson and Ed Rutter of Moore Products. Communication ideas came from Mike Tudisco, Mike Horn, and Mike Hogan of Moore Products Along with fields concepts this books communication ideas were also inspired by Bill Hodson, formerly of Leeds & Northrup and MAX Control Systems, and now with Honeywell. Bill Goble with help from John Cusimano, both of Moore Products, was the principle source of my education in critical systems. Along with Dave Stokes formerly with Leeds & Northrup (UK) and now with Asea Brown Boveri (UK) Bill Gobble also gave me many ideas for diagnostic systems. Phil Bur, formerly of Honeywell and now with Moore Products, worked together with me to design some operator station requirements. Bob Hubby, formerly with Leeds & Northrup and now with MAX Control Systems, spent many a bull session with me on human-machine interface, as did my longtime friend Renzo Dallimonti, now retired from Honeywell. Hundreds of conversations with Renzo since the early 1970s have helped me understand the many facets and implications of distributed control systems (DCS). I learned of the trauma of specifying systems from many experiences and people, including my colleague Scotty Moore, now retired from Leeds & Northrup; George Mabry, formerly of Honeywell and now with Sharp Design, and Ross Forman, now retired from Day & Zimmerman; Bill Shaw, formerly of EMC Controls, who I never met and whose affiliation I am uncertain of, authored a little booklet entitled "From Specification to Plant Installation," once published for EMC, that seemed to confirm all I had learned from many others. Larry Goettsch put together the first iteration of the large vendor comparison table in Chapter 43 from ideas we frequently shared at Leeds & Northrup. A lot of subtle learning came from Harold Wade of Wade Associates.

If you hadn't noticed by the way I described my contact points with the people I thank in these acknowledgments, the process control business seems to be a rather incestuous industry, especially in the Philadelphia area. We don't particularly exchange proprietary secrets, but through the ISA, Scouting, various youth groups, schools, and places of worship, we meet and exchange ideas. We quite literally learn from each other, teach each other, and have no idea who "owns" the stuff! That is why it is so hard to give adequate credit.

However, one gentleman, who was very instrumental in causing this book is Scotty Moore, who coauthored with me the first book devoted exclusively to distributed control back in 1982. I had all these lecture notes, and he had all this experience since

1944 with pneumatic, electric, electronic, and then digital control. He also had a new IBM PC and a WordStar processor program he was just itching to use. With support from Jim Fahnstock, Larry Heine, and Paul Taylor, all of Leeds & Northrup (and now of MAX Controls Systems) that first effort was brought forth and called *Understanding Distributed Process Control.* Scotty provided the overwhelming effort needed to make that book happen and inspired me to bring about this one.

Thank you, everyone.

..Sam 4/98

Table of Contents

Part A
Introduction

Purpose of This Book 1

In the preface of this book we talked of why the title reads "..Distributed Processor Systems for Control" instead of its original title "..Distributed Process Control Systems." We also discussed the nature of the expected readers, and their circumstances. In this chapter, we come to the reason the title begins with the word "Understanding..." as well as what issues are involved.

Figure 1-1. What System to Select?

Can This Book Tell Me Which Control System I Should Buy?

In all likelihood your boss sent you to this book to find out which system to buy and commissioned you to return with the answer. You will be expected to turn out a flawless specification to get the ideal system. *This book will provide no such answers*! Go back to ISA and get another, if you think *any* book can do this.

What this book does hope to give you, however, is at least the ability to know what are the right *questions*. If we are successful, you will return to your boss with many more questions than you had at the beginning. These should give you a running start on how to efficiently go about discovering what you will really need.

Will This Book Tell Me How to Find Out?

Buying any system is like buying an automobile—no one can make the decision for you. You must first take a serious look at how you will *use* it before you begin. Otherwise, you will surely waste your money. Even if you are not reading this book in order to *buy* a system, if you pretend that you are while you are reading and you will learn much more. If you are in fact buying a system, we have included a section—Part J, "Control System Implementation," that should help you bring all the pieces together.

Buying a control system and buying an automobile both require you to ask some critical questions. When buying a car you must first ask, "How is it to be used?" Driving to and from work? Must it hold the whole family on outings? How big is this family? Must it be used to carry large items from the hardware store? Is it used only for pleasure? In what part of the country will it be used?

These kind of questions will determine if you buy a small or large vehicle, a sedan or pickup truck, a station wagon or a van, four-wheel drive or a sports car, and so on. When you understand the *function*, you can move on to the brand(s) that make the most appropriate versions, are the most durable, are the least costly, have the best service record, have the most convenient dealers, and many similar issues. Only then you will be ready for smaller features, such as color and convenience items.

To Start, You Must Look at the Issues...

What is the purpose of the specific system? What do you want it to do for your plant? This obvious questioning is often overlooked! Everybody knows the current system you are probably using must be upgraded, but *why* should it be upgraded? Specifically, what will it do differently than before? Since the introduction of the microprocessor in every type of controller, very unique and powerful capabilities have become available for even the smallest operation. We cannot afford to do process control the same way as before!

You should expect any control system today to improve production, product consistency, operating efficiency, safety, and cost of operations. It is imperative in the very beginning of the project to define on paper an agreed-upon statement spelling out exactly what improvements *of the process* are expected from the system. You must also provide some sort of cost analysis of the value those improvements give you so as to justify the investment required.

In other words, the *real* reason you buy a distributed control system (DCS) is to improve plant *productivity*. Any control system, by whatever name, *must* contribute to that productivity! We will return this productivity theme throughout the course of this book to show you where new technologies allow improvements that could not even be considered in the past.

Productivity is the real bottom line—not all those cute new features that the vendor claims are the panacea for your problems. Don't confuse the hype of cute features, with *real* technical advantages. Sometimes the hype overlooks the real value of these same features!

But look at all the things that are working *against* productivity (Figure 1-2)! Factors that have a legitimate impact on all businesses include social pressures, changes in workforces, government regulations, cost of energy, and environmental effects. Perhaps the greatest impediment is the ever-changing technology! The control system must overcome all of these and also be flexible enough to overcome new ones that have not yet happened—ones that we do not even know about. Throughout the book, to help point out some of the many subtle issues that contribute to productivity and cost savings, I will use a little icon of a moneybag.

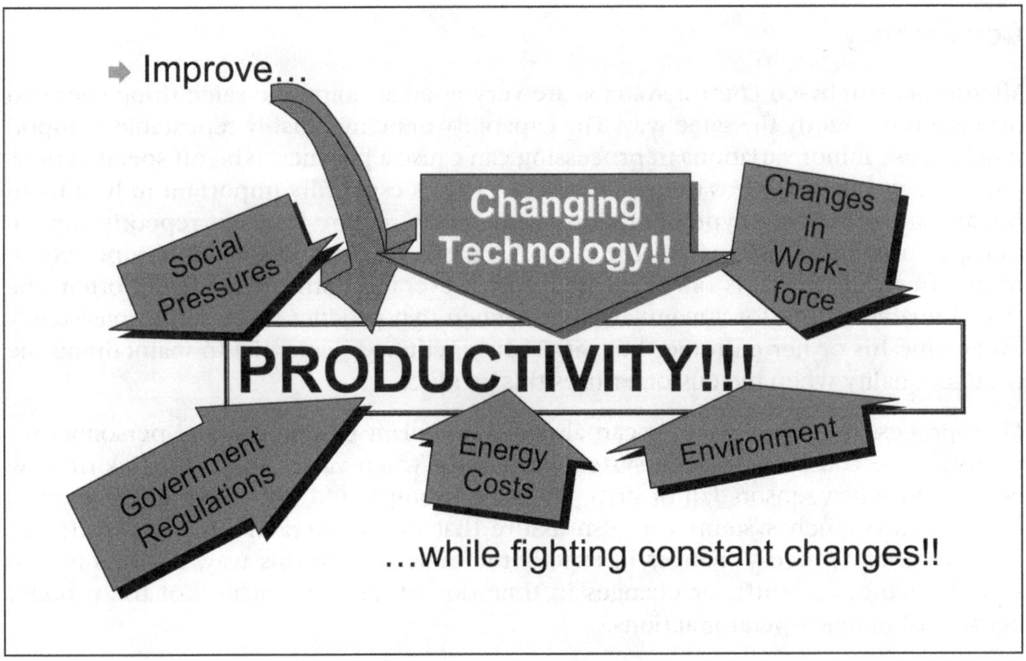

Figure 1-2. Many Factors Work Against Productivity

There Must be Goals for Improving a Plant Control System

Since the advent of the microprocessor into every type of process controller, very unique and powerful capabilities have become available for even the smallest operation. We can now improve production, product consistency, operating efficiency, safety, and cost of operations.

Production

Microprocessor control can optimize the production schedule and equipment assignments to achieve the best available product throughput with the optimal use of equipment. For example, in operations that have multiple units in a particular stage of a process, the equipment can keep track of the hours the equipment is in use and alert the operator when it is time for a cleaning or maintenance shutdown. The system then can redirect the process flow through the alternate equipment while this cleaning or maintenance takes place. Cleaning or maintenance will occur as needed, rather than on some arbitrary time schedule, which usually wastes of replacement parts, as well as the time and energy lost in unnecessary downtimes.

Microprocessor-based systems are also quite capable of prompting the operator when the production flow deviates from normal or begins to drift from recognized limits. This allows the operator to be on top of the process flow and make fine-tuning adjustments as needed to keep production flowing smoothly. Quite often, the control system can make some of these adjustments both automatically and consistently without requiring the intervention of the operator.

Consistency

Microprocessor-based control systems are very good at doing the same thing over and over again in exactly the same way. The capability of being reliably repeatable is important because minor variations in processing can cause a product to be off specifications and to be worth much less than it should be. This is especially important in heat treating and any other batchtype operations, which may require frequent repetitive operations, an operation that ensures the correct ingredients are added in the proper order, or an operation which is only repeated every several months or so. Quite often, the most valuable output for a manufacturer is when that product is the same consistency every time his or her customer buys it. That repetition is essential to maintaining the product quality when the customer uses this product.

Microprocessor control systems can also monitor plant equipment and personnel for performance consistency. Such systems can warn when valves begin to stick or slow down, and when sensors fail or drift. By using prompts and improved information to the operators, such systems can also assure that every operator on every shift can respond to any process changes in exactly the same way. In this way, changes in personnel, changes in shift, or changes in time do not alter the quality of the product because of unique operator actions.

Efficiency

Microprocessor controls not only allow the use and management of more process loop or discrete control actions but also the use of flexible control strategies. Quite often, the concept of a control strategy was not new, but it was never practical because of the limitations of the earlier control equipment. Because it is now more practical to configure cascade loops, which were not easy to do in the past, it is now possible to use control strategies that interlock various control loops. Now temperatures, pressures, flows, and levels can be monitored more precisely, allowing tighter controls and reducing wasted product. This is especially true when trying to achieve more precisely blended ingredients of a product so there is less waste due to the proper ratio of the ingredients.

Microprocessor controls also allow the control of any excess energy so energy is not wasted in a product. With improvements in sensors, particularly where analyzers can be online, a continuous signal can now be fed back to the controller, enabling the governing of operations that were not practical before. Examples of these operations include measuring the composition of stack gases for the correction of the fuel/air ratio in burner management, pH for control in boiler processes, chemical reactions, and the pharmaceutical industry, and the monitoring and controlling of relative humidity to help reduce corrosion of equipment. Many other unique control strategies provide greatly improved efficiency in overall production.

Safety

There are three safety issues: the safety of the plant, the safety of the product, and the safety of the personnel in the operations. If a valve sticks open too much and too much raw material is used, if a level doesn't rise once a fill valve is opened or if the temperature starts rising too fast, the microprocessor control system can initiate a fail-safe procedure automatically. Moreover, it can also record the operator actions, the control actions, and the process response to those actions, so that in the event of a failure the steps leading to the failure can be analyzed and failure avoided in the future.

> The control system can often be used to double-check direct measurements by computing an expected result from a related measurement. For example, the flow into a vessel could be checked by examining the level changes in that vessel. A temperature rise also may be seen in a pressure change, and so on.

In another circumstance, if an operator misses an entry of some value by a decimal point, the system can compare the reasonableness of that entry. The system will prompt the operator with a signal to assure that the entry is truly the desired one before the action is implemented. Of course, the control systems themselves have checks and balances to monitor their own failures. This includes redundant systems that are far easier and more economical to implement in today's control systems than they were in the past.

Cost

Especially when an existing plant is being targeted for an upgrade, a justification must be done to assure that the advantages provided by the new system will in fact be an improvement over the current control capabilities. Quite often the microprocessor-based system is considerably less expensive than the conventional instrumentation that it replaces.

The cost loop by loop is not enough for a complete analysis. Consider the equivalent cost to perform the additional functions that can be inexpensively done with microprocessors, such as the following:

- Automatic sequential control capabilities
- Proper management of additional data for sensible, informed operator actions
- The use of considerably more annunciation to gain a better understanding of the process

- Tremendous capability to keep records and manage data
- Expanded opportunities to make process comparisons for product improvements that were never before possible or realized.

Investing in the new system generally is far cheaper than any existing system it will replace.

Distributed System Issues

Several issues that impact distributed systems are as follows:

- Problems of open standards
- Impact of fieldbus
- Configuration made easy
- Significance to batching functions
- Inclusion of safety systems
- Challenge of advanced control methods.

Dilemmas to Resolve Using Distributed Processor Systems

The tools used on the road to increased productivity present us with some real dilemmas. We cannot make light of them, but we can at least acknowledge them. In this book, we will attempt to put these issues into some perspective as we go through the search for the most appropriate system for your plant.

How open is "open"? Initially, proprietary systems provided far more efficient solutions for real-time control and simple configuration. Unfortunately, however, no one company can "do it all," and the cost of proprietary systems is prohibitive. More and more, corporations ("enterprises" is now the current buzzword) want to avoid being held hostage to a single vendor. These corporations also have the very real problem of communicating between several systems from different vendors and of different vintages.

New architectures are emerging as microprocessors get more powerful and ubiquitous. In Chapters 26 and 46, we will talk of the fieldbus structures that are emerging to alter the fundamental way plants are run, again causing openness, and moving the control action back into the process itself.

With the trend toward so-called lights out plants, which will have little or no supervision on every shift, safety concerns for plant, process, and personnel are becoming much more imperative. As more users become aware of all the implications and issues involved, the inclusion of safety features, especially in complex control strategies, is continually increasing.

The advent of the S88 Batch Control standard has made people aware that the concepts of this standard transcend traditional views of what is included in "batch processes." As you read Chapter 31, you will become aware that most all of the manufacturing and process Industries operate as a batch. Even "continuous control" is an extended batch! All the elements are there, and in Chapter 31 we will try to point out how batch strategies are important, especially in light of "Enterprise Control."

Advanced Control is becoming more common in all forms of systems automation. Distributed processor systems have made this possible. Their increased calculating power and phenomenal memory capabilities have made the formerly impossible concepts like fuzzy logic, neural networks, genetic algorithms, and chaos theory much more practical and economical. The challenge now is to learn how to properly *use* these tools as they become available, without burdening the system with "techno-toys." While it is necessary to "play around" with a process to create improvements, the latter sometimes present credibility problems when you are attempting to sell management on real solutions—the two-edged sword dilemma again.

Control Systems: Discrete vs. Process

From an enterprise viewpoint, both factory automation and continuous process control look like batch systems. The author of this book has come from the process industries, but sees much of the phenomenon of distributed processor systems as having many of the same problems (at least from the standpoint of digital computing and communications). There are, of course, differences in the fundamental role of factory automation and process control. I suspect that the simplistic difference is that most of process control must deal with real time while most of factory automation must deal with "real enough" time.

Table 1-1. Differences Between Process Industries and Discrete Industries

	Process	Discrete
Products	Fluids	Devices, objects
Operations	Continuous, batch	Job shop, batch, repetitive
Product Design	Done in labs	Done with CAD/CAE
Equipment	Uses processes	Uses machines
Equipment Cost	Very high	Medium to high
Labor Cost	Low	High
Sensors	Numerous analog and discrete	Mostly discrete
Control Products	DCSs, PLCs, SLCs, PCs	PLCs, CNCs, robotics, PCs
Supervisory Control	Process optimization, scheduling	Cell control, scheduling
Business Management	In-house developed, MRP II, MES, ERP	MRP II, MES, ERP
Implementation Approach	Bottom up	Top down

I suppose you could compare a discrete operation with stamping out cookies with a cookie cutter. If something goes wrong with the shape, you toss out the cookie and continue to crank out many more. If several start coming out wrong, you fix the cutter shape, or the person doing the stamping.

A process, however, is more like driving your automobile to work everyday. It is the same automobile, and you go from the same home to the same place of work. Nevertheless, the trip is never the same experience two days in a row. Traffic flow is never the same, traffic density is never the same, traffic timing is never the same—even the chosen route isn't always the same.

Evolution of Plantwide Process Control 2

To better understand the concept of *distributed* control, we need to look at some history of control rooms, and of computer control. We also need to look at some arbitrary distinctions between DCSs, PLCs, and PCs. These will be very imperfect comparisons, of course, because of the many creative innovations by specific vendors. Nevertheless, for the sake of *understanding* (the title, remember?), we must make some generalizations which will no doubt bother some purists!

Early Control of Processes

In early fluid processing plants, controlling the process frequently required many operators. They continuously circulated around each process unit observing locally mounted, large-indicating instruments and manipulating the valves. Overall plant operations would often require operators to "tour the plant" with a clipboard, recording many key parameters. At the end of the first pass, appropriate calculations would be made for the second trip to adjust valves, dampers, drives, and other end elements.

This required each operator to develop his or her own "feel" for the process, which was very much an art. One of the challenges in running a plant this way was coordinating the many operators so they handled the flow of product from one portion of the plant to the other in a similar way. Because this "feel of operation" was very subjective, plant performance would vary with different operators and also with their different emotional states. The resulting time lags and other inefficiencies were usually the limiting factors in plant productivity.

Beginnings of Local Control Room Panels

Technology improved and the ability to transmit pneumatic signals became a reality, so the control room came into being at larger plants. The large indicating instruments were now moved to one location, along with some controls that transmitted signals back to the closer valves in the field (Figure 2-1). Several operators could now record their readings in log books and make some adjustments in the operating process without touring the plant as frequently. There was, of course, still a need to tour the plant to adjust the more distant valves, dampers, and other end elements.

This was the beginning of the concept of bringing the plant to the operator rather than requiring the operator to go out into the plant. It reduced the time lag in his or her decisions on the process performance because he or she had much of the necessary information nearby. It was easier and faster for him or her to spot interactions between different portions of the process. All of this was done through local control and monitoring, using direct wiring and analog signals. Now, the positive side was that there was not much wiring (or tubing, in the case of pneumatic installations). The negative side was that there was also not much control, not much monitoring, and not much "alarming."

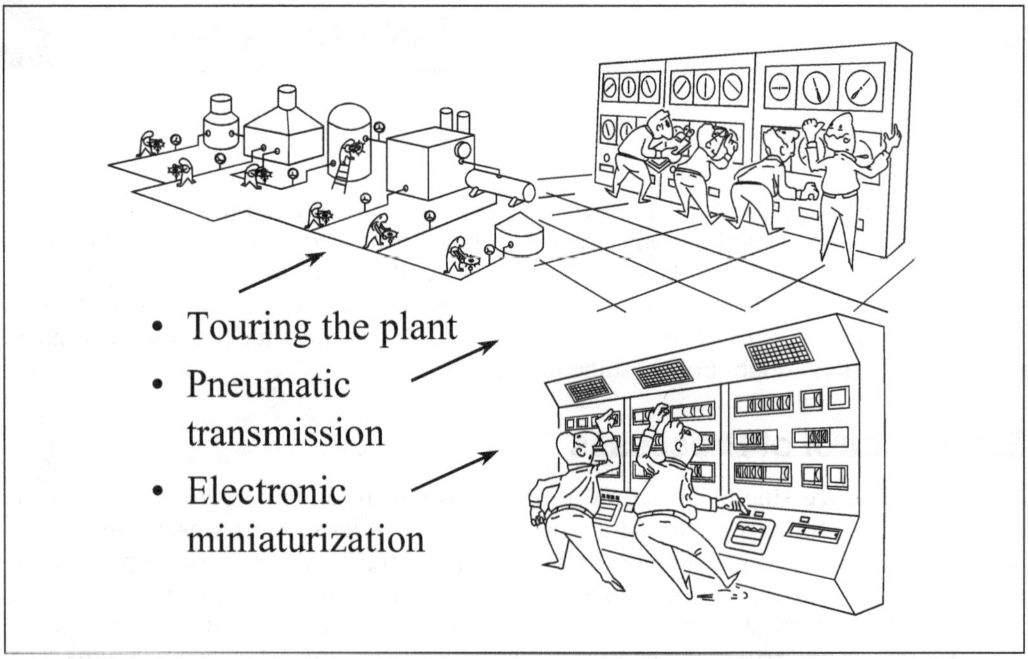

Figure 2-1. Evolution: These Were Distributed

More Sophisticated Control Rooms

Following World War II, electronic controls became more rugged and practical for industrial environments. More measurements were becoming possible because the cost of sensors was coming down. There were also newer types of sensors to measure parameters not previously measurable. Further, it was becoming possible to measure more parameters in line, rather than take laboratory samples.

The size of controllers was smaller, so more of them could fit on a panel, in a smaller area. All of this led to a more complex control room, as well as the need to bring more wires to that location. This presented information management problems for the operators in addition to challenges involving the logistics of signal management for the instrument engineer.

Central Mainframe Computer Control

As changes in technology brought down the price of computers, their use became more common in large and more complex facilities. This allowed the single centralized control room to develop further.

While these computers were now able to cope with all this new data, one of the problems that emerged was that most computers were designed for businesses. During the 1960s and 1970s two types of computers emerged for process control:

- Direct Digital Control (DDC) (Figure 2-2)

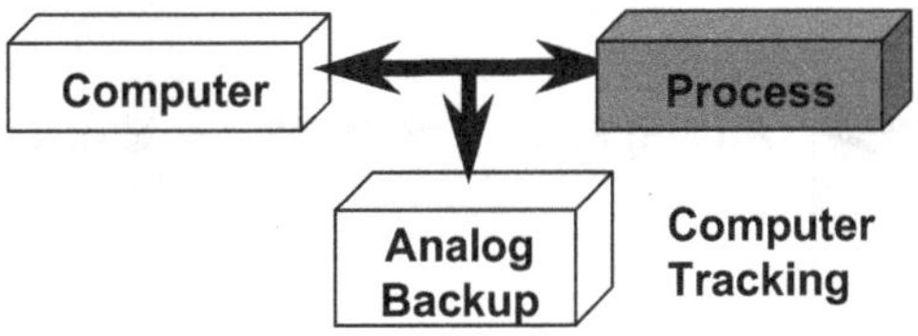

- **Advantages:**
  - Sophisticated control
  - Flexible control
  - Data acquisition and alarm
- **Disadvantages:**
  - Computer reliability
  - Redundant computer or controllers
  - Wiring complex and extensive
  - HMI required high-level operators
  - **Expensive**

Figure 2-2. Central (Mainframe) Computer for Direct Digital Control (DDC)

- Digitally Directed Analog Control (DDAC), or more popularly called Supervisory Control (Figure 2-3)

This central control room concept gave a much better picture of the overall plant operation, but when all the distant portions of the plant were connected to this one room the cost for the following elements was high:

- For the many control cable runs, wire trays, and handling devices
- For the engineering design
- For the craft labor of installing lines and making terminations
- For the problems involved in making changes in the control strategy

A serious problem also presented itself—a failure in the computer could shut down the entire plant! To overcome this, backup controllers were often used with the computer system. To make this system more reliable, it would frequently be necessary to duplicate control systems (which meant buying two sets of controls for everything). This redundancy often required the use of analog instruments to keep the plant running. Operators had to be able to operate computers as well as be knowledgeable about process control. Not very many qualified people could be found, and when they were, they were very expensive.

Using a supervisory computer to drive set points and other parameters in the analog controllers prevented the loss of signal to the end elements when the computer

- **Advantages:**
  - High reliability
  - Human-machine interface adequate
  - Data acquisition and alarms
  - Sophisticated control
  - Complete redundancy
- **Disadvantages:**
  - Complex wiring and installation
  - Difficult to make strategy changes
  - **Expensive**

Figure 2-3. Central (Mainframe) Supervisory Computer Control—Called Originally, Digitally Directed Analog Control (DDAC)

stopped. It still meant buying the control system twice, but at least the operators did not have to learn to run the process through the computer. When the supervisory computer was implemented properly, operators sometimes could even be oblivious to the computer's presence.

This centralized computer control and monitoring had several advantages and disadvantages:

- *On the plus side*. There was a more organized centralized view of the operations, control strategies became more flexible, alarms became much more flexible and effective, and the ability to have meaningful history and events was increased.
- *On the negative side*. There was much wiring, there was considerable risk to the plant, and it was not very "scalable," meaning you could not scale up a little bit more without reprogramming the whole computer. Correcting these disadvantages would cost money.

The high cost of central mainframe computer control meant that computers were used only when the operations were large enough or the process was critical enough to justify the effort required to automate this way.

Computerlike control has become more necessary, however, because as each industry matures it needs to optimize its processing methods. The cost of raw materials, waste, pollution, and compliance with government regulations—all are growing factors in the efficiencies of each industry's operations.

Distributed Process Control

The onset of distributed control was made possible by the ability of the emerging video technologies to display data and even to allow the operator to initiate control actions "through the video" (Figure 2-4). The central control room provided centralized *information* without having to have all the processing in one vulnerable location, thus distributing the risk.

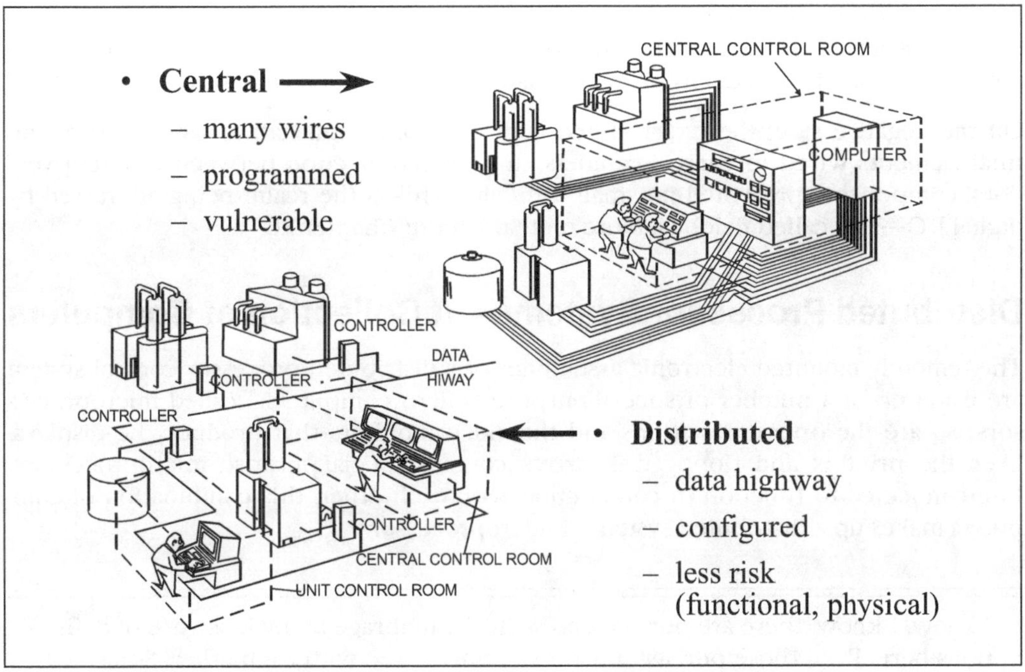

Figure 2-4. Central Mainframe Computer Grew to Distributed Computer

The cost and complexity of wiring could also be reduced by using a digital signal passing through a single cable used as a communication network (data highway), thus connecting the diverse portions of the plant. The magic behind all those signals running through a single wire is an old technology, called the telegraph. The use of Morse code was really the digital communication of analog values (voice-based information, like radio). More on that later in Part E on Networks.

The distributed process architecture permits a *functional* distribution of the tasks among many processors, reducing the risk of everything failing at once. As methods for reducing ground loops emerged it was also possible to allow *physical* distribution as well. These critical features began to open up many new possibilities for tying central information to local control in those plants where this was important.

This central control room view of plant operation gives the operator a single window into the process. Now operators no longer have to tour the plant. They can literally "let their fingers do the walking" as they call up each controller or group of controllers on their screen to check the progress of their process. If necessary, they can easily make a set point and output changes from their keyboard, as well as respond to any alarms if a process is "off-normal."

Furthermore, if a plant process requires it, there also can be several operator stations along this network. A local operator station can be positioned in a specific portion of the plant, either working from the same data highway or wired directly to a cluster of some loops of control.

On the plus side, distributed control and monitoring meant shorter wiring runs, no wires between controllers and control room, less risk of failure, and a more scalable system if you wished to gradually grow the system without much cost for replacement.

On the negative side, these distributed control systems still had to have sensors and final elements wired to control cabinets, and interconnection between different vendors' components presented no small difficulty. This is the realm being addressed by digital I/O—also called fieldbus. More on that later in Chapter 26.

Distributed Processor Systems—A Collection of Computers

The remotely mounted electronic assemblies of a distributed processor control system are made up of a number of special-purpose "micro computers," called microprocessors. So are the operator stations and the video monitors that produce the displays. Even the printers and floppy disk drives contain special-purpose microprocessors. Interconnected to function in conjunction with each other, this combination of computers makes up a distributed system of microprocessors.

I know, I know, there are purists who will take umbrage at my loose use of definitions here. Even those purists, however, cannot agree with each other! Some generally accepted definitions:

Microprocessor, μP—Electronic integrated circuit, typically in a single-chip package, capable of receiving and executing coded instructions; performs functions of both CPU and arithmetic logic unit (ALU), but excludes memory and I/O systems.

Microcontroller, μC—Microprocessor with timers, counters, RAM, and ROM included.

Microcomputer—Based on a microprocessor or computer that is physically small, usually fits on a small printed circuit board and works with a data word of 4, 8, or 16 bits (and, yes, 32 and 64 bits) but now often with all the power formerly found in minicomputers; also called a personal computer.

In its hardware context, the distributed processor system is an information handler, a communications device that operates in accordance with technologies far different from those of the applications for which it is used. In its system context, it has the purpose of controlling industrial processes. While the assembled system components do the old familiar jobs, they do them in far different ways. As one's understanding of the functions of microprocessors increases, their capabilities can be better appreciated. New control strategies will be evolved and new sensors and actuators will be developed to take advantage of the power for manipulating information offered by the microprocessor.

As we said earlier, these advances in hardware are a function of the smaller size, the lower cost, and the higher reliability of the technology of these components. The evolution of the controller architecture moved from a single central computer that did all of the controlling tasks and shared the display, operating, and communicating with inputs and outputs to an architecture of distributed processors throughout the system. These processors all combine to perform the specific functions of process control, of communication between controllers, and of the display and manipulation of information from the control system.

The intermediate step between these two stages was the evolution of these specific "microcomputers" into proprietary controllers and operator stations. The hardware was proprietary because in the 1960s, 1970s, and 1980s, normal computers did not have the processing speed and the memory capacity to function in real time, that is, to respond immediately to the actions of the process, informing the operator and prompting the operator what to do next.

Proprietary Systems

Because each vendor had to find a way to pull data up as fast as it was needed, each had to modify the existing technology, leading to these various proprietary systems. I'm not aware of any time when vendors purposely designed their systems so that they could not work with someone else's. Proprietary systems were an expediency to provide the customer, as economically and quickly as possible, with a functional digital system at a time before there were standards.

Role of Programmable Logic Controllers (PLCs) in Process Control

Programmable logic controllers (PLCs) were designed for use in factory automation functions when the operation required many rapid, repeatable operations, as on most assembly lines. This is not typical in a traditional process plant, but there are some operations that can use the powerful capabilities of a PLC.

Today's PLCs can be more efficient than ever before in performing sequencing, regulatory, and interlocking operations. Real-time control for interlocking motors and related equipment has become very practical within PLCs used in the process control world.

A good example of this is batch process control with process management functions configured through a personal computer (PC) or PC-type of operator workstation. More recent PLCs have been used for distributed computing through an operation involving several PLCs on networks. Sometimes, but certainly not always, these networks are peer-to-peer, meaning that one PLC can talk to another one directly without going through some intermediate device.

Decentralized control is available in many of today's PLC systems through intelligent remote input-outputs. Typical applications are equipment start-stop and safety interlocks, filtration, simple batching, packaging, bottling, and material handling. PLCs are quite frequently a cost-effective alternative to DCSs where sophisticated process loop control strategies are not needed.

Powerful advantages of PLCs in process control include the following:

- Excellent logic-handling capabilities; operating and maintenance personnel in the United States like and easily understand ladder logic!
- Very fast, with the ability to detect a malfunction within a few milliseconds
- Very cost effective, allowing them to be customized to the product functions
- Can withstand rough environment; they do not need the clean room required by many computers and "traditional" DCSs (but typically not corrosive atmospheres)
- Highly reliable, a proven product that is easy to maintain
- Offer high level of flexibility and expandability
- They are usually very compact and do not have large space requirements.

Table 2-1. Comparison of Computer Control Types
Warning! Generalizations Here!

	Typical Strengths	Typical Weaknesses
DCS	Distributed risk Real-time throughput Advanced control strategy PID (3-mode control) Operator interface Low integration cost	Entry-level cost Proprietary network Proprietary OS Complex interlocks Control room environment
PLC	Environmental Uptime Real-time throughput Complex interlocks RLL easy and repeatable	Human interface Integration cost Sequencing Reporting Application software Recipe handling
Central Computer	Data acquisition Advanced control strategy Database storage History and trending Networking	Programmed Environmental limits Costly redundancy Real-time throughput

The main drawbacks of PLCs in process control include the following:

- Nondeterministic; no ability to predict response time, which is disastrous for PID control! (PLCs are deterministic only if real-time interrupt is available [and used for PIDs])
- Limited in its continuous loop control capabilities, particularly in process control strategies such as cascading several controllers, and in the control optimizing techniques frequently available in most DCSs
- Need for host computer or personal computer to interface with process controls and other more complex operations
- Batch control software is typically not available for the process control vendor in hybrid systems using both DCS and PLCs
- Available user interfaces do not always have the capability of those provided with distributed controls; use of human-machine interfaces (HMIs) from other vendors limits PLCs capabilities (need more than a pretty face)
- The need to configure the PLCs is separate from configuring computers and DCSs in those systems that combine these
- PLC vendor companies and their distributors generally lack process expertise, requiring the services and costs of an independent integrator.

Table 2-2. Comparisons by Execution (Scan) Times
Warning! Generalizations Here!

Scan Time	Typical Functions	Likely System
1 Month	Corporate update of plant Operations summary	Computer ⇓
1 Day, Shift	Production report	
1 Hour	Off-line optimization	
	Batch management Batch scheduling	DCS ⇓
1 Minute	Unit process optimization	DCS ⇓
1 Second	Display update Analog control Process calculations Batch sequencing	
100 mSec	Flow control	
20 mSec	High-speed sequencing Interlocks	PLC ⇓
1 mSec	Sequence of events	

Table 2-3. Consideration of I/O Types and Amounts When Comparing Use of PLC vs. DCS

Warning! Generalizations Here!

Loops of Modulating Control		Channels of Discrete I/O: Under 200	200 to 600	Over 600
	Over 150	Large DCS	Large DCS with Medium PLCs	Large DCS with Large PLCs
	30 to 150	Small DCS	Small DCS with Medium PLCs	Small DCS with Large PLCs
	Under 30	Small PLC with PC or PC and SLCs	Medium PLC with PC or with SLCs	Large PLCs with Integrated Workstation

Warning hereby posted that any comparisons of DCSs, PLCs, mainframe computers, PCs, and PCs with PLCs are all generalizations!

Everyone regularly requests these comparisons, but products are continually changing. Each vendor has so many differing features that address specific situations. The reality is that most PLCs are in the manufacturing world and the packaging portion of process plants. Sophisticated control (multiloop control) typically cannot use PLCs for an assortment of reasons. Computers, DCSs, and PLCs all suffer from cost/performance trade-offs, just different ones. **Valid arguments can be made for and against nearly every point of comparison** made in this book or in nearly every magazine article you will read! Like so many things in life, there are *no* formulas for making decisions, otherwise you would not need to study how to buy the product that is best for your plant. (No engineers needed; just mail-order everything.)

Of course there are exceptions to all of these tables! The idea of all these tables is to highlight the areas where a particular system tends to be better, not to say the other systems cannot do the same. Example: Some DCSs are now beginning to perform *all* the batch management within their "domain."

When someone is looking for a system, it is the *combination* of issues that must be considered. Just as when comparing brands, when deciding between PLCs, DCSs, and dedicated or general computers (or PCs), the *functions needed* are what is important—the buyer must always follow the rule, "Understand thy process!" (Most know their process, but do not *understand* that process; sometimes the understanding comes from the information gathering that a new system can provide.)

The comparison figures in this chapter can only be *guidelines*, to be used along with several other guides. There is no single rule of thumb *nor* any simple formula to determine which is best. *Everything* depends upon *how* the system is to be used..and by whom. Know thy process!

Comparing DCS with PLC for Ease of Configuration

Proprietary DCS systems were initially configured as function blocks representing various instruments and controllers made by the same vendor. Those blocks usually represented the same strengths and weaknesses of that vendor, based upon the vendor's application expertise in the markets he or she understood. There were no standards in this area, but many of these systems were rather straightforward to configure. Part of this was because the vendor also designed the workstation to assure a matching operator interface to those "instruments." This also guaranteed the user of real-time operation and a lower chance of inadvertent "contamination" of the software.

PLCs, on the other hand, were usually replacements to relays and were either programmed using relay logic, or when more complex control was needed, programmed in one of the "higher languages" such as Pascal, Basic, or some blend of the two. There generally was a far simpler operator interface, very minimal communication, and not as much need for real-time communication between devices.

Typical PLC System Configuration (Figure 2-5)

Each PLC must be configured separately; discipline is needed to avoid duplicating process tags, etc.; complex strategies are generally confined to individual PLCs.

PC must be configured to communicate with *each* PLC to find specific variables, then configured for views, then for history, then for trends; etc.

PLC systems usually have multiple databases to configure and keep matched.

(Although used for data acquisition and control, this kind of system is not truly a SCADA system. *SCADA* is a term that has been used for well over four decades to mean systems that switch equipment some distances beyond the plant site using conventional phone, microwave, even satellite connections and that require a unique communications technique to assure integrity under conditions that are not in the user's control.)

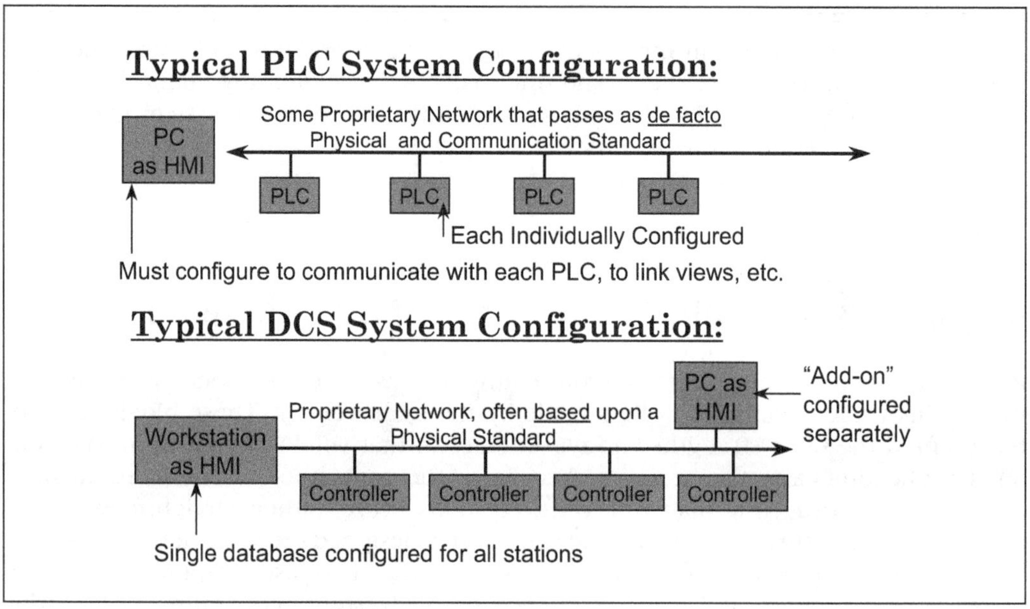

Figure 2-5. Comparing Configuration Approaches Between a DCS and a PLC with a PC

Typical DCS System Configuration (Figure 2-5)

Configuration is generally done from a workstation designed for that specific system. All controllers are as one database that allows for peer-to-peer communication in complex strategies. The database may reside only in workstation, with copies in controllers; sometimes downloading is needed during the backup of redundant controllers. Views, history, and trends will also have to be configured. Some of these will have a common database, depending upon the vendor (and system vintage).

Separate PCs, usually add-on, must configure unique links to control and views, etc., on separate database, as with PLC systems.

DCS systems usually have a single database; it does not have to be regularly matched with another.

Open System Configuration (Figure 2-6)

Controllers with both DCS and PLC capabilities at the price of PLCs have recently emerged. These controllers can be configured as a single system, but the database is distributed so each individual controller stores its own configuration and with some brands even all of the graphical documentation. Tag names, HMI "calls," peer-to-peer links for complex strategies, and the like are all included for each process tag. Open communication allows connection to **user's choice of HMI**, while "bridge software" presents the database to HMIs to populate the database within it. In that way, the creation of duplicate database entries is unnecessary.

User may select a human-machine interface (HMI) specific to the needs of the plant, perhaps to match equipment already in use there. The controller database in HMI can then be used with HMI database to allow construction of views, history, trends, and the like depending upon the features in HMI that are selected.

Expect to see more systems like this in the future.

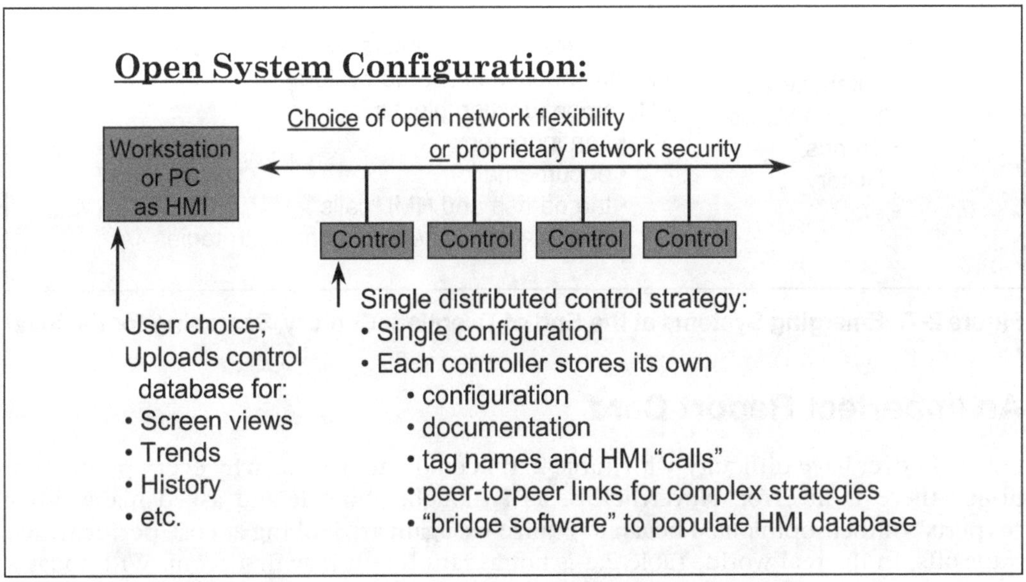

Figure 2-6. Configuration in the Mid-1990s of a System that Allows User to Choose a Workstation from any of Several Separate HMI Vendors

Emerging But Still Quite Ideal Configuration (Figure 2-7)

Beginning to emerge, but with de facto standards for network, not universal fieldbus (will that ever be now, or have too many alternatives been introduced to have users return to some common standard?)

Each vendor supplies the user with a disk to load into the PC so the device can be configured with all the features provided by that vendor, but the software for this must be written in terms that are "universal" to all systems!

In 1998 this is more vendor hype than reality for anything more than "simple" data acquisition and control (DAC) systems (do not call them SCADA), but it is available with some smart transmitters and valves.

As learning experiences increase, this structure will become more robust.

See the discussion at end of this book (Part L) on "Future Trends."

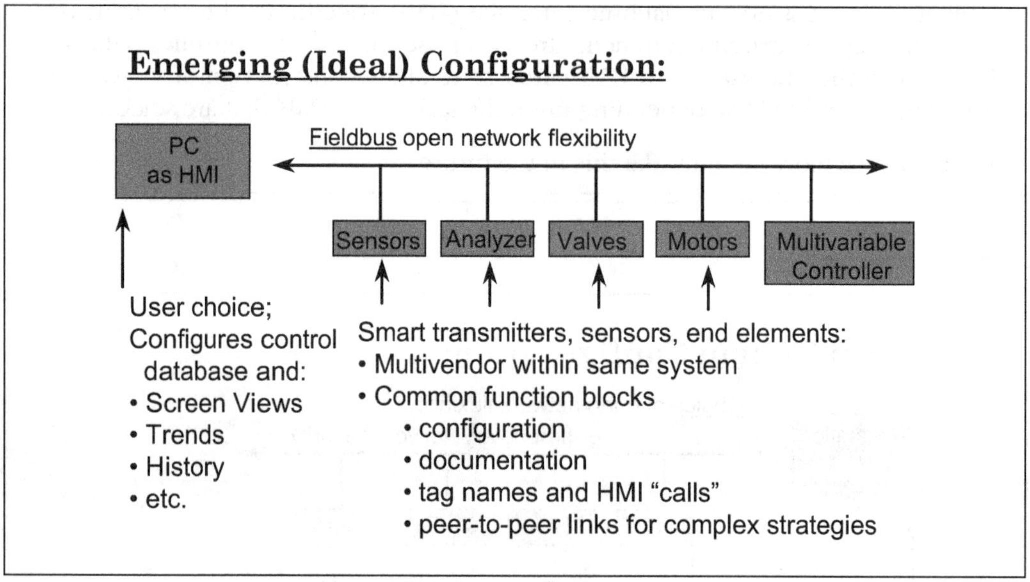

Figure 2-7. Emerging Systems at the End of Twentieth Century, Searching for the Ideal

An Imperfect Report Card

Boy, did I ever have difficulty with Table 2.4! I could cite reasons why every point mentioned there is in error. Nevertheless, as I thought about it and asked many other "experts" of their opinions, I began to realize we again are looking at cost/performance trade-offs. In the real world, Table 2.4 is not as far off as it may first seem. With today's fast-moving technology, however, we cannot pin *anything* down long enough to be accurate. Like report cards, "As" are excellent, "Bs" are good, "Cs" are passing; no one flunks here, and keep in mind the distinction made with PC/PLC: PC with PLC is *not* the same as some of the new systems emerging at the end of the 1990s. It is just what it says: any vendor HMI with any other vendor PLC!

Hybrid DCS and PLC Architectures

In the early to mid-1990s, when a process required a high level of discrete action, along with sophisticated process action, quite frequently there have been architectures that can combine distributed controllers and PLCs in the same network. Sometimes in these type of networks the PLC communicates serially with the distributed control station, and then, in turn, that control station is attached to the distributed control communication network, often called the data highway. On more recent versions, there are several PLC interfaces that will connect directly to the network of the DCS. This limits the user, however, to the brand of PLC that will work with a specific vendor of a DCS.

The advantage of these hybrid systems is that they allow the more complex system user to tailor the equipment selection by unit operation requirements. It also segregates the addressing of safety issues, splitting the configuration and troubleshooting tasks between the DCS for a portion and the PLC as a separate part of the system so they don't interfere with each other.

Table 2-4. Another Table of Generalizations!

	DCS	PLC	PC/PLC
Control Capabilities:			
Process I/O	A	A	A
Multivariable regulatory control	A	C	C
Complex interlocking	C	A	A
Sequencing	B	D	C
Recipe handling	A	D	B
Batch process control	B	D	C
User interface:			
Ease of configuration (links and displays)	A	C	D
Ease of operator use	A	D	B
Ease of creating custom displays	A	C	B
Cost:			
Hardware	C	A	B
Installation	A	C	D
Application programming	A	B	C
Additional Considerations:			
Ease of expansion (interactive functions)	A	D	D
Flexibility	A	D	C
Redundancy	A	C	C
Reliability	B	A	C
Hardware maintainability	B	A	B
Software maintainability	B	C	D

A big disadvantage of these hybrid architectures is that complexity is considerably increased. There are high integration costs for the configuring, the programming, the documentation, and the training. It may be necessary to match different systems with no common protocols. And you will have to rely on data links between these PLCs and DCSs. Remember, every time you have a link, there's a point of vulnerability with a potential for failure, and it's a possible slow link for moving data or, more accurately, for moving information.

When a complex process needs a blend of both discrete and analog, a hybrid system has been used. Usually it is custom tailored, so complexity is significantly increased, and there are high costs for the configuration, programming, documentation, training, and troubleshooting. There is also a need to rely on links to match different systems that use different protocols.

Every time there is a communication link, this becomes a point of vulnerability, which tends to slow the movement of data. The delay will reduce the quality of *information* about the process.

The example in Figure 2-8 shows most types of combinations, including single loop controllers (SLCs). Note also the *local* operator interface (OI), which can be used with DCS controllers or PLCs (Figure 2-8 is rather simplistic due to space limitations). In systems such as this, the configuration of DCS and of PLC is done separately in most systems, not with the same configuration "station."

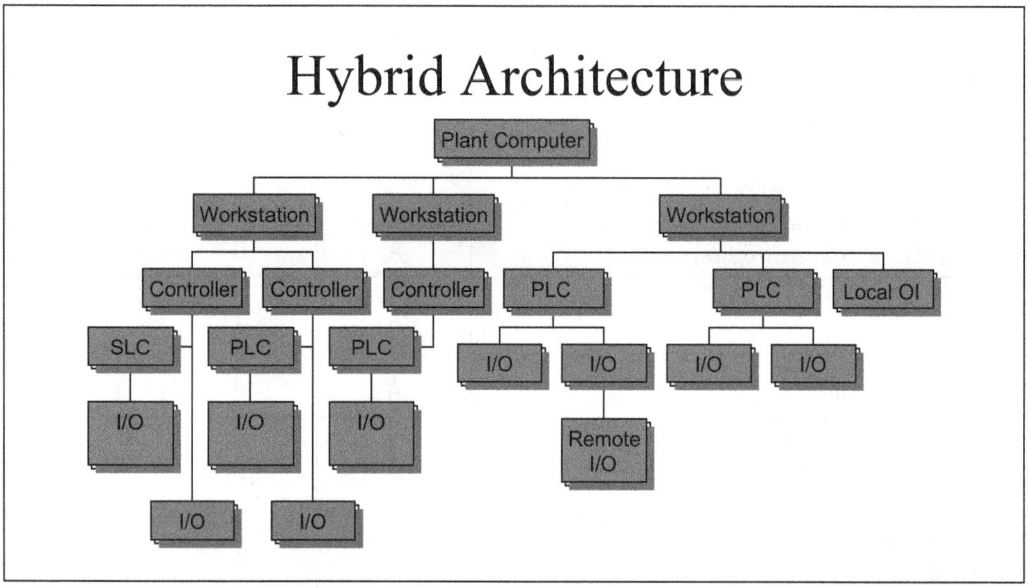

Figure 2-8. Different DCS and PLC Hardware in the Same Architecture is Called a "Hybrid Architecture"

Systems have been emerging in the 1990s that offer these "hybrid" capabilities without the cost, complexity, and limitations of this architecture. The need for this type of hybrid is already past, but because enough of these are in user's plants, and will be there for some time, this architecture should be shown.

SCADA Systems

In recent years the use of the term *SCADA* has been increasingly been applied to what are really data acquisition systems that now also do control. This has not been the definition of this term for over five decades. Used on a large scale, "real" supervisory control and data acquisition (SCADA) systems have been used for control actions and information gathering from *beyond* the plant (Figure 2-9). These SCADA systems have *not* traditionally been used in process control but rather in the starting and stopping of remote units, such as those found in remote power transformers or remote water or gas pumps on pipelines.

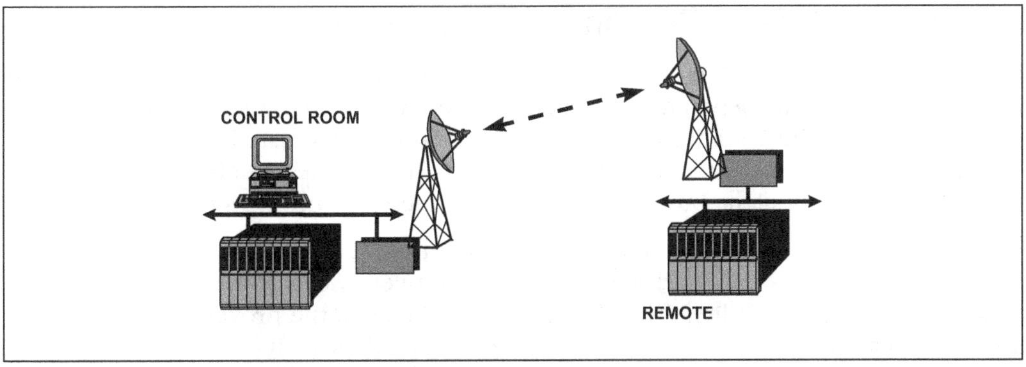

Figure 2-9. Traditional SCADA System

Quite often, the communication is not through wire, but through radio transmission, phone lines, and even satellites. The time delays on these SCADA systems have usually made it necessary to *not* rely on monitoring and controlling the details of the process itself from a distance. The supervisory control portion was only expected to merely turn specific units on or off or to bypass units that may have been damaged, for instance, in a storm or in an accident. Power distribution companies must live with these conditions all the time.

Any communications in such remote transmissions as a SCADA system have to allow for long time delays between the request for action and the action's occurrence. Also a concern are frequent unexpected interruptions of any communicated signal. This generally precludes any continuous process action, which needs a more responsive operation. For decades, unique technologies have been used to accommodate these control limitations, such as some very stringent "check-before-execute" routines on any transmission of data.

CDPD—Cellular Digital Packet Data. This is one of the emerging wireless digital communications technologies useful for "true" SCADA systems. CDPD sends packets of data using existing cellular communications technology for a given region. While cost is still a constraining factor with CDPD, this technology has proved effective for regions without direct telephone or leased lines.

To further confuse the issue, since the late 1950s, "supervisory control" in the process world meant to drive the set points of control loops using a central computer. This action could be overridden at the controller itself by the control room operator, who could switch any controller from "supervisory" to "automatic," or to "manual." The practice of referring to a personal computer (PC) connected to one or more programmable logic controllers (PLCs), which has been happening in the mid-1990s adds still another layer of confusion. In this book, I will try to distinguish these three different uses of the term "SCADA" by identifying them by their more direct terminology.

Increasing Role of Personal Computers (PCs)

Like it or not, the mid-1990s has become the era of Bill Gates' Microsoft®. More and more Microsoft is influencing all of our technology. The shear volume of Microsoft products, and of the volumes of compatible products, has created de facto standards and unbeatable pricing. In a short few years, this has permeated all levels of process control products, let alone business products and therefore business practices.

The first area of the system architecture in which the PC shows up as the device most asked for by users is the workstation. UNIX has been *the* workhorse of processing power capacity and stability. Over the years it has become the proven platform of reliability for use in "mission-critical" operations. Nevertheless, it will be overtaken by Windows NT or its successor. Price, power, and universality will cause users to demand it. They will then demand that vendors make it robust as well.

The process controls industry has never had the advantage of volume for most of the products used by it. Certainly not like business systems, and nothing even close to consumer products. Just how many cement plants can the world's economic requirements support? Yet how many television sets, microwave ovens, video games (and the list goes on) can there be? Price comes down as the volume goes up. Research on new technologies will always go to those markets that can support the effort. Other users must wait for the results, then modify the technology for their own use.

There are exceptions. In 1970, Honeywell Industrial Division (Fort Washington, Pennsylvania) commissioned the development of the first 16-bit microprocessor from General Instrument in order to create the TDC2000, the first commercially successful distributed control system. They had to "amortize" the cost across eight loops of control to justify that expense and then match the cost of single loop controllers. Eight bits could not do the job. This was a decade before the first 16-bit PCs!

The Issue Is Real-Time

The real issue is not UNIX vs. NT, because neither are real-time by nature. There are almost as many definitions of real-time as there are manufacturers of systems. Generally, for any control system real-time means doing the task when it needs to be done. Brayton Paul of *Chemical Engineering* magazine and David Cawlfield of Olin Corporation have called this "meeting deadlines." They identify deterministic real-time as hard real-time that always meets deadlines and nondeterministic as soft real-time meets deadlines only part of the time, depending upon the circumstances. They go on to describe the properties of soft and hard real-time.

In a hard real-time system, lateness is not accepted under any circumstances, results are useless if late, catastrophic failure results if the deadline is missed, and the cost of missing the deadline is infinitely high. Soft real-time, on the other hand, is characterized by rising costs for lateness of results and the acceptance of lower performance for lateness. A robust real-time operating system must include several capabilities, such as preemptive multitasking, so that the most critical software processing always takes place, even at the complete sacrifice of the less critical.

In addition to the real-time required to perform a control action, there is the perceived real-time by the user of some screen view, who expects an action to occur immediately. At a minimum, this user needs some *confirmation* that the action called for will really happen, even if the inertia of equipment (often beyond the control system itself) causes normal delays. This subject is covered in Chapter 17, which is devoted to the appropriate philosophy and creation of screen displays.

Impact of Windows NT

With the "steam-rolling effect" of today's PC technologies, there is no choice for process control vendors but to "go with the flow" and be creative in making up the differences "where the holes are." In Table 2.5, which compares UNIX, Windows 95, and Windows NT, we have created a comparison that is imperfect at best because of the many complex issues that underlie it. Nevertheless, the thrust of Table 2.5 is merely to point out that nothing is simply "better." Some considerations to recognize include the following:

- UNIX has "flavors" offered by many vendors, limiting the creation of "standards"; however, many do not like being single-sourced only by Microsoft.
- There is no "one size fits all." It appears that NT is finding a niche midway between UNIX and Windows, taking a piece from each.
- While Windows NT is currently less compatible with hardware and software applications than UNIX, Microsoft *claims* that NT provides ease of administration, simplicity, and cost advantages over UNIX and security and robustness over Windows 3.1 or Windows 95.
- The cross-platform compatibility of NT is a strong plus for designers and should result in better products for users.
- So far, among controls vendors NT is not yet being used for better *user functions*; there are clearly some developer advantages, which should result in benefits to the user.
- Microsoft caters to office functions, not process control. It is up to control vendors and third parties to hammer it into process needs!

Table 2-5. Probably Unfair Comparison of Computing Platforms, but Our Best Effort for 1998

Technical Issues	UNIX	Windows 95	Windows NT
Hardware Needs	Highest; Multiprocessors Multiple platforms	Lower; 486 with 8–16 MB; Intel only	Higher; Pentium with 16–32 MB; Multiple platforms
Scalability	Yes, favors larger systems	No	Yes, favors smaller systems
Data Warehouse	Excellent	Little	Good

Table 2-5. Probably Unfair Comparison of Computing Platforms, but Our Best Effort for 1998 (Continued)

Technical Issues	UNIX	Windows 95	Windows NT
Client/Server	Central server in larger systems	Client	Local server or client (in large systems)
Software Compatibility	High; relative to use, but many different "flavors"	Higher, but office-based	Lower, but growing rapidly
Hardware and Device Compatibility	High; relative to use, but many different "flavors"	Higher	Lower, but promised
Install and Deployment	Most by far in industrial applications	Comprehensive but desktop	Less so; mostly for office desktops, but also industrial
Plug 'n Play Functions	Designed for mission-critical	Built in but for desktop	None (promised with Cairo)
Performance	Higher	Lower	Higher
Reliability, Stability	Excellent	More than DOS, Win 3.1	Good
Ease of use	Complex	Simple	Simple
Ease of Administration	Complex	Simple	Not so simple
Security	Robust	Weak	Good
Cost	High	Low	Medium; grows when more functions required (like UNIX)

Note: All of the above is oversimplified so as to compare what is far more complex than any chart can show!
Generalities: UNIX vs. NT is currently a standoff: *"If you don't know why you need NT, you probably don't need it!"*
—Bill Gates

Using PC for Control

The next generation of controllers is also being influenced significantly by Microsoft! This is equally true for factory automation and process control. Although in the mid-1990s there is still the need for "mission-critical" robustness in function-specific hardware, the trend is toward "off-the-shelf" hardware and away from proprietary systems. The value-added by controls vendors will be by their software. These products must not only provide control capability but will still have to overcome the obstacles to "real" real-time. There will also be a significant need for standards in many places in order for this to become a full reality.

Unlike PCs for business use, however, control system users expect the vendor to supply very reliable, thoroughly tested components with an obsolescence period that is much greater than the typical three-month period for business machines. The ability to perform in harsh and severely variable environments, be compatible with existing systems, and have long mean time to failure (MTTF) are just as important as price and performance.

Emergence of PC as a Controller:

- Robustness is still a serious concern
  - "Industrial strength" for processes is far more severe than factory floor
  - Corrosive atmosphere and vibration significant
- Potential to "liberate" end user from being a proprietary hostage
- All serious vendors are preparing to grow into selling software rather than hardware
- *Process* control unlikely to be "shrink-wrapped"
- Standards still an obstacle.

All of the major control system vendors were working on PC-based controllers as the 1990s moved well past the mid mark. Several smaller companies already have release products for process control, as well as factory automation. I know of a major cement plant in Canada that has had a PC-based controller in a full system since about 1992 and is quite happy with it. A major chemical company has been using theirs for over three years without a reboot. Although the reliability of a PC-based control system is measured in much the same way as any other system using MTTF, what is less obvious is that the most common mode of failure is not hardware, but an operating system "crash." Although this is not such a concern for the business community, it is extremely significant in process control!

A control system has failed if it cannot do what it is designed to do. In a PC-based system, this happens every time there is a need for a reboot. This is no mere inconvenience, but will likely cause a partial or full shutdown of the process itself. The time required to restart the process is usually quite longer than the time needed to restart the PC. Wasted raw material and product out of specification are just some of the costs. The need for fault tolerance is critical. When noncritical portions of a system are separated into independent computing processes, these can be shut down and restarted while the balance of the system remains on line. Even when a noncritical hardware fault causes the failure of some related software component and it cannot be restarted, safety-critical portions of the system will continue to work correctly. Fault-tolerant design organizes the system so that the most critical functions are located in the smallest possible computing processes, and very little information needs to be shared *between* these processes. Is that not called *distributed* processor systems (and why we originally called them *distributed* control systems)?

The Nuts and Bolts of Computing Devices 3

This chapter discusses the basic developments that made distributed processor systems possible. It may not cover anything new for someone who has been around the industry for many years, but many who have just begun exposing themselves to the explosion of digital technology in the measurements and controls field have found it useful.

Electronic Circuitry

The technological developments that brought about distributed processor systems were the large-scale integrated (LSI) circuit and the microprocessor. Computer design was well established during the 1960s, but during the following decade large amounts of circuitry packed on small silicon chips became available. Computers became smaller because the size of the circuit-bearing components could be markedly reduced. As corollary effects, the amount of heat generated was smaller, the reliability was increased, and the cost was brought down. A computer that made use of this new technology was developed. Intermediate in size but very powerful, it was called the minicomputer.

Large-Scale Integrated Circuits

Silicon seems a poor choice for a circuit component because, by itself, it is a poor conductor. An atom is made up a nucleus with "shells" of electrons rotating around it. The scientific name for the shell is "valence." An atom with eight electrons in its outer shell is inert and not a good conductor. An atom of silicon has only four electrons in its outer shell; put two silicon atoms together, share their four electrons, and each has a valence of eight.

Semiconductors are deliberately created by introducing impurities (other atoms) into the silicon crystal, a process called "doping." Adding phosphorus gives the semiconductor the ability to pass a negative current. Phosphorus has a valence of five; the phosphorus atom displaces a silicon atom and that extra electron is left over.

Silicon can be doped with boron, an atom that has only three electrons in its outer shell. Again, the boron atom can take the place of a silicon atom in the crystal lattice. But now there is a deficiency of one electron. This state is called a "hole." Semiconductors with holes allow the passage of electric current with a positive charge.

The LSI chips are silicon wafers (substrates) in which doped areas are created and then modified by photographic etching masking diffusion and overlaying to construct and interconnect the equivalent of diodes, transistors, resistors, and capacitors. Very small wires connected between the semiconductor and a number of connecting pins bring signals into and out of the circuitry. The semiconductor is embedded into a protective mounting with the pins protruding, creating a "chip." The pins can be pushed into a socket and assembled into a printed circuit card to become part of the electrons of the distributed processor equipment.

For several decades, the design of the semi-conductor that has been used most successfully for the circuitry of distributed processors is called CMOS (Complementary Metal-Oxide Semiconductor). Although the miniaturized components do not create much heat, there's a limit to the number of circuits a chip can hold, as more and more are packed into a given volume. The CMOS design reduces the heat generation to a minimum because current is only passed through the circuit when there is a transition in the state of a component. In the static state, which is a relatively large portion of the service time of a circuit, the only currents drawn are junction and subthreshold leakage currents, and these are minute.

LSI has made it practical to build the central processing unit (CPU) of a computer into one chip called a microprocessor (Figure 3-1). Combining the microprocessor with other chips that perform the services required by a computer has resulted in the creation of the microcomputer. Circuits and components seem to become smaller and smaller. So what is known today as the microcomputer may seem large to the next generation. But by today's standards, it's unbelievably small for the tremendous power and computation and data manipulation that it provides. From this power and capacity has come the ability to generate the design represented by the current proliferation of distributed processor systems.

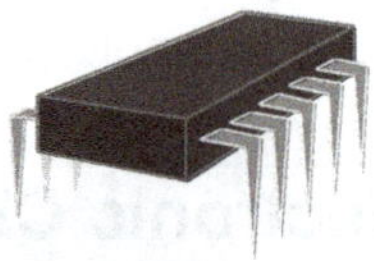

Figure 3-1. LSI Chip

Basic Training Camp Analogy

It may help you to understand the operation of the microprocessor by comparing it with an army camp for basic training. Recruits are brought into the camp and processed. They are assigned to a group called a squad (Figure 3.2). After the assignment is made, the squad is marched into the barracks where it will be located. The area is specifically identified by a company number, a squad number, and a barracks number, and each recruit has a number that identifies him or her uniquely.

Figure 3-2. Microprocessors Function Under Orders

From the barracks, the squad is called into the company street, graded in a parallel formation, left-or right-faced and marched serially to some other location to be trained to perform some activity or to intersect with other squads. This is done in accordance with a program or an agenda. The program may assemble the squad for a class at a training area A in grenade throwing, direct it toward an officers' quarters to police the area, send it back to the barracks to prepare for inspection, and so on.

Everything is done "by the numbers." Rifles are disassembled by the numbers, beds are made by the numbers, clothing is issued by the numbers. The squad members do what they are told to do, when they are told to do it, and in the manner in which they are commanded. There is another organization in camp that is a directing agency. The instructions making up the programmed activity of the recruits are issued from this agency, but it in turn operates in response to other programs. These programs, which are designed to make the camp functional, define such things as mail delivery, trash collection, payroll, hiring and firing, making steam in the camp boiler facility, requisitioning supplies, and other necessary activities.

All actions in the camp operation as well as at the company level—where the recruits exist—take place in accordance with commands. The supply sergeant, for example, receives a requisition for a certain number of items of clothing. He fills the requisition and then waits for another order. While he's waiting, he may be doing some utility functions, but these too will have been outlined in the series of standard operating procedures. A person can enter or leave the camp if he or she has the right piece of paper, but there must be some formalized orders that specify the purpose of the entry or the departure, a destination and probably a time limit. Recruits who have completed training leave the camp on the basis of orders that define the port of departure, the destination for the next assignment, and the route required to get it there. The result of all this organization and unquestioning following of orders is the efficient accomplishment of specific objectives. The microcomputer exists for much the same purpose and functions in a similar manner. The microprocessor is a CPU for a special-purpose computer that is designed to perform a specific library of instructions. This makes it different from a general-purpose computer that can be programmed to do many different things. A special-purpose computer directed by the microprocessor is called a minicomputer. A pocket calculator is a special-purpose minicomputer—so is a digital watch. These devices are microprocessor based. A microcomputer is analogous to the army camp, and the microprocessor is analogous to the headquarters section of the camp.

How Microprocessors Function

So we see that a microprocessor is the central part, or brain, of an electronic device, such as a calculator, personal computer, microwave, car phone, and so on, that retrieves information from various sources, performs many predetermined simple functions on that data, and outputs that result. For a calculator, the device for which the microprocessor was created in the first place, the CPU reads the numbers you put in and the function key that you hit—add, subtract, divide, and so on—and then outputs a result to the display. The reason the microprocessor has made such an impact in all aspects of our lives is its ability to perform millions of instructions per second, or MIPS.

The microprocessor (CPU) has several sections called units, each of which is designed to handle specific tasks (Figure 3-3). In general, a microprocessor has at least three units:

Figure 3-3. Microprocessors Have Several Units for Specific Tasks

- Bus unit—This connects the CPU to various devices in memory, moving data instructions to or from the chip.
- Instruction unit—This decodes the instructions received from the bus unit and puts them into a format understandable by the execution unit.
- Execution unit (also known as the arithmetic logic unit or ALU)—This performs the actual data operations as commanded by the instruction unit and passes the result to the bus unit for output.

The bus unit is where much of the speed is gained or lost. The bus unit is broken up into a data bus and an address bus. The data bus is used to send and receive data with devices inside the computer itself. The address bus relays the information to or from the place in memory where the data is being sent or received. The data bus signals are transmitted in binary (0s and 1s) throughout the computer. A five-volt signal is considered a "1" and a 0 volt a "0." The larger the size of this bus, measured in bits, the larger the chunk of information that can be carried each time.

Let's take, for example, a signal that needs to be carried to the CPU over a 4-bit data bus. The signal's value is, for instance, 254. This number would be represented in binary as 11111110. This signal must be broken into two sections, 1111 and 1110, and sent in two passes in that processor unit. If this were an 8-bit bus, the CPU would only need one pass to receive the entire number, increasing the speed of the operation dramatically. It would thus seem logical that to increase the speed, you just need to increase the bus size, but it isn't that simple. Economics come into play because, if the bus width is doubled, so must be all the associated wiring, which also dramatically increases the cost.

Processing Speed: Not Always the Processor

Eight bits are called a byte. Although a byte has been called a word, words today are frequently 16-bit, 32-bit, and higher in "length." Bits making up one piece of information can be thought of as being stored side-by-side in consecutive boxes. This side-by-side group of boxes is called a register. Microprocessors compute one register at a time, but the register sizes must be compatible. For convenience, let us first look in Figure 3-4. at only an 8-bit processor computing 8-bit information:

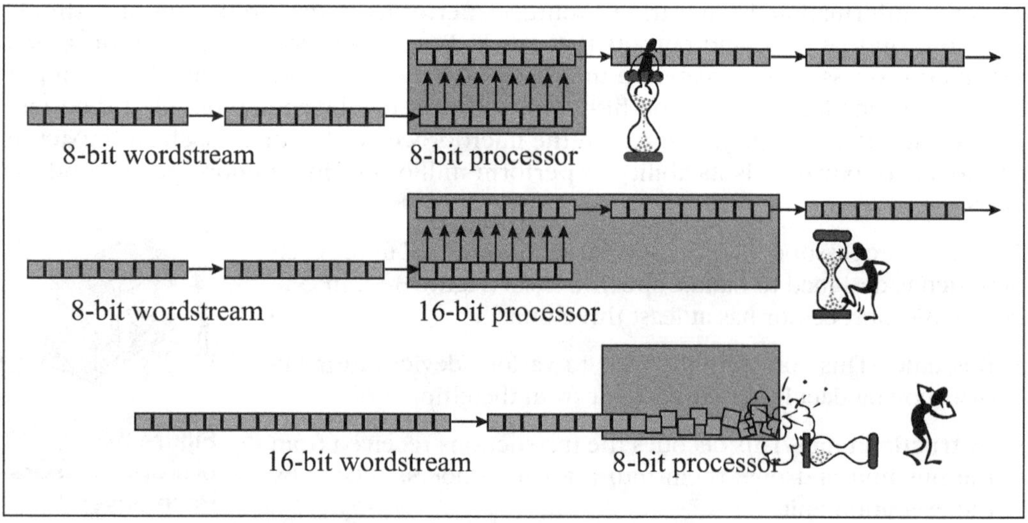

Figure 3-4. 8-Bit versus 16-Bit Processors

You will notice that even if a computer has a 16-bit processor, it still must process one word at a time. Clearly, the performance will not improve unless it is designed to process *two* words at a time. The 8-bit processor is not designed to process larger words. This explanation, of course, applies equally to 16-bit, 32-bit, 64-bit, and higher levels of data processing.

Some system users have been left with a wrong impression that performance improves when they upgrade to a larger processor (register size). However, there is no advantage if the system code is the same as before (same word size), unless that processor is designed to *also* run with the existing code.

Clock Speed: Keeping Everything in Time

Figure 3-5. Tempus Fugit

Clock speeds, measured in megahertz (mHz) provide a "base beat" like a metronome that the CPU operates upon. Actions are performed in steps to the beat of the clock speed. The higher the clock speed, the faster things get done (Figure 3-5). The clock is necessary because computers process information in the form of very brief electrical pulses. Each pulse is dealt with separately in a linear sequence, one after another. The system clock synchronizes all the pulses by allotting a given period of time to move the electrical charges, then triggering the various computer parts to see what they have done. Once all the pulses throughout the system are registered, the system can move to the next beat. Rating a CPU's performance isn't solely based on the clock speed value. Different CPUs go about processing the information differently. Speeds should only be compared for similar CPUs. For example, a 386-33 is faster than a 386-25, but a 286-20 is not necessarily faster than a 386-16.

Brief History of Microprocessors

Just as an example, let's look at one microprocessor manufacturer, the Intel Corporation, which was founded in Santa Clara, California. In 1968, when it was founded, Intel's sole business was trying to integrate large numbers of transistors into small silicon chips. By 1969, a Japanese calculator company approached Intel to manufacture a line of integrated circuits for their calculators. The 4004, the world's first commercially available general-purpose microprocessor was developed. In fact, all personal computers owe their heritage to the 4004. In 1978, IBM went looking for a microprocessor on which to base its new PC. It looked at Motorola, Zylog (now defunct), and Intel. IBM chose Intel's 8088.

With the public outcry for more power, in 1982 Intel released the 8286, which is more commonly known as the 286. The 286 is able to run in two modes, a real mode, which acted like a fast 8088, and a virtual mode, in which it could address much more memory, making it more powerful. It also used an early version of multitasking. By 1985, the 386 was released, and it addressed a bus twice the size of the 286 and four times the size of the 8088. This, coupled with the higher clock speed, made it the most powerful microprocessor of its time. Multitasking was improved by using a technique called pipelining. To bridge the cost gap between the 286 and the 386, Intel introduced, in 1988, the 386SX. This chip had basically the same internal 32-bit structure, but the SX communicated with the outside world with a 16-bit bus. This made connections less expensive and reduced the total cost with only a small sacrifice in clock speed. By the end of 1989, the 486 was released, which was basically the same as the 386 but with a dedicated coprocessor to perform math functions. This significantly increased the speed by 20 to 40 percent. By the Mid 1990s, the Pentium processor was developed, which had it followed the numbering pattern would have been called the 586, hence the name "Pentium." But it had several other design features, making possible for IBM and specifically Microsoft to expand the capability of *Windows*.

Coprocessors

In numeric coprocessors, a special microprocessor is built in to do one thing well— arithmetic. The coprocessor works in conjunction with a CPU to handle all the functions required by the system (Figure 3-6). Since it is dedicated to that task, it's very fast and accurate. Crunching numbers hundreds of time faster than a stand-alone CPU, they have the same size and appearance as a CPU, and many PC manufacturers place the coprocessor socket on their main board. Coprocessors are especially handy when you're using math-intensive programs, such as spread sheets, like *Excel*, *Lotus 1-2-3*, *Quattro Pro*, and so on, or computer-aided drawing (CAD) programs, (such as *Auto-CAD* and generic CAD), and so on. Intel makes most of the available coprocessors, using such names as 8287 and 8387, although other vendors also sell coprocessors.

Figure 3-6. Coprocessors Work in Conjunction with CPUs

Memory Devices

As with all microprocessor systems in use today, several variations or varieties of memory are used in distributed processor systems. Two considerations to look for in any memory device used in these industrial systems is the ability to be nonvolatile, that is, a memory whose stored data or code is retained when power is removed from the memory cells. It should also have the ability to be updated while a memory whose contents can easily be modified by the system processor is operating in the active system.

Computer Memory Parking Lot

In early computers, there were solid-state (i.e., no moving parts) memory cells, which were designed by having a grid of ferrite donuts (miniature donuts) lined up in rows and columns. A single wire would intersect and wrap around each of the donuts for each row going across and another series of wires would go down in columns, wrapping around each coil. The address would be the intersection of any two wires, one in a row, and one in a column, intersecting in the donut they both had in common. When the wire was energized, a magnetic field would be stored in that ferrite core donut.

This would be very much like having a grid of inner tubes sitting in a parking lot, all holding a different pressure. They would hold that "memory" so that three days later you can come back and test the pressure in any one of those tires. If you wanted to give that "memory" (a pressure number) to someone, you would give them a grid position, such as H3. They could go to column H and row 3, take a tire gauge and measure the pressure, and retrieve a number. So in a grid of these tires, across a large parking lot, you could have a considerable memory of different numbers, and all you would need would be the proper address or location of each tire to know which value you wanted to retrieve. Finding the ones and zeros in any memory media is very much the same concept.

RAM versus ROM

In today's modern memory devices, the principles are the same, but the technology allows the signal to reside in significantly more dense locations. Very much as described in the previous section, read-only memory (ROM) and random access memory (RAM), have similar storage patterns where the memory is retrieved from an address. The difference between those two types, read-only memory and random access memory, is in the different functions you may want to perform, either long-term or short-term.

ROM-type memory instructions are taken for a general-purpose computer class to create a special-purpose computer designed, for example, for a distributed process control system. These are usually the fundamental functions of the computer, such as how to multiply or how to divide, and they are used for instructions for routine scanning, communications, and display. Random access memory, on the other hand, is usually used for collecting data that's stored for a short period of time, perhaps only minutes or sometimes hours or days. It is sometimes saved so it can be used, for example, to show the trends of a process variable.

Random Access Memory (RAM)

Random access memory is similar to all the various paraphernalia and notes you have left for yourself on your desktop (Figure 3-7). If you go to your desk and move a note, it changes position, and you have to remember the new location. If you want something that you know you'll be going to go back to after a long period of time, you want a more permanent record. If you only need to remember something for a few days, you can leave it laying on a given place on your desk or in your house, and you'll probably remember where to get it. With you, it is only "probable" that you'll remember it because of your limits of memory. The computer is more likely to remember, except the limits of *its* memory are reached when the power is removed!

Figure 3-7. Your Desktop is Like RAM

This family of fully bit alterable memories can be updated while operating within a system. RAM is easily rewritten by the system's CPU. RAM does not retain its stored values, however, when power is removed. RAM is used to store temporary data and also to shadow the contents of both ROM memory and magnetic mass storage during normal system operation for high-speed access.

SRAMs and DRAMs

Battery-backed static RAMs (SRAM) integrate a battery so data can be stored when the system's power is removed. These batteries are, of course, ultimately volatile and are also sensitive to temperature variations. Dynamic Random Access Memory (DRAM) today is the technology that drives new manufacturing processes for many semi conductor companies. Each Dynamic RAM cell consists of a transistor and a capacitor that must be refreshed or occasionally rewritten in order to retain the stored contents after the leakage. SRAMs requires no periodic refresh and has a faster access time, but at the price of density and cost. SRAMs typically use between four and six transistors per cell, affecting the attainable device density and significantly increasing the memory cost at a given density relative to DRAM.

Read-Only Memory (ROM)

Figure 3-8. Preprinted Book is Like ROM

Read-only memory is like the pages in this book (Figure 3-8). You can read them, but you cannot change the typeface. The only way that can happen is to go back to the printer and have the page reset to new words. This memory family is nonvolatile but cannot be updated while it is in the system. The family members, ROM, PROM (programmable Read-only memory), and EPROM (Erasable Programmable Read Only Memory), are distinguished by their varying degrees of flexibility. ROM memories are used to store permanent code and data that are required to initialize the operator system and that must be accessible at relatively high speed (differentiating them from magnetic disk drives, for example). Most ROM technologies employ a single transistor or fusible link per cell and are therefore capable of high memory densities.

Programmable Read-Only Memory (PROM, EPROM, EAPROM)

Programmable read-only memory (PROM) is memory that you can reprogram, and it will hold that memory until it is programmed again. The most common type is the floating gate type, where the basic memory cell is a metal-oxide semiconductor (MOS) transistor with two gate electrodes. Threshold voltages provide charges for determining the memory state. An erasable programmable read-only memory (EPROM, sometimes EROM) allows you to erase the memory clean with an erasing device, such as an ultraviolet field, and then replace it with an entire new program. An electrically alterable programmable read-only memory (EAPROM, sometimes EAROM) is erased with an electrically charged field rather than by exposure to an ultraviolet field.

Electrically Erasable Programmable Read-Only Memory (EEPROM)

This device can be written upon within an active system on a byte-by-byte basis, like RAM, but it is also nonvolatile like ROM. Write operations to an EEPROM cell will store or remove electrons from areas of the cell transistor, resulting in a zero or a one, respectively, when the cell is subsequently read. Since EEPROM is per-byte alterable, cell erase is a selected part of rewrite. To speed this process, high internal voltage potentials (and subsequent high electric fields) are generated. This has the potentially unhappy consequence of compromising cell reliability over time, causing cell oxide to break down as the transistor is repeatedly rewritten. EEPROM vendors often strive to extend memory lifetime by means of on-chip cell redundancy and error detection and correction (EDAC) logic. This added cell complexity, along with on-chip high-voltage generation and considerable peripheral logic, limits EEPROM density and increases cost per megabyte compared to other types of storage.

Magnetic Data Storage

The resident hard disk drive and removable floppy disk drive are extremely dense, inexpensive (on a cost-per-megabyte basis compared to semiconductor memory), and nonvolatile and can be updated within an active system (Figure 3.9). However, the relatively slow access time caused by "platter seek" and "rotational delay" makes direct read of code and data unrealistic. Instead, nonvolatile magnetic mass storage contents are copied to faster but volatile RAM for CPU access. The fact that hard disk and floppy disk drives contain moving parts (the motor and heads) also suggests that they are potentially less rugged and consume more power than solid-state storage alternatives.

Figure 3-9. Floppy Disk Provides Inexpensive Removable Memory

Optical Memory

The optical disk is a very-high-density information storage medium that uses light to read (engrave) and write (reflect) digital information. It comes in read-only and write-once types, frequently called "write-once, read-many" (WORM). Unlike magnetic media, it is not inadvertently changed or erased because of electromagnetic or radio frequency fields, such as power surges or "walkie-talkies." It comes closest to "paper storage" in its permanency and can be extremely dense, holding the equivalent content of tens of thousands of sheets of paper (100 to 200 megabytes on a 3-inch disk).

Flash Memory

This is the first significantly new solid-state memory technology to appear in over a decade. Its nonvolatility, and high density and the ease which it can be updated can enhance existing applications and make new ones possible. Although by in the mid-1990s it was still considered a relatively new approach, flash memory was by then already in its second generation. These devices have been produced in volume only since 1993, but moved rapidly from novelty status into the main stream within five years. As of this writing, flash memory chips are available in densities of up to sixteen megabits with a random access times of sixty nanoseconds. In addition to providing complete nonvolatility, this capacity makes the chips a potential fit in applications that otherwise might have used ROMs, PROMs, EEPROMs, and battery-backed RAMs or magnetic mass storage. Flash memory can also be updated within an active system. The simplified architecture of using only one transistor results in significant density advantages over both EEPROM and SRAM. Flash memory can even be as dense as ROM and DRAM.

Part B

Controllers

Controller Hardware Structures 4

Here we go with that word *understanding* again. To understand the microprocessor-based controller needs a little understanding of the traditional analog controllers from which it evolved. Different vendors took different approaches to their respective designs based upon how they viewed the role their analog counterparts.

Traditional Process Controllers

Recall that programmable logic controllers (PLCs) used in factory automation began as replacements for banks of relays, with no operator interface other than "start/stop" buttons to initiate action and lamps to follow the progress of an operation and notify the operator of its completion. The origins of process control were quite different.

Early process controllers were physically one with the operator faceplate. They included not just a process variable (PV) indicator on a calibrated scale but also a set point (SP) indicator on that scale and a control signal output indicator. On some instruments, the later was not an indication of the controller output, but rather the actual position of the end element (valve, motor drive unit, etc.) coming from a feedback signal. This was all part of a "process loop" (Figure 4-1): process to sensor, sometimes through a transmitter, to report process conditions to the controller, to drive the final (end) element, which adjusted the process.

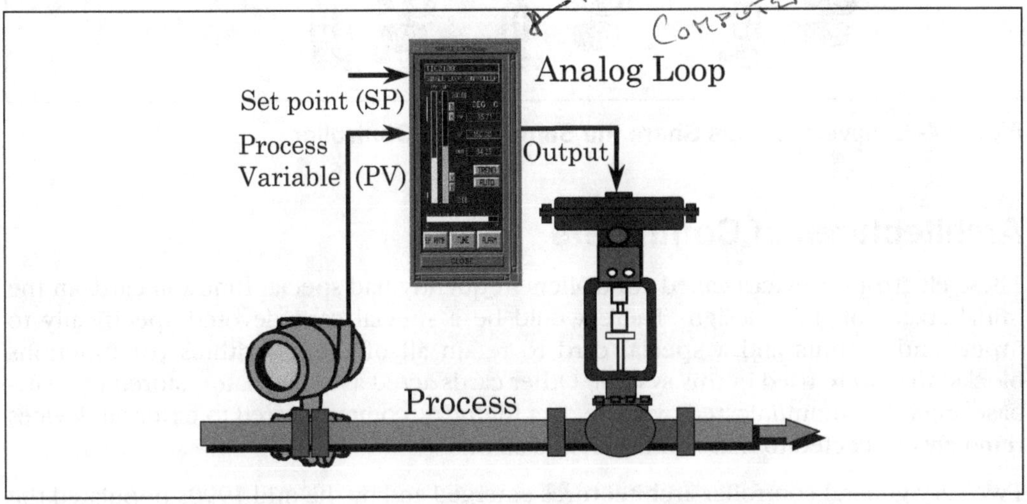

Figure 4-1. Simple Process Loop Using a Traditional Single Loop Controller

In the distributed controller "file" or "rack" the "card cage" became the location of several loops that shared a processor (Figure 4-2). Like before, there were still hard wires to sensors and final elements, but within this controller rack there were no longer direct wires and traditional connections. What starts to be quite unique about a microprocessor-based controller compared to the traditional controller is the opportunity for significant interconnection of the analog and discrete. They both had to be converted to the digital domain. Now alarmed values in one loop could trigger actions in another. There was even the not-so-obvious fact that an "endless" number of "wires" can be connected to a digital point in the system with no voltage/current "loading." In the past, this last idea placed a severe restriction on one's ability to develop many kinds of control *strategies*. This new "freedom" from hardware and hard wiring is permitting many control strategies, that were merely hypothetical in the past to become practical and inexpensive. Hence they offered another opportunity to introduce "productivity" where it had been not possible in the past—a new way to see!

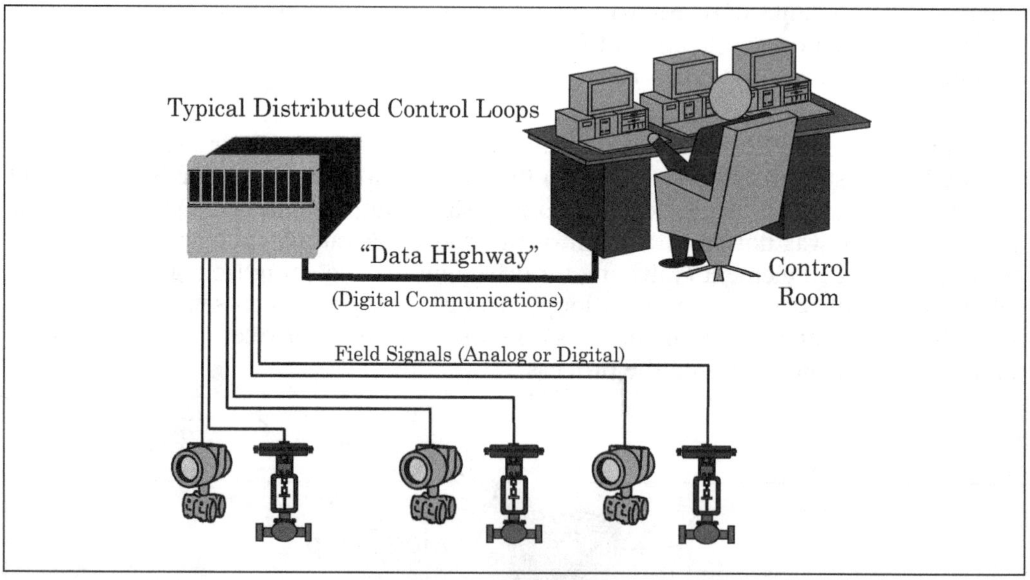

Figure 4-2. Several Loops Share the Same Digital Controller

Architectures of Controllers

These electronic devices called controllers frequently had special function cards in the initial stages of their design. There would be a special card devoted specifically to inputs and outputs and a special card to retain all of the algorithms (or functions blocks) that were used in this system. Other cards acted as a calculator, stored the database, digitally communicated over the data highway, communicated to external devices remotely connected to that controller, and so on.

Two very general controller architectures emerged and by the mid-1990s populated the majority of DCSs still operating by the tens of thousands worldwide. Both types influenced the approach used in the newest of designs and are worth understanding, especially if your company owns a few. Each version has distributed processing, but they distributed it in different ways.

In what I call the shared-function version, all the loops coming into that particular controller shared several microprocessor cards (Figure 4-3). Microprocessors were *functionally* distributed into I/O processing, control processing, communication processing, and so on. In this particular structure, the same card sets were used for all versions of control in most cases. As a result, all the controllers were alike from a hardware viewpoint and relatively easy to maintain and expand in their own way. They could be recognized by their having such cards as an output card (or a hold card, perhaps called a hold station), an input conditioning card, a database card, an algorithm card, and an external communication card. These cards were usually accompanied by the other required cards, such as a power supply card and a data highway card. The earlier controllers made by EMC, Fischer and Porter, Foxboro Microspec, Honeywell TDC2000, Leeds & Northrup's MAX 1, Moore Products MYCRO and Powell System's Micon tended to be of this type.

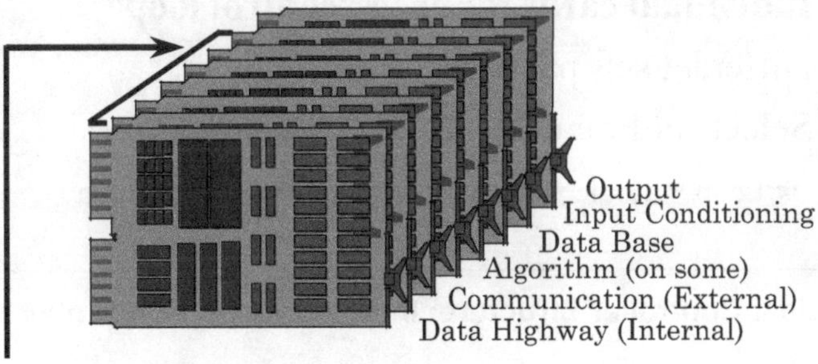

- **All "control loops" share several cards**
- Same sets for all
- Function processing is distributed:
  - I/O ● Control ● Data highway ● Communication

Figure 4-3. Physical Controller Structure: Shared-Function Controller Rack

---

The major advantage of the "shared function controller" is that all the controllers have the same hardware/software sets, making ordering, installing, changing orders, training, maintaining, and storing of spare parts very simple.

The other generalized construction was to have individual microprocessor cards for each loop or loop set (Figure 4-4). Some cards were for loop control, different ones were used for logic control. The functions of output, input, signal conditioning, and so on occurred on each card by the same processor. There were also separate cards for "programming" beyond the vendor's "standard set" of algorithms. Frequently, these cards are called "multifunction," "multipurpose," or similar names. Different combinations of cards were unique in each controller rack depending on the customer's order. Each controller rack would also have a highway card and a power supply card, sometimes another card for diagnostics, and still another card for a bus driver to connect these cards together. These systems in those days tended to be Bailey, Fisher Controls, Foxboro IA, Rosemont, Taylor, and Toshiba.

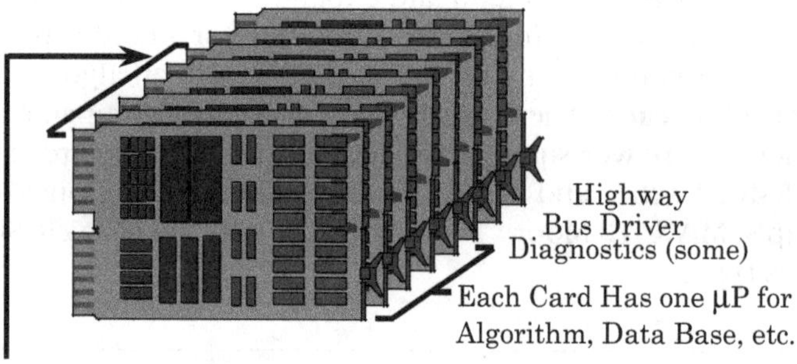

- **Individual cards for each "control loop"**
- Different sets per order
- Select card for each needed function:

● Loop ● Logic ● Data Acquisition ● Multifunction

Figure 4-4. Physical Controller Structure: Individual Loop Controller Rack

---

The major advantage of the "individual loop controller" approach is that the loss of a processor only impacts one loop or small cluster of loops.

Later designs began to combine these ideas in ways not so easy to classify, taking advantage of ever increasing processor power and memory capacities. Emerging from both of these earlier designs is a more current design in which all the functions are embedded on a single card, or module (Figure 4-5). Most architectures being sold in the mid-1990s use what are called multifunction controllers rather than loop controllers, logic controllers, and separate application controllers. This approach also provides the advantages of the single hardware/software set. This is the form that "soft control" within PCs is taking.

The advantages of having multiple loops residing within the same card makes it even more possible to create some very powerful multiloop control strategies. This capability defeats the purpose of "single loop integrity," which is near impossible to achieve with any kind of interlocking control strategy. The only protection for today's control strategies is redundant controllers, which are now more practical and reasonably priced than before. (I personally have always called single loop integrity a marketing myth that was based upon a battle between two vendors in the late 1970s.)

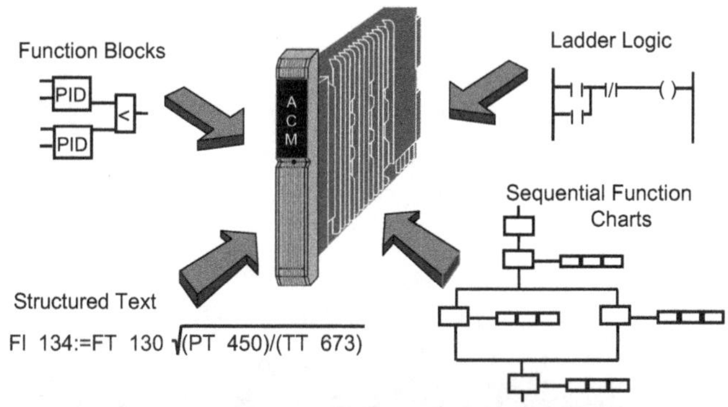

- Continuous, discrete, sequential control
- Four blended languages (IEC 1131-3)

Figure 4-5. Single Control Module with Multiple "Languages" (and Capabilities) Within the Same Module

Expect to see wider use of multiple configuration languages within the same module. The International Electrotechnical Commission's standard IEC 61131-3 defines five such languages, each of which has been popular with various PLC vendors. Four of these languages are function blocks for continuous control, ladder logic for discrete requirements, sequential function charts for sequencing and batch control, and structured text for complex calculations. (The fifth is like assembly language, not very useful as a "user-friendly" language for process configuration). One process vendor has been using multiple configuration languages within the same module since 1992, and offers the ability to blend the configuring of all the languages in the same graphic technique. More process vendors are beginning to employ one or more of the IEC languages in their control configuration.

Controller Software Structures 5

Just as the original analog controllers influenced initial hardware designs, so also did they influence software. The software had to perform the actual functions of the controllers, but as the unique capabilities of software were learned, new functions emerged. More precisely, new combinations of functions were now possible, which continue to lead to far more capabilities than ever before, at far less cost. This is the exciting area of development which is significantly altering and expanding the whole field of process control.

Programming

When talking about computers, you often encounter the terms *hardware*, *software*, and *firmware*. Hardware, of course, is the tangible part of the computer that you can see and touch. Software, on the other hand, is the set of instructions in the computer that tell it how to function. Firmware, however, is software that is burned into a PROM and always stays the same, so that certain routines are always done the same way, such as an algorithm for a three-mode controller, or a multiplier, or a divider.

> Handheld calculators function using firmware. Because of PROM, the "plus" button always adds and the "multiply" button always multiplies. If you remove the batteries, then return them, those buttons continue to do the same thing. The machine, however, cannot remember the last numbers it calculated before the batteries were removed! Those values were held in RAM.

The programming of firmware must be complete and very specific. The microprocessors within a process controller have generally been programmed to perform a specific number of basic routines, defined by commands. This is similar to the standard operating procedure in the army camp analogy we talked about in Chapter 3. The routines are untouchable; their combinations of bits reside in read-only memory (ROM), inaccessible to the user. There is a very basic routine that causes a CPU to look up an instruction for a particular register, perform the command that the instruction defines, and then go look up the next instruction. If there is no instruction, wait and periodically look again, and when another instruction appears carry it out.

To generalize to some extent, the instructions will direct the information stored in a specific address in memory, which is to be brought to the microprocessor, where it is then put into a data register. From there it goes to an arithmetic logic unit (ALU), where arithmetic or logic operations are performed on the data. The information may be temporarily stored in another register called an accumulator, to be combined with another portion of data called by a subsequent instruction. And as quickly as possible the modified information will be sent from the CPU for storage in a memory again. In this way, specific tasks are executed.

The memory units in which this manipulated information is stored are not read-only memory (ROM) but random access memory (RAM). This memory is accessible to the programmer. The programmer can combine the commands that the microprocessor can execute in specific consecutive arrangements that will accomplish his or her purpose. In our army camp analogy, this program is comparable to the series of activities carried out by the recruits that are designed to teach them to become soldiers.

Minicomputers differ from most microcomputers in that they can be programmed in a high-level language like FORTRAN, or Pascal, to perform any task that a programmer can describe. By assembling commands from the list that the computer will obey, the minicomputer is a general-purpose computer. Microcomputers generally do not have such flexibility. They are not general-purpose devices but are called special purpose computers, such as a process controller. They can be "configured" to perform programmed tasks selected from a list of available routines to accomplish a desired result. But in most cases, it is not possible to create new routines. For example, a pocket calculator can add, subtract, multiply, and divide, but it cannot call for the selection of the highest of three numbers. A routine to do this could be written, but if it were not, this operation would be denied to the user unless he or she can figure out a way to do what he or she wants, using the functions that are already available to him or her.

Organizing Execution Time for Control Action

The way the software runs within each vendor's box takes on different characteristics depending on the design that vendor has chosen. Just as hardware designs have different appearances, so do software designs even though the function may be the same. In a software program, the microprocessor is going to read all the lines of code that have been written to perform a function. The time it takes to go through all the lines of code is called scan time. The designer is faced with several approaches to make his or her software execute, just as a designer of hardware is faced with different approaches regarding the way his or her parts are assembled.

In the traditional computer, a program is written, and however long that program is, whether it be minutes or hours, the computer has to go through every step of that program before it comes to the end and then recycles and goes through the entire scan again. It is a very rare computer program that can stop in the middle, although there are designs that allow that. Within a process controller, the designer can decide to have each function of the controller, whether it be three-mode control, mass flow calculation, or whatever, as an entire routine written in his or her program. When these different routines are assembled into an entire control configuration, each of these small scans is added together in a way that properly executes a given control loop.

With no standards available, most control venders made their best efforts to incorporate real-time execution of loop functions within their design. By the way of a simplistic explanation, I have invented "styles" that typically have been used, shown in Figure 5-1.

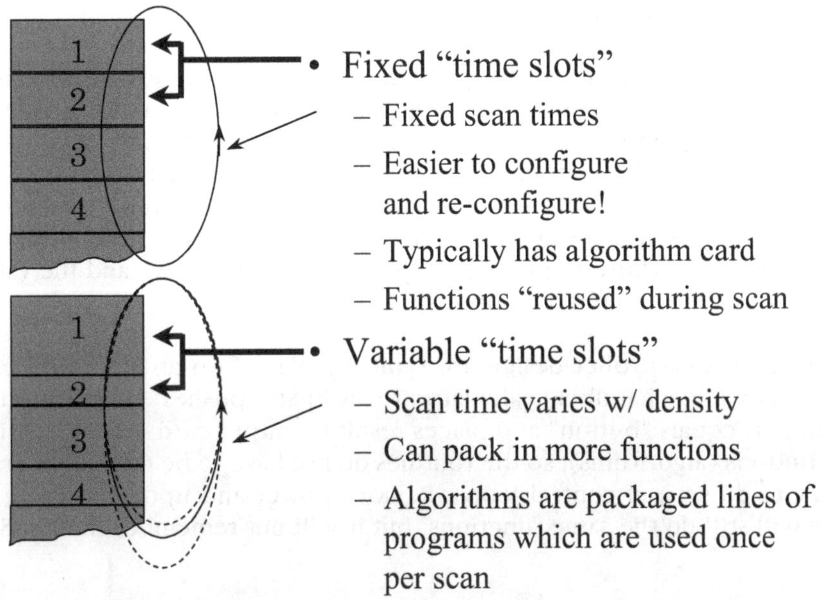

Figure 5-1. Control Function Execution: Fixed Times for Flexibility vs. Variable Times for Capacity

The earliest form is what I call the "fixed time slot" approach, in which all functions (firmware) each execute within the same time length (say, 1/64th of a second). Early examples of this approach include the Honeywell TDC2000, Leeds & Northrup MAX 1, and Moore MYCRO.

In these "fixed time slot" controllers there may be, for example, thirty-two subdivisions through which this controller scans to develop the control strategy. Each piece of the strategy would fit into those time scans or time slots. So there would be thirty-two functions available within that controller from a library of many functions. During the controller operation, each of those time slots would be scanned in the same order every time the microprocessor goes through its routine. The first time slot might have a three-mode (PID) controller. The second time slot might have a cascaded controller that links to that first three-mode controller. The third time slot might have a summing block, the fourth a multiplier, and so on.

Note that whatever time it takes for a controller to do a full three-mode algorithm, it will probably take much more time to do a multiplier. But in a fixed scan type structure the same time is allotted for each operation (perhaps 1/64th of a second). There is, then, some wasted time in the multiplier "slot," which causes the processor to sit idle until the scan gets to the next time slot. This is somewhat inefficient for controller performance. Yet by providing a fixed amount of time slots as well as the same time "length" within each, the user is guaranteed the same complete scan time for every controller, no matter what function is used and no matter who configures it! Furthermore, when changing control strategies, every function fits in any "position" so reconfiguration is just as easy, especially online changes. These are very important considerations in a plant.

Usually, in this kind of controller the operation of the action of the controller is to take a calculation from a database and put it through a subroutine, say, a three-mode controller. This is like the operation of a hand calculator. In a hand calculator, when you enter a value, push a "plus button" or "multiply button," it performs that function. When you push the "equal button" it will then give you an answer. You can do thousands upon thousands of calculations, always using the same plus routine or multiply routine within the calculator. Those routines are typically saved in PROM, and the values you are entering would be brought temporarily into RAM.

Algorithms in this controller design are typically placed on an algorithm card and perform exactly like a handheld calculator: reads in SP, "pushes" PID "button," reads in PV, "pushes" equals "button" and places result to output card. All calculations use the same buttons (algorithms), so the routines do not have to be copied several times in memory to do several control loops. Remove power and upon returning its, the controller will still do the same functions, but it will not remember the last SP or PV readings.

The other software execution style I call the "variable time slot." In that controller type, the scan of a three-mode (PID) control might take one length of time, the multiplier far less time and a sequencer a far longer length of time. All these irregular time slots are added together, of course. Usually, in this type of controller the engineer who is configuring the system must keep track of all the scan times and add them up so he or she knows how long it will take for the controller to perform a function. The length of time it takes for that controller to perform a function depends on how many different scan times or, in other words, how many different kinds of functions and their individual lengths are put together. Unlike the "fixed time slot" type, the scan time differed between any of the controllers in the same system.

Because the "variable time slot" approach allows each algorithm to use only the time needed for execution, many more functions could be run in the same amount of time. Nevertheless, the user had the responsibility of determining the scan times to assure that execution does not take too long! This made configuration, and especially reconfiguration very difficult. Unlike the "calculator push button" approach, multiple control loops required additional subroutines of those functions (versus reusing the same routines). Before enough memory was available, the user could also run out of a function if enough were not placed into library! Early examples included Fischer & Porter's DCI and Powell Systems' Micon.

Now these two approaches to controller software had been a serious consideration in the buying of controllers throughout the 1970s and 1980s and even into the 1990s. Thus, most of the tens of thousands of DCS controllers in operation today will reflect one of these two designs in some general way. The technology of processing speed and memory capacity available today has removed many of the limitations to this approach, and as well have diminished the impact of either of these different controller software structures.

Software Structure Advances

The advances made in distributed systems have also relied heavily on new and evolving approaches to make it convenient to configure computer based systems without having to be a programmer. The idea is that the plant engineer whose responsibility it is to develop the control systems that operate the process involved may fully understand how to program but should not have to be a programmer in order to make his or her control system work.

Now, the elements that go into a control system have evolved over the years from "programming" to "configuration."

Programming vs. Configuration

> You may very well know how to design a light bulb, but you should not have to design and build a light bulb every time you want light to appear in the room. You merely want to throw the switch and get enough light for the job at hand. Building a control system is very much the same kind of problems.

Machine code was the original programming language, and, in fact, all code that goes into any processor is reduced to this eventually (i.e., compiled).

More memory and processing power made possible assembly language, which made programming "easier" because it was somewhat translatable. The assembly language example shown in Figure 5-2 says the following:

- Load accumulator register A with the value stored in the memory location named TEMP
- Subtract 150 from the temperature value stored in accumulator A and put the result in A
- If the accumulator value is less than zero, go to the instruction labeled LOOP1, otherwise
- Load A with a specific number (which will turn on the motor)
- Store the contents of accumulator A in a location called MOTOR (turns on fan motor)

Relay logic grew out of relay hardware and provided electricians in North America with an easy understanding of solid state troubleshooting. Programming complex functions like PID are very cumbersome! Engineers prefer to use Boolean logic to express the same programming information.

Even more memory and processing power made higher-level languages possible, through still often cryptic to nonprogrammers. These languages often focused on specific endeavors, such as science (Pascal), business, machine tools (APT), simulation, circuit analysis, and so on.

All of these languages have had a role in the history of the methods of programming controls, whether for programming logic control or for distributed controls. All have been continuously evolving.

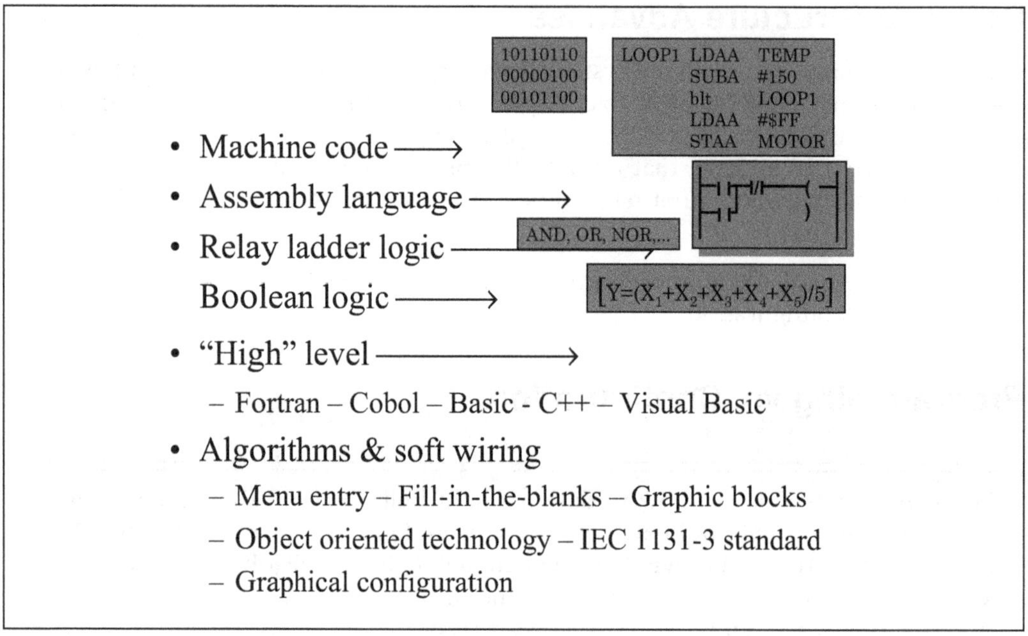

Figure 5-2. Growing From Programming to Configuration: Advances in Software Structures

Function Blocks

Process control vendors found most of these software languages difficult for users who needed easy tools for configuring rather than programming! This led each vendor to develop function blocks to "arrange" control strategies by connecting them in various ways with "soft wiring."

- Vendor X says he has forty algorithms
- Vendor Q says he has four hundred!
- Who has more functionality? Maybe neither!

The first vendor may have large function blocks, but very complete and powerful, ones probably with appropriate alarms and discrete status links embedded into them. If you need to later add to these alarms or link to the status of a function, you merely need to connect to what is already there and go—probably without changing scan times or "finding room" to somehow squeeze the function(s) into the configuration. Typically, those vendors who took the "fixed time slot" approach used larger function blocks.

The second vendor may have many more smaller function blocks. Several function blocks may be needed to create the same operation done with a single one of the first vendor's function blocks. (One vendor I recall took forty-two small function blocks to perform a cascade control action, which took another vendor only two of their own function blocks to perform.)

Smaller function blocks clearly have more flexibility, but making any changes will probably require a more significant rearranging of the control strategy, a painful recalcula-

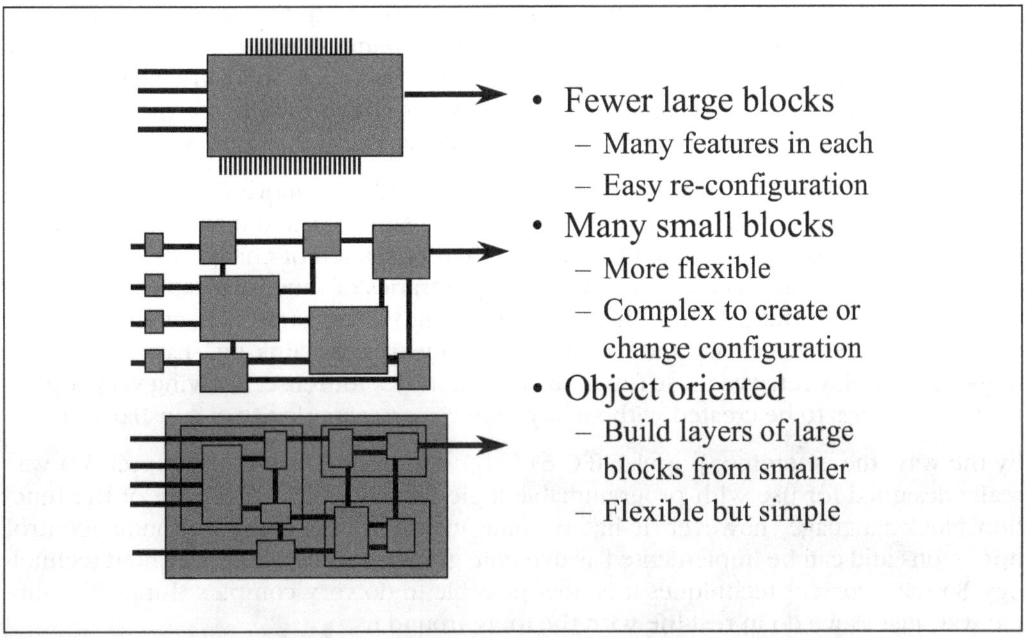

Figure 5-3. Software Structures & Direction: Function Blocks Grow to Object Oriented Configuration

tion of scan times, and the consideration of *any* other interactions. Sometimes it requires checkout and verification as is needed with computer code. Typically, vendors who took the "variable time slot" approach tended to have smaller function blocks.

Object-Oriented

Now, wouldn't it be nice to have the advantages of both types—the convenience of the large blocks and the flexibility of the small? Emerging to answer this need is the concept of object-oriented configuration.

Object-Oriented Analogy

We define a pencil as a "rod of graphite surrounded by wood, capped on one end with metal ferrule holding a rubber tip for erasing incorrect marks made with the graphite." Instead of reciting the full definition every time you want to ask someone for this writing instrument, you would merely ask for..a pencil. So "pencil" would be the object, and all of the components of the object are implied in that single word pencil. In fact, you don't even have to know the components of that object in order to use it.

The object-oriented configuration allows you to build layers of larger blocks out of smaller blocks. This means you can assemble the exact type of three-mode controller you like, with whatever alarms and status conditions you wish it to report. Then you save it with the identity of a single unit (large block). Using the advantages of copy/paste-type routines and other word processing techniques, you can then build very complex configurations of control strategies without having to build all the details each time. Your view of that large block remains very basic. You merely see the inputs and the outputs that are attached to that block without seeing all the detail within.

At some later time, you may discover the need to add or remove functions from the (small block) details of that large block. "Open" the large block and make the modifications. You could use that changed block as a different version or change all those blocks in which the original was used, or both. Whole libraries of functions can easily be custom developed by the user and then configured into larger strategies, without seeing every detail unless necessary and without fear of unexpected "linking." Easy-to-use techniques can readily retrieve these functions from libraries for reuse, allowing very sophisticated strategies to be created without any unnecessary complexity of construction.

By the way, the emerging, popular IEC 61131-3 standard (covered in Chapter 32) was really designed for use with programmable logic control. With clever use of the function block language, however, it has become just as useful with continuous control operations and can be implemented as dynamic graphics using object-oriented technology. So with current techniques it is now possible to do very complex things in a simple way, just as we do in real life with the tools around us.

Connecting the Blocks

Vendors have created the equivalent of many instrument hardware types by building software function blocks that perform the same computations. The set of these is usually in *firmware*, which is software that thinks it is hardware (as compared with vaporware, which is what the salesman sells before a product is a product).

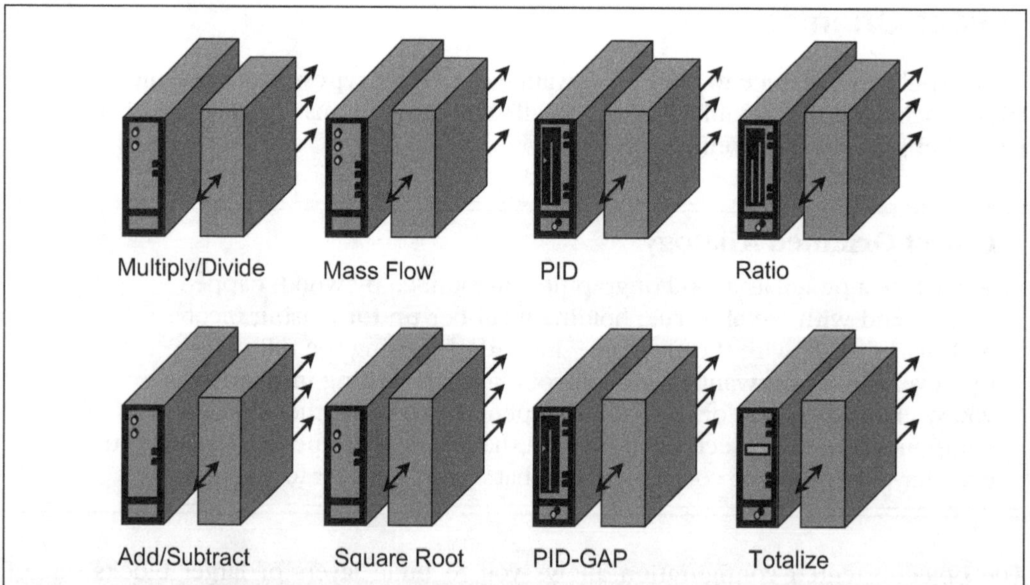

Figure 5-4. Hardware to Firmware: Function Blocks can be "Instruments"

These standardized function blocks will generally vary from one vendor to another and are designed so the fundamental action cannot be altered by the user, but many "adjusters" and "terminals" are available, just as with the hardware they replaced. This is so the "programming" of those functions does not have to be tested repeatedly for each use. The person doing the configuration can fully expect that they will work the same way every time, without having to resort to what programmers call "linking."

Linking Analogy

You are making eggs one morning, and you are being helped by a four-year-old child. Now anybody who knows four-year-olds, knows that they desperately want to help but don't have enough experience to be useful! Nevertheless, you give in hoping this learning experience will pay off in the future. "Quickly get me two eggs," you ask. The youngster proceeds to throw two eggs at you. (You said you wanted them quick!) They arrive scrambled. "*No,*" you say, "bring them to me in something safe!" The youngster places each in a pocket, where they are immediately crushed. Still not wanting scrambled eggs, you modify you request again: "Place them in a container to bring them over." The child finds a grocery bag and carefully places two more eggs inside. Arm length and bag size combine to allow the eggs to bounce along the floor (while "protected" within the bag) as the child happily skips across the room to present them to you.

Now, each of your commands was correct, and the responses were just as you asked, but the eggs arrive damaged each time. Programmers call that "linking." That is, *anyone* can tell a computer what to do, but only someone with the proper application experience can tell it *all* that it also should *not* do!

Let us combine a few function blocks in a simple configuration, like the one in Figure 5-5. The power of this combining function concept is astounding to someone who is familiar with the old hardware methods of building control strategies!

Just imagine the many possible versions of this optimizing capability of connecting some function block as an input to the gain of a three-mode (PID) controller. For example:

- An eight-position switch function block could select various gains based on operator input..or inputs caused by different stages of a process.

- A ramp generator function block could vary the gain by some relationship to a changing variable..or the difference between two variables.

- A function generator could change the gain by some uniquely nonlinear response to a changing variable..or the changing relationships between two variables.

And so on; the possibilities are limited only by the process engineer's imagination!

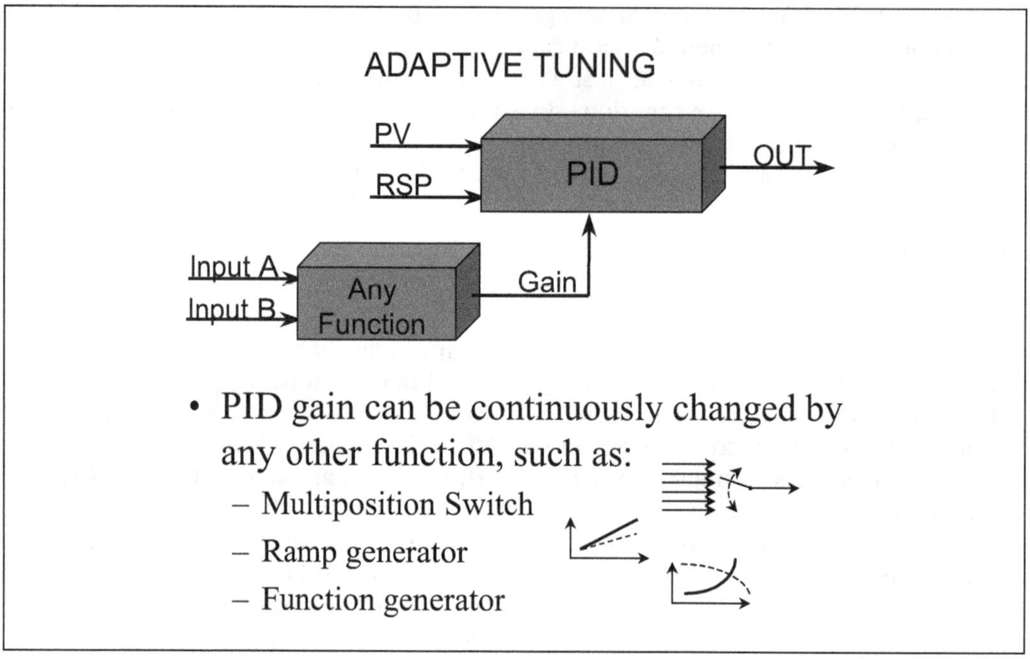

Figure 5-5. Combining Function Blocks for Powerful Control Strategies

A few years ago, all of this was only possible by using some single, central computer passing through vulnerable and slow communication links. With hardware it probably was not possible at all—or at least not practical! From this ease of configuration will come those changes in process techniques that will provide *productivity*. Productivity was the real reason we said your boss wanted you to look into a DCS.

On the left and right of Figure 5-6 we see hard connections coming into a controller from the real world of sensors and final elements. In between the vertical bars we see function blocks connected by "soft wiring," which make up a control strategy. Here we see a small industrial boiler that combines analog control of both fuel and oil, which are connected together so that if the set point of the air controller is modified there are links and overrides to keep the fuel in proper balance. There is no need for the operator to have to manage these independently—with imperfect results.

You will also notice the discrete trips for flame failure, low oil, and so on. These are also linked to logic overrides so as to shut down the boiler if it is required by the combination of conditions. Notice also the impact of steam pressure, oil flow, header pressure, and air flow. There is even a boiler efficiency equation there. Of course, a power utility boiler would be far more complex, but it could also be done through function blocks and soft wiring.

Changing Control Strategy

Rather than the small industrial boiler shown in Figure 5-6, the example could just as easily illustrate the strategy for making tomato soup. Anyone who has ever tried to

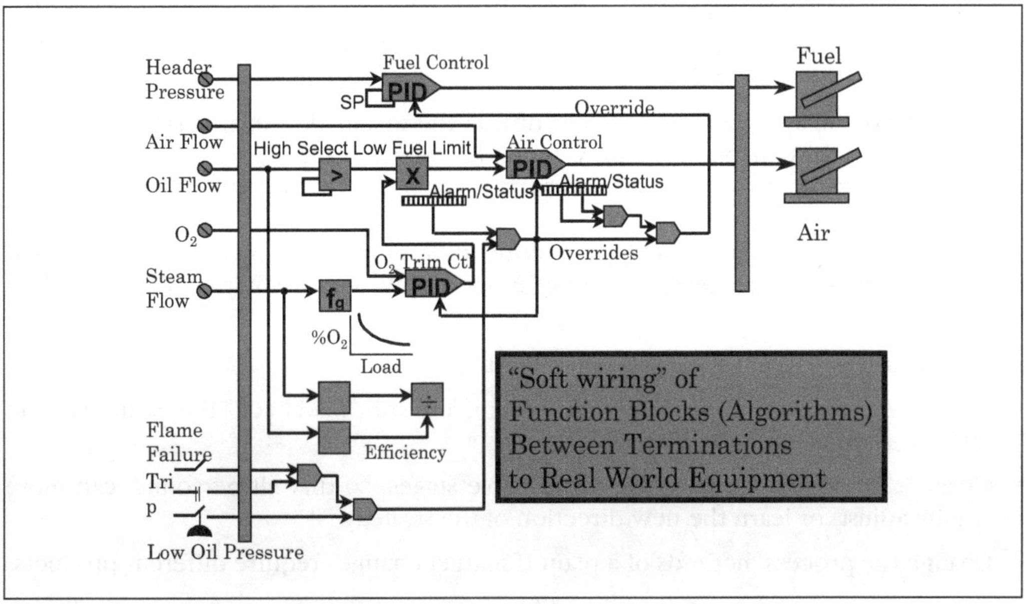

Figure 5-6. Connecting Function Blocks Through "Soft Wiring"

make tomato soup from scratch can tell you that when you try to mix high acid, like tomatoes, with milk it wants to curdle badly, especially when subjected to heat. There is a cooking technique to do this and a control strategy, just as in the process industries. In commercial production all the post and pans are really vats and piping, but the "cooking" techniques and control strategies are similar.

The same set of pots and pans, or vats and piping would be used next month when the company could be making split pea soup instead of tomato. If you ever burned your tongue on split pea soup, you know that its characteristics are much different than tomato. Different controlling techniques are needed for different applications. Instead of rewiring the controllers and placing different ones on the line, one would merely download a different control strategy. It could easily use different "instrumentation" (firmware function blocks) that is "softwired" in a different way. The different configurations for the several products made at this plant could be saved in memory, even kept on some removable memory media, to be used whenever they are needed.

Everything Changes

Even while you are in the middle of building something the project will change. Have you ever done a project around a house? Did it ever end up the way you first envisioned it? Take a simple shelf in a closet, for example. All you need is two boards on either side of the closet, and a plank across them on top. You cut the two boards and plank, then try to attach them but discover that there are no studs behind the drywall on the sides; they are in the rear. You then toss the two boards aside, and go down to the hardware store for some simple shelf brackets. As you prepare to install them, someone in the household says, "Don't use those ugly things, I want the gold-colored ones with the curlicues!" So you go down to the hardware store again for the prescribed brackets, and as you are again preparing them for installation and someone else says, "They're too high." So you lower them. Just as you get out the can of paint, a cry goes up, "That's a terrible color, it clashes with the room color!"

Look at how many changes occurred during the installation of this simple shelf. What do you think happens when you build an entire plant!

Instead of food, the plant could be making different grades of paper, steel, glass, cement, or any other process. The significance points are that with soft wiring, it is easy to:

- Make changes while the plant is being built.
- Create new ways to run a process, test them, and still "load back" the earlier version if the first turns out to be better.
- Create a major change in small, manageable stages, so that all personnel can more readily adjust, or learn the new direction of the strategy.
- Change the process methods of a plant if market changes require different products.

In contrast, none of these changes would have been likely when only traditional hardware was available. When using pneumatic, electromechanical, electrical, or even electronic controllers, doing involved strategies was very complex. You had to buy a collection of hardware, and then you had to hook it together. The tuning of all of these different control loops was very difficult, especially if you needed to make them play together in a multivariable control scheme. There were physical limitations to the levers, gears, balance beams, and pneumatic components, even to the electronic components in controllers.

To make a simple change like switching from a two-mode controller into a three-mode controller, frequently required that an extra component, or for that matter a different kind of controller, be purchased. So change was always very expensive. To make a change in your control strategy, you frequently had to do the following:

- Determine the additional hardware and instrumentation that would *probably* work.
- Look in catalogs for the correct combinations and sizes needed.
- Develop a purchase order.
- Perhaps go out on bid to several vendors.
- Wait for delivery (often months).
- Develop a work order, perhaps involving more than one of the crafts (and unions).
- Turn off the process or plant (sometimes scheduling it to fit normal maintenance time).
- Change all the appropriate wiring and/or plumbing.
- Test what can be static tested.
- Turn the process or plant back on.
- Make dynamic tests.
- Hope that it worked the first time, or do it all over again with new "stuff."

Today, with microprocessor-based controllers, you can pretest control strategies even before you go online, and you can do it within the same controller while that controller is performing the original function. Online changes are becoming practical as well. The microprocessor-based controller makes possible an entirely different approach to the design and use of plants. It also has great implications for redundant systems.

REDUND... OR TRANSMITTING

... THE FAILURE OF

FUNCTIONAL DISTRIBUTION

PHYSICAL DISTRIBUTION

Controller Redundancy 6

In the "olden days" of single loop control hardware, it was rare for a process loop to actually be backed up with another. Usually, the fallback position was to switch to manual. On critical processes, however, the expense of another controller was justified for a one-to-one control loop backup (Figure 6-1). If the process had any kind of interlocked control, even as simple as cascade control, such a backup was very difficult and also very expensive. If interlocking relays were needed, redundancy got very complicated because of the additional components, which could perhaps cause the strategy to be more unreliable!

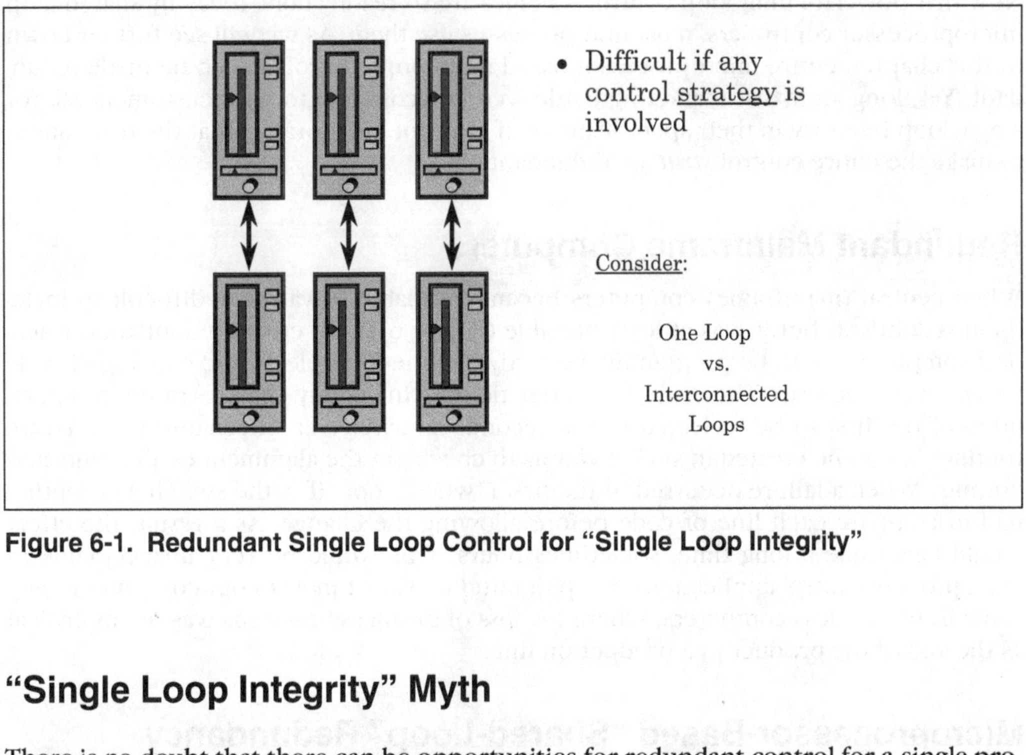

Figure 6-1. Redundant Single Loop Control for "Single Loop Integrity"

"Single Loop Integrity" Myth

There is no doubt that there can be opportunities for redundant control for a single process loop. I believe, however, that more has been made of this than is necessary. Most microprocessor-based controllers are on unit processes with more than a simple variable, say, temperature. Quite often that loop is connected with pressure, flow, and some analyzer as well as other devices. When that occurs, the loop is no longer independent, and if the loop fails the entire operation stops. To prevent this, the entire *strategy* must be redundant, or the single loop must be entwined with many vulnerable relays and cutouts, which, as we stated before, are even more likely to fail than the control loop itself.

The battle cry for "single loop integrity" started in the early days of distributed systems, when shared loop control was the only economical way to use microprocessors. In a sticky *marketing* situation, a vendor without a DCS was selling against a vendor with one and was losing jobs. To change the cost/benefit factors of the DCS vendor, the second vendor mounted a campaign to write into specifications the need to back up each loop independently of the others. Redundancy was in its infancy, and the DCS vendor had developed a scheme to back up his multiloop controller files in a cost-effective way by sharing up to eight controller files with a single back-up "director" connected to a single "empty" controller file. Because of the expense, this scheme became economical only when four or more controller files shared this system. The second vendor, who was competing with traditional single loop controllers, developed an advertising program insisting that only one-to-one loop backup was reliable. This convinced several customers to require a one-to-one *loop* backup, causing the DCS vendor who was using the "shared backup" approach to bid four times the equipment (and cost!) to comply.

Now that powerful multiloop control schemes are so readily done today by shared-loop microprocessor controllers, most unit processes use them. As we will see further down in this chapter, entire microprocessor-based multiloop controllers can be made redundant. Yet, long after that marketing battle, vendors continue to have customers ask for single loop integrity in their specifications, if only out of ignorance that the real issue is to make the entire control *strategy* redundant.

Redundant Mainframe Computers

When central (mainframe) computers became available it was very difficult to make them redundant, but it was at least possible (Figure 6-2). To create redundancy, a second computer had to be programmed exactly like the first (electronic copying of code was not yet practical). There was no automatic tracking of any changes in the programming of the first to be reflected in the second. A switchover "mechanism" (software routine) had to be created in such a way as to check out the alignment of all inputs and outputs. When a failure occurred in the first ("when," not "if"), the switchover routine had to compare each line of code before allowing the change. As a result, the effort would take quite a long time, sometimes hours. This would be very unacceptable in most process control applications. Keep in mind now, that most of our computer legacy came from business computers, where the loss of business functions was not as critical as the loss of the product in a production line.

Microprocessor-Based "Shared-Loop" Redundancy

With the advent of the first microprocessor controllers, the first designs were shared-loop controllers, because of the cost. In these were eight loops situated within the same box. It was realized that these digital versions of process loops residing in the same box could actually transfer information between loops, allowing complex control strategies. Because of this, it was next realized that it was best to back up the entire control strategy. By now it was also necessary to run diagnostics on these new processors and their circuitry.

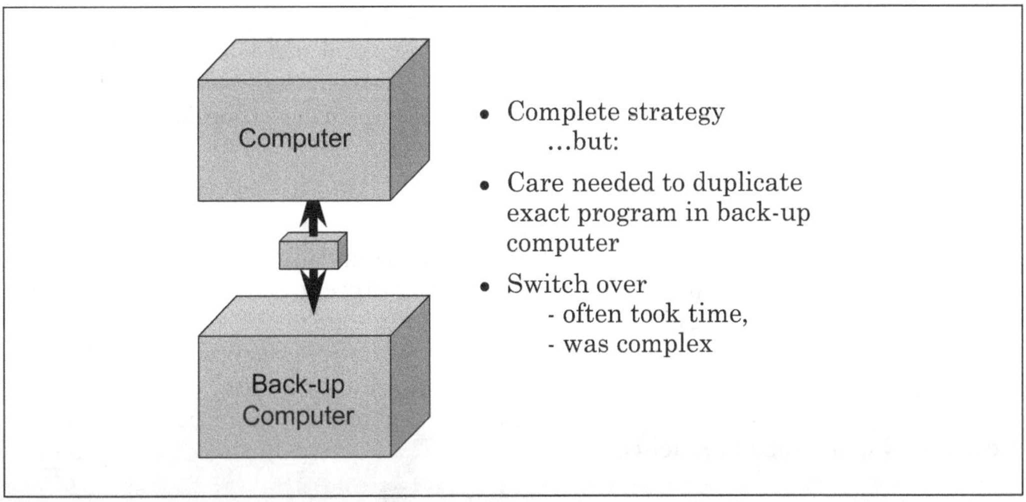

Figure 6-2. Mainframe Computer Redundancy

A separate monitoring circuit was needed to view the diagnostics within that controller to determine when it was necessary to switch to the backup. In these earlier days, this process was an expensive affair. It was decided to share several controller "files" with this "backup control director" to keep the costs reasonable (Figure 6-3). Through the control director and the digital communication link between it and the controllers, each controller was able to maintain the same input/outputs without physically switching them, instead using a spare "empty" controller to hold the configured software control strategy.

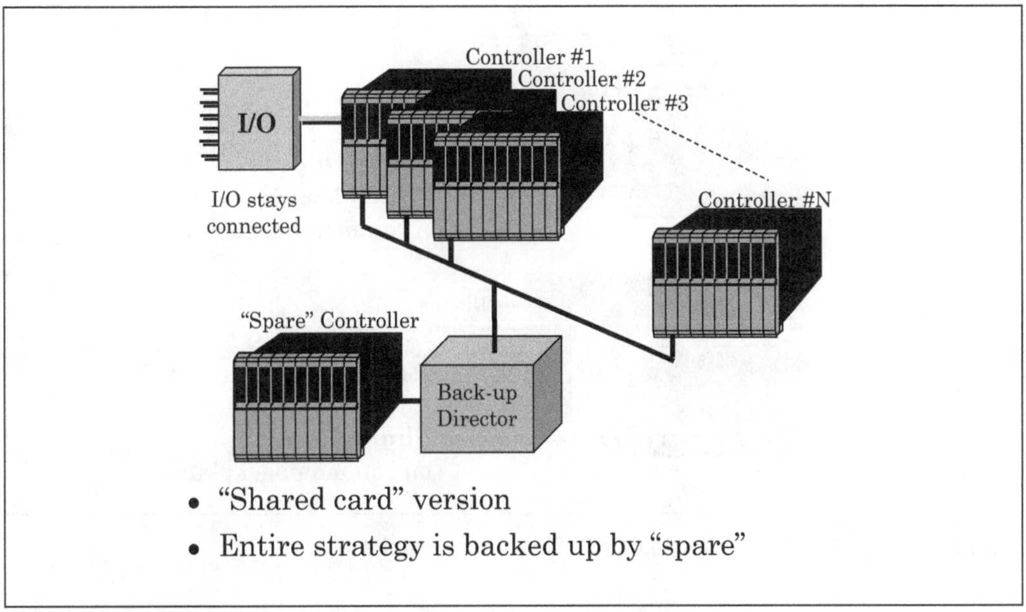

Figure 6-3. Shared Loop Redundancy Among Controllers

When the control director saw the diagnostics of one of these eight controllers going down, it would then immediately switch the database from that failing controller into the spare controller, redirect the inputs and outputs, and continue to operate from the spare controller as if it were the main controller or the primary controller. This was all done well within the decay time of the failing controller.

In an architecture in which all the hardware/software sets are identical, the selected control strategies within these controllers do not have to be. A "1 to N" backup is possible because entire control strategies are backed up. Redundancy is transparent both to the process itself and to display views of the operator (except, of course, for a diagnostic about the primary failure). The system relies on the statistically low chance that an additional controller will fail before the first primary controller is brought back in service. This was a relatively secure method of back up, but of course, the fact that you were moving a database out of a failing controller frightened a lot of people. I believe the fear was unfounded in practice.

Microprocessor-Based Redundancy in "Single Card" Controller Racks

In the controller design architecture that uses different card sets for each controller "file," redundancy is a rarity (Figure 6-4). (Actually, I do not know of any instances at all.) When vendors of those same structures offered a "multifunction" version, a variety of backup versions then emerged. They are summarized by two very generalized types, shared and one-to-one. Although only some of these versions are still being sold on the market, many tens of thousands more continue to operate in plants worldwide.

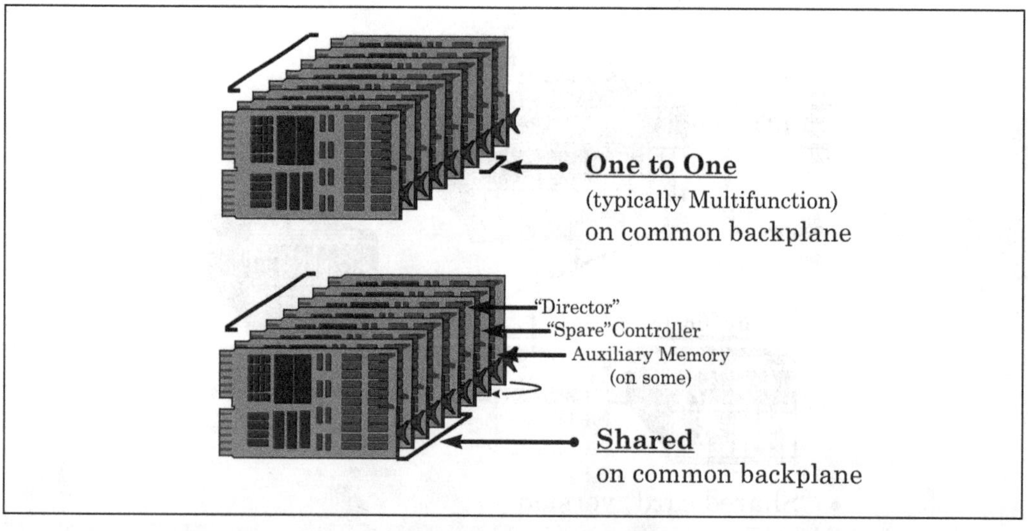

Figure 6-4. Redundant "Single Card" Controller Racks

In those "single card" controller racks that are made by several vendors, only "multifunction cards" can back up their identical twin. Most, but not all, will automatically refresh with any changes that occur in the primary controller. Some vendors permit the backup to be loaded with a different configuration and call that a benefit, namely, to allow "live reconfiguration." (I personally find this dangerous because it requires that rigorous discipline be exercised consistently by everyone using the system to ensure that the correct configuration remains in the backup should a failure occur. Otherwise, some very exciting things could happen in the process!)

A form of shared backup, "one-to-N," is available from some vendors in cases where more than one identical (hardware) multifunction card is backed up through a "director" to an empty spare. In this case, like the shared controller racks, each configuration strategy can be unique. There is a switchover of I/O to the redundant card from the one that failed. In some of the shared versions, a separate memory card retains each of the configurations (but not the current values) from all the cards in that rack and downloads the appropriate one as needed. Some others download the configuration for that controller from a workstation.

Both types (shared and one-to-one) have redundant cards on the same backplane, some use redundant circuit pathways on that backplane. Some vendors use redundant bus paths on the backplane to assure security, claiming that the backplane is passive and susceptible to any failures. Many vendors do not place the redundant card on a separate power supply. There is also the consideration of having an independent power source should the nature of the failure include problems with power. Some systems will permit a rack-to-rack backup using different cabinets, with different power sources going to each cabinet, and those power sources could possibly have different power source pathways for each of these cards.

In many of the multifunction programmed controllers, their configuration has been assembled as if it were one big program. If the controller is in mid scan through this program and there's any kind of an interruption, the control action will then have to start over at the beginning of its scan in the redundant controller, often restarting any sequential process. This will happen where the configuration must be downloaded from another location to a "spare" module. In a heat-treating furnace control, a pharmaceutical plant, or a chemical batch process, this could be quite a concern. Some vendors have designed the redundant controller as a "hot spare" to continually track the current values as well as any online or offline changes in the configuration in the primary controller. This assures that switchover happens more smoothly and that the process continues rather seamlessly.

In that architecture in which all the hardware/software sets are identical (selected control strategies do not have to be), and also with some single module-type controllers, a one-to-one backup strategy is possible between separate controller racks (Figure 6-5). It is also possible to select either shared or redundant I/O, and with some both shared and redundant I/O to each controller. With some systems, redundant I/O is available on *each* controller. Not all vendors offer this exact grouping. In this arrangement, the controllers can be in different cabinets, with different power supplies, if that level of integrity is needed. Vendors offer these many variations to allow the user to selectively trade off economy with redundancy, whichever is most appropriate within the same system.

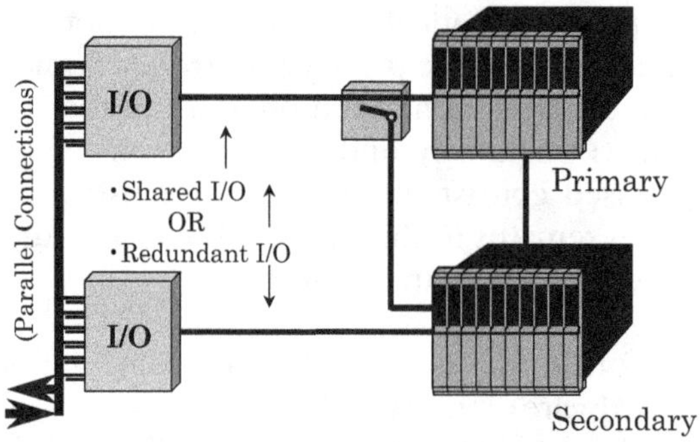

- "Shared card" version; some module versions
- Entire strategy backed

Figure 6-5. One-to-One Redundant Racks, I/O, Even Power

Windows NT as Controller

Some very important issues must be considered in order to achieve proper one-to-one control redundancy in any platform and/or hardware. These include the ability to

- Assure exact duplicate databases when the controllers are first configured to a control strategy.
- Maintain exact duplicate databases when later configuring any strategy change, especially when online changes are made.
- Maintain synchronized timing within both controllers.
- Monitor dynamic process value and condition changes within the primary controller during operation, and provide rapid update of the redundant controller *or,* even better, directly receive those process changes into both controllers and compare them.
- Detect failure in the primary controller very quickly.
- Switch over very quickly upon the detection of failure.
- Upon switchover, continue control, especially of ramped values and sequential events, so that these actions are transparent to both process and operators.
- Upon switchover of control, appropriately switch both local and remote inputs and outputs, in a way that is transparent to process and operators.
- Upon switchover of control, appropriately switch all digital communications in a way transparent to other connected devices, processes, and operators.

In the mid-1990s there have been several issues of concern when using a general-purpose operating system and general-purpose hardware to create a robust system for specific "mission-critical" purposes like process control. Microsoft® and others, however, are trying to simplify the coordination of two hardware boxes running NT in a "redundant mode." This is the clustering technology called "Wolfpack" which is in beta testing as of this writing. "Wolfpack" is a series of application program interfaces (APIs) and extensions to the NT operating system that allow applications to be developed in a "redundant manner."

Power Interruptions

We stated earlier that an interruption of power often meant that the sequential control strategy would be forced to start its routine from the beginning again. This may still happen with several models of programmable logic controllers. Quite often this is not a problem in factory automation situations, but with process control this could be unfavorable to the process itself depending upon the complexity of the system. Today, many of the controllers have internal timers to mark the duration of a power loss, so that when power returns the controller strategy will act accordingly.

If power is suspended and then returns, the control strategy may work quite well and continue where it left off, particularly if it is a temperature operation. In fact, if it's a very large furnace, the power could be off for an hour, and it may not affect the temperature change of the "work" within. In highly volatile operations, however, you may wish to decide whether to change the strategy depending upon the length of the interruption, and even have a battery-backed automatic shutdown procedure. With some controllers, the configuration can include several thresholds of interrupt time, each initiating a different control action.

- Where are you in "strategy cycle" upon switchover? ...Loops? ...Sequence state?
- Typically programming restarts at beginning.............................
- What about power outage? ...and return?

(Internal timer to mark duration, ...can act upon: Time/State/Conditions)

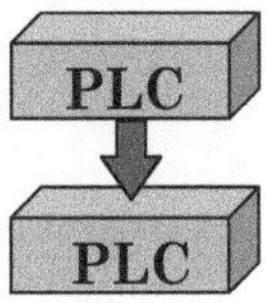

Figure 6-6. Power Interruption Impacts Control; Back-Up Considerations

While there are still controllers that must reload their configuration after a power interruption, many are equipped with built-in batteries to protect RAM memory, where the configuration resides. The charge on these batteries is often monitored, and significant warning time is provided through internal diagnostics. That warning, usually given weeks in advance, will display at the controller itself with an LED or alphanumeric code and will also be presented as part of the diagnostic video display(s) for the operator and others.

7 Connections to the Controller

The two main sources of inputs and outputs to the controller are the interface with the process, and the interface with the operator. This chapter merely discusses the hardware involved. The interface with the process must manage all of the signals to and from the process, whether they come directly from sensors, or are modified through transmitters. Technology is rapidly changing this whole scene, not just with digital fieldbus networks, which is covered in Chapter 26, but also with the fundamental nature of sensors themselves. The other critical interface is with the human operator. The very complex issues in how to present information from the controller begins with Chapter 8 and runs through Chapter 21. Within that discussion, Chapter 16 discusses the current tools on manipulating the control functions.

Input/Output Subnetworks to Field Devices

In most control systems, the control "station" on a network manages all the inputs and outputs as well as the control functions. In the process control loop, the connection from the sensor through the controller and back out to the final control element should be unimpeded. This means that any path from the inputs and outputs into the controller should be as direct as practical, even though it may be shared among several inputs and outputs.

Inputs and outputs to a controller traditionally have been analog or discrete switching. Some pulse inputs have been available over the years for devices such as frequency measurements, and pulse outputs have been available for certain motor drive units and the like. Signal conversion generally occurred within the controller itself, along with all the analog/digital conversion of the digital controllers.

> Connecting I/O to the real world means including all those messy issues like ground loops, radio frequency interference (RFI), electromagnetic interference (EMI), surge protection, hazardous atmosphere protection, and so on. Although changing technology is also impacting that part of the system, this book (which is getting long enough) is going to leave those many "standard instrumentation wiring" issues to other publications.

Connected to most controller modules today are many versions of input/output (I/O) *modules* (Figure 7-1), which are generally offered for both discrete and analog values. I/O modules are typically dedicated for all-discrete-in, all-discrete-out, all-analog-in, and all-analog-out, and some vendors may offer a single module in which each terminal can be configured as an input or an output. Other inputs can also be received for the many signals from sensors, analyzers, and the like (such as low-level signals from various thermocouples, thermistors, resistance temperature detectors [RTDs]; digital signals from chromatographs, and so on).

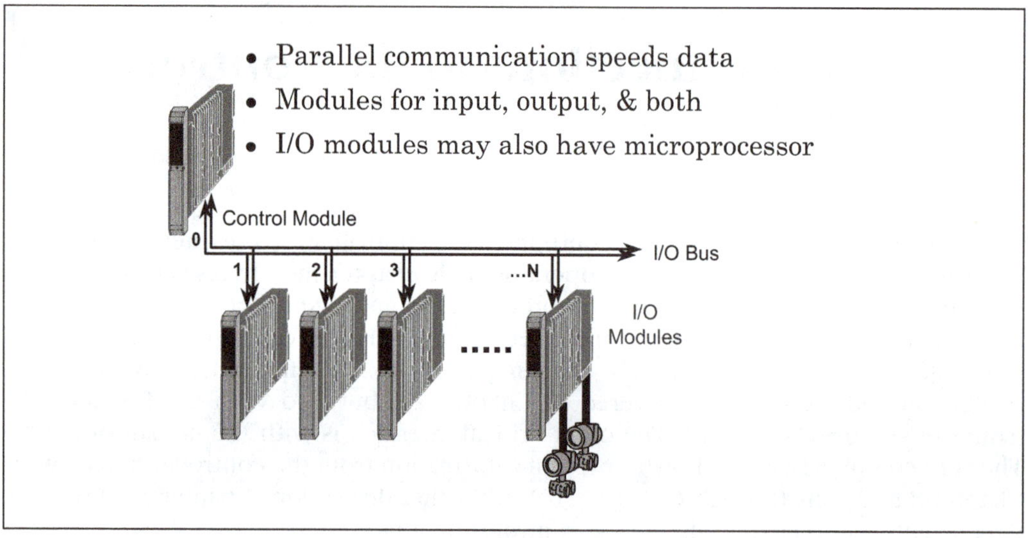

Figure 7-1. Even Local I/O Comes In on a Bus Within the Controller "Card Cage"

Selections and combinations of these modules, along with the number of terminations available on each module, can make a significant difference in the cabinet space required on a given job.

Rather than using the controllers, the I/O modules themselves more and more contain microprocessors for conversion from analog to digital (and back) and for linearization and signal conditioning.

Digital Conversion of Inputs and Outputs

Many kinds of signals come into the controller, for example, from discrete switches and relays, from light, from temperature, from flow, and from pressure. Digital communication signals can even come from operator keystrokes. And all these signals, which would come in either from discrete or analog values, must now be converted to digital. In process control, these analog signals are typically 4 to 20 milliamperes (mA), DC.

Once the manipulation of these digital signals within the controller is complete, they must then be converted back to discrete and analog outputs. Sometimes pulse, the analog output signals are usually 1 to 5 volts (V) dc (4–20 mA) to drive valve actuators and positioners as well as motor drives. Discrete output signals drive solenoids, clutch brakes, relays, annunciator lamps, and the like. Digital communications is also being used to bring data out to various operator displays and printers.

There are many techniques for converting between analog and digital signals. In Figure 7-2 we show the concept which changes a digital bit for each threshold the signal passes through. The more thresholds that can be used, the closer the conformity between the actual signal and the detected one.

As the analog signal passes various thresholds, those thresholds would be recorded in bits. In our example, we show a 3-bit conversion as the signal flows from zero to plus four volts and then swings over and back down toward minus four volts. The regular

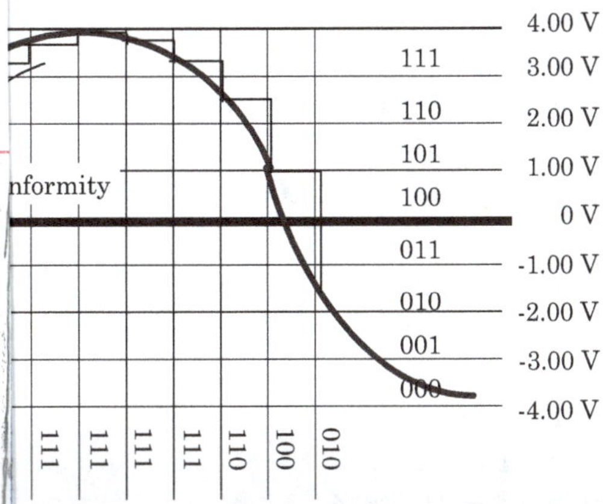

on conversion (a coarse conformity)

ion ≈ 1 in 8000

ion ≈ 1 in 16000

sualize Analog to Digital Conversion

› right, and at each intersection that bit forms a stair tread
ırve. This would be converted into three combinations of

f how close that curve is represented by the staircase. As
risers become steeper, the less accurate you will be in
ınversely, with very narrow steps and very short risers,
vould more accurately represent the real curve. This
reads and risers gives you an increase in resolution. So,
fine the rise and fall of the analog curve, the better the
hnology, you will typically see numbers of about 14-bit
10-bit resolution on the output. To give an example of
ould represent a one-in-eight-thousand resolution and a
nt a one-in-sixteen-thousand resolution–a significant

ion:

7-bit resolution = 1 in 128

8-bit resolution = 1 in 256
9-bit resolution = 1 in 512
10-bit resolution = 1 in 1024
11-bit resolution = 1 in 2048
12-bit resolution = 1 in 4096
13-bit resolution = 1 in 8192
14-bit resolution = 1 in 16384
15-bit resolution = 1 in 32768
16-bit resolution = 1 in 65536
17-bit resolution = 1 in 131072
18-bit resolution = 1 in 262144
19-bit resolution = 1 in 524288
20-bit resolution = 1 in 1048576

(Note: Inputs have higher resolution than outputs to allow for rounding off in the calculations. Real-world resolution of sensors and final elements rarely requires this, but the addition of quality codes carried through these calculations could.)

More resolution on the input or the output is probably unnecessary. A higher resolution in the input allows the calculations to be rounded off as the numbers are processed. The accuracy of the sensors themselves usually falls below that level of resolution. As for output, a 10-bit resolution probably exceeds the capability of most output devices to follow. Of course, as technology moves on, these limits will probably change significantly, particularly as sensors and final elements become digital themselves and have less need to convert to analog signals. Fieldbus like digital I/O communication is becoming the norm.

Remote Input/Output Connections

Remote I/O (often with signal processing) is becoming available more frequently. This has become the controller's own digital communication subnetwork, and quite often the connection is parallel rather than serial. Being parallel, of course, is not required. This all depends on the nature of the vendor's communication link and how promptly the process information can get into and out of the controller. Up to the mid-1990s this subnetwork was by necessity a proprietary link by the vendor to fit the real-time speeds for good loop control. Several vendors have been offering these designs as a "de facto" standard. It is in this area that the ideas of fieldbus have been emerging.

More systems today use advanced data highway communication techniques that allow direct peer-to-peer links with other controllers (Figure 7-3). Real-time data does not have to pass through other devices, such as the workstation or some "traffic director," which can cause serious delays. In this way, a signal can enter the system at one controller and be used within another on the same network, making possible much more sophisticated control functions.

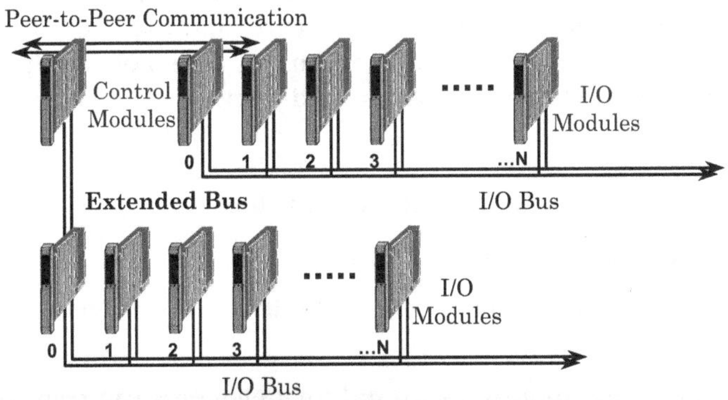

- When controller not needed in remote area
- Local & remote may be from same controller

Figure 7-3. Remote I/O showing Peer-to-Peer Connections to Other Controller(s)

Many, but not all, vendors offer communication to a remote cabinet for the inputs and outputs (Figure 7-4). Because of the distance, the signal may have to be different from the normal I/O bus, sometimes fiber-optic. This will save considerable expense in locations where the controller itself is not required at the remote site.

- Local I/O
- Remote I/O
- Extended remote I/O (fiber optic)

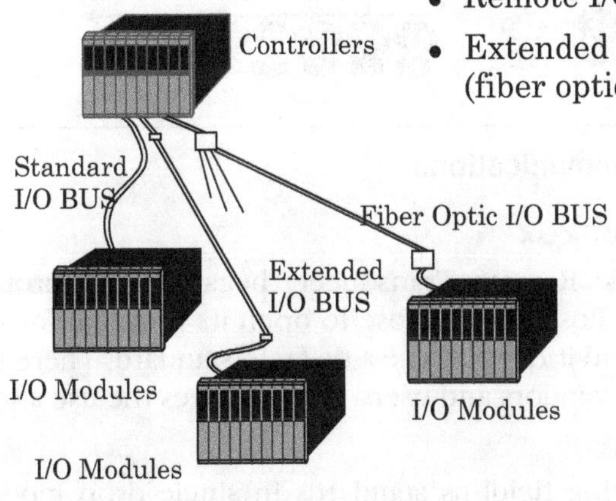

Figure 7-4. Extended Remote I/O Connections

Considerable cost savings not only results from far fewer terminals but also from savings in the significant cost of making each termination, the cost of expensive thermocouple extension wire, and the like. The use of fiber optics can add to the savings because it does not require protection from EMI, RFI, lightening, and ground loops.

Fiber optics:

- can pass through puddles of water without shorting
- is impervious to nearly all corrosive atmospheres
- can pass through hazardous atmospheres with little fear of triggering an explosion if broken

In the late 1990s more and more sensors and final elements can transmit data through digital field communication networks (Figure 7-5). Usually, systems will use a communication card or module to link a controller with different digital protocols. Changing the card changes the capability to work with a different protocol. These protocols often began as proprietary, but through common use (often encouraged by the vendor), they became "de facto standards."

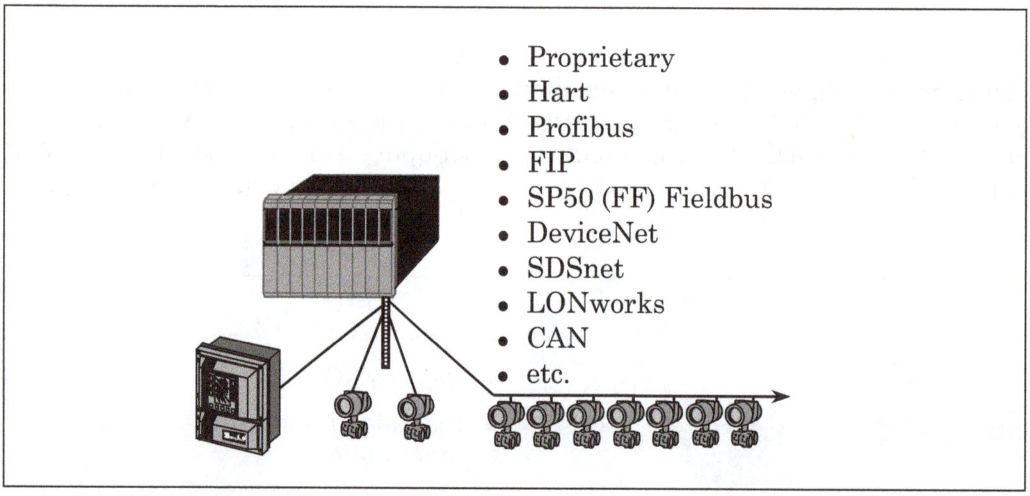

Figure 7-5. Digital Field Communications

HART (Highway Addressable Remote Transducer) began as the protocol for Rosemount's "smart" transmitter. Rosemount chose to open its protocol for others to copy. Other vendors used HART, and it has become a de facto standard. There is now a HART committee made up of many vendors and users, that oversees the use and definitions of the standard.

There are benefits to following fieldbus standards in single drop mode, such as the interchangeability of sensor and final element hardware from different vendors for the same function. Multidrop expands these benefits to include reduced wiring costs, which are estimated to be at $20 per foot.

Influence of Fieldbus

There's considerable pressure from vendors and users alike to develop a digital link to sensors and final control elements, rather than the traditional analog 4 to 20 mA. This digital link will allow not just a single input coming in from a sensor or going out to the control element, but a viable, two-way communication between these elements. On most systems today, the link to the process itself is still analog. Now, there is the possibility that a digital link can be made that can move more information, be more accurate, and be less vulnerable to signal conversion activity.

The advantages of fieldbus are as follows:

- Greatly reduced wiring and the cost of checking out that wiring
- More scalable so you could gradually grow as your needs require
- Offers even less risk and has more fault tolerance
- Begins to open the door for multivendor interoperability
- Allows more direct connection between distributed control systems (DCSs) and programmable logic system interconnections
- Control can be local..again

These advantages create new opportunities to review how a plant is controlled. The proper use of fieldbus will provide the installation benefits of less wiring, improved remote configuration, more automated documentation, and compatibility with multiple suppliers. It will also provide the operating benefits of more accuracy, more precision, better and safer control, increased information, more reliability and security, and less downtime. It also provides the maintenance benefits of increased reliability, competitive replacements of equipment, automated documentation, and remote diagnostics.

What are the disadvantages of fieldbus? Well, the biggest thing is that it requires a common standard among a large number of people and many different companies—all of whom have different interests. Because of this, it raises political problems between the many vendors, each of whom has many kinds of often very different types of information to move over the communication system.

For example, a vendor with a mere thermocouple input might have to live with the cost of providing expensive software overhead to allow someone with an intelligent transmitter to communicate on the same network. A complete communication system must require numerous software function blocks to allow such a large variety of sophisticated products to reside in the system. This could make a simple temperature transmitter very expensive with the current technology.

There are many additional problems. For example, how much information should be on this fieldbus? There are many vendors, and they and their users must communicate considerable amounts of information, but that increases costs to those who do not communicate as much. Other vendors feel there is only a need for a small amount of information, which saves on costs but reduces its flexibility. All of these issues are in committees, and, as is typical of committees, there is a lot of discussion and background to work through before coming up with a common, unified idea that is global (i.e., applies in Asia, in Africa, in Europe, and in the Americas).

MOST COMMON FIELDBUS IS FOUNDATION FIELDBUS.

More on the "mechanics" of fieldbus, and Foundation Fieldbus in particular, will be discussed in Chapter 26.

Input/Output Subnetworks to Humans

Some controllers can link directly to PCs for an inexpensive configuration terminal and operator interface (OI). Some controllers even have a PC built into the same card rack, along with the I/O modules (Figure 7-6). A nice compact system like this provides a user with economical control but also with powerful DCS capabilities on a small unit process. This also allows for a very powerful "starter kit" for the user, which can be scaled up with the expansion of the process. More typically, such a system is purchased as a trial before investing in a major system from that vendor.

Figure 7-6. Local Operator Interface Directly Connected to Controller

---

As the 1990s draw to a close, some major vendors have released "PC-based" products, which are claimed to be open but in fact do not offer the upward migration path that might be implied by their design technology nor enough connectivity to their existing large DCS.

The next level in scaling up would be the ability to connect a PC onto the backplane bus of the controller(s) for the local operations of a larger unit process. "Above" that could be a proprietary network to a more centrally located control room with several PCs (Figure 7-7). This network could also be based upon any of several protocol standards, but these standards by themselves are not "real-time." By imposing design restrictions on their use, vendors have been able to achieve "real-enough-time."

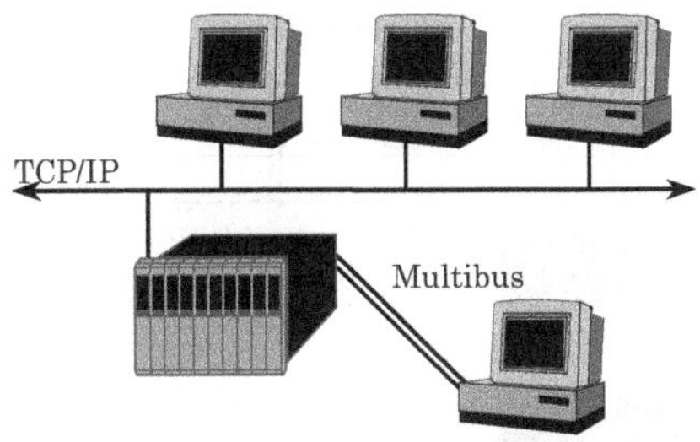

Figure 7-7. Larger, But Simple System Networked to Several PCs

---

IEEE (Institute of Electrical and Electronics Engineers)—international professional society that issues its own standards and is member of ANSI (American National Standards Institute) and ISO (International Organization for Standardization).

- **IEEE 802.3**—Ethernet LAN standard except for type field (10 Mbps); physical-layer standard using CSMA/CD access method on bus-topology LAN.
- **IEEE 802.4**—Physical-layer standard using token bus-topology LAN; nearly identical to MAP (Manufacturing Automation Protocol).
- **IEEE 802.5**—Physical-layer standard using token-ring topology LAN.
- **IEEE 802.6**—Metropolitan Area Network (or High Speed Local Network) standard.
- **IEEE 802.11**—Radio and wireless LAN.
- **IEEE 802.12**—Draft standard for 100BASE-VG networking.

More sophisticated functions can be achieved from the more powerful (and more expensive) workstations, which are usually built around one of the several UNIX variations (Figure 7-8). WindowsNT is emerging in this role, but UNIX will be around for a while to come!

Generally linked in a client/server relationship, UNIX workstations will offer the ability to manage many more system "points" and "tags." With the ability to use X terminals, more views can be added in the control room, providing significant savings. X terminals are merely that which use the electronics in the workstation server.

Note in the example shown in Figure 7-8, redundant controllers are likely to have unique addresses. This may not be true in all systems. The redundant link permits "instant" transfer regardless of the data highway activity.

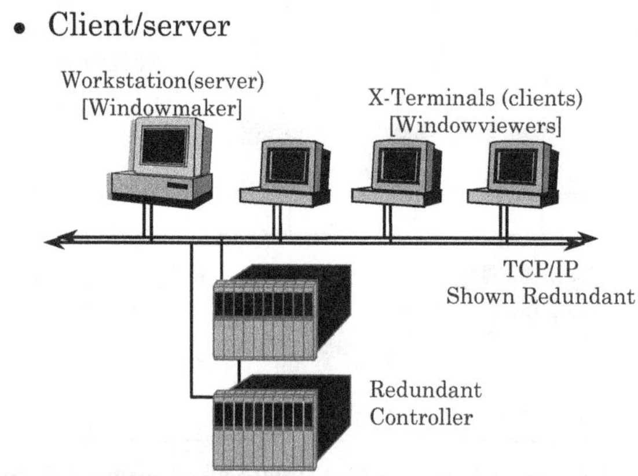

Figure 7-8. More Powerful User Interface

Client/Server Architecture—An approach to computer processing in which the functions of applications are shared between multiple computers on the same network Client/server distributes the computing load among several computers on a network. It is not exclusive to UNIX and is becoming very popular with NT as well.

Client—One of usually several devices on a computer network that are being supplied by another processor acting as server of data, memory, or function(s); the client's software requests and receives these from the server's software.

Server—A processor that supplies the network with a specified service, such as a routing function, and acts a common source of data, memory, or functions to be shared by many devices requesting these.

X Windows

With the development of RISC-based processors, we now have an abundance of powerful, low-cost workstations that are getting even more powerful and still dropping in price. Moreover, on these platforms in the mid-1990s, one operating system—UNIX—and one graphical windowing system—the X Windows—predominate.

To say that X Windows is a graphical windowing system does not do it justice. It's really much more. There have been graphical systems in the past, but their objective of allowing applications to be more portable was not realized because not enough vendors agreed to use those standards. This was especially true in the real-time graphics arena, such as in process control. It was therefore necessary to build specialized graphics hardware and software. Since the hardware was slow by today's standards, the software had to be highly optimized. In fact, every clock cycle was important. This all tended to be very proprietary.

The first thing to know about X Windows is that it is a graphical system that has had a lot of momentum behind it and has gained wide acceptance. It is considered the unofficial graphical standard on UNIX platforms, and there are now implementations that run under DOS and Microsoft® Windows as well. It runs on anything from personal computers to supercomputers.

Furthermore, X Windows is a graphical system that is rich in functionality, providing support that ranges from simple user interfaces to complex three-dimensional computer-aided design packages. X Windows makes it possible to have multiple applications running simultaneously in separate windows. Each application can have its own hierarchy of windows and subwindows on the same screen view. With the presence of a window manager, these windows can act like stacks of paper on a desk, thereby exploiting the desktop paradigm that many people can to easily. These windows can overlap, be moved, be restacked, be converted to icons, and be resized dynamically by the user.

Applications can be device interdependent, that is, not need to be rewritten or recompiled to work with different display hardware. Just as you can replace one disk drive with another disk drive, the display hardware can be upgraded without changing the application program. This is one of the desired characteristics of an open system.

X Windows is a network-transparent window system—another area where it really shines in the world of open systems. It provides a common interface across many types of computers with different types of display hardware running different operating systems. An application does not care where its window is physically rendered. It could be on another workstation somewhere else on the network or on its own local screen.

X Windows: A De Facto Standard

In 1984, Project Athena was initiated by the development team at the Massachusetts Institute of Technology (MIT) working in association with Digital and IBM. Its purpose was to find a way to link together the many incompatible workstations acquired through donations and purchases by the school. The immediate goal was to build a windows system running under UNIX on BS 100 terminals for debugging multiple distributed processing. Little was available at that time that was not encumbered by license or portability issues.

The team did find a software package called "W" at Stanford University. In the summer of 1984, Robert Scheifler modified it from a synchronous to asynchronous and called it "X." In 1985, a key decision was made not to license "X," but to make it available to anyone for the cost of production. By 1986, it was ported to IBM PC/AT, Hewlett-Packard, Apollo, and Sun workstations.

In January of 1987, the first X Windows technical conference was held during which many vendors announced their support for the X Windows version 11 (X11). In 1988, the MIT X Consortium was formed, which included as members Apple Computer, AT&T, Bull, Digital, Hewlett-Packard, IBM, NCR, Sony, Sun, and Xerox. When one considers the rich functionality X Window offers, the kind of vendor backing it had, and the fact that it was offered by MIT practically for free, there can be no doubt why it became so popular.

X-Window Architecture

In the high level architecture of X Windows, the peripherals associated with the display (screen, mouse, keyboard, etc.) are managed by software referred to as the X-Server. The X-Server itself is linked with the device-dependent routines so that application programs can be device-independent. The X Server can provide display services for application programs which are referred to as X-Clients running on the same machine or on any other machine on the network. If a remote application has been given access to talk to the X-Server on a different machine, the X-Server will interface with that application as though it were running locally on the same machine.

The backbone that allows this to occur is the X-Protocol. Every vendor that supports X - Windows must support this protocol. Therefore, it is possible to mix different types of computers and workstations running on different operating systems and with different hardware. Note that even the window manager acts like any other application and does not even have to run on the same machine as the X-Server. The window manger, however, is usually running on the same machine as the X-Server for efficiency, that is, because it helps to cut down on the amount of X Windows traffic over the network.

An application program can link directly to the X-Library calls, which take care of the X Protocol, or it can interface with a "tool kit." A "tool kit" is a software library that implements graphical user interface (GUI) objects, thereby providing a higher-level interface for application developers. For example, instead of drawing individual boxes and text, the application could request that a menu be drawn. In this case, the elements of the menu object for that particular "tool kit" will be rendered on a screen.

For those who want to tie their process control systems to the management information system network, X Windows is a great fit. Applications can be invoked in such a way that data is accessed from the process control system but displayed on the terminals in the management information system network. A feature of many workstations is the ability to interface to more than one network at a time. This allows some degree of isolation to keep the management information system traffic separate from the process control network traffic. Furthermore, this feature can be employed to bridge between two different types of networks, such as between DECnet and TCP/IP (Transmission Control Protocol/Internet Protocol). An area of particular concern in this age of networking is security. X Windows has several access control mechanisms. For example, each workstation can enable or disable access to its display from any other workstation, Alternatively, there are several schemes for controlling access by individual users.

Incorporating X Windows in a Control System

One aspect of X Windows that was heavily used by one vendor who incorporated this concept in its product line was the ability to program at the X-Library level. This provided the vendor with a way to port their product graphics application programming interface (API) so that existing products could be brought to market quickly on the next platform. The clear advantage of this approach was that users of these products did not have to be retrained on the new platform since the "look and feel" was ported to the X-products. They were also able to remain independent of the GUI battles by not becoming dependent on any particular window manager. Today, X-Library is the highest common denominator with regard to the interconnectivity of heterogeneous X platforms. By using the X-Library interface, the porting could be done successfully without having to give up any of the powerful features of X Window managers, such as having multiple windows displayed at the same time, or the ability to resize windows, restack them, and convert them into icons. The X-Library interface provided the capability to have a process graphic with "live" data in one window while using a display folder in another window. Modifications can be made to a display and then called up in the other window with "live" data without having to exit the display builder application when configuring the graphics.

X Windows requires that applications be written in a way that allows them to be event-driven. For example, one event that applications should handle is the "exposed" event. The X-Server will send this event when an overlapping window is moved off of an applications window. Hence, the application should have the ability to repaint the contents of the window that is now exposed. This is a good discipline to learn in order to make software more object-oriented. However, not all existing products are prepared to handle this because they were written for a system that has allowed only one window at a time. Thankfully, the designers of X Windows anticipated this and provided a way out. They supported a feature called ***"back in store"*** in which the X-Server keeps a copy of the contents of the window in off-screen memory, so it can handle the exposed event itself.

Among the obstacles that had to be overcome was the fact that the X operating environment favors the use of a three-button mouse. In some process control sites, the only peripheral device available is a touch screen and a totally encapsulated keyboard. X Windows does not directly support touch screens or special keyboards. X Windows does provide mechanisms for adding "extensions" to accommodate such special needs.

In this case, however, the vendor implemented a device driver to handle the touch screen and custom keyboards. To overcome the lack of blinking colors, programming at the X-Library level allowed them to successfully implement a scheme that was transparent to the applications.

Customer Response

An interesting lesson was learned when the merits of X Windows was discussed with customers. There was much excitement about the new capabilities that X Windows brought to the table, though it was mainly for use by process engineers. There was concern, however, about giving process operators too much functionality. In some sites, the process operators interact only with process displays and do not need to have multiple applications effective at the same time. To accommodate the customer who was concerned about this, the vendor decided to implement a scheme to allow customers the choice of optionally restricting access to the whole X Window functionality for process operator environments.

The end result is that the X Windows that has been incorporated in the process control system has been found to meet the demands of display response and alarm handling while at the same time offering such powerful features as having multiple applications on the screen at the same time and networking capabilities. In areas where it did not exactly meet the needs of a process control system, it provided enough openness and flexibility to allow these shortcomings to be overcome.

Admittedly, the ideal situation has not yet arrived. However, there will continue to be real progress with the establishment of standards and their widespread acceptance by major vendors, and with the development of enabling technologies. The X Windows system represents one milestone in this saga. It has been shown that it is not only applicable to the computer industry but that it can be gainfully applied to the process control industry.

Putting this all together, as shown in Figure 7-9, we may find various combinations of capabilities within a plant. The numbers of controllers, workstations, local PCs, and the like can be used as needed, of course, with a practical eye to both costs and sophistication. Note the extension to the business planning computer network. This may have a separate interface or be a part of one of the workstations. In Figure 7-9, because of the batch workstation, it is likely that the business planning software will have some control of the scheduling of these batches and will be connected there. More will be said on communication networks in Part E, and on connecting the enterprise in Part F.

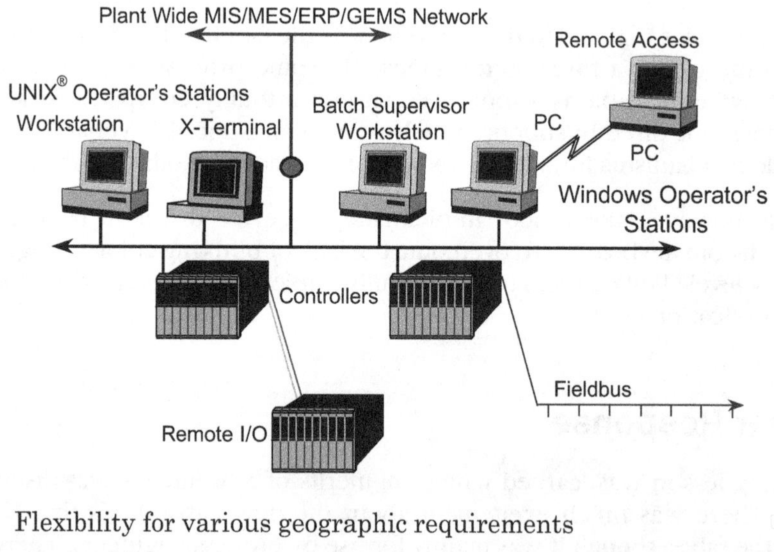

- Flexibility for various geographic requirements

Figure 7-9. Networks Built Around Controllers in Large System Architectures

---

UNIX®—*Unified* multitasking; time-sharing operating system designed originally by (and a trademark of) AT&T for communicating, multiuser, 32-bit minicomputers and which has become widely accepted because of its versatility. The trade name now belongs to X/Open Corp. Ltd.

Windows™—GUI environment developed by Microsoft® that permits users to run more than one application on a desktop computer simultaneously.

Windows NT™—Windows™ Next Technology; developed by Microsoft® as a significant upgrade to Windows™.

X terminal—Dedicated platform (terminal) that is transparent to the user and designed to run X-Server software. Used with powerful machines that run 680x0 processors such as RISC computers; X is a standard base-level windowing architecture for UNIX® machines and their terminals.

X Windows™(trademark of MIT)—Major element of the open systems concept; it allows video terminals in one vendor system to present views and operate as if they were video terminals in other vendor systems that reside on same network.

Part C

Human Interfaces

8 Humans in Control

Just as our present-day architecture grew out of simple controllers then to control systems and now to open control networks, our techniques for interfacing with the control process itself have been evolving as well. Since the beginning of mankind, humans have been making "stuff." The trick is to make the "stuff" the same way every time it is made. The intricacies of converting how you make the stuff consistently and repeatable is parallel to the way mankind has always interacted with the inanimate. It is imperative to understand this human process before any progress can be made in developing useful operator interfaces (and any other user interfaces) to make a plant *PRODUCTIVE* (remember that goal?).

The Process of Control

Much as in the act of cooking, ingredients are mixed for a length of time, and perhaps heated for a period of time until they are "just right," whatever "just right" is. If this person had an apprentice, he had to literally live with him. That's why apprentice programs lasted long periods of time, like seven years or so. The apprentice had to learn what it was that the master did when he made the stuff. How long did he do it, how much did he do it, what were the ingredients, and what changed when conditions changed, (e.g., if it was winter or summer, day or night, or if different kinds of wood were used on the fire, etc.).

And at one point the master would turn to this apprentice and say, "Charlie, come over here, look into this cauldron. This stuff is just right." Charlie would come over and look in the cauldron and see what "just right" looked like. Now he didn't always know whether he was looking at a texture or a consistency or a color or whether he was smelling it or feeling it or getting close enough to it to feel the temperature. It was actually a combination of all of these, and somehow Charlie had to understand what "just right" was every time it was "just right."

Figure 8-1. Process Control is the Art of Making "Stuff" the Same Way... Every Time You Make It!

If you tried to convey all of that experience through a sensing device, a measuring device, or some kind of display, you have the problem of sharing the sense of "just right" in the same way to everyone who observed the process. Unlike Charlie, who has seven years or more to learn what it's like, a control room operator of today will be a different person from one shift to the other, from one day to the next, or after many emotional strains. So somehow vendors must make existing technology convert all of those indicators of "just right" into whatever each individual can sense understand, and respond to.

Brown's Instrument for Repeatability

As time went on, the master might find a method for helping the operator understand this. For example one Eddie Brown in Philadelphia in the 1850s was managing a salt bath to temper steel. He wanted to assure that apprentice followed the exact same procedures as he. He capped one end of a pipe and inserted the closed end inward through the wall of the salt bath, which had had a metal rod of a different material welded on its inside end. The dissimilar materials changed lengths differently as the temperature changed. The rod would protrude from the open end of the pipe by different amounts as the temperature changed.

Figure 8-2. Eddie Brown's Instrument to Measure Temperature

When the temperature was just right, the master etched a mark on the rod, and he could say to his apprentice, "When that mark gets to the edge of the rod, the temperature is just right." That became both the sensor and the indicating device. In fact, as time went on it was part of a control system. The person doing this, Eddie Brown, repeated this in other vessels, and eventually began selling the device, forming the Brown Instrument Company, which later (in 1934) became part of Honeywell. This was the beginning of a series of many different temperature measuring devices using different forms and shapes. The point is that on this device, the user didn't know the precise temperature of the vessel. He did know, however, that the vessel was the identical temperature that it was last month or even last year. The whole key to industrial process control is *repeatability*, which is more necessary than the accuracy of absolute measurement. Oh yes, accuracy is involved, but it is not accuracy in the sense of an absolute temperature or measurement, but rather the accuracy of a measurement's repeatability.

Touring the Plant with All the Senses

Figure 8-3. All of the Senses Were Used When "Touring the Plant"

Now this challenge of using the senses to determine the progress of any industrial process often required someone whom was the expert or the master. Frequently, as in Figure 8-3, he would tour the plant, look at all of the different parts of the process, and sense when everything was running smoothly, based on his experience. There would come a time when he would be walking through the plant and would determine that perhaps the conditions weren't so perfect. He would stop, listen, smell, feel, and look to see what had changed. Many times it wasn't obvious. He had to determine what was different this time, to make note of it, and to come up with a correction. As time went on, the capability of measuring different parameters was developed so sense and measure pressure, temperature, flow, pH and many more factors could be sensed and measured. These were frequently placed in the specific location near the process.

As we pointed out earlier, this was all a form of distributed control. These distributed sensors and measurements were brought into a local area on what was called a control panel. Sometimes there were several local control panels within a large plant because of the limitations on how far you could convey the measurement. Usually, this distance was limited because of pneumatic transmission lines. This transmission saved the operator some part of his tour of the plant, so that he could at least look at all the meter positions and recognize the appropriate measurements and with his clipboard make a note of them and compare them with the last time he made those measurements. He still had to tour the plant, but this time, it was only to adjust the valves and the other end elements to modify and alter the process—not to measure it.

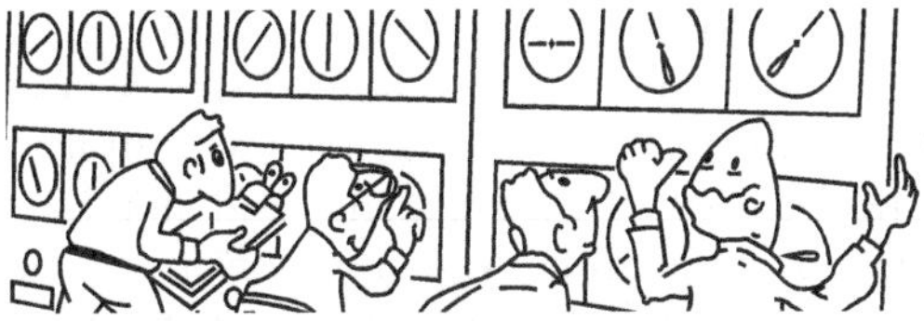

Figure 8-4. Pneumatic Transmission Allowed Local Control Panels

Now you will remember, the whole journey recounted here was down the road to better plant productivity. Better plant productivity sometimes meant being able to make more of the product, and do it faster. This could only happen when the operator was able to observe the proper indication of the process conditions and be able to quickly respond to any change in the process. The faster he would recognize change and the faster he could respond to the change, the more confident he could feel in running the process "faster." Up to now, however, the operator's control room was quite frankly scattered about the plant, depending on its size and operations.

As electric sensors, measuring devices, meters, and transmission devices emerged over the years, it became easier to bring all the information to a central panel and even operate the plant from some central location (Figure 8.5). The challenge now was to make the plant values make sense when they were all jumbled together on this panel—because you now had more and more kinds of sensors and more and more of each kind to better measure what was going on in the process. This meant that the panel board layout was very critical. The various size and color and shapes and direction of meters sometimes were limited by the technology of manufacturing those devices. For example, gauges often would be concentric or eccentric depending on whether they were driven by bellows or bourdon tubes or other mechanical devices, which expanded and contracted, thus rotating needles in different ways.

Figure 8-5. Electronics Made Central Control Panels Possible

Indications for Control of Process—Blame the Early Railroads

In the evolution of man's relationship to the inanimate, the psychology of conveying information has always been complex. The control of mechanisms and machinery in the industrial revolution as it occurred in the United States, first appeared publicly with the operation of the railroads. Now, railroads are a process. You are trying to move goods and people from one point to another, usually in multiple directions, usually on multiple paths, and in the least amount of time—not unlike what happens in a factory. To control the flow of traffic, which moved at different speeds depending on the locomotives pulling it or the weight of the train, a signaling system was set up. It consisted of a large ball suspended from a rope, which was raised or lowered through a set of pulleys (Figure 8-6). When the ball was raised to the high position, it was a clear signal to go, and when the ball was lowered the operator should stop his train. This was the origin of the term high ball as a signal to go. (How this relates to a certain alcoholic party drink of the same name, no one knows, but it can lead to some interesting speculation.)

Figure 8-6. Highball: Up Meant Clear to Go

As time went on, a large board was put on a pole and pivoted so that when it swung upward it meant the track was clear, and when it was downward—as if to block the path—it meant stop. When nighttime operations were possible, the board was extended to the other side of the pivot, a lantern was hung behind it, and colored lenses were inserted into the board (Figure 8-7). This caused red to be on the top and green on the bottom, which is why most traffic lights and panel boards still use this orientation. We are still using today the signaling methods that were developed over two centuries ago.

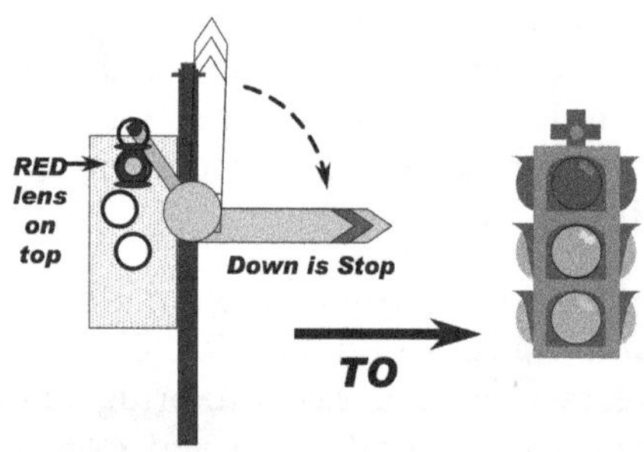

Figure 8-7. Highballs to Semaphores to Traffic Lights

These same signal conventions moved into factory production lines, a de facto standard if you will. People have become used to the fact that when the signal is up, conditions are good or improved, ready to go or full, or complete (Figure 8-8). The down direction means a warning or low, level is down, speed is down, temperature is down, and so on. So, a natural instinct has apparently been generally built into all of us that up is good and down is not so good or stopped. That impression affects how we view most things that operate

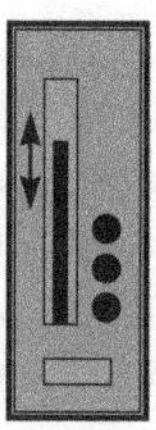

Figure 8-8. In Faceplate Presentations, Up is Generally "Good" (Full, On, High, etc.)

even today when we drive our automobiles or use household appliances. This simple idea should never be overlooked when designing devices to control and convey information to humans who are operating those controls.

Back to Control Room Panels

The layout and organization of a control panel is very essential in helping understand conditions in the process itself. How instruments are clustered and the way those clusters are placed on the control panel give a better understanding of what is happening within the process. Quite often, some flow lines and diagrams are also drawn on these panels, but, of course, these are static, so the ability to understand what was happening in the process is somewhat limited to merely the gauge positions. As plants and processes grow larger, so also do the control panels. Sometimes they became so large that operators would sometimes literally navigate them on roller skates.

To understand what is happening at all ends of the process, alarming devices and alarming annunciators already very important. Flags, bells, klaxons, and other such annunciators are used to alert operators to what part of the panel to run to next to determine if anything that is out of normal. This in turn limits how a complex plant can be run, and of course that limits the productivity of that plant. As it became economically possible to add more sensors and more kinds of sensors, it was necessary, of course, to manage all of that extra data.

This led, fortunately, to the advent of the computer, which offered an opportunity to manage all the data and present the operator with only the part that was important to him or her. The introduction of the video screen around the same time made it possible to bring all of this data to the operator rather than have the operator run out to all the data. So, unlike traditional control panels, the video screen allowed the control panel to come to the operator and make it easier for him or her to look for alarms, chains of events, and all the changing parameters. *BUT REMEMBER*, isolated in the control room the operator no longer has all his or her senses working as when touring the plant (Figure 8-9). Any operator interface must therefore replace those inputs!

Figure 8-9. That Computer Screen Must Convey All the "Feel" of Touring the Plant!

Remember: It is, and has always been, the responsibility of the system engineer to design *ALL* of the control system, especially the way in which the operators fit into the operations plan! In the past, there was little the system engineer could do except make the most out of the instruments and instrument features provided by individual vendors. There was no way to change the faceplates; for example, one could perhaps just paint some lines on the panel in which they were mounted. Today, with the use of video systems, the possibilities have become so expansive as to be confusing. But the responsibility to design everything is still there, even if it is little understood. Maybe the many words and pictures presented, in the following chapters will help promote that understanding. User interfaces are as important as the control strategy in improving plant productivity!

Video for User Interfaces 9

The advent of both computers and video screens have made a lasting impact on running processes. In fact, we have hardly scratched the surface of how to use these emerging technologies!

Computers, of course, have been invading all parts of the process plant. Computers are used for finance, order entry, inventory turns, production management, product management, process management, and equipment management. All of these are generally considered to be different and independent functions, and they are often run by different departments using different computers.

But today, computers are becoming more "general purpose" in the construction of their operating system platforms. Distinctions between systems is now primarily a result of the application packages that run on them. Of course, it is necessary to "isolate" computing functions for such needs as having "real-time" control. Nevertheless, the use of multiple microprocessors and network communications makes it possible to share data among the many different groups. But the *presentation* of the data, usually through the video screens of "workstations," varies depending on the function of these different groups.

Video Display Workstations

Interaction with process control generally falls to proprietary operator stations, commercial workstations, and personal computers (PCs). The role of a proprietary operator station is now leaving us in the late 1990s, but we have had several decades of creating and installing large quantities of operator stations to deal with. Many tens of thousands of these continue to perform the real-time operation of process throughout the world.

Commercial workstations were designed for business transactions that could take minutes, or hours, even days. These are not practical time frames in which to run most processes that need interfaces to work within a half-minute or few seconds. As a result, vendors had to make their own unique modifications to cope with the real-time data.

Average computers, and certainly the home computer, could not work with the same kind of graphic processing needed in typical process operation. Operator workstations must also be able to link to the real-time data, receive data as it happens, and cause actions exactly when needed. The network and display capabilities of the average PC could never meet those requirements. This limitation is rapidly changing as the 1990s draw to a close, and we are already seeing some rather dramatic changes.

Through changing technology, we are beginning to see the convergence of what used to be the separate fields of television, computers, and publishing (Figure 9-1). By the millennium we will see computers, television, and publishing functioning within the same kind of electronic hardware. That hardware will also make these *FUNCTIONS* indistinguishable!

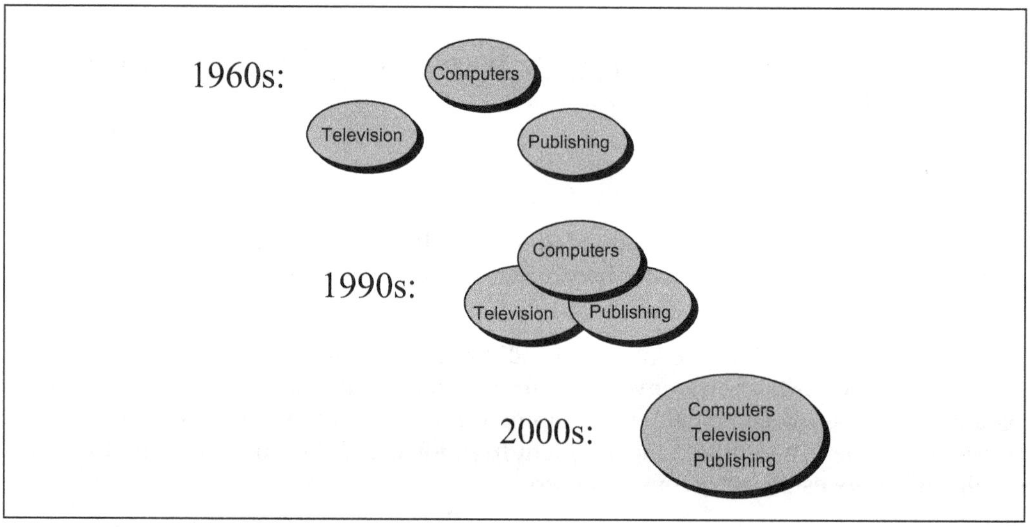

Figure 9-1. Changing Technologies are Causing Workstation Differences to Disappear

This convergence will have a very significant effect on the automation systems as well as human-machine interfaces (HMIs) It is influencing interface capabilities and it's even influencing how we communicate with each other, let alone how we communicate through machines for processes control, factory operations, and businesses.

The workstations of the late 1990s are far superior to today's personal computers..so far. They're replacing many full mainframe computers. These workstations didn't even exist in the mid-1980s. Workstations now provide incredible processing power at low cost; they offer high-resolution graphics, and they are consistent and easy to use. They can be networked. Their performance can be expanded merely by adding newer processors as they are developed. In this way, the user can upgrade without replacing the entire computer and all of the configuration in it. These workstations can do multitasking, which means they can perform multiple tasks in a very short time on the same microprocessor. They typically run in UNIX or some variant of it, but the NT platform is rapidly overtaking UNIX.

Workstation Development

- Far superior to today's desktop PCs (so far)
- Replacing minicomputers
- Did not even exist in the middle 1980s
- Incredible processing power at low cost
- High resolution graphics
- Consistent, easy to use
- Can be networked
- Performance can expand
- Typically run UNIX or variant
- Multitasking (Figure 9-2)
- Expect Windows NT to make more change

The Future Continues to Develop

Most DCS vendors have grown away from providing workstation hardware of their own design. With the improvement of processing power and memory in those stations now provided in general-purpose computers, most vendors found themselves competing in both price and availability. This is unnecessary. The business of controller companies is just that business—controllers. With such good workstations already being made, most vendors have designed software that works with one or more models. With the arrival of software graphics packages, even those are now being carefully incorporated.

As PCs develop more processing power, capabilities, and memory, the scene will change again. Some workstations have been made up of a cluster of personal computers to help overcome the need for real-time data handling. This again makes the workstation itself distributed. Commercial platforms are becoming available that assure the expandability of both capacity and capability without replacing the system. Multitasking of single processor allows many functions to be performed in what appears to be concurrent (Figure 9-2). Working with multiple processors, it really is done concurrently. This helps bring the cost of the workstation down, and the workstation is now approaching the cost of a PC. Of course, the more function you need and the more power you add, the more the price will increase. Workstations allow the user to control and monitor more processes simultaneously, to toy with more "what ifs," to perform a detailed analysis of data, and to do all of this at the same time.

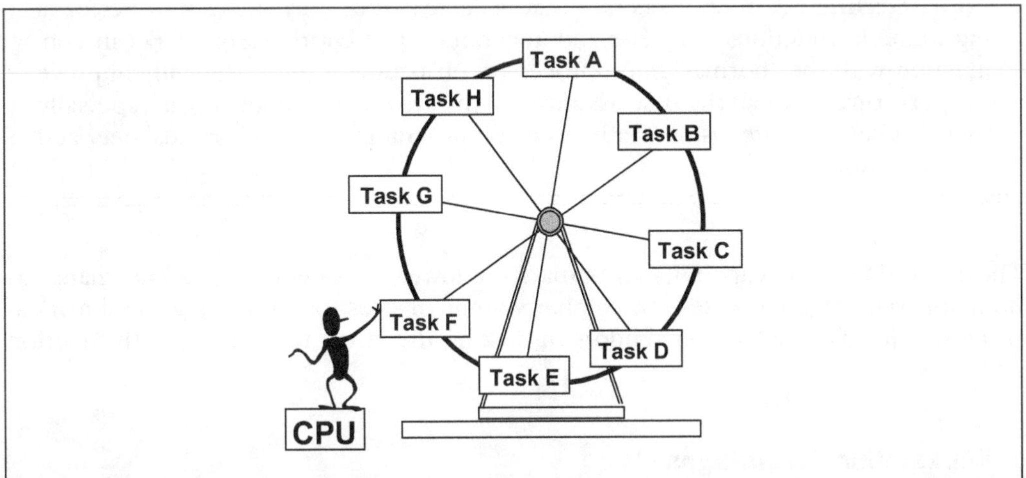

Figure 9-2. Multitasking of Several Functions with a Single Processor

Multiprocessing—Where the operating system allocates different programs and tasks to different processors without intervention by the operator, saving considerable amounts time.

Multiprogramming—The ability to run multiple copies of an application program on a single computer.

Multitasking—The concurrent execution of two or more tasks or applications usually separate but interrelated by computer at the same time; may also be the concurrent execution of a single program that is used by many tasks (not always real-time).

Context switching multitasking—Multiple applications can be loaded into the computer, but only the one in the foreground is given processor time. This simplest level of multitasking is how Microsoft Windows works; that is, once an application is in the foreground all other applications stop.

Cooperative multitasking—Common to the Macintosh platform, this is a step above context switching; background applications are given processor time but only when the foreground task is idle and allows it, such as while waiting for a keystroke.

Time-slice multitasking—The truest form of multitasking, found on sophisticated workstations, in which each task has the microprocessor's attention for a fraction of a second, and then tasks are then performed in sequential order by priority.

Parallel processing—The concurrent or simultaneous execution of two or more processes or programs, within the same processor, as contrasted with serial or sequential processing.

Coprocessing—A microprocessor that is dedicated to only the task of performing numeric functions very fast and accurately. The coprocessor works in conjunction with the "normal" microprocessor, offloading it to dramatically improve the performance of all the tasks required of the system. Coprocessing is especially useful when you are using math-intensive programs such as spreadsheets and CAD functions.

The demand for more capability and capacity at lower prices will bring about change as nonindustrial usage increases. The higher volume of sales found in the general marketplace will justify workstation vendors in making the effort to improve both function and price.

Workstation Advantages

- Increase and improve users ability to:
  - —Design control strategy
  - —Design functional screen views
    - Operator
    - Engineering
    - Maintenance
    - Business
    - etc.
  - —Deliver completed project faster
  - —Upgrade performance of process

Workstations also increase and improve the user's ability to design control strategy and, in the same machine, design functional screen views. These views within the same station, can be separate for the operator, for the engineering department, for the maintenance department, for the business people, and so on. The views can focus specifically on the required jobs without confusing the user with meaningless data. Sometimes too much data without explanation can cause a well-meaning, but disastrous action. Security codes can be incorporated as passwords so this separation is assured.

Properly used, workstations can be instrumental in delivering completed projects faster. Not only can the configuration process allow you to easily and rapidly "rearrange" control strategy, there are also system tools to help you analyze the appropriateness of the strategy selections and offer alternative suggestions. This can be a part of the "what ifs" which can be incorporated into the control system operation. The workstation can also be a part of the "loop testing" that can be done at the factory test before shipment, saving you valuable time.

Workstation platforms today can allow you to upgrade hardware, such as the latest microprocessors and memory media. This can improve performance without altering the software, sometimes even while the process is in operation.

"Look and Feel"

Graphical user interfaces (GUI) are characterized by their "look and feel." This includes the visual appearance of the objects, such as menus, buttons, dialog boxes; and how selections are made from menus; and so forth. For example, does a pulldown menu appear when the mouse button is pressed or must the mouse be clicked over a menu button? Does stay down while the mouse button is pressed, and is the selection made by dragging the pointer over an entry and releasing the mouse button or must the mouse button be clicked?

During recent years, there have been so called GUI battles, in which different vendors have tried to push their "look and feel" as the standard. Motif is the "look and feel" specified by the Open Software Foundation (OSF), which has Digital, Hewlett-Packard, and IBM behind it. Open Look was the "look and feel" specified by UNIX International, which has Microsystems and AT&T behind it. For a long while it appeared that the emerging de facto standard was Motif. In March 1993, announcements were made for a unified UNIX GUI that would be adopted as standard by the X/Open Consortium. The members of the coalition backing this standard included IBM, Hewlett-Packard, Sunsoft, UNIX System Laboratories, Univell, and the Santa Cruz Operation.

In X-Windows, an application's look and feel come from two sources. One source is the look and feel provided by the window manager that is running on the machine where the applications windows appear. The window manager determines how the desktop paradigm is implemented. That is to say, it determines how the windows are moved around, restacked, converted to an icon, and resized. The window manager manages the windows by placing a "wrapper" around each application's windows. These "wrappers" are referred to as "window decorations" and usually contain a button that pulls down a menu displaying choices such as converting the window to an icon or exiting the application. The wrapper usually contains handles that may be grabbed with the mouse to resize the windows.

The way these figures look, rectangles versus oblongs, two-dimensional versus three-dimensional, and so on, and the way they work, click versus press-and-drag release, and so on, account for the look and feel that comes with the windows manager. The other source of the "look and feel" comes from the application itself, that is, what is inside the "wrapper." If an application is built on a "tool kit," such as Motif from OSF, or Open Look, from Sun, it will exhibit the look and feel of that tool kit.

If a vendor of the control system uses the X-Library calls directly, however, that vendor can define its own look and feel. This has some advantages, especially in the area of process control.

X-Windows in Process Control Systems

As mentioned earlier, X-Windows is a graphical system rich in functionality. Yet something as common to the process controls industry as blinking colors, which are used to denote alarm conditions, is not a standard feature of X-Windows.

Process controls tend to push the capabilities of graphical systems in the following areas:

- Display call-up time and display refresh time
- Real-time updating of many data points, alarms, and dynamic graphical objects
- Displaying large amounts of graphical and textural information simultaneously
- Having the ability to switch quickly between displays from different applications
- Screen resolutions for clear presentations of very dynamic data

Neither the time element or screen resolution are directly addressed by X-Windows. These are hardware issues. It is really the development of low-cost but powerful workstations that has enabled X-Windows to be suitable for process control applications. One advantage of X-Windows is that the applications can be independent of platforms. As mentioned earlier, once an application is developed it can be run on different platforms, which can be selected based on the desired level of performance or on budget constraints.

For many applications, the low end of the middle-range workstations is quite sufficient. If more performance is needed, the same application can be used with a high-end workstation. If less performance will do, such as terminals, used just to monitor a process from a remote location, a low-cost X-Window terminal can be effectively applied. Even personal computers with X-Windows software can be installed and used.

Process control needs to have the ability to display lots of information simultaneously and to switch quickly between different displays. X-Windows offers multiple windows at the same time and the ability to quickly move, resize, convert to icons and restack the windows. With this kind of functionality, it is possible to have a process graphical display in one window while having a systems management display in another. At the same time, alarms could be displayed in yet another window and a display builder configuration in an additional window. Keep in mind that all of this power does not come without cost. In this case, the cost is the need for higher network loading and processing performance for all the increased activity.

Use of Video Screen also Changing

- Originally for peering into process itself
- Then replaced static graphic panels
- Much later to operate plant from faceplate views, replacing panelboard instruments, providing
  - —Overviews
  - —Groups
  - —Details (points)
  - —Alarm lists
- Currently includes dynamic graphics with continuing improvements to interaction

Role of Workstations Is Also in Transition

During the 1950s and 1960s video was used in the control room to show the process itself. This was especially useful when the process was at some distance or was inaccessible, such as when viewing the interior of a furnace. Early uses of video to build and show graphical panels during 1960s and 1970s were to save money in the changing of the artwork needed on traditional panels. But even these took little advantage of the dynamics available, mostly because of the massive and expensive programming required. However, no one considered using video techniques for actual *CONTROL* of the plant. Only when *CONFIGURABLE* techniques rather than programming become available could any kind of interactive graphics be considered practical. We also had to learn how to *USE* the new technologies.

How many video monitors are needed in the control room? In the late 1970s it was assumed you needed one for the overview monitoring of the process, one for the working displays (group views), and one for alarm lists. With the emergence of windowing technology in the late 1980s and early 1990s, these functions could easily be performed on a single monitor. There is, however, the consideration of task analysis. How many individuals are needed to operate the plant or process, and what functions are they to perform? The response given to these question will tell you how many video monitors you need in the control room.

As large screen technology and large projection techniques improve, the use of semi-permanent displays for monitoring overall plant performance may reduce the need for a hierarchy of screen views. This was the purpose of the traditional dedicated operator panel board and control desk instrumentation used in the past. New discoveries involving the way people interact with the processes themselves will have a strong influence on the number and locations of video monitors.

Adjusting Technology to Fit— Use the Medium 10

A number of years ago, Marshall McLuhan of the University of Toronto wrote of society's learning curve as it adapted to each new media type to convey information. His observations of how the development of printing dramatically changed our society as we moved from oral communication to written (and visual) communication. More dramatic social changes will come as we return to oral communication but conveyed, visuals (radio, motion pictures, television). As an example, he described the way visual communication evolved in the entertainment and advertising industries. According to McLuhanan, "The medium is the message" (Figure 10-1).

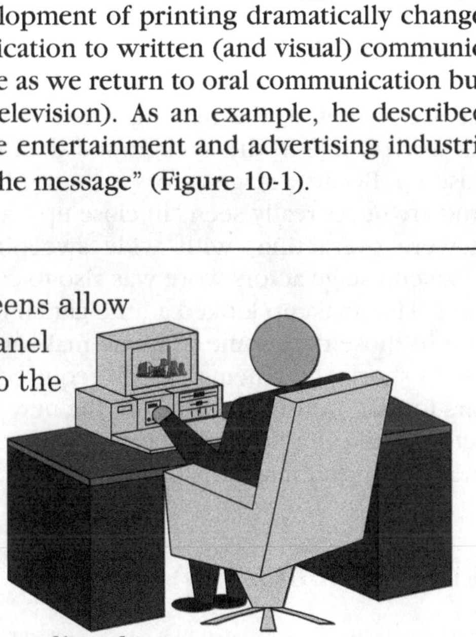

Figure 10-1. Coping with New Technology for Shared Human Interface Displays

It is important to understand how people respond to different media used to communicate between the process and those who try to understand and control it. We are currently experiencing many significant changes in the control room. Keep the control room in mind as consider at the following changes in the entertainment industry, which has also been undergoing great change during this same period of time. Look for all of the concepts to that relate to process control

Theater

In the old control room there was a long panel with meters and gauges but no graphics. In the theater is a stage with a backdrop, but there is very little detail and little, if any, reality to the scenery. The actors convey some of the ideas through their costuming and their positions on the stage, but mostly they convey ideas through their emotion and how well they act. The audience is engulfed in the emotion of that theater. The actors had to learn how to perform in that emotive way so they could convey the full impact of what they were saying. Remember now, it isn't the words that are used, it's how they're said and in what context. The lighting and perhaps some music contribute to the atmosphere. If the actors are any good, within about fifteen minutes of the play's start, the audience will have a pretty good feel for what is going on, and few will notice the lack of scenery detail on the stage.

Black and White Cinema

When the cinema was invented, the moving pictures were in black and white, and many more details were visible in the background than in theater. All the actors were usually viewed close up. Because stage actors learn to play to the full audience, including the balcony, and are never really seen "in close up," at first the actors in the cinema looked like they were overacting, with wide sweeping gestures and exaggerated expressions. The makeup stage actors wore was also to convey their emotion across the length of the theater. That makeup looked a little garish on the black-and-white screen, although to be sure in those days some extreme makeup was needed to overcome the contrast problems. In short, the cinema this all required a very new way approach to acting. It took years for the industry to adjust to the new techniques and try all the possibilities. Some actors could not do both stage and screen, so they only performed in one medium. Some could never make the transition at all.

Black and White Cinema with Sound

Before long, black and white cinema included sound. This novelty was quickly used in all pictures, with as much sound as possible—lots of talk, lots of music, lots of everything. It was years before certain producers and directors, such as Alfred Hitchcock, discovered that information could be conveyed with *silence*. By carefully placing the absence of sound, the emotions of anxiety or anticipation, or fear could be evoked to convey information that otherwise wasn't there. This again required a very approach to acting. Again, it took years for the industry to adjust to the new techniques and try all the possibilities. And again, some actors could not do both "talkies" and silent pictures, so they only performed in one medium.

Figure 10-2. Each Medium has Unique Characteristics and Capabilities

Color Cinema

Then came the technology to color motion pictures. The problem was now that everyone filled the screen in like a coloring book, In the landmark film, "Gone with the Wind," the color was used to evoke emotion, like the oranges and reds during the burning of Atlanta. Though not everyone used color well, outdoor scenes could now be far more effective. It took years for the industry to adjust to the new techniques and try all the possibilities. Some studios never made it.

Radio

Many of the actors and entertainers in the medium of radio had to learn to "speak in pictures." Those who remember old radio shows, recall envisioning what was going on just by the way the actors expressed themselves, and their choice of words, and the sound effects around them. The audience participated with their imagination to fill in the details. Radio program sponsors who understood this phenomenon did very well selling their products. This again required a very new way to act. It took years for the radio industry to adjust to the new techniques and try all the possibilities. Some actors could not do both radio and cinema and so they only performed in one medium and some could never make the change at all.

Television

Television was just "radio with picture," until the industry learned how to use exploit the fact that this was a very different medium. Cinema keeps the audience focused by using a dark theater with a huge screen, which today virtually wraps around the audience. Television was a small screen in the middle of a well-lit room in which much unrelated activity might be going on. A far different kind of programming was needed here, especially to keep the audience's attention on the same channel for all three of the prime viewing hours. Lot of dynamic action was required, with changes every four seconds or better. "Made for TV" doesn't mean they took out the "dirty words," it means they had to reformat the image to a different aspect ratio, edit to different time formats, and in the case of many wide-screen films decide which part of the overall to select for the "tiny screen." This process requires about forty hours of effort for every one-hour broadcast. To keep the audience from switching to competing channels for the three hours primetime, studios review every minute of what goes on the air, including commercials. To return to process controls, some control room operators must be in front of *THEIR* "television set" for eight hours! What has been done for them? And, unlike the TV Viewer, operator loses if operator loses attention, the very expensive product could be destroyed or worse, even the plant could blow up!

Psychologists tell us that you *cannot* pay attention to the little tiny screen called a TV for more than a few minutes. Commercial video studios spend over forty hours of preparation for every one on the air just to keep your attention for three hours of prime time. So what have you done to keep your control room operator's attention during his or her eight-hour shift?!

Life Is Not Just Video Games

We could go on to discuss the ramifications of videotapes, computer games, virtual reality, and so on. However, the point is that the video screen is a vital, critical link in plant productivity. Most people have no idea how best to use this vital tool! While the plant engineer is creating a critical control strategy, someone says, "Oh, let's get some co-op student to crank out a few pictures." It is quite possible that some co-op students could do an even better job than the manager! The manager probably has not considered that the *PRESENTATION* of information to the operators may very well be half of the entire equation of improved productivity for the process or plant.

Picture, if you will, using your video screen to "walk through your plant." With today's technology it is possible to "walk" through the piping and vessels looking for leaks, hot spots, or damaged vessels and equipment. This is already being done wholesale in the video game industry! What's wrong with this picture?

What you must have in every system is *REAL* feedback to the operator regarding the conditions of the plant. Picture walking through that pipe again. You see a leak thirty feet down from that elbow, at two o'clock high. Now, how do you know that leak is precisely there? There would have to be a detector of some kind at every inch, both laterally and around the circumference, and for every appropriate variable—temperature, pressure, and so on! This is not very practical and certainly very expensive. I never want to say never, but the technology to do this just isn't there right now. Unlike computer games, operator stations have to have their screens "wired" to a real process (Figure 10-3).

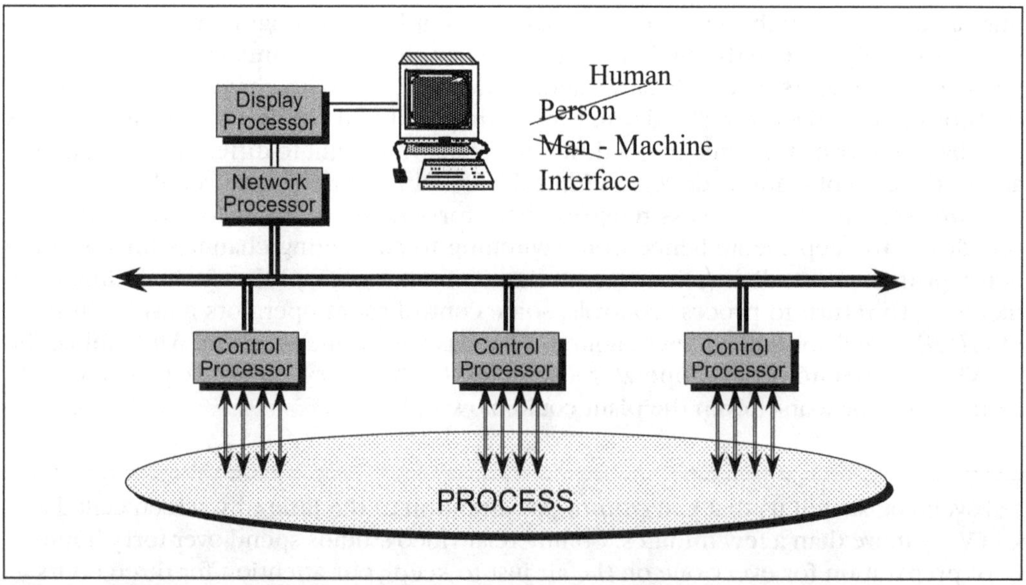

Figure 10-3. Unlike Video Games, the Screen is "Wired to the Process"

The big difference between home computer graphics and a process operator station is that the operator station must do the following:

- Link to real-time data
  - —Receive data as it happens
  - —Cause actions exactly when needed
- Not allow display and network performances to limit each other
  - —High activity of one processor should not slow down the capabilities of the other

Video Monitor Hardware 11

Just some more "nuts and bolts" on what is rapidly becoming commodity status; that is, the hardware for the workstations. At one time these were rather proprietary with each distributed control system. For some time now all vendors of control systems now merely purchase assembled monitors from any of several suppliers of video equipment. There are many tens of thousands of monitors of earlier technologies that will continue to be operating for many years to come. We discuss in this chapter some of their characteristics.

Screen Size and Resolution

Typical video screen sizes are 19 to 20 inch resolution diagonally and for most purposes this is quite adequate for most consoles. It is not unusual to find a 25 resolution diagonally inch screen or even 40 resolution diagonally inch screens. Projection systems, of course, allow an even larger community projection, perhaps along a wall. Considerations to keep in mind for the console itself include the density of the pixels (dots) and the amount of colors controlled by the processor within the video electronics.

In the mid-1990s typical density had been an array of 640 × 512 pixels, with 1,280 × 1,024 in a high quality screen. By the end of the 1990s, 1,280 × 1,040 is standard. Of course, the computing requirements increase with the density and therefore the cost as well. Like everything else, as the cost of processing power comes down, the higher density machines will increase in availability.

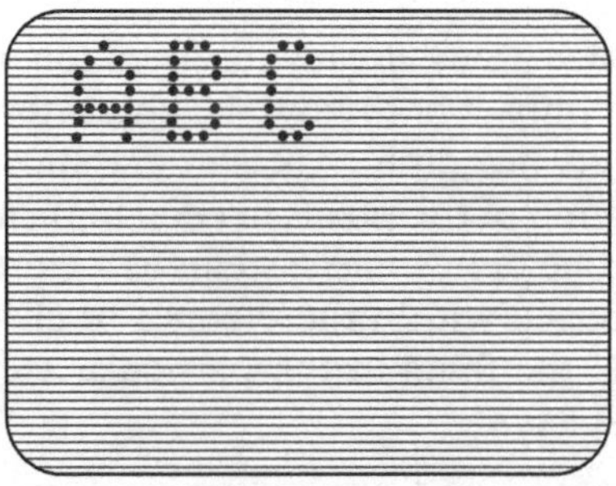

Raster Scan Character Generation

Figure 11-1. Scan Lines are Part of the Screen Resolution for Characters as Well as Pictures

Higher density cannot be achieved without increasing the raster scan across the screen. This is essential to furnish higher graphic resolution. Computer monitors are made to provide denser raster scans than television sets designed for commercial broadcast. Home television sets are limited to broadcast standards, otherwise they could not produce a recognizable image from the received signal.

Commercial broadcast standards vary, and they cannot simply be changed without preventing huge numbers of peoples from viewing. These standards are as follows:

- **NTSC (National System Television Committee)** = 525 lines, 60 Hz, 110 Vac. The world's first compatible TV service, introduced in 1953 and used in North America. "Never Twice the Same Color."
- **PAL (Phase Alternation Line)** = 625 lines, 50 Hz, 220 Vac. Introduced in 1967 and used in the United Kingdom and Europe. "Peace At Last"
- **SECAM (Système Electronique Avec Memoire)** = Introduced in 1967 and used in France and Eastern Europe. "SomEthing Contrary to American Methods."
- **PAL-M** = 525 lines, 50 Hz, 220 Vac. Used in Brazil. "Pay A Little More."
- **HDTV** = High Definition Television with a pixel resolution of 1,920 × 1,080, HDTV is still a broadcast issue (transmitters, receivers, and a large enough audience to justify). The higher volume of commercial products will probably significantly lower costs of current high-resolution monitors now used with computers. There is a very good possibility that other new technologies will emerge from the HDTV market that will be useful in the control room.

Raster Graphics

Tens of thousands of control systems already in operation around the world have character-generated screens that impact both how the characters can change size in a zoom and the monitor's ability to create graphics. Raster graphics, as this is called, require an *x-y* matrix to define the location of the pixels needed to turn each dot on or off. Characters are defined as a single zone or in some systems as a cluster of zones. To further save memory, the pixels are managed within these zones or clusters. Fonts are a fixed size, so when they are "zoomed" the fonts in the particular view may bounce to the next nearest size, with mixed results.

As long as characters are being displayed, the use of alphanumeric characters to control the color for this array is quite suitable. When used for trends, graphics, or piping and instrumentation drawings (P&ID), the character oriented approach requires that these individual characters be linked together to form the graphical display. If the type of characters used matches those needed to construct the desired display, the results will be acceptable. Otherwise, the display will look quite ragged.

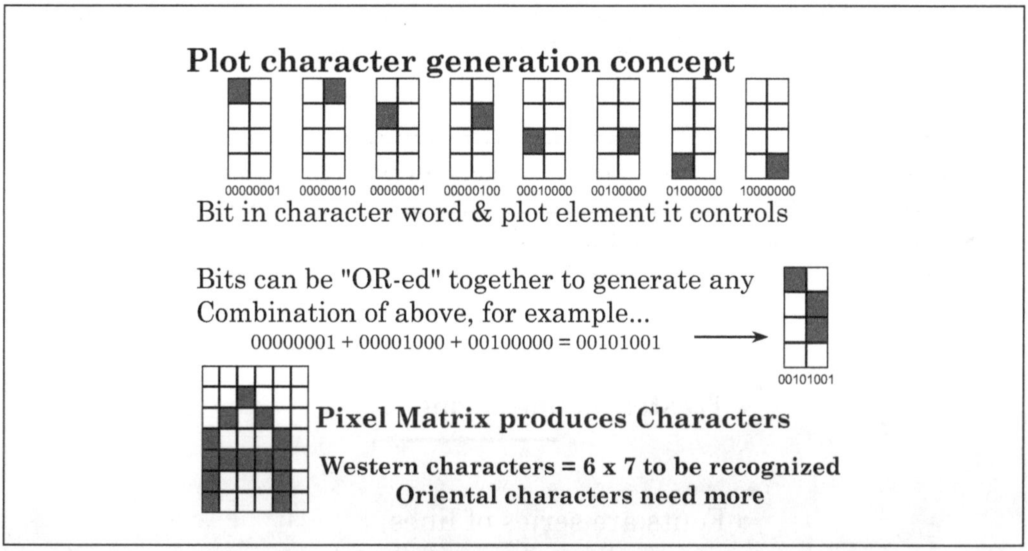

Figure 11-2. Raster Graphics to Plot Characters and Character-Based Graphics

Because of the limits in memory and processing power when most of these systems were designed, each "zone" of pixels typically could be switched to only a single color. If two intersecting lines passed through the same zone, the last selected color "wins," leaving irregular spikes (within each zone) along its length. Clever placement of lines is needed to avoid this (such as intersecting at the corners of the zones).

Western characters are constructed more simply and require fewer pixels than Eastern language characters to be readily recognized. The characters themselves represent only a portion of a word and several of these characters in a string are used to complete any given word. Oriental characters need more pixels to define their image because those more complex characters represent entire words and phrases and require more pixels than if the same thought were expressed in Western form. The complexity of Oriental characters led some Asian vendors to create systems sold and used in Asian countries, that displayed Western characters and Western transliterated forms of Oriental words. This use of Western phonetic words for Oriental sounds was just to save "real estate" on those screens.

Vector Graphics

In contrast to raster graphics there is vector graphics, a newer technology, that does not define the location of pixel switching in the same way. When defining a line, vector graphics first places end points and then it "connects the dots" to fill in that line. Treated as line segments, rather than individual pixels, they allow a more flexible size of fonts because they can be changed to "any size" (nearly). As a result, they can take on far more shapes and stay smooth. This allows many more illustration techniques, as well as the use of a complete range of type fonts, including some of the more complex characters used in many countries around the world. With vector graphics, these characters all tend to "zoom' much better, although there are limits.

Cathode ray tubes (CRTs) wear out over time; they will get dim and lose focus. All systems must support the replacement of CRTs through a standard video format. Users should plan on replacing their CRTs at a minimum of five-year intervals.

- Treated as line segments
- Fonts are series of lines; allows "any size" fonts
- Tend to "zoom" much better

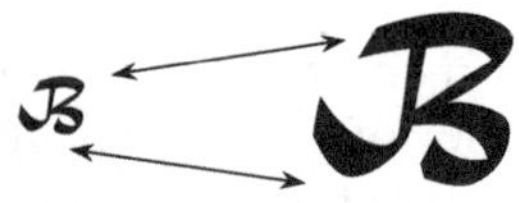

Figure 11-3. Vector Graphics Provide Smoother Lines

The Future of Cathode Ray Tubes (CRTs)

Flat panel displays (FPDs) are rapidly catching up to CRTs in their acceptance in the control room. Some of the many issues that need to be considered are screen brightness, for visibility in bright rooms, and operator visibility at a wide range of viewing angles. The end of the 1990s, the CRT is still the most flexible and least costly solution for complex control system monitoring. As time goes on, of course, the increased use of FPDs in domestic equipment and other commercial enterprises may eventually change the economics of this state of affairs.

A rough estimate of the mean time to failure (MTTF) of an operator station (the CRT and the electronics to drive it) is about 40,000 to 50,000 hours (five years), excluding support items, such as hard drives, keyboards and other input devices. Electronics that are subject to factory floor or outdoor environments and require protective enclosures will likely have reduced ratings.

Much More to Video Monitors

Explaining the many technical aspects of video monitors in depth is outside the scope of this book. Because they play such a vital role in distributed processor systems, you will encounter many terms that need only to be identified, rather than a lengthy explanation. This will no doubt occur when some technician is installing your system, and you find yourself intimidated by technology. For this reason, I have added the following list of definitions:

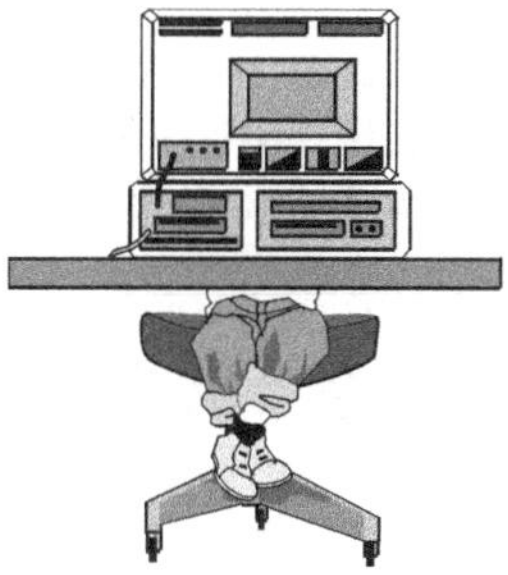

Figure 11-4. Your Video Technician May Try to Intimidate You with Terminology

active-matrix displays (AMLCDs)—A liquid crystal display (LCD) technique in which the pixels on a screen are controlled by voltage signals applied in rows and columns. An array of thin film transistors (TFTs), one per pixel, keeps the pixels energized at all times with no need to reenergize on each scan. AMDs thus respond faster and are brighter than PMLCDs (see *liquid crystal display* and *passive-matrix displays*).

additive primaries—In color reproduction, red, green and blue; when lights of these colors are added together, they produce sensation of white light.

AGA (Advanced Graphics Architecture)—A chipset for driving high-resolution multimedia tools.

antialiasing—In digital graphics, a technique for reducing the jagged appearance of aliased bit map images, usually by inserting pixels that blend boundaries, especially color boundaries.

artifact—In video development, the area within the image or characteristic of the image that is the result of system limitation, for example, weird shimmering, jaggies, or other undesirable distortion. Also in digital graphics, image imperfections caused by data compression.

ATPG (Automatic Test Pattern Generator)—Used in video raster alignment.

AVD—Audio/video driver.

AVI (Audio Video Interleaved)—A digital file format by Microsoft developed for dynamic graphics.

AVK—Audio/video kernel.

AVL—Audio/video library.

AVSS—Audio/video subsystem.

bit depth—In digital graphics, the number of bits used to represent the color of each pixel in an image. A bit depth of 2 = black and white pixels, 4 = 16 colors or grays, 8 = 256 colors or grays, 16 = 65,536 colors, 24 ≅ 16.7 million colors, and so on.

bit map—In computer imaging, the electronic representation of a page or a chosen area of a page, or illustration indicating the position of every possible spot (zero or one.) A bit map is pixel-based (typically higher resolution on video screen) rather than object-oriented (typically higher resolution on printer).

brightness—also luminance; in video displays, the greatest light that a monitor can emit without losing focus; measured in units called footlamberts.

CGA (Color Graphics Adapter)—A video standard (for IBM PC in 1981) offering 320 × 200 pixels with four colors, or 640 × 200 pixels with two colors; in text mode, up to sixteen possible colors; see *EGA, PGA, SVGA, UXGA, VGA, XGA.*

CLUT (Color Look-Up Table)—Used by a video display station to define its color palette to use an 8-bit or lower digital image file.

CMYK (Cyan, Magenta, Yellow, Black)—Model or color space to convey color information; combining differing amounts of these *subtractive* secondary colors produce all the colors in color space; used by most printers, it works by starting with all light waves (white paper) and then *subtracting* quantities of cyan, magenta, yellow, and black wavelengths with pigments, (theoretically, maximum of CMY produce black, but inks are not pure so usually result is muddy brown, hence addition of black); compare with *RGB.*

color depth—In video development, refers to the number of bits of data used to define the pixels' color (8 bits = 256 colors, 16 bits = 65,536 colors, 24 bits = 16.7 million colors).

component RGB video—In video development, red, green, blue, and luminance signals are processed as separate signals (or components), thus achieving higher quality; generally found in professional-grade equipment; see *composite video and RGB.*

composite video—In video development, a video signal that combines chrominance (colors red-green-blue) and luminance (brightness of black, white, and gray) information into one signal relayed on a single waveform or over a single wire; used by most consumer-grade products.

CRT (Cathode Ray Tube) video screen—Used to display information.

distortion—The extent to which a system or component fails to reproduce accurately at its output the characteristics of the input. Also called pin cushioning in video displays, manifests itself at distortion the sides of the screen image by inward or outward bowing of vertical lines, such as those in spreadsheets and tables. Distortion can vary after a switch of resolution and tends to worsen as a monitor ages.

dithering—Electronic graphic technique of filling the gap between two pixels with another pixel that has an average value of those two so as to minimize difference, to add detail to smooth the resulting line, or to create a color not in the palette supporting the given display.

DTV (DeskTop Video)—Combines animation, image metamorphosis, photography, etc., within a common data manager.

DVI (Digital Video Interactive)—Brand name for a variety of Intel product families having to do with digital video and audio.

EGA (Enhanced Graphics Adapter)—Video standard (for IBM PC in 1984) that allows 16 out of a possible 64 colors to be used; can emulate all modes of earlier CGA, adding 320 × 200, 640 × 200, and 640 × 350 pixels with 16 colors; see *CGA, PGA, SVGA, UXGA, VGA, XGA.*

ELF—Extremely low frequency radiation in CRT-based video monitors; see *VLF*.

field emitter display (FED)—Flat-panel display that works much like a CRT, shooting electrons at colored phosphors (pixels) to create an image on screen, but rather than illuminate the phosphors with a single electron gun, a "flat cathode" chip is placed behind each phosphor, allowing the use of a flat panel in lieu of a bulky picture tube.

field of view—Volume in space defined by angular cone extending outward from the focal plane of an instrument or video screen.

flicker—Flashing of a video screen as the electron beam that creates the image follows its raster pattern.

focus—In video displays, the crispness of text and lines, the contrast of adjacent single-pixel-wide black and white lines.

footlamberts—Unit of brightness in video displays.

full-motion imaging—Video image that is completely smooth; see *raster imaging*.

gamma (γ)—In digital graphic video, gamma measures the contrast that affects the midtones of an image; adjusting gamma allows the brightness values of middle-range gray tones to be changed without altering shadows and highlights.

HDR (High Data Rate)—Usually used in the context of digitizing video information.

HGED (High-Gain Emissive Display)—Flat LCD-like panel containing color phosphors similar to those of CRTs but modified to operate at extremely low voltage (under 100) and activated by a matrix grid instead of beam-steered, high voltage electron gun. Unlike LCDs, the matrix needs no transistors to address pixels; phosphors are instead excited by electrons guided to the grid by a process patented by Telegren, Inc. HGED is less than one-tenth the cost of LCD and has no viewing angle restrictions. It has the brightness, color palette, resolution and refresh rates needed for high-definition video, without the concern of X-ray emissions of near-field viewing.

hypermedia—Hypertext function expanded so that documents contain links not only to other pieces of text but also to other forms of media—sounds, images, and video. Images themselves can be selected to link to sounds or documents, and so on.

interactive video—A fusion of video and computer technology, in which a video program and computer program can be run in tandem under the control of the user. With interactive video, the user's actions, choices, and decisions genuinely affect how the program unfolds.

interleave—In data communication, to send blocks of data alternately to two or more stations on a multipoint system or to put bits or characters alternately into time slots of time division multiplexer. Also, on a video screen, to alternate raster scan lines so as to transmit higher-resolution frames per second.

liquid crystal display (LCD)—Reflective visual readout of alphanumeric characters, generally of two types: passive-matrix displays (PMLCDs) and active-matrix displays (AMLCDs), which refer to how pixels in display are controlled. See *active-matrix display* and *passive-matrix display*.

luminance—also *brightness*; in video displays, greatest light monitor can emit without losing focus; measured in units called *footlamberts*.

MDA (Monochrome Display Adapter)—Video standard introduced by IBM in 1982 for IBM/PC, PC/XT and AT computers and compatibles that handled only textual data and was eventually replaced by a card.

MMX (MultiMedia eXtension)—Performance-boosting technology incorporating fifty-seven multimedia-centric instructions into Pentium processors by Intel, to achieve a 10 to 20 percent improvement on standard CPU benchmarks and up to 60 percent improved performance when running software specifically designed for audio, video and graphics technology. MMX involves a processing trick known as "single instruction, multiple data," that enables the MMX chip to package and process many pieces of information as one value rather than in a one-at-a-time sequence that could cause bottlenecks.

MTF (Modulation Transfer Function)—Video focus test to measure the contrast of adjacent single-pixel-wide black and white lines.

PALC (Plasma Addressed Liquid Crystal)—Technology in which gas-plasma channels perform pixel-triggering duties much like the thin film transistors in active-matrix LCD panels, with standard LCD-style backlighting providing illumination.

passive-matrix displays (PMLCDs)—A liquid crystal display (LCD) technique in which the pixels on a video screen are controlled by voltage signals applied in rows and columns, and the crystals respond by reorienting along field lines to transmit or block light to create the image and then return to their original orientation when the voltage drains away. Compare with *active-matrix displays* and *liquid crystal display.*

PCI (Peripheral Component Interconnect)—Bus architecture by Intel that increases physical capacity for high-speed data transfer in graphically intensive applications such as human-machine interfaces (HMIs) and video systems on personal computers.

PIXEL (Picture Element)—The smallest unit on a video display screen that can be stored, displayed, or addressed. A computed picture is typically composed of an array of 450 × 300, 720 × 560, and so on. In color video, a pixel contains red, green, and blue values, and the color depth refers to the number of bits of data used to define the pixels' color (8 bits = 256 colors, 16 bits = 65,536 colors, 24 bits = 16.7 million colors).

PGA (Professional Graphics Adapter)—For PCAT and PCXT high-resolution graphics; see *CGA, EGA, SVGA, VGA, UXGA, XGA.*

raster imaging—Video image that stutters slightly when depicting motion. See *full-motion imaging.*

raster—In the display on a video screen, the raster is the grid pattern of vertical and horizontal divisions outlining all the small elements of which the picture is composed.

RGB (Red/Green/Blue)—Analog NTSC video signal between commercial monitors and equipment such as VCRs and some computers. Also, a model or color space to convey color information. Combining differing amounts of these additive primary colors produces all the colors in the color space. Used by most monitors and most desktop scanners, RGB works by starting with no light (black) and then *adding* quantities of red, green, or blue light (the maximum of all three produces white.) Compare *CMYK*; see *additive primaries.*

scale-ability—The ability to vary the information content of a program by changing the amount of data that is stored, transmitted, or displayed. In a video image, this translates into creating larger or smaller windows of video on screens.

sharpness—In video displays, the crispness of screen displays, like focus. Sharpness is generally due to the convergence of red, blue, and green electron beams into single white "dot" on the screen.

stochastic screening—In electronic publishing and video screen displays, a digital screening process that converts images into very small dots (14 to 40 microns) of equal size and variable spacing. Second-order screened images have variable size dots and variable spacing; also called frequency modulated (FM) screening.

SVGA (Super Video Graphics Adapter)—Introduced in 1988 as a refinement of VGA that offers higher resolution, of at least 800 × 600 pixels, and greater color compatibility, of at least 16 colors, compared with VGA; see *CGA, EGA, PGA, VGA, UXGA, XGA.*

S-video—In video development, a way of dividing the signal so luminance is on one wire or signal while red-green-blue (RGB) mix is on another. Is of higher quality than composite video. S-video is also called Y/C video for luminance/chrominance (lumination/color); compare with *composite video* and *component video.*) Used in "prosumer" equipment but available on some consumer-grade video products. See Y/X video.

TBC (Time Base Corrector)—Electronic device that corrects inconsistencies in the rhythm of a video signal.

Uniformity—In video displays, the evenness of brightness across the screen display, without which the image appears dirty and the colors distorted.

UXGA (Ultra eXtended Graphics Adapter)—video standard introduced as a refinement of SVGA which offers higher resolution of at least 1600 x 1200 pixels; see *CGA, EGA, PGA, SVGA, VGA, XGA*.

VDS (Variable Definition Syntax)—This is DDL (data definition language) renamed (copyright granted to SP50 Committee by ISP Foundation.) Also, Video Direct Slot; provides port for additional video monitors using a common signal source in a workstation.

VDT—Video display terminal.

VDU—Video display unit.

VESA—Video electronics standards association.

VGA (Video Graphics Adapter)—Video standard introduced in 1987 for IBM PS/2 series which can emulate CGA and EGA modes and additionally provide 640 × 480 pixels with 16 colors and 320 × 200 pixels with 256 colors; see *CGA, EGA, PGA, SVGA, UXGA, XGA.*

Video for Windows (VFW)—In digital graphics display, a multimedia architecture and application suite from Microsoft that provides an outbound architecture that lets applications developers access audio, video, and animation from many different sources through one interface. As an application, it primarily handles video capture and compression, as well as video and audio editing.

Video Ram (VRAM)—Random access memory with parallel-to-serial conversion for generating video display signals. Provides capacity for number of colors and resolution (amount of pixels.)

VIW (Video in Window)—Placing a continuous video image (from, say, an RGB input) into a computer's (typically VGA) screen view.

VLF—Very low frequency radiation in CRT-based video monitors. See *ELF.*

VR (Virtual Reality)—Three-dimensional (3-D) computer simulation of real-world activities and events allowing "walk-through" of various proposed designs or situations; a 3-D doorway versus a 2-D window (video screen).

XGA (eXtended Graphics Adapter)—Raster than VGA and causes less eyestrain, but works only on Micro Channel® 386SX or better PCs; resolution is 1024 × 768 pixels and 256 colors are supported;. see *CGA, EGA, PGA, SVGA, UXGA, VGA.*

Y/C—Video Y (luminance) and C (color) video information on separate signals. Is of higher quality than composite video but not as high as component video. Available on professional and some consumer-grade video products. Same as S-Video. See *composite video*, *component video* and *S-video.*

Exploring Displays 12

Navigating through screen views of your process requires some screen display techniques as well as screen layout. The screen display techniques are somewhat standard among most video equipment suppliers, based upon the computer operating systems that they use. Our discussion here is what is typical.

Other view arrangements, however, will be based upon how the control system vendor has chosen to portray his standard views of his screen hierarchy, if this was done at all. Some vendors with proprietary workstations provide an "out-of-the-box" set portraying overviews, groups, and detail displays in one form or another. Some do not, especially if they connect with "generic" workstation packages from providers of HMI software (only). Still there are few vendors of control systems who create "framework" packages to provide some standard order onto generic workstation packages from those suppliers who sell only HMI software.

Windowing

New technologies offer users the dynamics of using multiple, different windows on the same screen, allowing direct access to diverse areas of the plant. Windowing capability provides users with a powerful way to obtain selected details and support information on the main monitor without losing the principle screen view (Figure 12-1). Windowing capability also gives users the ability to emphasize the important control process information while de-emphasizing the less relevant. However it also keeps the latter always available upon request. While it is helpful to open several windows at the same time to look at different parts of the plant at once, this feature also reduces the need for access to be only by way of a screen hierarchy.

Windows can be tiled so they do not overlap. They can be cascaded, which allows them to be stacked so you see just the edges of each window, usually with a title exposed, and you can select the one you'd rather see.

Windowing borrows terminology from commercial video:

PBP (Picture By Picture)—This is a split screen video display, with simultaneous adjacent views or channels.

PIP (Picture In Picture)—This is a video screen with more than one simultaneous view or channel, usually one or more insets within a larger view. It is usually used with live camera views of process.

POP (Picture Outside Picture)—This is a simultaneous multiple-view video screen but without insets.

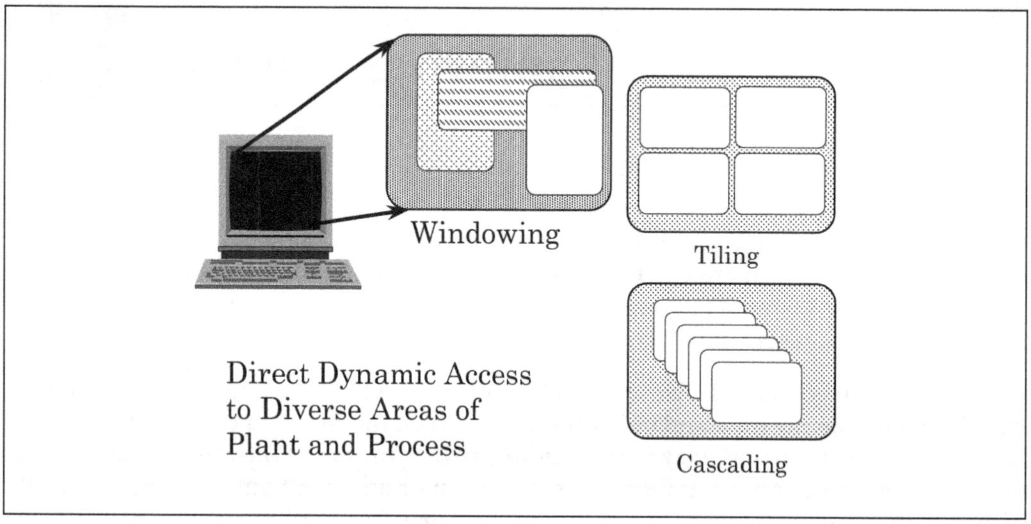

Figure 12-1. Examples of Windowing

There are some practical considerations to keep in mind when using windowing techniques:

- How many screens can be opened before the user gets lost? (Some systems put an arbitrary limit on this.)
- Do all opened views continue to update?
- Do those opened views continue to update at the same rate?
- Do those opened views continue to process data in those areas that are hidden behind other opened views?

In some systems opened views will continue to process data in those areas behind other views. This places considerable pressure on the display generator and can slow the refresh times for all views. If the hidden layers stay live, however, the data is more readily available if these views are rapidly switched.

Zooming

Zooming allows you to "step up to or back from the panel" (Figure 12-2). This may be done in one smooth motion, or it may be done in stages. A possible disadvantage of smooth zooming action is that when you "back away" from a highly detailed display, all that detail clusters down into an unrecognizable blob. There are decluttering mechanisms that switch off certain symbols or switch to a simpler icon as you move out. Then as you move back in, more detail will be added in increments.

Certain creativity in the construction of the illustration could be necessary to avoid confusing the operator. Some prefer switching through a series of stages from close to far to control font and icon sizes within a readable range. Others prefer to merely change views through a select "button" built into the view.

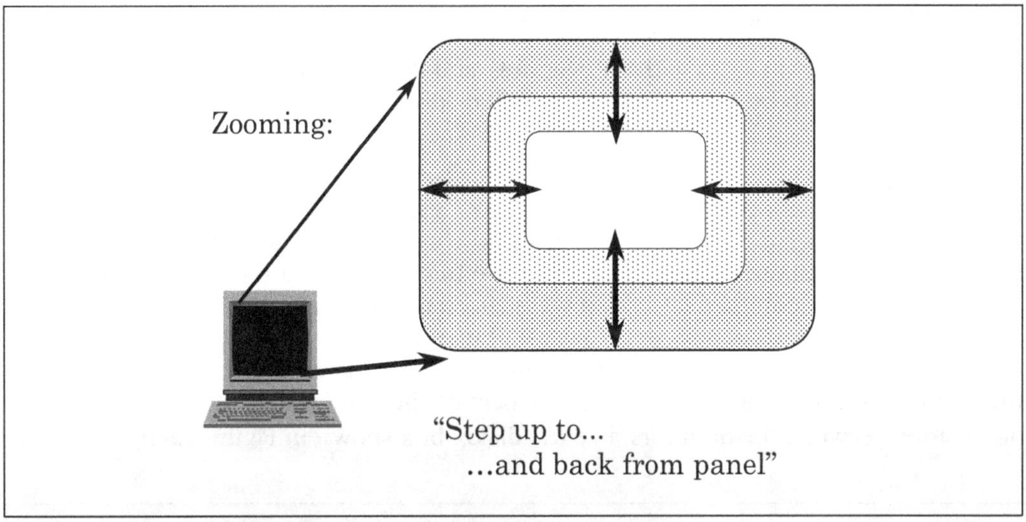

Figure 12-2. Zooming Into/Out of Displays

Panning

Panning provides a feature in which you can literally walk around the panel and it acts like having a smaller open window on a very large page. You slide the window around the different areas of the page to focus on a specific area of interest or concern (Figure 12-3).

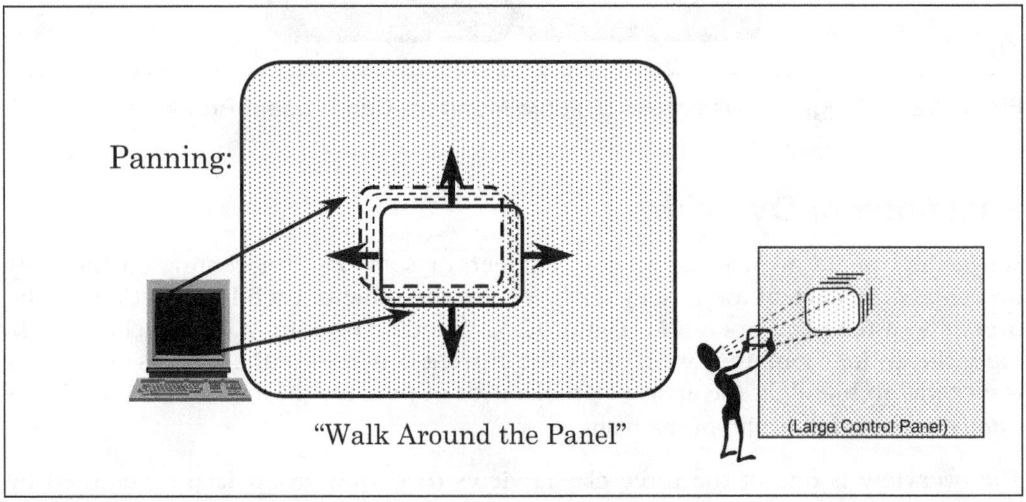

Figure 12-3. "Touring the Plant" by Panning Smaller Window Around Larger "Panel"

Panning, and even zooming, involve issues similar to windowing in general:

- Do you refresh the hidden area?

- Can you get lost in navigation?

Some systems offer an inset with an overview and cursor that you can use as a locator. This feature can also be used as a selector when "diving into" a display.

Video Wall

Console designs permit multiple screens to be clustered together but still functioning as one view. This allows a much larger picture but maintains a high resolution. Examples of this are the commercial "video walls" used for entertainment centers and advertising displays. Be careful how these are used! If you merely transform your usual views to such an array, without making modifications for the change in presentation, you may find some surprises, such as viewing that part of the screen that crosses through the boundaries between the monitors, like the dialog box shown in Figure 12-4!

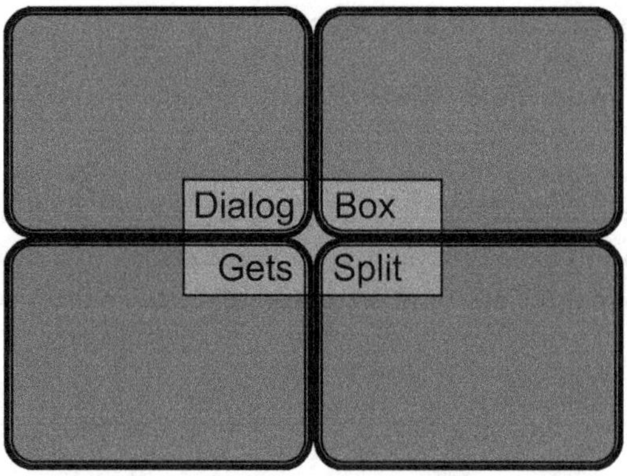

Figure 12-4. Single Views across Multiple Monitors Can Present Problems

Functions of Overview

When the operations manager, plant engineer, or someone just coming on the shift first enters the control room, they don't require the value of each loop, but rather the overview of the plant operation (Figure 12-5). Standing back from the panel and looking at the entire room, they want to see the current concerns of the process or plant. It is essential to highlight the areas of problems or of potential problems. They are interested in the overall health of the plant.

The overview is one of the three classic views (overview-group-detail) identified by Renzo Dallimonti in the early 1970s as the three standard needs in the typical control room. The view shows some grouping of major loops and process states, sequence stages, alarms that are already there, or areas that are in danger of going into alarm.

A general grouping of loops will show only deviations between set points and process variables for one or two hundred loops. Deviation limits between setpoint and process variable are generally set individually so that "full scale" to the limit mark can be

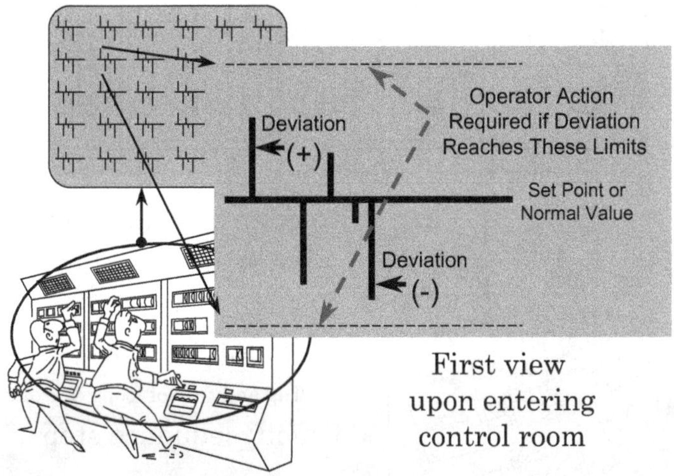

Figure 12-5. General Plant/Process Conditions

3 percent, 11 percent, 26 percent, or whatever is an appropriate critical limit that should be a concern to the operator. Overviews provided by some vendors may also show major steps in sequences, depending upon the information needed at this level.

Invoking one of the groups with a keystroke or a touch on the screen will present you with a group screen view (faceplate or graphic style), which will give you a closer look and provide you with the ability make a change at that level.

Today, this overview screen will very likely be in the form of a dynamic graphic, but the elements are the same. Interactive operator prompts can also be included; for example, to give direction and focus to an alarm or plant upset.

Functions of Group View

After viewing the general health of the process or plant, the operator will walk up to the control panel to make adjustments to the controllers. He or she will only pay attention to those few instruments involved in that portion of the process. This is the origin of the group view (Figure 12-6).

The group view is the second of the three classic views identified by Dallimonti in the early 1970s as the three standard needs in the typical control room. This is the group cluster of loops (ramp generators, sequences, "switches," etc.) that together define a unit process. It is the normal operating view of the "panel," and typically it has no more than eight or sixteen "instruments" in that group. As with the control panel, the operator should be able to view and/or manipulate the process variable, the set point, and the output. When the loop has a problem, the operator will want to see any appropriate alarm limits and perhaps the operating mode to which the controller is set—automatic, manual, or computer, and so on. Of course, he or she will need to see the tag and title of that process loop.

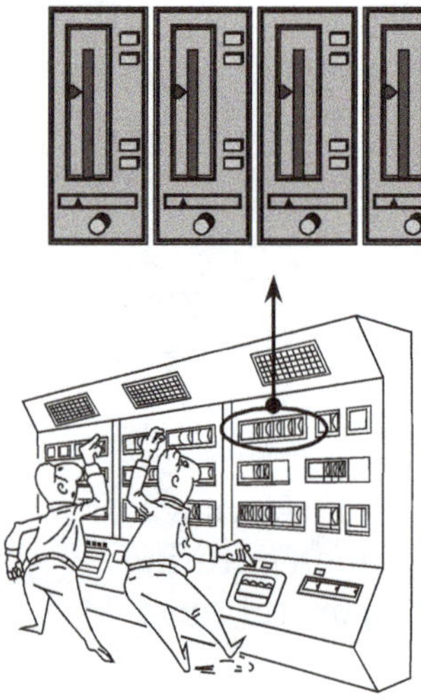

Figure 12-6. Functions in the Operating Level

When an operator invokes one specific controller of that group on the screen, that faceplate should be highlight red in some way to verify that it is ready to receive commands. It is helpful if a line of text also appears that it enhances the information about that loop or function, such as where it is located on the process and in the plant. In addition, more detail regarding the condition of that "device" can appear in a second line of text, such as alarms or diagnostics in natural language (as opposed to alphanumeric codes).

The group originated view with an early grouping of controller faceplates known as "clothesline indicators." These were a group of instruments designed so that the scales behind the process variable (PV) pointer could be moved with a thumbwheel. The set point was placed by moving that scale to the center of the viewing window. The center was marked by a green line painted across the front of the instrument. When the red process variable pointer was on set point, that pointer fell out of view behind the green line. If the loop was off normal, the red pointer came out from behind the green line and was visible from a distance. The advantage of this was that when a large group of instruments was lined up side by side, a quick glance by the operator was all that was needed to spot discrepancies in the operation. This concept also gave rise to the deviation bar in the overview display.

Of course, like the overview, *today the group view usually will be the graphic equivalent of the same function.* Quite often, however, you will find a faceplate either embedded into that graphic view or faceplate "pop-ups" when a cursor is placed over that part of the process needing adjustment.

A major difference between this screen view and the hardware version is that the screen view can provide dynamic operator prompts on the same screen, such as "Must enter Manual," if the operator tries to adjust the output while operating in automatic.

Many different procedural prompts can assure consistent operation from a crew with a wide variety of individual experiences.

Functions of Point Detail Display

Now, the other operator action that could happen in a control room in a traditional control panel would be the ability to walk up to a group display and slide the instrument out of its case (Figure 12-7). It would now be possible to adjust the control parameters (gain, rate, or reset) of a loop or the alarm settings.

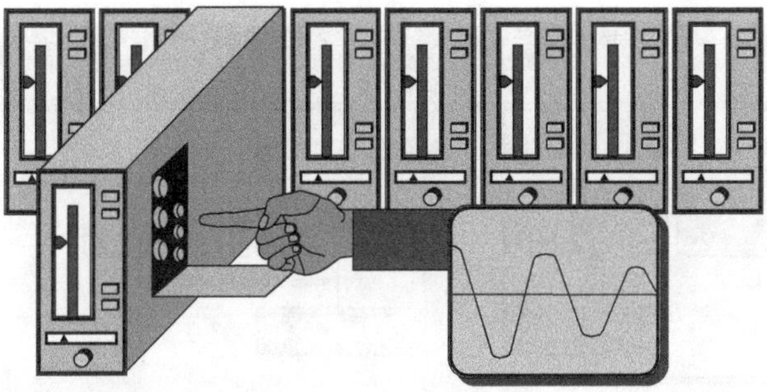

- Like sliding instrument out from case to adjust tuning, alarm settings, etc. ...
- On screen, also tuning "chart," to/from wire list, "hold value," SP ramp/clamp, etc.

Figure 12-7. Video Screen Version Can Add Tuning Trend to "Instrument" View

This is the third of the three classic views identified by Dallimonti in the early 1970s as the standard needs in the typical control room. This view is now called by some as the Point Display and by others as the Point Detail Display. In the video form, and with the many features that are now easily possible in microprocessor-based controllers today, this view can also be used to adjust set point ramps, set point clamps, emergency shutdown settings, set values for hold ring output at some desired safe setting, and whatever other attributes the vendor supplies with the function blocks for control. A process variable trend for tuning is often added, which can even have some "zoom to close-up" capabilities.

By its nature, the detail view is rarely graphic. It can, however, be used to invoke an input from the to/from wire list within this view. This can be convenient for checking on the condition of the signal source, rather having to run out to the I/O cabinet with a test set of cables and multimeter. By "clicking" on a selection in this input/output list, an additional view appears that shows the conditions of signals coming from a terminal board. From this view comes more detail about that input, such as the signal range, input alarm settings, and the linearization curves that were configured into it.

The view may perhaps instead show that part of the configuration strategy in which this "instrument" is used. With some vendors this is a dynamic piping and instrument diagram (P&ID) that also conveys the quality coding of signals as well as current values.

In Figure 12-8 we see an example of a screen view that shows the progress of a batch operation with windows for operator instructions and interactions; definitions of specific phase parameters; the availability of equipment; material tracking and genealogy; ingredient quantity, location, amount available and consumed, and so on. Some of the requirements of batch operations necessitate more than Dallimonti's "traditional" overview-group-detail scenario.

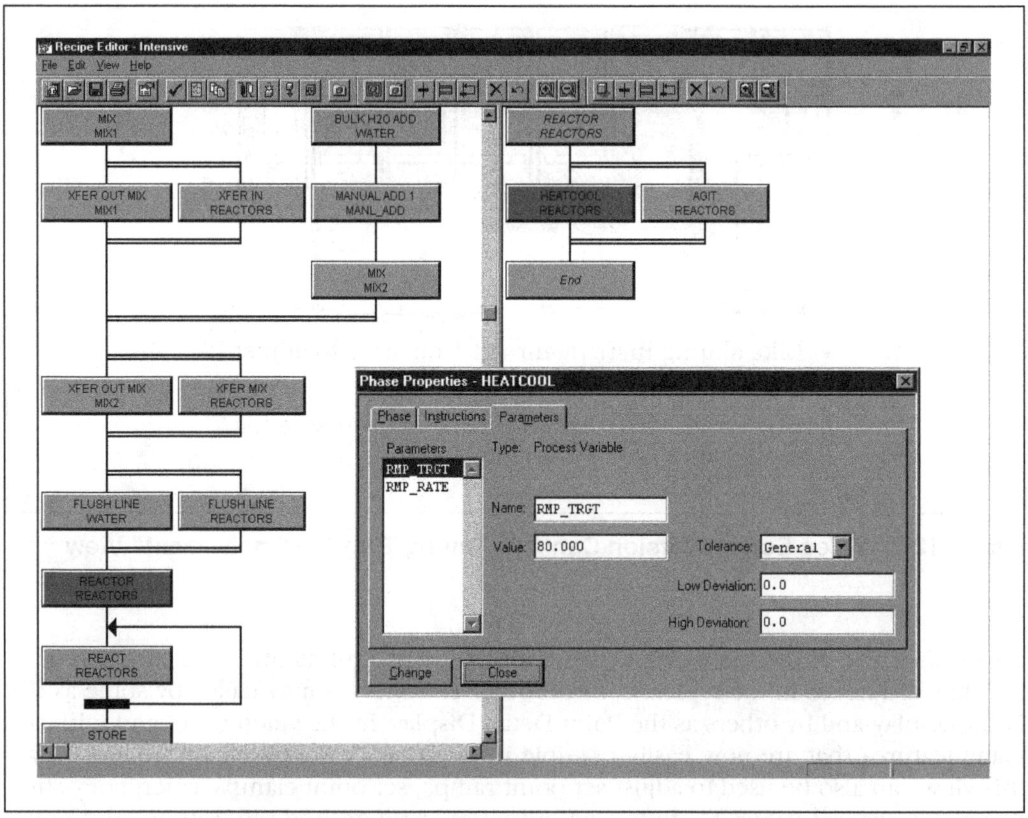

Figure 12-8—Batch Progress View

Additional Views

Besides the fundamental operating views discussed in the preceding sections, there are many more views that will help the user of control systems. There is no limit to the imagination of the system design team, except to not become so carried away that they overwhelm the people who must run the process or plant. The way to develop operating views is to think FUNCTIONALLY.

For example, the other requirement that was in a traditional panel board was alarm annunciators. However, it is necessary to quickly find the area of concern and just as quickly gain as much information as is needed to make corrections (but not so much data as to overwhelm). While doing this, the operator should also be able to silence any audible alarm and/or acknowledge that alarm. Support views such as alarm lists, which can be used for filtering, qualifying, and sorting problems quickly, should be available. Their design, though somewhat generic, ought to be "custom" designed to the specific need of the processes involved. This will be discussed later in Part D on plant upsets.

Similar problem-tracking views should be available for system diagnostics. When responding to a system alarm (the control system itself had a failure somewhere), the operator, or the maintenance person, should also follow a "trail" leading to the offending component. Lists for sorting, qualifying, and filtering are useful here, as well, but serious consideration should be given to dynamic graphic maps to locate and resolve problems. Additional displays include system summaries, component status, control sequence status, historical and trend information, line safety and tie-in flow summaries, energy costs, maintenance and red-tag (out-of-service) functions, and many sorts of help windows.

All of the technologies for achieving these goals are evolving and will continue to leapfrog through the different vendors as they experience installations in their clients' locations. As time goes on and processing power permits, operator prompts should be included in these views to support and remind operator(s) of best practices.

Other Typical Screen Views

- Ability to use interactive and dynamic displays offers interesting variations on the traditional
  - I/O connections on terminals show values, limits, alarms, signal conditioning and linearizations
  - Alarm list by various sortings, qualifiers, filters, etc.
  - Diagnostic lists, also by various sortings
  - Equipment "map" can also show locations of failures
  - Historical data by various sortings, including RDBM
  - List of alarmed points defeated by plant engineer during start-up or plant repairs
  - Statistical process control charts (XbarR, etc.)
  - Just about any type of view desired

Learning to use the video medium, as we said earlier, takes time. Only when people experience the advantages of change in meaningful steps can new ideas what is useful begin to happen. Limitations on screen refresh speeds have been an obstacle to involved graphic displays. Yet as technology overcomes performance restrictions, more creative displays will be tried, and even demanded. That is just one of the exciting components of the controls business.

Historical information is becoming an operator's tool as well as for the engineer and plant manager. This is true especially with the emergence of relational database managers (RDBMs), which help make it possible to sort data quickly into useful information. This also is a topic for a later chapter, but it follows the same basic rule—think FUNCTIONALLY.

13 Trending Data Through Video

In the operations of a process or plant, you often need to have more than the immediate values; you want to have the perspective of history (Figure 13-1). Some indication to guide future direction, immediate or long-term, helps cause operation repeatability. Trending also helps you show the activities prior to some upset. Then you can play them back at a later time and determine what events occurred leading up to the upset.

Beyond Immediate Values

Traditional trending was done on circular charts or strip charts. What both had in common was messy ink that dried too slowly and clogged the pens or dried too fast and ran down the chart paper, "feathering" into wide blobs and smears.

Circular charts were favored for easy storage of data from each shift, day, week, even month. They were nice and flat and filed easily, and the entire report was on a single sheet. Problems with circular charts were the non-linear scales and the need to change the span of each analog signal, so as to cause the trace to favor the outside third of the scale. Low values fell into the narrow part of the pie shape, making them hard to read. Any change in the measured signal meant the mechanism had to be recalibrated.

Strip charts are linear, but only a small portion can be viewed at any one time. The storage of chart rolls was very cumbersome at best, and retracing a value at some past event that occurred a week, a month, or, heaven forbid, a year ago was a nightmare. I know, I had to more than once. The new video recorders, which emerged in the mid-1990s have been able to provide corrections to these limitations. Their technology came from that developed for the DCSs.

Charts and Clipboards to Video Trend

- Need more than immediate values
- Provides perspective of history
- Indicates future direction
- Allows operation repeatability
- Shows activities prior to upsets
- "Entry" to historical archival

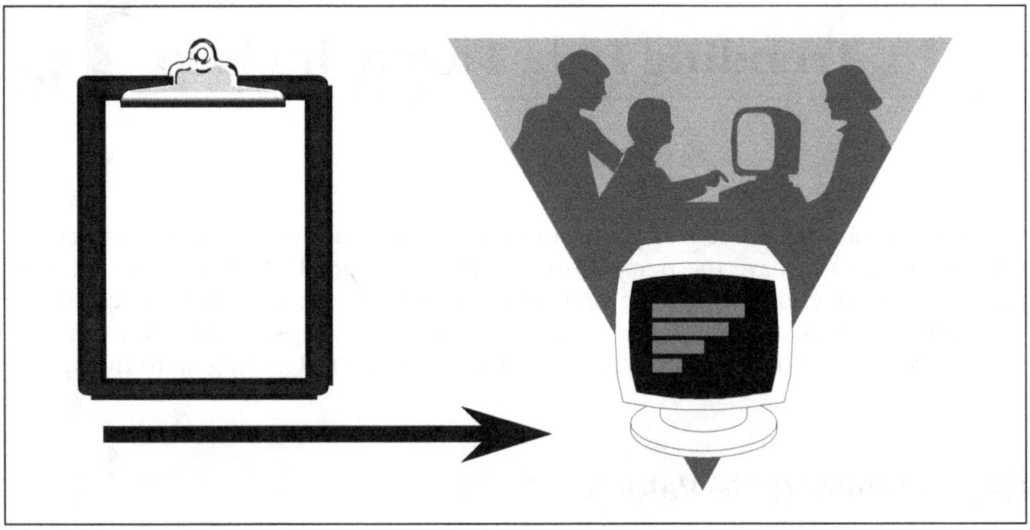

Figure 13-1. Clipboards to Computers—More Thorough Recordkeeping

---

A New Way to See

With the difficulties presented by traditional trending methods, most parameters were never tracked. Very easy and economical video trending is now allowing many more values in a process to be recorded. This has been leading in turn to the discovery of process characteristics that were never realized before. Many people have learned that they may KNOW a process, but they do not UNDERSTAND it! There have been significant boosts in PRODUCTIVITY as a result of the changes that have been made because of this emerging understanding.

On most systems, the workstation dynamically collects current data and stores it into local history (within that station):

- Active trend, Dynamic trend, and Current trend are just some of the terms used to define displays that show data as it is being collected.
- Historical trend is generally that which is "called up" from local memory.
- Archived trend is data that has been transferred onto some removable media, such as magnetic or optical disk.

Using Trend Displays

Of course, every system handles trends unique to the design of that particular vendor. The features of such systems will vary depending upon the experiences of that vendor in serving customer requests. Expect those features to represent the needs of the industries that vendor serves.

Considerations for trend placement (Figure 13-2) are:

- Will a single trend group fill the screen view for better visibility?
- Will multiple trend groups be placed on the same screen view? (as multiple "windows" tiled, cascaded, or either tiled or cascaded?)
- Can a trend group be embedded within a graphic and other views?
- Can a trend group be a "pop-up" within another view?
- Can "window" be resized as needed on line?
- Can the "window" be repositioned on the screen view as needed on line?

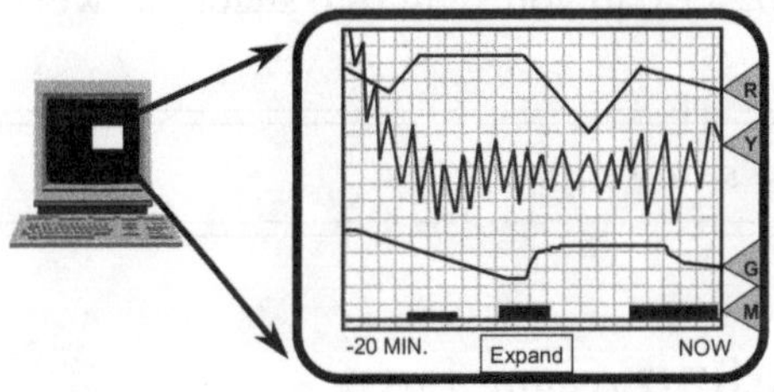

- Trend placement
- Trended points
- Trend trace dynamics

Figure 13-2. Considerations for Trend

Considerations for trended point limitations (Figure 13-2) are:

- How many traces (pens) will fit within a single trend group?
- What is the total number of traces (pens) available per screen (multiple groups)? (There could be a processing performance limitation)
- Can you trend any parameter of any tagged point (process tag): that is, set points, process variables, outputs, status, operating mode, control parameters, and so on.
- What is the total capacity of the number of trended points (traces or "pens")?
- What are the smallest samples that can be taken? (This could be a performance limitation of controller scan time more than a question of screen refresh time or even the data communication network. It could be possible to time-stamp a high scan rate at the I/O, then whenever the data reaches the screen, those values could be presented.)
- What is total capacity of sampled data? (This is a complex question because memory will be consumed much more by smaller samples of a large number of parameters. More on this later.)

Considerations for trend trace dynamics (Figure 13-2) are:

- Is there a choice of colors for each trace?
- Does the trace change colors (it can go red) when the point goes into alarm?
- Can you place discrete and analog values in the same group?
- Will the trace start and stop with the equipment or process? This would indicate rapid recognition of these changes; also no need to save flat lines in memory.
- Can you switch shading on and off while on-line? (Shading will especially improve the visibility of "stray dots" that are off-normal "spikes," which can otherwise be lost from view.)
- Will the trace shade to base? Can you switch to shade between traces?

Not all systems have the same capabilities!

Analog Value Trending (Figure 13-3)

Note that by allowing span changes to be done individually, as well as by groups, users are able to "play around" with comparisons between different trended points. This is very useful for overcoming the problem that "all the important areas are crunched together at one point", and assures the readability and correct interpretation of data. View changes like this are harmless as long as the database is not altered or destroyed.

Not all systems have the same capabilities!

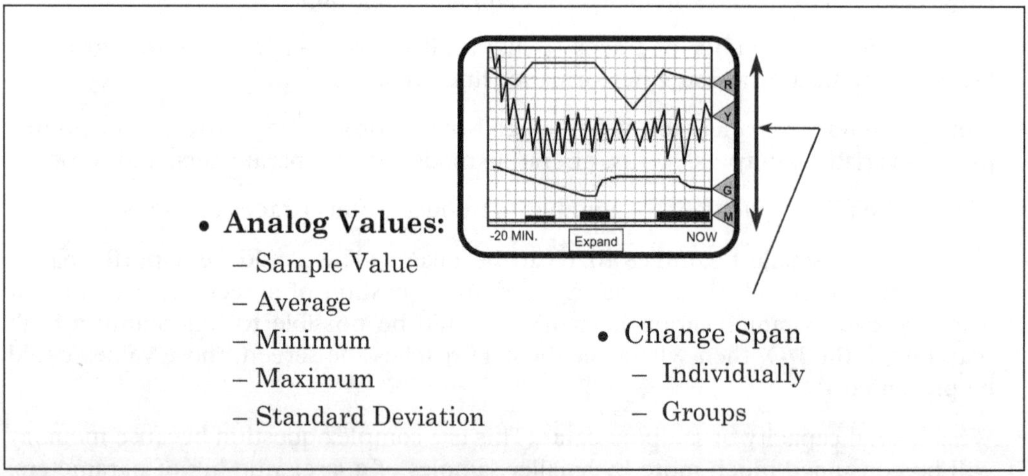

Figure 13-3. Trending Analog Parameters

Discrete Value Trending (Figure 13-4)

Note that discrete values show THREE conditions; ON, OFF, and a mid height for those conditions when the signal was both on and off, such as during a transition during the time increments selected, or when the "switch" is cycling. Having discrete actions shown with analog values allows events to be compared with process fluctuations.

Not all systems have the same capabilities!

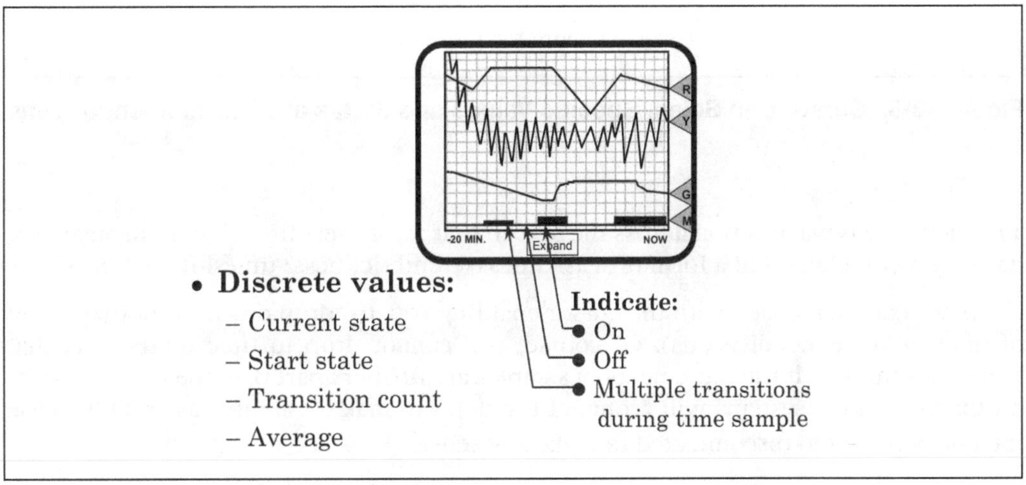

Figure 13-4. Trending Discrete Parameters

Uses for Trend Cursor (Figure 13-5)

The cursor can be moved over analog and discrete traces to make accurate comparisons at any given time sample. At each intersection, the time and date appears, along with the specific values of the conditions at that point in time. All traces are identified with the process tag, the parameter being measured, and the description of that process tag.

Not all systems have the same capabilities!

Trend Navigation (Figure 13-6)

Panning is moving "back and forth" along the same time divisions within a much longer trend than fits in a single screen. In most systems, this is done in half, quarter, or even eighth screen "jumps." Although processing power is a factor in the choice of which of these "jumps" to move in; the real reason for using these jumps is that a so-called smooth transition is not really smooth because of the nature of time sampling. As

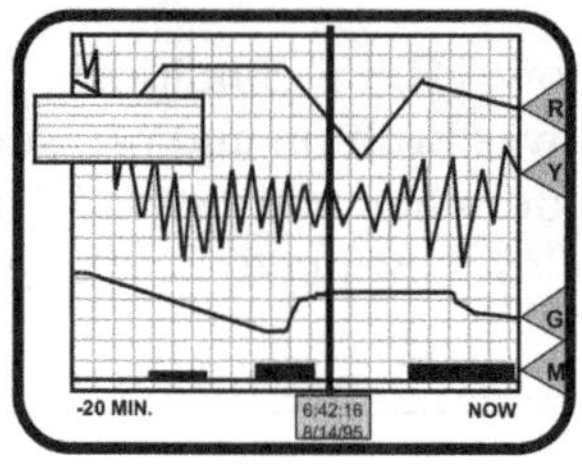

- **Cursor:**
  - Time/date of placement
  - Value/state of intersected traces
  - Tags and titles of all traces viewed
  - Select area of zoom for more detail

Figure 13-5. Cursor Can Select Specific Values and States at Same Moment of Time

a result, there is wave action across the screen that most users find objectionable. Some have even complained of a form of seasickness (trend sickness? timeshift sickness?)!

Zooming can be focused with the cursor enabling you, to "drop down to another layer" of time increments (divisions). Of course, you cannot drop to time increments that were not sampled! If the increments of samples are further apart than the time divisions on the grid, some systems will "connect the dots" to make visibility easier. Otherwise the dots will be too disconnected to make any sense.

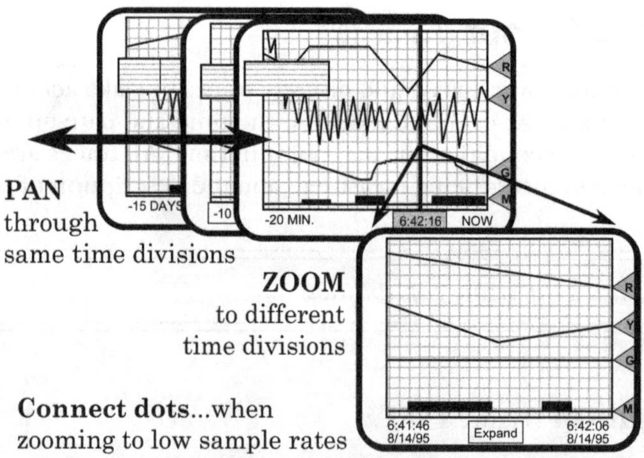

Figure 13-6. Cursor Can Be Used to Zoom In for More Detail

Some Trend Guidelines

Trending is far easier in systems today than it was only a very short while ago. The tendency is to trend everything that moves just because it is there! You should consider trending parameters that have not been observed in the past. It could lead you to understand much more about your process, even if you think you already know enough. You must, however, be organized or you will be buried in data. Some guidelines to consider include the following:

- Use consistent trend layouts throughout the display system.
- Trend multiple variables only when they are related or are needed for comparison to each other.
- Provide labels for all the trended variables, and provide them always in a consistent location.
- When displaying multiple trends, code each label to correspond to its respective trend line by color, shape, or some other means.
- Provide all important labeling, such as trend variable range and time scale.

History, Archiving, and Record-Keeping Subnetworks

All information that moves into the controller, or even that which moves into the I/O modules, whether or not it is viewed or acted upon, can be retained. The hardest part is deciding WHICH data to actually retain. Some users will save data only until a process has successfully completed a run or only after preestablished, continuously uneventful periods of time.

Sometimes an operator may wish to have past data to compare to previous runs of a particular process. This would happen in repetitive operations such as heat treating. In some metalworking processes, the final customer requires a record of the process, especially the annealing or hardening of material. This is certainly true of the pharmaceutical industry, which has critical government regulations requiring documentation.

When trying to picture how historical data is stored within the operator or workstation, picture if you will storage history saved on multiple "trend barrels" (Figure 13-7). The height of the barrel is the number of traces being saved, and the circumference of the barrel changes with the length of time saved, so you can predetermine how many parameters will be saved and how long they will be saved before they "pour off the barrel" or get "painted over."

The example in Figure 13-7 shows but one way to visualize how data is saved. The idea here merely is to try to understand how memory is often allocated. Even if the station seems to have "infinite memory," someone will always want to save thousands of points at one millisecond increments for fourteen years!

HISTORICAL DATA is usually that data stored within resident memory within the workstation itself. In each different system, the vendor will have to explain how to precisely calculate the total "pieces of data" that can be saved in history. Essentially, you will have to determine the number of parameters that must be saved and the time increments for

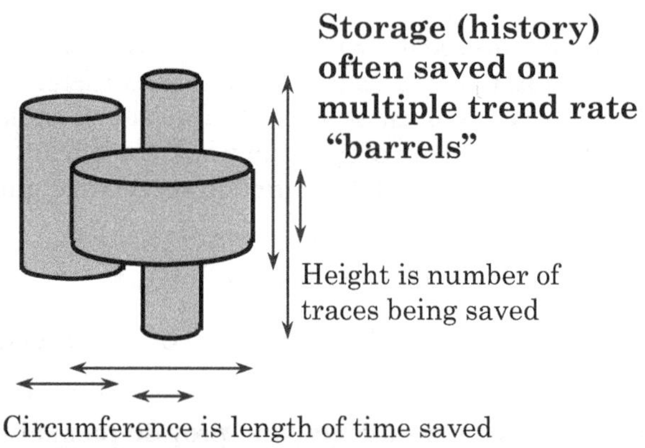

Figure 13-7. One View of How Data is Saved

each parameter. Of course, this calculation will not be so simple because of the internal structuring of the database done by the vendor.

To organize the data so it can easily be retrieved, the vendor may have an assortment of restrictions based upon how the data is grouped within that particular system. For example, all those trends in the same "trend group" must all have the same "save rates" or time increments. When averaged, they all must be done at the same point in time. If they are not, they could not display on the same time grid. Depending upon the digital manipulation methods you may find that larger clusters of points may have to be in the same "save rate" category. Look at the example in Figure 13-7, for instance. How many "drums" are kept in a system? The user may very well have the option of defining each drum "circumference" and "height," but there will have to be some limit to the number of drums that can be provided. In any case, there will be some "wasted space" on each drum.

This is not as great a problem as it may first appear. Usually, there is plenty of overall memory for normal use and provisions to archive data for long-term storage.

Off-Line Storage of Data

Sometimes the volume of history, particularly the collection of all the events that happened on a given shift, day or week, or even month becomes so large that it will not be analyzed until a much later time. This is when an archiving system would be used. Archiving can "continuously" pour data off this drum before it's lost or "painted over," or the system archiving could be designed to create a series of snapshots sometime after it's saved but sometime before it's painted over (Figure 13-8).

In the event of a plant upset, some systems have provisions for capturing a snapshot of all the data around the event on a separate part of memory, or onto another disk, for a "post trip review." This is especially helpful in those systems that sample data at a more dense rate for a few hours or more, then average it when the operation is uneventful.

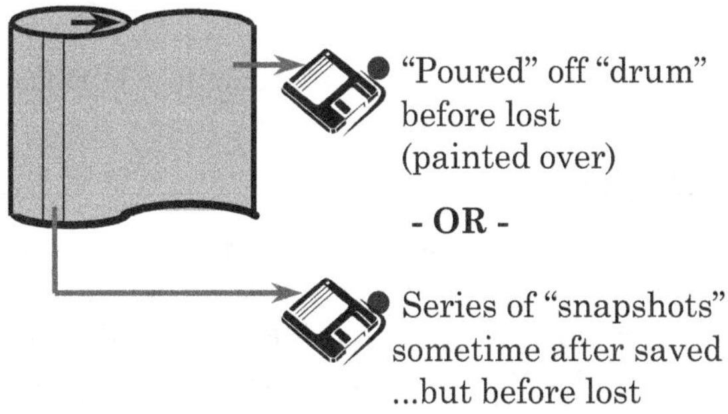

Figure 13-8. Archiving Data Allows It to Be Saved Off Line

Archiving allows the history to be moved onto a removable media whether it is magnetic tape, floppy disk, optical disk, or solid state. Generally, when the historical information is archived, a record is maintained indicating which archived disk volume the information is kept. This may be an automatic and/or a manual process. Nevertheless, it provides a technique for retrieving data that could be months or even years old without having to memorize where everything is located.

The data can then be placed on a removable medium like a floppy disk or an optical disk. Archive data is usually defined as data that is stored on a removable media.

In some systems, a library of the disk titles is kept in a station. At some later time the user may invoke a trend view that includes history that goes further back than what's resident in the station. The station goes into its memory and notifies the user which disk volume number to locate and insert into the station. The station will then be able to blend this additional data into its own resident memory for display in that trend.

Trended, historical, and archived data do not carry the same degree of urgency as alarmed and operating data. The movement of historical data from distant stations will carry a much lower priority in the data management of the "process operating network." Historical and archiving activities for report generation and management reviews are likely to be operated over a separate subnetwork, connected to the operator stations but operating independently of their primary role.

There is a whole field of data compression which is beyond the scope of this text. Nevertheless, when talking to vendors, or their engineers, you may encounter some terms and acronyms that are equally mysterious, but should not intimidate you. Some of them I list here, but I wish I knew even more about this myself (such as what the "SS" stands for in "LZSS" below):

asymmetrical compression—Data compression system that requires more processing capability to compress an image than to decompress it; typically used for mass distribution of programs on media such as CD-ROMs.

CGM(IF) [Computer Graphics Metafile (Interchange Format)]—A standard for archiving and transferring graphics data.

compaction—See *compression*.

compression—Any of several techniques used to reduce the number of bits required to represent information in the storage or transmission of digital data (saving memory or bandwidth), in which the original form of the information can be reconstructed. Also called *compaction*; see *asymmetrical, delta save, JPEG, MPEG, symmetrical, compression.*

DCT (Discrete Cosine Transform)—A data compression technique.

EDM (Engineering Data Management)—Controls access to online and archived engineering data; prevents unauthorized users from getting information and erroneously making changes that others don't know about.

JPEG (Joint Photographic Experts Group)—Working committee under the auspices of the ISO that is attempting to define a proposed universal standard for the digital compression and decompression of still images for use in computer systems and for image exchange between computers. The JPEG algorithm reduces image size by as much as 65:1 while maintaining image integrity by eliminating imperceptible color information.

lossless—Digital data technique that reduces the size of a file without sacrificing any of original data; this tool allows an expanded or restored file to be an exact replica of the original file before compression.

lossy compression—Digital data compression technique in which some data is deliberately discarded so as to achieve massive reductions in the size of the compressed file.

L-Z algorithm—Lossless data compression technique developed by two researchers named Lempel and Ziv.

LZH Compression (Lempel-Ziv-Huffman)—A method of data compression that can reconstruct data exactly like the original with no loss.

LZSS—A refinement of the L-Z algorithm for data compression that can reconstruct data exactly like the original with no loss.

LZW (Lempel-Ziv & Welch)—Patented by Unisys, another refinement of the L-Z algorithm for data compression that can reconstruct data exactly like the original with no loss.

MPEG (Motion Picture Experts Group)—Standards committee under the auspices of the ISO that is working on algorithm standards that will allow the digital compression, storage, and transmission of moving image information such as motion video and CD quality audio and control data at CD-ROM bandwidth. The MPEG algorithm provides interframe compression of video images and can have an effective compression rate of 100:1 to 200:1.

MPEG 2—Proposed standard for ISO adaptation that allows for a higher than normal resolution motion video compression than the MPEG standard.

PLV (Production Level Video)—Video encoding using the oldest digital compression scheme, by Intel/IBM.

RLE (Run Length Encoding)—Data compression technique that saves data by a single count byte and a repeat byte rather than by using memory to save a repetitive group of bytes, for example: 777777 becomes "count of 6 with value of 7 (two bytes).

symmetrical compression—A system that requires equal processing capability for the compression and decompression of an image. This form of compression is used where both compression and decompression is used frequently.

Communication of Information 14

For the past five chapters the discussion has been on the workstation as a tool for humans to communicate with the process. Most of this discussion, however, has really been on how the process provides data. What about how humans provide data to the process? To discuss that, we will have to briefly look into how humans communicate in general.

Communication between people in normal human discourse isn't really about what we say, but *how* we say it. In Figure 14-1 we see that the meaning of our words is only a very small part of how we communicate. We usually communicate with pictures, symbols, and objects. A gift is a form of communication. For example, there is meaning behind a gift of diamonds and it is more than an advertising slogan to "say it with flowers." Even in verbal conversation, the information is usually passed through "body language." There are dramatic differences between the meaning of words, the *way* they are said, and our *use of actions* or pictures. The *correct* picture is truly worth a thousand words. Consider the implications in the control room!

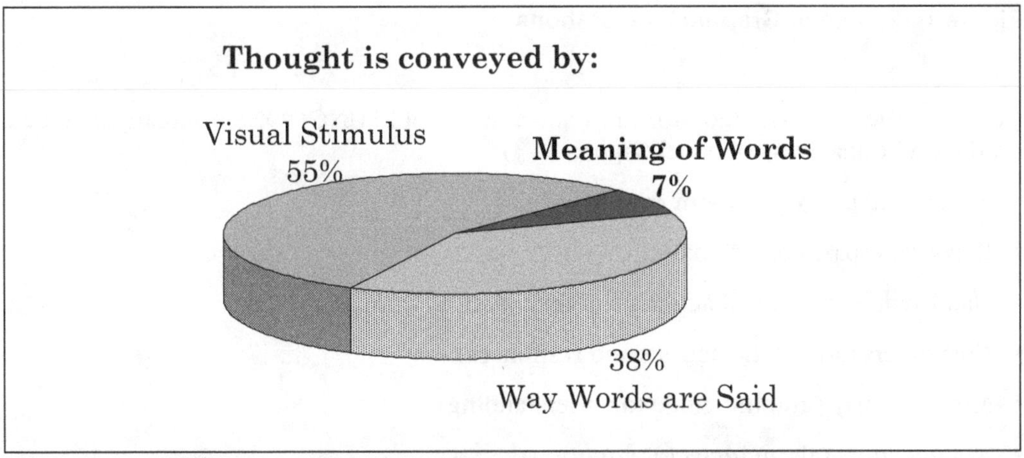

Figure 14-1. Dramatic Differences Between Communication Methods

Interacting with Processes

We have seen that much processing is needed to enable the human interface with the process. That is why so often a sophisticated workstation is used. In Figure 14-2, however, we see that graphic presentations are only 10 percent of what the workstation is doing. Although the other 90 percent involve a lot of computational effort, these stations are really designed to help us understand through pictures. Sometimes pictures are the *only* way to understand. It's a fact that optical paths to our brain carry the equivalent of fifty million words per minute, which is ten million times more than the ears can handle. That's why we learn more easily, quickly, and accurately with pictures. According to Louis Platt, CEO of Hewlett-Packard, what is challenging is to meet this potential with realism, speed, standards, and integration with other media.

Graphic Presentations

- 10% of workstation use
- Help us understand
- Sometimes **only** way to understand!

Optical path to brain carries equivalent to 50 million words per minute...

...which is 10,000,000 times more than Aural!

(we learn more easily, quickly, accurately ...with pictures)

Figure 14-2. Use of Graphic Workstations

Certainly, the graphical monitor must show and do all FUNCTIONS originally included on the traditional control panel (Figure 14-3):

- Meters and gauges (present conditions)
- Recorders (past conditions)
- Hand switches (manual actions and responses)
- Controllers (automatic actions and responses)
- Mimic display (graphic guide to understanding)
- Annunciators (alarm focus for attention)
- Other functions

Time As a Parameter—Analog or Digital?

Remember, certain operations are intuitive, and their appearance on the screen should be consistent with the operator's experience in his or her own life. Let's take the example of an analog portrayal of a parameter such as time. Many of us have probably been raised in a household with both analog and digital clocks. The analog clock portrayed time as a pattern around a circular face, with the progression of time proceeding in increments of sixty-sixty seconds, sixty minutes, and so on. As a result, the average

Carefully consider role of Graphic Monitor:

- Do all functions of traditional panel
- Picture and animate process
- Show process variables (analog and discrete)
- Signal alarms and upsets
- Show change in status and conditions
- Provide instructions
- Present analysis for higher order decisions

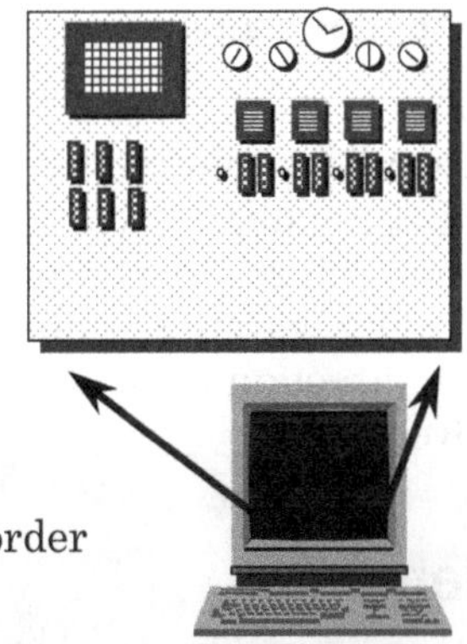

Figure 14-3. Graphic Monitor Is More than Just a Control Panel

faceplate of an analog clock would show the numbers one through twelve evenly spaced around the circle.

When my oldest son was growing up and learning to tell time, we didn't have any visible digital clocks in the house. He had to figure out somehow that there were occasions when 11 meant 5, as in five minutes to the hour. Over time, he adjusted to a base 60 and did in fact learn how to figure time. When my youngest daughter was being raised, there were digital clocks that she could see in the house, and if she were asked what time it was, she would quickly reply that it was, say, 2:50. To her, however, that seemed to mean that it was halfway between two and three o'clock. Without the analog clock's representation of the base 60 system, she initially had no concept of how time was being used.

Now, think carefully, is time absolute or a relative measurement (Figure 14-4)? Unlike all other measurements, it could be argued that it is both, but if you think about it, how do you *functionally* use time in the normal course of events?: Usually to determine how much time *until* something happens or how much time since something happened. So, we're always looking for some *relative* placement within time, which is an analog concept. Therefore, we usually like to think of using time with an analog display rather than just digital values.

Figure 14-4. Analog vs. Digital Presentation?

Many of our clocks use fancy displays, roman numerals, or no numerals at all. Yet none of this variety prevents us from using them quite easily, even accurately (for the purpose intended). In fact, the latest digital clocks are showing *digital* displays of an analog hand position. So it is with most of the things we measure. We try to translate many measurements into some analog sense because most of the parameters we encounter in nature are analog, not digital. *Most of our presentations should portray information, not data.*

So out of context, digital numbers could be confusing, particularly if the operator isn't used to looking at the digits themselves and relating them to a particular analog function. If an absolute value is being used, the *digital* representation is important, particularly if you're dealing with precision to multiple decimal places. But if you're looking at the approximate direction or action as with time, sometimes the analog display is far more informative.

Display Elements

Display elements consist of letters, numbers, shapes, and/or colors. In developing display elements, it is important to consider the best coding method for proper communication with the intended audience. Display organization and the coding of information are covered in Chapter 17. A number of display elements are described in ISA-TR77.60.04-1996, which include the following:

- **Numerical value**—A digital readout of a parameter value that uses the amount of digits given to provide the precision (the exact value) needed. It requires a label or symbol to identify its meaning, including appropriate units of measure.
- **Analog indicator (bar chart or meter)**—Shows the relative value of a parameter, using a continuous change in the size or position of a shape. This element is best used for conveying qualitative information, such as the direction of movement, relationship among values, and (inferred) rate of change. Bar charts are the usual method for comparison readings, but some users may be more familiar with, and prefer, using the pointer and scale of a meter. Pointers may be combined with a bar to show a target (set point on a process variable measurement) or alarm limits, used as scale markings, and even used with numerical values if both comparison and precision are needed. If pointers are used as scale markings, do not use more than the precision of the reading can support.

Generally, five scale markers along a 0 to100 percent bar graph are all that is needed to provide the right balance between having enough to understand and cluttering of view.

- **Discrete indicator**—Used to display a device status that can have one, two, or more discrete states. Each state must be easily distinguishable. States are displayed with labeling (ON/OFF), supplemented with color-coding (red/green), and possibly enhanced with shape coding (breaker OPEN/CLOSED). Labeling or coding is critical since misinterpretation by the user would cause him or her to infer the opposite of the intended message. Avoid using color alone as a means of conveying device status.

- **Mimic (process or system graphic display)**—A symbolic picture reflecting the user model (archetype) of a process, including relationships among variables. To avoid misrepresentation and any resulting confusion, care must be taken to conform the mimic to that model. See Chapter 15 for more discussion of mimic displays.

- **Plots or Graphs**—Show a parameter-to-parameter plot and are useful for process diagnostics, such as marking normal versus abnormal operating regions.

- **Trends**—Show the history of one or more variables, including the rate of change, the approach to limits, and a way of comparing current activities with similar operations from the past. More on this trending data through video is found in Chapter 13.

- **Tables and lists**—Used to show large amounts of information, so they must be well organized and coded to reduce the time required to read or interpret them. Guidelines for tables and lists include:

  — Label rows on the left, columns on the top.

  — Align lists of data vertically with labels on the left and the type fonts left justified. The corresponding numerical data for these labels should be on the right and right-justified and if a decimal is involved, right-justified to that decimal (so the decimals align top to bottom)

  — Separate rows of more than three to five items from each other with spacing.

- **Text**—Is very flexible but is probably the least desirable display item because it is slow to read and interpret. Text should be limited to labels and brief messages such as operator prompts and "help" messages. Color suggestions include the following:

  — Dark colored text (red, blue, black, etc.) should have a light background.

  — Light colored text (white, green, yellow, etc.) should have a dark background.

  It may seem foolish to state these obvious points, but, amazingly, these ideas are not always followed. This is not to suggest that the entire background must be dark or light; often it is appropriate to just have the band immediately behind the characters be the contrasting color.

- Combining these elements into a standard library for the process or for plantwide use is highly recommended. Sometimes the vendor offers something of a library to use as a start. Using these will save time, but with many systems you are not limited to that basic library. Do not be afraid to experiment, but also look into why the vendor chose the design he or she provided. There may be good reason. Some typical examples include the following:

  — **Control station**, often called a faceplate, is a combination of labels, bar graphs, meter pointers, numeric value fields, discrete status fields, and push-button hot spots (selection targets) arranged as a standard "instrument" symbol familiar to the user.

  — **Selection target** is a combination of shapes and labels for creating standard symbols used in display call-up selection, control selection, sequential action list and so on.

  — **Trend/Indicator** window with standardized "chart recorder" elements, which has been discussed in Chapter 13.

Use the Full Potential of Graphic Creation

Imagine if you will that you just unearthed a large stone covered with hieroglyphics. You know it tells you everything you need to locate an ancient king's treasure! Try to read it. What, you can't? All the data is there, isn't it? Why can't you do what it says and find the treasure? Oh, then you have to learn to translate the meaning of the symbols! What, there's more? Oh yes, that's right, you will then have to learn how those symbols are used in context with each other.

All humans communicate in "idiom" or what you might call "local jargon," which uses *combinations* of words differently than you would expect—the same words mean different things when used in different phrases. Gee, my kids do that all the time! Without an understanding of idiom, what you're telling me is that you have all the data, but NO information!

The idea of the graphical monitor is to show more than the functions that were originally on the control panel. These were meters, gauges, recorders, hand switches, controllers, annunciators, and sometimes a static mimic display. Today, you have the opportunity to carefully consider the *complete* capability of the graphical monitor, that is, the ability to picture and animate the view of the process to show the effects of process variables, both analog and discrete; to dynamically show change in status and conditions; to signal alarms and upsets; to provide instructions and present analysis for higher order decisions (Figure 14-5). In developing these graphics, you must understand the transition of personnel from the use of traditional panels to the *different* use of video screens, and you must use this different medium to its full potential. Remember that the purpose of graphics is to provide *information*, not data.

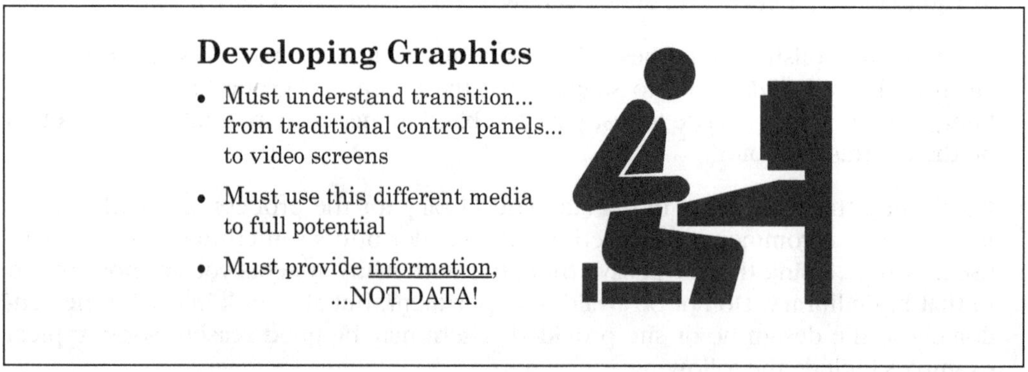

Figure 14-5. Graphics Are More than Pretty Pictures!

Goal for Creating Video Screen Views:

Try to allow the user to interact directly with the process itself as much as possible and not have to be aware that he or she is a piece of interacting with equipment.

---

15 Video Screen Animation

As already mentioned, the video screen provides unique opportunities for communication of the process conditions to the operator. This communication must be unambiguous. It must be done in a way that reduces the effort needed by the operator to fully comprehend the significance of any changes, good or bad. The animation potential of screen views gives us powerful capabilities to bridge that gap between unfolding events and operator understanding. It is imperative for the system engineer to understand the full use of these too.

Dynamic Displays

When creating the display, you can assign hot spots or enter fields anywhere on that view and you can activate them with a cursor. When you activate a hot spot, it provides status changes or value entries, parameter changes, menu selection, screen changes, or guided response to plant upsets. When you touch a hot spot it will sometimes open up a dialog box for some appropriate entry, such as a value, text, or response to a list of choices (Figure 15-1). You may also have pulldowns where you reach up to the top of the screen or window under a listed topic and then click to pull down all the subheadings under that topic.

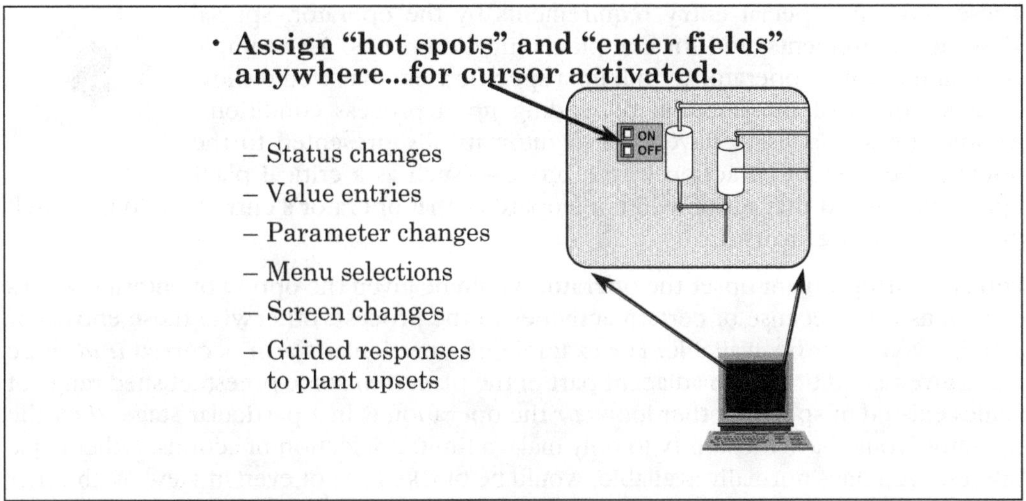

Figure 15-1—Action Capabilities through Animated Screen Views

Tool bars may also be available that have icons for different actions and are continually viewed on the screen or requested upon making some selection. Hot keys look like pushbuttons on a screen, which, when you cursor and click on them, appear to depress, as if you were pressing a button. That movement is important because you need to have some feedback, both visual and audial, to know that you made an action. In this way, when you make an "imaged" keystroke on the screen (or for that matter on any keyboard) you want to have some way of knowing that the action has *begun*, even if the screen does not yet reflect the *completion* of that action.

Hot spots, called poke points by some, allow you point to a certain part of the mimic, which responds with a "pop-up" showing a series of buttons permitting the entry of selections or a choice of actions. This pop-up can offer an on-off function or an analog drive that ramps a set point, output, or other function. Perhaps the pop-up portrays a small instrument faceplate embedded at that point that displays during the time you're on that poke point.

Natural Language

Keep in mind that you want to provide the operator with as close to a natural language dialog as possible in any screen view and especially within dialog boxes. *This is an opportunity to significantly improve productivity.* Try to avoid local jargon unless it is industry-specific and promotes quick understanding with all users of your system!

IF-THEN-ELSE Statements for Screen Dynamics

One interesting feature in animation is the use of an IF-THEN-ELSE statement with the math equations built into the graphics package. These allow for special entry requirements by the operator, special viewing requirements, and for complex animation needs. An example is the ability for an operator to pull up a specific view that would show different fields of information, depending upon process conditions. Another possibility is to have a view automatically presented to the operator because of an action in the process (such as a critical plant upset), but only if that action will not jeopardize that operator's current actions (which might make things worse).

Perhaps during a plant upset the operator would be given the option of entering values or actions only because of certain activities in the process, otherwise these entries or actions would not be available. For example, if a particular alarm occurred *and* there was a given condition in an adjacent part of the plant *and* some preestablished range of values existed in specific other loops *or* the operation is in a particular stage, *then* the operator would have the ability to only make a limited selection of actions. Other capabilities, even ones normally available, would be blocked or not even in view. With other conditions of plant environment, stage of operation, and specific loop upsets, *different* selection criteria would show up for the operator, and all other options would be masked from him.

Picture an operator presented with an emergency condition. He would have the option, for example, of pressing a button that says, "emergency down," meaning to shut the process down in an orderly way. That same operator action would result in a different process change depending upon what other conditions existed in the process and plant.

This IF-THEN-ELSE feature is very useful for presenting an appropriate screen display for unique conditions. Remember, the object of the game here is not to present the operator with as much data as possible but rather to present to the operator information that is appropriate for the condition of the plant. So this animating feature seems to be very useful in helping to filter out some of the options of operator actions. *What is important here is that this SCREEN feature be used for animation NOT for control action!* In other words, you want to be able to portray information on the screen, but you do not want to use this feature to create automatic action down in the controller itself. Only features and processors in the controller should be used for control action.

On Constructing Mimic Displays

Guidelines for building mimics, which are based upon ISA-TR77.60.04-1996 include the following:

- Conform abstract symbols to common electrical or mechanical symbol conventions as much as possible.
- Reduce the details of goal/task/function analysis data to present only the required content so as to avoid clutter.
- Provide labeling inside symbols wherever possible.
- Locate data used with symbols in a consistent position (always under, or to the left, etc.).
- Locate data for mimic lines and symbols as near as practicable to those items.
- Distinguish dynamic display symbols from nondynamic symbols (those static symbols needed for coherence of the mimic.) The user must recognize those symbols that are providing information about a state or condition.
- Use redundant coding of dynamic symbols, for example a valve can be red or green, show OPEN or CLOSED labels, and hollow or filled symbol to express its state.
- Use dynamic mimic flow lines to show the operation of the process if this is important information for understanding the process conditions. The presence of flow or pressure can be shown by line color or by hollow or filled pipes (area between two parallel lines). Flow direction can be shown with arrows and also with alternating line segments that blink like "chase lights."
- Use dynamic electrical line mimics to show charged or uncharged lines. The presence of power can be shown both with color and with the symbol of an open or closed breaker.
- Make touch screen or mouse targets distinguishable with respect to the kind of information to be accessed. Targets that call up controls should be coded differently from those that access other displays. Similarly, analog control call-up targets should be distinguishable from discrete or digital ones. All targets must be identified (a three-dimensional effect is useful to imply a "button" metaphor.) Nontargets must not share a similar appearance.

Color As a Dynamic

Part of animating displays is the use of color conditionals for two positional discrete status. Displays may also show a series of colors, marking the passage of some value through several thresholds of analog indication, such as temperature levels. In this way, an operator can quickly view the progress of temperature change within a vessel at a glance when a precise reading of values may not be necessary. Color conditionals can also be used for blink action rates. Blink actions can show motion or show the progression of events across the screen through the optical illusions brought about by these dynamics.

Of course, colors may be used to trigger events. If you "clicked" on a pump, you might want it switched ON or OFF. The pump may be red when it is OFF. It may turn yellow in a start-up stage and then turn green when it's running.

In a screen that is highly congested, color can help to highlight special groups of information. Grouping is perhaps one of the most efficient uses of color for screen display purposes.

Combined Capabilities

Combining animation capabilities gives you some very good dynamics while freeing the operator from studying unnecessary details. For example, a tank may be automatically filling or emptying, perhaps because product within is being consumed at another part of the operations or is being filled by a process upstream from it. A bar graph could show the level. The bar graph would probably be more useful in showing the level of the tank, because the tank is only a variation of a bar graph. Bar graphs can also be used downward as well as up and are sometimes based in the center to "grow" both ways simultaneously.

Back to our tank; you could use a fill pattern to indicate the change of chemical composition, for example, pH or conductivity. Change in pattern could indicate thresholds of composition values. At the same time, there may be a temperature constituent. Temperature could possibly be shown through changes in the color of the fill, level through the "bar graph" height, and composition through changes in the pattern of the fill, all at a glance by the operator, without the need to read individual numbers or the faceplates of instruments. All of these parameters would, of course occur concurrently.

If the analysis reached some critical point, the fill could begin to flash. This could also trigger a message specific to the problem (level, temperature, composition, pressure, vessel wall stress, fluid on the floor around the vessel, etc.). Be careful, however, that you don't make the activity so involved that it distracts or confuses the operator. All of these changes of parameters, of course, depend a lot on what is important in the process. Good screen management will unambiguously present to the operator the conditions of the process and what actions you expect him or her to take because of them. You want to use shapes and colors to *help* the operator!

Not by Color Alone

The use of color is a supplementary thing. *Color should be used only to enhance information.* Color provides redundant coding, as well as a shape (text is a shape) as pointed out in Figure 15-3. Consider, for example, if the operator has a diminished capability to distinguish colors. At least 10 percent of males and some small number of females have one of the forms of color blindness. None of us sees colors exactly in the same way nor very likely with the same intensity. Research on color indicates that in the human brain it is processed in parallel. Interestingly enough, shapes are processed in serial, so your perception of them is different. Furthermore, humans have trouble distinguishing the meaning of more than four colors simultaneously. Colors, therefore, should be used sparingly and consistently to help the user understand the desired message.

Figure 15-2. Example of Using Color, Shape, and Dynamics to Draw Attention to a Situation

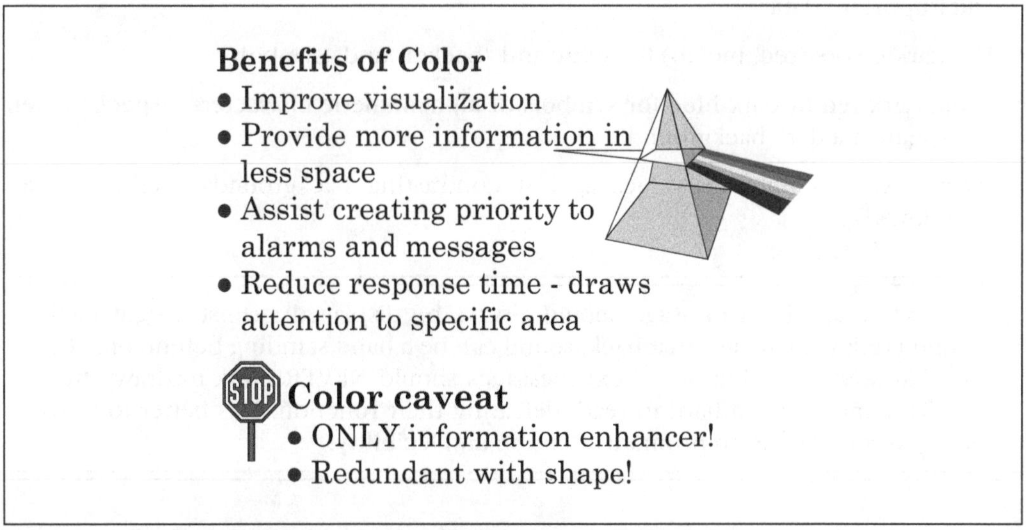

Figure 15-3. Color Should Be Used CAREFULLY

Using shapes as a primary indicator, for example, would mean making a pump solid when it's running and a hollow when it's off. This would provide the more secure communication and as a supplement to that might also include the use of red or green. The purpose of supplemental color is to improve visualization, to provide more information in less space, to assist in conveying priority in alarm messages, and to reduce response time by drawing attention to a specific area.

Considerations for Color Use

Color for coding has two general uses—to convey meaning and to distinguish one item from another. Some guidelines for use of color are as follows:

- Define the meaning of each color consistently
- Be consistent in using this meaning throughout the system
- Use color as a *redundant* indicator
- Keep large background areas neutral, such as gray or black (25 to 50 percent is best to avoid glare). With higher resolution color choices, teal and manila are becoming popular as neutral backgrounds that offer good contrast to other color lines and objects
- Use compatible color combinations ("circus" combinations distract from task)
- Avoid using more than seven (give or take 2) colors
- Use color to indicate quality, not quantity
- Match colors with those already in use on other (legacy) systems
- Use bright colors (white, yellow, light green, cyan) for dynamic values and symbols and important data
- Use dark colors (red, indigo) for static and "background" symbols
- Avoid dark red or dark blue for symbols or alphanumeric characters, especially hen used against a dark background
- Place text and numeric values against contrasting backgrounds (perhaps small "windows")

Red text as an alarm message should always be displayed against a light background (yellow or white) that background can be a band standing behind only the text (like a small "window"). Text messages should NEVER blink to draw attention. This makes them hard to read, defeating their function. It is better to blink the background color to promote attention and legibility!

Using a neutral background is consistent with reducing the big display of colors, which only distracts the operator. You should design with no more than seven colors. Look for colors with high contrast, such as blue and white or black and white. When you get beyond the magic number of seven, plus or minus two, then you start to lose the operator in a sea of colors that begins to feel more like a circus display than a good medium for the needed information. To convey meaning, the limit on colors used should be four or five. If you merely want to distinguish between different items, the range of color-scan is broader. Since the eyes are quite sensitive to color differences, the limitation of four or five optimum colors is not as important. An example of this is the use of subtle shading to create the illusion of depth, which could actually reduce the feeling of clutter. For the most part, any combination of text and background colors is suitable, so long as the combination maintains adequate luminescence and/or chromatic contrast.

Limit the Colors

Choose from any of 256 × 256 colors, but use only 7! (Actually, recommendations vary from 4 to 11, depending upon who is the expert.) As the number of colors increases, the relative effectiveness of the color-codes decreases. Perhaps allow for some color shades to show curvature of vessels. Too many colors, especially incompatible ones, will obscure, not enhance information.

The idea of compatible color combinations is to make the total appearance pleasing to the eye. This is not just a nicety; it is essential for directing the operator's attention towards what is not natural versus what is natural in the process operation. The human eye perceives color only in the center of the retina. Actual color perception depends on the different degrees to which various wavelengths of light stimulate the eye. Placing two colors with wavelengths at opposite ends of the color spectrum next to each other will strain the eye muscles trying to focus on them. It is best to avoid such combinations.

Picking color combinations for the screen is not the same as picking the color combinations in a room. Color has many psychological impacts and they should very much be considered when laying out the control room and establishing its atmosphere. These impacts are not as critical in the displays. Part of the reason for this is that rarely do you have operators staring at the same screen all day. Yes, in some plants the operator DOES, but in most places the operator periodically addresses the screen display in addition to several other activities in the control room. That is not to say that common sense color schemes shouldn't be used, but the primary goal of the colors that appear on the screen is to help the operator recognize changes in the process.

What Colors Should I Use?

The use of color consistently throughout the plant may be part of an overall code or scheme adopted by that plant or in that industry. For example, a typical color scheme for lines of text and numerals might use green for normal, red as an alarm, yellow for out of scan, cyan for of instrument range, blue as a raw signal, magenta as deleted from the database, and white for the text. But keep in mind, no two plants are alike. It's a good idea to place data values of importance in a bright color (white, yellow, light green, and cyan) to make them more noticeable.

The color convention for power plants is to use green for OFF (safe) and red for ON (hot, energized). In the paper industry, which has rotating machinery, red means OFF (stop) and green means ON (running, online). Industries involved with furnaces and heaters sometimes use red for hot (thermally) and green for cold. In the chemical industry, colors are used for different chemicals and gases.

More important than the choice of colors is to be *consistent* with the them so that any operator in any other part of the plant will easily understand their significance. Many corporations have multiple plants and strive to have a consistent display that means the same thing to every individual, on every shift, and in every location of their operations. When designing screen views, be aware of differences between distinct cultural perceptions of color and shape, especially for operations located in foreign countries.

A Video Screen Designer's Opinion

What I found empirically, then supported with some literature research, is that background colors should be of similar luminance to the surroundings—in most cases 25% to 50% gray (0% is black, 100% is white). I found that the highest contrast could be had with green on black, followed by yellow, then white and cyan on black. Red and blue are difficult against any background—as is magenta for similar reasons. All of this is for a computer screen, of course, and would be different on a physical instrument or panel.

When building screen views, I used large gray areas with black windows to emphasize alphanumeric data and indicators. I also used dynamic background colors to display secondary data on a gray background in normal cases, and changing to a higher contrast background in an alarm case.

I look at the screen's dynamic range. If everything is maximum contrast, then the screen looks cluttered. If most of the screen is low contrast, then only the most important high contrast dynamic values call attention. I think Renzo Dallimonti was a proponent of having everything in shades of gray unless attention needed to be called to a particular item. Then, the **change** would be perceived even before the color.

I also would do a dynamic range test on a screen by ranking the importance of objects. This is done by standing far enough away that I can no longer read anything, and then slowly approach the screen. Objects should become readable in their order of importance, which should also track from high to low contrast. If everything becomes visible at the same time far from the screen, contrast is too high... or if everything becomes visible at the same time when very close to the screen, contrast is too low. In either case the screen would look cluttered due to the lack of dynamic range.

Separation of data items is a tricky business. I think a soft 3D metaphor gives the perception of separation without being too cluttered. For example, you can make a 3D frame with white highlight and black shadow on a 50% gray background. But it would be less cluttered with a 75% gray highlight and 25% gray shadow...softer, but still effective.

Marc Lombardi, Human Interface Designer formerly of Honeywell and Leeds & Northrup

Not All Systems Are Alike

There are many different animation capabilities built into the various vendor products and they will vary from one company to another. Some companies provide only operator interface packages to function with other systems, typically PCs with programmable logic controllers (PLCs). Many of those companies originally served the needs of PLC companies that traditionally did not have operator interface packages beyond an on-off switch arrangement. These graphical packages generally run in "plain vanilla" PCs and come with software packages that can be attached to a variety of programmable logic control products.

These PC-based graphical packages are also used for several single loop products that are networked into small DCS-type systems. They have concentrated on the operator interface rather than on the control tactics. These packages provide a wide variety of animation capabilities, but their flexibility in being "all things to all people" reduces their chances of contributing to convenient structure. They are like having a blank sheet of paper and a dictionary of thousands of words but with little or no ability to provide sentence structure. The challenge is to interconnect those wonderful capabilities with the control system vendor's product.

Proprietary distributed control systems, however, were originally left to their own devices. At the time they initially developed their operator interfaces there were no standard packages, and each vendor had to create its own. These creations generally were developed around the control capabilities of that particular vendor and were ordinarily tightly interlocked with them. Although the processors themselves were distributed, the linking of the animated display and that vendor's control scheme was critical in minimizing the configuration limitations of the interconnection between them.

For this reason, not every vendor provided the same level of animation. However, now that operator interfaces are becoming more standard through the adoption of common architectures like the UNIX, MS-DOS, Windows, and Windows NT platforms, there will be, and already is emerging a more standardized approach to some of these animation features. There still remain many clever interlocks and features that individual vendors had "hard coded" in the early days. What is elusive, however is how to economically port these interlocks and features into the current platforms, which may have more universal capabilities but lack some of the specific features of the control actions of each vendor.

A Word on Performance

With so much graphic and animation capability, it is tempting to get carried away with cleverness. Such excess features will pay the price of performance for video screen "call-ups" and refresh rates. You will quickly find yourself pressing a key to make an *appointment* for a screen view! Remember that the overuse of animation and clever graphic pictures can seriously impact performance of the operator station. In addition, the processors used in the operator display should be reserved exclusively for graphic animation. Keeping them separate will ensure a secure system, and you will not have a problem in the plant if for some reason the communication link is lost.

Screen Navigation 16

The challenge of using graphic monitors is not just presenting the process to the operator, but also to present the operator to the process. How should the operator communicate to the process what must happen next? We are still exploring technologies which again have only begun to touch on methods to keep the interface tool (operator station) as transparent as possible. Of course, having said that, we must currently look to some very tried-and-true techniques of navigation and entry.

Video Screen Access Tools

There are several techniques (Figure 16-1) an operator can use to cause an action once he or she understands what's going on with the process or in the plant. With a few tools, he or she can make a change in the operation or perhaps change the view to get a better understanding of the operation. Ideas regarding what tools are needed vary with the requirements of the plant. Consider the nature the plant and the operator's environment of the operator to determine which of these tools are best.

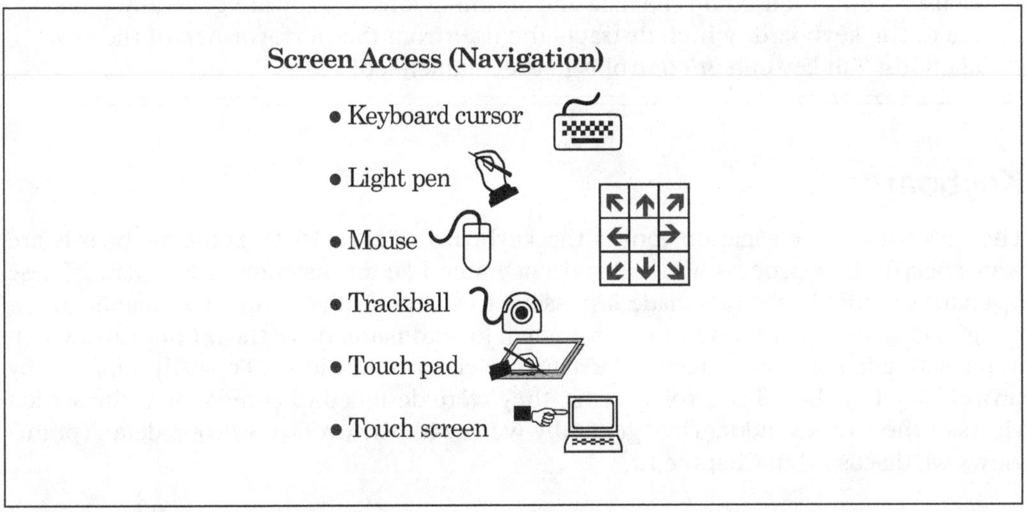

Figure 16-1. Control of Process is Navigational, Not Transactional

Screens typically used in business are for *transaction* functions, whereas the manipulation of control actions in a process through video screens is a *navigation* function.

Operators, in a bank, for example, will search their record's to verify account information, then modify those records as they complete the transaction of exchanging funds. An information finder in the video kiosk at a shopping mall is another example. Compared to process requirements, neither of these functions is time critical.

Some operator functions are, in fact, a transaction, such as to recording or retrieving historical information for comparison or analyzing. This is not a control action, and the microprocessors can operate at a more "leisurely" pace. Typically, keyboards are best suited for this, but well-designed screen views can be very impressive.

In the control room, however, operators respond to process changes by locating and pointing to the appropriate "instruments" and then altering their settings to correct for those changes. These actions are very similar to navigating a vehicle. It may surprise some people, but the "point-and-click" action with a cursor comes closest to the manipulation of traditional control panel functions. Once experienced is gained at it, point and click is probably the most comfortable method by which operators can gain access to the appropriate reaction process needs. The cursor offers many features for navigating through screen views and operational choices.

Regardless of the mechanism used, the whole idea of an operator access is that it too should be extremely consistent with the natural operation of that plant. As with screen views, any operator, no matter on which shift or which operation in that company, should expect certain actions and operating tools to result in the same responses in the plant. This should be true whether the actions are initiated through the layout of the keyboard, the use of a light pen, or the action of the mouse (right-click actions versus left-click, for example).

Access devices, such as a touch screen, mouse, trackball, or their equivalent, keep the user's eyes focused on the data and action involved. They are generally preferable to the keyboard, which distracts the user from the performance of the keys' functions. Tab key cursor control is not recommended!

Keyboards

The most obvious navigation tool is the keyboard (Figure 16-2). Some keyboards are very specific to a process and are laid out much like an instrument faceplate. These operator-specific keyboards made it possible to switch from automatic to manual operating modes, to adjust set point control when in automatic, drive the output valve when in manual, and sometimes access the alarm levels or tune a loop. Typically supplied by proprietary distributed control systems, they were designed to complement the screen views of the DCS's vendor. They generally went with the overview-group-detail (point) views we discussed in Chapter 12.

The QWERTY Keyboard

Named for the first alphabetic characters on the upper left of the typewriter keyboard, this "de facto industry standard" since the 1880s was *designed to be as inefficient as possible*! (so as to prevent speed typists from jamming the mechanism). Because it was used for nearly a half a century before the development of the electric typewriter, people around the world became used to the QWERTY keyboard layout. Many dozens of better designs have been suggested and implemented in the last three-quarters of a century, but none of them have become popular enough to justify any kind of standard. August Dvorak developed a layout that requires a good typist's fingers to travel only one mile in a normal workday, compared to twenty minutes with the QWERTY layout. These typists achieve twice the speed, make half the errors, and need only eighteen hours of training rather than fifty-six. The rejected Dvorak died in 1975, a bitter man: "I'm tired of trying to do something worthwhile for the human race; they simply don't want to change!"

Keyboard Layout

- Typewriter (QWERTY)
- Alphabetical
- Numerical – calculator
- Numerical – telephone
- Control pad – discrete actions
- Control pad – process actions
- Display pad
- Operator function pad
- Special-function keys

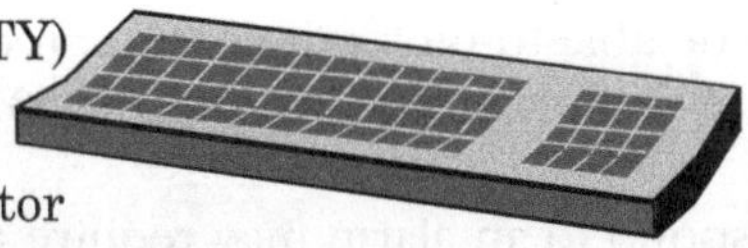

Figure 16-2. Keyboards: Operator-Specific? Process-Specific? "Standard?"

For years it has been assumed that most control room operators were not unfamiliar with the standard typewriter layout. Several vendors furnished alphabetic layouts on their "operator's keyboard." I know of one company that offered both the QWERTY and the alphabetical keyboards for anyone buying its system. After eight years of holding both versions in stock, they discovered that no one bought the alphabetic version when given the opportunity. All bought the QWERTY layout!

The other common keypad design question is how to allow numerical entry. The layout of the keypad could be that of a calculator or that of a telephone; each is different. Typically, a telephone is a three-by-four key matrix with the numeral one at the top. Early telephone rotary dials carried both numerals and alphabetic characters, both in ascending order. In the migration to touch pads, it seemed logical to have both begin at the top, to reduce dialing errors.

Typical calculator keyboards and keypads, however, are set "upside down from the telephone." This is probably because that was the position in the original mechanical calculators, where the internal gearing required that orientation so as to maintain "right-side-up" view of the digits while allowing incremental change from units through tens, hundreds, and so on. The numerals were arranged in columns of ten rows, with the number nine key at the top and zero key at the bottom in each row.

The migration to touch pads kept the larger numerals at the top for users who grew up with mechanical calculators and had to use both during their gradual transition.

For whatever reason, this apparently has not caused anybody any trouble. When you face a calculator or telephone, you seem to automatically go to the correct key, even if you use them interchangeably. It must be one of the paradoxes of the human system to be able to accommodate such switches. However, it would not be easy to make the abrupt change between those two keypad layouts if they alternated within control system keyboards. So whatever mechanism you choose, it should be consistent throughout the control system used by all the operators.

On operator-specific keyboards, another set of keys beyond discrete and loop control actions needs to be able to pick out specific requirements such as trend views, group views (instrument faceplate or mimic displays), and especially alarm-handling views.

The ability to respond to an alarm may require that the keyboard have its own display, such as you would have on an annunciator panel. Also needed are keys for other operator functions such as printing out a report, silencing an alarm, acknowledging an alarm, or similar arrangements. Then there are always the special-function keys that may be unique to that system, that process, or that plant. Some vendors supply special-function keys for the user with any of these needs.

Keystroke Actions

Several actions may come from a keystroke:

- A single touch produces a momentary contact, even if held down.
- A single touch latches contact and a second touch releases it.
- A single touch latches contact in one state and a second touch causes a second state (flip-flop).
- A single touch maintains the contact state as long as the key is held down (or perhaps causing a smooth ramp action).
- A single touch causes repeated short contacts as long as the key is held down (perhaps causes ramp action in repeated small steps).
- A single touch causes repeated short contacts as the key is held down for the first few seconds, then increases the number of contact increments while still held down. If the finger is lifted, the "slower" speed resumes are replaced.

The last item, using the "two-speed repeat action," allows this method to be used to drive an analog value a short distance with one touch, but if it is held it will speed up the change to reach a new position or value faster. If the user wants to stop more precisely, then by removing his or her finger from the key for a moment, he or she can then "bump up" the value to the desired point. This also helps with rapid cross-screen excursions.

Considerable controversy has occurred over the years about the best layout for keyboards used by process control operators:

- Should it be process-specific? Operator-specific?
- Should it be an alphabetical or the QWERTY key layout?
  — Should there even be any alphabetic keys?
- Should number pads be in the telephone or calculator layout? (often calculator)
- What keys, and layout of keys, should be used for process actions?
  — Auto/man-Raise/lower (separate for SP versus PV or mode-specific?)
  — Other?
- What keys and layout of keys should be used for discrete actions?
  — Up/down-On/off-Start/stop-Forward/Reverse-Reset-etc.
- What keystroke actions should be included? Where? When? When held down?
  — Single action unlatched-Single action latched-Flip-flop
  — Repeat action-Continuous steady drive
  — Non linear continuous drive
  (During full stroke should action speed up?)
- Should certain displays have unique keys?
  — Overview-Group-Detail (Point)-Trend
- Should certain functions have unique keys?
  — Print-Save-Last view-etc.
- What about plant upset?
  — Alarm acknowledge-Silence
  — Defeat (during start-up, maintenance, etc.)
  — Restore (after start-up or maintenance)
  — Emergency down key (various functions: all loops, only those shown, only those out of normal)
- Any industry-specific, plant-specific, or process-specific keys?

Keystroke Feedback

Important with any keyboard type, but especially important with the membrane type, is the absolute need for a sensory feedback. This ought to be some sound, like a beep or click, so you know that you pressed that key. This is essential. A sense of responding to the finger's pressure for the sake of tactile confirmation is critical, especially with membrane keyboards. Some offer this by using the pop-back "oilcan" effect.

Moreover, the operator should not only hear something but see something. This could be an intermediate state, something acknowledging that the key was pushed, but it should never show that the action is completed until there is a real feedback from the process itself verifying that the action was indeed completed. You do not want a screen simulation of process results. Consider some indication that the action has been requested but not yet completed, such as a color or shape that is associated with the equipment involved. Another method is to show the image of a depressed key on the video screen. One advantage of the video approach is that when activated the "key" has the ability to "change labels" (on can become off).

On one actual occasion an operator pushed the key to switch a loop from automatic to manual. There was a delay in the screen action before the operator was informed this keystroke was pushed. As a result, the operator pushed again to make sure of the action and toggled the loop back to automatic, creating a severe plant upset.

The system should respond to every user entry! It must be positive, obvious, and natural. Having no response is not allowed! When a request is invoked, there should be an instantaneous reaction (within two seconds). If the nature of the request requires longer processing time, then a response should show that the course of action is underway and even, when possible, how long it will take for the action to begin.

"Soft Keys"

Keys on a keyboard that change meaning in accordance with whatever screen display is being viewed are called "soft keys." In the earlier days of DCS, these took the form of several unlabeled keys at the base of the screen (usually eight) and labeled images of keys on the screen itself. For example, when you're looking at an overview display, the selector keys underneath that overview would determine which group you were getting. When in a group display, if there are eight groups on a screen, each of those keys represented a group. If a point detail display, then each of these keys might represent set point, process variable, output, or a tuning parameter. This is fine as long as these keys are used to select a screen view. In my opinion, however, soft keys should *never* be used for control action of a process.

A variation of this idea is the use of multiple functions on any instrument, whether it be stand-alone hardware or located on a video screen. For example, some vendors have decided to save space and appearance by providing one set of raise/lower buttons on a three-mode (PID) controller faceplate (hardware or screen view). If the loop is in "Auto[matic]," they drive the set point; when in "Man[ual]," they drive the output. Arggh! When the operator wants to drive a valve, he or she should always push the same button. He or she should not have to look to see what state the loop is in. Now, what if during an upset the operator thinks that a loop happens to be in automatic, stabs at the operating mode button to switch to manual, and didn't quite act on it. He missed, but thought he hit it—and now thinks he is driving the set point when in fact he's starting to drive the output, or worse, the reverse happened! Separate drive buttons for each control action is imperative!

The operator should always find critical action keys in the same place, these keys should always be in the same location, and they must always have the same meaning! This is equally true of the location of controls on screen views themselves: always be consistent with functions and locations! During normal operation there is time to carefully look for the correct keys, but during any kind of plant upset there must never be any ambiguity about control action.

Keyboard Role

Serious consideration must be paid to how a keyboard is going to be used. Is it something the operator is continually using, or is it something he or she occasionally uses. Should the keyboard be permanently attached, or should it be a plug-in. You may prefer to only plug it in on those occasions when it's needed, and remove it until it's needed at another time.

A number of years back, IBM researched the best position for typewriters and computers where the keypunch operators were working an eight-hour day entering data. The study found that the ideal keyboard angle was 10 degrees. This is probably true in a control room as well. But this goes back to the question of how the keyboard being used and by whom.

The size and shape of the keys are important. For occasional use, you can get away with smaller keys, but take much care to determine whether the person using it needs to wear a glove or has some ability limitations regarding when and where to push a given button. For example, in an emergency condition you don't want the operator to fish around looking for the right little tiny button to push. For emergency needs, there should be some very obviously clear "Push here when in trouble" arrangement (on a keyboard or on a touch screen).

Keyboard Considerations

- Continuous use versus occasional use
- Sealed versus not sealed
- Attached versus separate
- Size & shape of keys
- Depth key must travel
- Feedback sense to action
  - —Click (aural feedback)
  - —Resistance to pressure (sensory)
  - —Visual (response on screen)
- Keyboard angle (10°)
- Shielding from
  - —Radio Frequency Interference (RFI)
  - —Electromagnetic Interference (EMI)
  - —Other environment

Some guidelines for operator keyboard entry functions include the following:

- Provide a logical arrangement for function keys.
- Group function keys when many function keys are required.

- Provide on-screen entry fields with a cursor that shows the location of the next keyed entry for multiple-key entry (like typing with a word processor).
- Provide some means of distinguishing fields for (typing in) multiple-key entries so they are not confused with fields for current data displays.
- Locate edit fields, for changing current data, so they are in a consistent adjacent location to the items (values, text, etc.) to be changed. This is usually below or to the right but, in any case, should always be a consistent prompt location.
- Highlight the data to be entered, so it can easily be reviewed to ensure it is correct before invoking an enter key (or some similar entry action that is in addition to the creation of the entry statement or value).

Keyboard Types:

Mechanical

- Hermetically sealed reed relay

Electromechanical

- Magnet and saturable core
- Hall effect
- Capacitance

Membrane

- Flat surface
- Tactile feel (oil can effect)

To Seal or Not to Seal?

The use of a membrane is not the only way to seal a keyboard. Hermetically sealed relays are just as secure even though the keyboard itself shows discrete keys on the surface. Under the keyboard, the circuit card itself should be protected from spills and can be coated with a material to seal all of the electronic components. Then the actual keys presented on the surface will still look like traditional keys on a keyboard and depress and respond like the familiar keys with which most people are comfortable. Membrane keys have a place in an industrial floor where there is heavy dust, small filings, heavy humidity, or similar difficult environments. It is far easier to clean a membrane.

A Fluid Experience

A user spilled coffee onto the flat membrane keyboard of one vendor, and the fluid ran over the membrane as it should but then leaked through the side to short-circuit the edge connectors within the case!

Protection for keyboards must also include shielding radio frequency interferences (RFIs) from communication devices or electromagnetic interferences (EMIs) from lighting fixtures and appliances. Both can trigger "keystrokes" without an operator pushing anything. A surge or spike in some voltage level somewhere can also give a false signal to a keyboard and cause the operation to think a keystroke was made.

Mouse or Trackball

One advantage of a mouse and trackball over a touch screen is that the targets can be smaller because the selection is more precise. The mouse and trackball action is generally more secure because it doesn't suffer from problems of parallax when placing it in position and requires more deliberate actions. Both the mouse and the trackball are suitable for stand-up use as well as sit-down positions. One disadvantage is that the ball tends to pick up dirt easily, especially in dusty environments. Another possible drawback stems from the fact that these are easier and more precise tools that can be used on smaller screen targets, so the human tendency will be to provide many more targets. When that happens, the user must locate the cursor, then have a much better feel for the locations of the many targets. Both of these actions could require that more time be spent placing the cursor on the target. Again, layout is everything in problems like these.

Touch Screen Access Tools

A touch screen is a video screen (cathode ray tube) with which the user can interact by touching icons on a screen display rather than through a keyboard or mouse. It is ideal for selection-based activities because you invoke information and create responses just where you expect them to be on the screen. Touch screen is a natural human interface in that you actually interact with the process itself as portrayed on the screen, reducing the awareness of the system in between. Touch screen technology offers an operator only appropriate selections, that is, there is no need for unnecessary options to confuse decision making. Unlike operator-specific or process-specific keyboards, touch screen devices can readily be modified to fit changing operator or process requirements. Partly because of this, it is far easier and faster to train users on it.

Several Touch Screen Technologies Are Being Used Today:

- Capacitive overlay
- Resistive overlay
- Scanning infrared
- Strain gauge
- Forced vector
- Guided acoustical wave
- Surface acoustical wave

Vendors of each of these products have been continually working to improve the different technologies. Currently, there are many articles by people who analyzed each of these technologies and created comparisons through matrix tables. Although a noble effort, new development within each of these technologies has changed, and vendors have made improvements to overcome several of the limitations of each of these types.

Selecting through Touch Screen Targets

Employing a touch screen, the user must know when the correct target area has been reached. The field can blink, switch to reversed video, or draw a box around the text or zone. Now the question is how to execute. The action can occur when the finger first touches the screen. But what if the operator first touches the screen but isn't quite on the target or changes his or her mind and he slides his or her finger to a new target? What causes it to activate? It is very important to decide how that screen is activated so a purposeful action on the screen is distinguished from an accidental touch.

Another touch screen method is to activate when the finger is removed from the screen. In this way, the operator can make a location correction and assure that the proper target is invoked. If he gets into an ambiguous position or changes his mind, he can slide to a neutral territory and remove his finger.

Requiring two keystrokes or two touches of the screen is another way to distinguish when an action is intended or accidental. It also depends on whether you need to touch the screen with two hands. This is a dilemma. What if the operator is required to have something in the other hand, such as a clipboard or a microphone, or what if the operator has no other hand? Now, what should the touch screen action require? Should it require striking an enter key as a second action, which is possible using only one hand? This would take time, particularly if there's a sequence of actions that the operator must make. These issues are why some do not like touch screens.

The two acoustical wave technologies are interesting because they add the dimension of sensing the pressure of the stylus or finger on the screen. Although not yet exploited, they both have the potential to act more like a mouse in function. They permit the user to glide a single finger over the screen to locate an area of control. The screen responds by displaying a cursor, then when the finger presses harder, the action is created. One vendor claims that sixteen levels of pressure on the screen can be detected. A second hand or second keystroke is not needed to verify the selected function.

The latest technologies that have the potential to be the most "mouse like:"

GAW—Guided Acoustical Wave: Type of touch screen that channels acoustical energy into the full volume of the screen material; compare with SAW.

SAW—Surface Acoustical Wave: Type of touch screen that confines most of the acoustical energy to the surface of the screen; compare with GAW.

The response of the touch screen is very important. Just as with any keystroke or operator action, there should be some way to let the operator know that the "keystroke" was completed. Remember now, this is on a hard video screen. There is no oilcan effect or other tactile impression. There ought to be a sound, however, just as with conventional keyboards. Certainly, visual feedback can be the same as discussed earlier using color change, shape change, the "key" appearing to be pressed down, and so on.

Touch Screen Considerations

One advantage of a touch screen, as compared with a mouse, is the automatic movement of the cursor to the selected location. There is no looking for the cursor location before you start, it is on the end of your hand. The disadvantages are that significantly larger targets are required because the fingertip is too large for small, adjacent targets. Fingerprint smudges can also affect screen legibility, especially when glare is a problem.

Vibration

The touch screen should be visually transparent. Most use overlays that reduce screen brightness by varying degrees. The worst offenders are technologies, resistive and capacitive. This is becoming less of a problem, but some people feel very strongly about this. Infrared has no overlay.

Most touch screens can tolerate physical shock and vibration, but both the force vector and strain gauge version are especially sensitive. The thin glass in the acoustical versions could be susceptible to shock. No changes to the system should be caused by induced fields from EMI, RFI, or any other influences. Cell phones, other communicators, appliances, and machinery may impact capacitive and resistive overlays.

Figure 16-3. Most Touchscreen Versions are Tolerant of Shock and Vibration

The alignment of the screen to the operator's finger is important to avoid parallax. The resolution targeting must consider the average finger size and a gloved hand. The infrared type tends to be more of an offender, but all have some limitations.

The installation and maintenance should be simple and straightforward. This is an area that is also changing as technology improves. The frequency of calibration may be higher with capacitive.

Some touch screen *layout* considerations are as follows:

- *Place the targets consistently.* Just as with a keyboard, the targets should always be where they're expected. Alarm Acknowledge should always be in a consistent place on the screen, in every screen. Operator Response to Plant should be found in expected locations so that there's no question or ambiguity about it.
- *Provide differentiation among the targets* to make them easily distinguishable for the function performed. That is, the call-up of full screen displays (screen changes) should differ from pop-up windows for expanded information and also differ from control selection requests.
- *Keep the number of targets to a minimum* so that the operator doesn't have high density and too much confusion on the screen.

- *Surround each target with a dead zone* to prevent an operator from accidentally touching an adjacent target.
- *Make the target as large as possible.* A minimum of three-quarters of an inch by three-quarters of an inch for critical functions that must be made quickly. Smaller targets are acceptable if immediate and accurate response is not required. Even though the capability is for high resolution, there should be reduced ambiguity about touching the target.
- *Make all targets rectangular*, if possible, for while this is not absolutely required, quite often it is far easier on the operator and, for that matter, the designer as well.
- *Label the targets clearly*, again, with consistency, just as with colors, with shapes, and with all the other aspects of a screen view. Consistency makes for a better operation.
- *Highlight the selected target* so the user knows the correct selection is made.
- *Provide a multiple "keystroke" action* to confirm that the invoked function or entry is truly the one to be implemented. This avoids an accidental touch that triggers unwanted action.
- *Provide visible and auditory feedback* when the action is invoked. As we said before, let the operator know the entry was made successfully.
- *Provide all consoles (sit-down or stand-up versions) with suitable armrests.* This makes the user's arm extension to the screen as small as practicable and supports a more precise target selection that is easier to achieve.

Navigational Designs

Various standard features are embedded in systems today that help the user make the proper action for each occasion. That is, they provide some focus during plant upset, as well as consistent direction during routine functions, especially ones that require many steps for their performance (start-up, shut-down, changeover, etc.). These are frequently screen call-up sequences directed by on-screen selections:

- **Display targets** (hot spots) provide immediate access to any form of pop-up, which in turn, can include menu selections or control faceplates for operator actions. Because of its fast user-response system, this approach is very suitable for the real-time user.
- **Maps/menus** are a special form of display/pop-up in which a selected display can be called up by the user. These may include structured menu tables or menus coded by display elements (hot spots), which, in turn, can be used to make further decisions. Consistency of symbolic representation, selection, and selection response is critical in any use of coded display elements.
- **Context-sensitive** help allows "help displays" and/or any associated displays to the action at hand to be called up based upon the current display, the control faceplate selected, or the state of the process. These associated displays or pop-up windows can provide interlock, override, and/or permissive information for the related device.

Make touch screen or mouse targets distinguishable with respect to the kind of information to be accessed. Targets that call up controls should be coded differently from those that access other displays. Similarly, analog control call-up targets should be distinguishable from discrete or digital ones. All targets must be identified (a three-dimensional effect is useful to imply a "button" metaphor). Nontargets must not have a similar appearance.

Entries for Control

Earlier in this chapter we discussed the need to use display elements that are standard throughout the plant. This reduces confusion during plant upsets and ensures consistent operation during normal running. Based upon ISA-TR77.60.04-1996, the following guidelines are offered.

Control station—a standard control station display element should

- Provide consistent target functions, including the way targets are presented across all controllers, so that if the operator can click and drag a bar graph to change a variable, it should be expected this can be done in all similar devices as well.
- Use standard keyboard interaction, so that separate keys are consistently used to provide the different needed functions, to avoid errors through ambiguity.
- Provide a consistent location for the basic display elements that comprise the control station, such as labels, bar graphs, meter pointers, numeric values, digital indicators and the like.

Optimum user interaction—guidelines include:

- Provide coding to highlight which items can be selected to be actually controlled by the operator, which control is currently active, and which is not controllable. This differentiation is critical for mimics, where some devices are not controlled by the specific operator (level of training, level of responsibility, etc.)
- Provide clear indication of control states, such as
  - —Is the item automatically controlled?
  - —Is it manually inhibited by other actions?
  - —What is the current operating mode (auto, manual, local control, etc.) of plant areas, units, loops, or equipment?
- Follow a consistent loop-operating philosophy for control of an analog process variable or a discrete state of equipment. This should include
  - —A well-defined act for selecting a control. (A two-step operation should be provided for any significant control action, including a means for deselection.)
  - —A feedback that the control is active.
  - —A separate, second act to adjust the selected control.
  - —A feedback from the actual piece of equipment being controlled (not just a verification of the requesting signal).

—A means to invoke context-sensitive help if control is not allowed for the selected device (such as through an interlock).

—A Cancel Selected target or button to clear the currently selected object.

- Perform analog control adjustments by

—Selecting and entering a target value that has an acceptable slew rate built into the firmware, which drives the change

—Having raise/lower keys on a keyboard or displayed on the screen view and have them accessible with either a cursor or a touch screen.

—Selecting a target element at the top of a bar graph of the variable and dragging it to the desired position, so the variable will move at a predetermined acceptable sleMw rate.

- Design displays for sequential automatic control functions to include display windows that

—List all sequence steps and start/run permissives.

—Indicate the current sequence step.

—Indicate the target sequence step.

—Indicate the steps satisfied.

—List the inhibits present that prevent further progress.

—Display the elapsed time for any time-based holds.

—Include controls to start/stop the sequence

—Provide direct feedback indicating completion or failure to complete a second command.

- Never allow an item to be controlled but not observed (e.g., if a set point raise key is active, the set point must be displayed).

Audio Access in the Control Room

One other method of human-to-process interface that we did not mention in our list in the beginning of this chapter is the fascinating, but unproved, realm of using audio as a communication medium. Though so natural for humans, it is not fully understood enough to be applied to the subtleties of a control room. We shouldn't feel badly about this. If we are to believe archaeologists, speech as a communicating tool among humans seems to have appeared very late in our development.

There are two sides to this. The voice to the operator from the control system (presumably through the operator interface), and the voice of the operator as an access to the operations. Remember our earlier observation in Chapter 14 (Figure 14.2) that the optical path to the brain carries the equivalent of fifty million words a minute, and that's over ten million times more than the aural reaction of the brain. We can learn more easily, quickly, and accurately with pictures then we can with sound. This difference may also be involved in the cause/effect of the late development of speech in humans. By nature, we are more a visual people.

Figure 16-4. More Must be Learned for Effective Use of Audio in the Control Room

Voice Commands

The interpretation of voice commands involves the quality of the microphone, background noise, and, as we have said, the many speech idiosyncrasies of humans. Grammar, accents, inflection, pauses and red tones are all part of the challenge. Systems used commercially at the end of the 1990s either limit the vocabulary of the user by informing him or her of the words to select or required a trial-and-error "training period" so the computer can learn the voice patterns and foibles of each user. Also by the end of the decade, Microsoft had already invested over $50 million to develop the easy ability to instruct computers through spoken commands for word processing, spreadsheets, and so on. There is at least one alarm monitoring system that can place a phone call to announce plant status and respond to specific interrogations regarding conditions.

I can see where a "hands-free" approach could be useful in a control room in selecting screen views for plant conditions. This would probably be necessary only during plant upsets, which is a dangerous time to require that an operator speak precisely. Considering the complexities of human communication, I would personally have reservations about using voice commands to set control parameters (set points and outputs) during stressful situations. How does the process know the difference between asking for an action, inquiring for information, or having a discussion with an nearby partner in the control room that might impact the action or strategy of the process. Much still needs to be done in this field beyond just the "mechanics" of voice recognition.

Pretty Girls in the Airport

We still have to consider that the aural range of operators is not consistent, either spoken or heard. My own experience while going through a very busy airport several years ago confirmed this. I noticed that there were voice directions, a pleasant female voice giving information about which stairway to use to get to another level. Upon reaching that lower level, I began going down an escalator and "she" gave information as to what to expect at the foot of the stairs (walk, ride a gliding footpath, or take a tram). When I was standing by the tram, "she" said when the tram was coming and which door to use. Once inside the tram, "her" voice also asked passengers to stand clear of the door, brace for the acceleration, and brace when the tram stopped as well as announcing we were approaching.

Figure 16-5. The "Girl in the Wall" at the Airport Gave Information

All this was fine and good, but I noticed a change about a year later while going through the same airport. Here again was the pretty girl somewhere behind the walls melodiously telling us all of those same instructions until I got on the tram. There the pretty girl had been fired and replaced by a machine! This very mechanical voice curtly commanded us to "Stand clear of the door" and as the door

Figure 16-6. The Machine on the Tram Gave Warnings

closed, "Car will accelerate" and so on. Well, I had to ask the management why this change occurred.

Control Room Lesson from the Girls

I was informed that for giving informational data, the pleasant, fluctuating, melodious voice was very nice and helpful. When it came to warnings and attentions and alerts, however, a mechanical voice was needed that would be heard by all. The fact was that the frequency range of the melodious girl's voice was often not heard by all of the travelers. In fact, the full range was only heard by about 60 percent of them. So the mechanical voice, which had a very limited frequency range, was designed to fit the many varied, and even very limited, frequency ranges of most people.

I reflected on the impact of this for the control room. These natural variations and limitations would change the kind of information that could be portrayed to the ears instead of the eyes, and how you would distinguish absolute urgent actions from suggestions. Because the information receptivity of the eyes is far more acute and processing speeds than that of ears, it would seem that most information would be best conveyed through the video screen rather than through loudspeakers. Loudspeakers could be used mostly for alarms, plant upsets, similar warnings. These should be *duplicated* on the screen, so that once the audible message passed the memory of that information would be reinforced. Now the operator would never overlook or forget information given in the past and records could be more easily kept.

We may have to live with the limitations of bells, whistles, Klaxons, buzzers, and the like. Much can still be accomplished inexpensively with multiple tones, tone levels, and, yes, some voice warnings. As for voice inputs, well, science is coming along with that, but more progress needs to be made to be truly effective.

Human Information Processing 17

With automation we have tried to emulate all of the activities of the human facilities. The brain is the information processor that tells we humans how to perform. Our challenge is to discover how to learn from this to really create and use meaningful operator interfaces.

How We Think and Do

Looking at the human being as a computer, we can identify different actions within our brains (Figure 17-1). Of course, it probably works just as well the other way, looking at computers as human, at least to some limited extent. That's because in all design, probably our best model or template for any kind of computing function, communication function, or even motor function comes from that wonderful model called the human being. Within the human brain, we can see several operations.

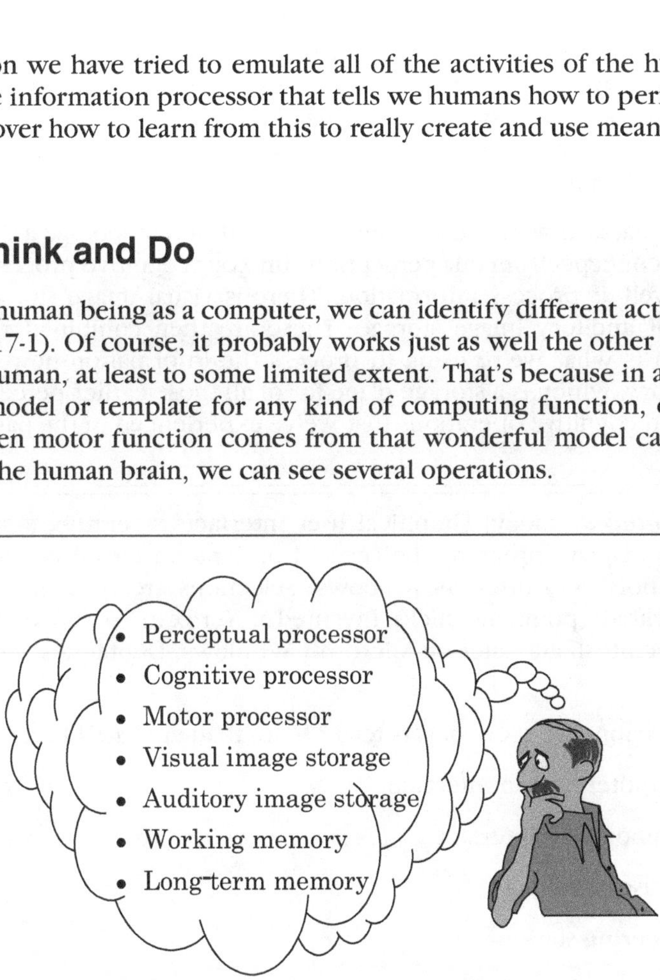

Figure 17-1. Computers Mimic Human Brain Processing Categories

The brain's perceptual processor is where we perceive actions or recognize what's going on around us through various inputs, tactile feel, auditory and visual frequencies, and probably several frequency senses we haven't yet identified. We have designed process sensors based upon many of these human capabilities.

The cognitive processor is where we possess the ability to define our experience or to apply our reasoning power to previously learned information. From this capability we determine the significance of all those things we are perceiving through our many sensors. We have also attempted to mimic this function with our measuring devices and controllers. Some exciting refinements are being explored through our efforts to develop practical forms of fuzzy logic, neural networks, genetic algorithms, and chaos theory, all of which we learn from nature and other life forms.

The motor processor is the response to all of those perceptual and cognitive capabilities, the conversion of our decisions into actions. It is where we make our limbs respond to what we have been perceiving and computing in our head and resolve it into some form of decision. Motor processes give very subtle directions to our limbs, even for extremely complex functions. A good example is writing, which involves the operation of several motor actions in arms, hands, and fingers, using the writing tool to record in symbols the concepts working in our brain. The whole process of writing involves constant feedback and optimizing control.

For all of this to happen well, we also need to have different storage areas, from which we transfer the concepts from our perceptions into our cognitive processors. The brain must store as well as process information. There is visual image storage, and there's another area for auditory image storage. These are then combined with a working memory, which is what we're using to process the information now at hand, and a long-term memory, which is a storage place for of all those earlier perceptions, images, and auditory and cognitive operations that we've experienced in the past.

GUI—[*pronounced:* gooey] Graphical user interface; operating system or environment that displays program choices and options on the screen as icons (pictures or symbols) and often as windows. Selections are typically made with a mouse or trackball (point and click). Invented at Xerox in 1970s, was first used on the Apple Macintosh and later on Microsoft Windows, Digital Research GEM, and X-Windows.

How many versions are there of this term? More than are listed here!

- **CHI**—Computer human interface
- **CUI**—Common user interface
- **EUI**—End user interface
- **ES**—Engineering station
- **HCI**—Human-computer interface
- **HMI**—Human-machine interface.
- **HPI**—Human process interface
- **MMI**—Man-machine interface
- **MS**—Managing station; maintenance station
- **OI**—Operator interface.
- **OS**—Operator station
- **UI**—User interface I

Think of the Interface

How should the operator interact directly with the process? Everything between the operator and the process should be very transparent. This interface is really a gauge of how well we have people interact with a more sophisticated technology. This brings up two fundamental questions that must be asked before designing any operator interface, or for that matter any interface between a person and the function you want operated upon. These two fundamental questions are as follows:

1. **Why do you want this interface?** What is the fundamental purpose for putting this interface here and having something happen through it? You are defining what is really supposed to go on rather than all the nice neat little toys that go with it.

2. **Why would you not want to get rid of this interface?** What you really have to ask yourself is "Do I really need it?" What would happen if I did not have it at all? Very carefully think this one out, and write down all the reasons why it must be there. That will give you the first clue about what functions should occur on that interface.

Differentiate User Needs

The designer of this interface must think like the user who is going to use it, and take into consideration all the phases of the system functions. Be sure to design screen views and dynamics to fit the requirements of each user. What people work with this particular process?

- Plant or process operator?
- Maintenance technician?
- Plant or process engineer?
- Automation engineer?
- Quality assurance personnel?
- Business manager?

All these people have different functions to perform, and therefore they need different information from the control system. The presentation of the data for converting this into information is probably going to be significantly different for each of these six people, or for any other people who should use it. The tools that each of these people need to perform their functions on the process or on the plant will also be different. Yes, sometimes there will be things in common, but more typically even if those common things are performed they are performed in a different context. If you have an action item that can be created from the screen, it's probably going to be surrounded by different forms of information depending on that person's role.

Operator Action Philosophies

Surprisingly, there's only a small body of work on the design principles for operator interfaces. Some of the most interesting contributions have come from researchers at the Georgia Tech Multi-Satellite Operations Control Center, who authoritatively tested the implementation of a new real-time operator interface on a variety of operators.

Such research is expensive, which may account for its rarity. Most research on human-computer interaction is relatively narrow in scope, focusing on individual aspects of shape, coding, color, and menu design. Incorporating all the different aspects of computer capabilities and human aptitude into a usable product is one of the jobs of any serious designer. To achieve success in interface design, it is necessary to understand the ways in which humans think conceptually and to understand how they process this information physically. The physical and conceptual are closely related when working with any type of interface. Designers should ask themselves what type of information is useful to the field operator.

Consider some important issues involved in designing the operator interface:

- Easy to navigate through video screens
- Reduced chances for misunderstanding
- Accurate representations of process or functions
- Consistent and predictable operation
- Pleasant and engaging interface that conforms to operator's understanding

Two major elements determine the display type:

- **Display content**—established by user functions (task analysis)
- **Display organization**—must be logical to the user

Users with different responsibilities may need the same content to be organized according to their specific responsibilities. The display types provided should offer enough flexibility so that, when used in conjunction with the display system's capabilities, a user's needs can be comfortably accommodated. For example, some operators may prefer to operate from process mimics, where others may prefer to work the control station faceplates. The amount of detail on the screen at any moment in time should be left to the discretion of the user.

In planning video screen display types, it is important to consider various techniques for expediting display recognition, including the following:

- Reduce the display types; use flexibility only in response to specific user's preferences.
- Enhance user recognition with consistent formats and methods for showing information.
- Use standard elements such as symbols, colors, names and abbreviations for all displays, even if the display content and organization varies because the intended functions are different.

When a standard format and especially a standard layout are used, displays will tend to look alike. To avoid confusion and errors, it is equally important to make each display and layout distinguishable from each other by using unique titling and possibly other coding techniques.

For example, if multiple units of the same process are accessed from a common console, the unit number must be clearly displayed. Consider using along with that number some shape and color (like a unique team logo) for that unit alone, and with everything that is associated with it. Another method would be to use a different background color or "wallpaper" pattern. Refrain from getting carried away with the idea and creating a visual circus!

Intuitive versus Learning by Rote

User behavior for programming was organized by Schneiderman and Mayer in 1979 into either syntactic or semantic knowledge. Syntactic knowledge is learned by rote, involves little system understanding, and is only short-term. An example of syntactic knowledge is using combination keys such as "CTRL-C" to copy a selection or "CTL-ALT-DEL" to close an application, as is done with many DOS-based computing applications. These actions or key assignments are frequently different with each different system, so the knowledge is not transferable to other systems in even the same plant.

Semantic knowledge, on the other hand, is taught through concepts, relationships, and analogies. Semantic knowledge is often conveyed through pictures, is task-based, and once learned is not easily forgotten. An example of semantic knowledge is the use a picture of file folders or icons that resemble the functions performed, as is done in Macintosh computer applications.

By not working with abstractions, users usually have a much better idea of what the program does. This semantic thought process is one of the ways humans break complex problems into manageable pieces. Learning is much faster, and the user becomes far more comfortable with the operation. Semantic knowledge leads quickly from running the process to managing the process.

Range and Uses of Operator Interfaces

Later, in Chapter 28, we will discuss the linking of local process control and factory automation systems directly into the corporate business planning systems. The focus today is not only process control and process management but also equipment management, production management, order management, procurement management, personnel management, and financial management. All of these fall under the category of business planning. In the future, using an operator interface will change significantly. For example, in the process management area, you are monitoring the parameters of the process itself, the accuracy of sensors, the operations of the valves, and so on. Today, in addition to controlling the recovery of plant upsets, there is also environmental monitoring, product yields, predictive maintenance of the process equipment, and many other requirements.

The system designer must provide tools through the screen displays that are capable of navigation through many more diverse activities. They must support the operator's ease of access to a large database and simplified decision making through presentation, interaction, and analysis displays. The operator is also responding to plant upsets and alarms or changes in process conditions. He or she must follow intuitive screen prompts and must navigate through the screen displays and various windows to discover the different aspects of the operating plant.

Under the area of business activity, there's financial management and product production management. Product production management is the raw material usage, the inventory, the logistics of getting the material to where the operations occur. It is also production scheduling, production monitoring, the product's quality control, material movement and storage, energy usage, the unit product's production costs, lab analysis, and so on.

Philosophical Issues

Key issue:

— Do customers and vendors really know what the *application* needs?

Technology is not the issue:

— The issue is commercializing technology into useful products!

— We have ten years of technology we are not yet using!

The human today is a manager:

— The computer/distributed control system *operates*

— The human *manages*

Process control is the art of making food, pharmaceuticals, steel, glass, paper, cement, power, clean water, and the like. The *computer* merely helps perform the art better and make it repeatable!

On a level above project management is financial management, which includes invoicing and billing; the accounting functions of general ledger, accounts receivable, and accounts payable; purchase order tracking, and sales and marketing forecasting for the products. This enterprise resource planning (ERP) must dynamically link with the production management to preorder materials as the inventory of raw material goes down as well as track the requirements of customers and their orders to determine how to optimally custom fit each production day to meet the customer's requirements.

This dynamic linking of two types of information flow presents both interesting possibilities for the concept of the control room and also some exciting challenges. The operator is now exposed to business parameters that previously only existed in paper reports that came out monthly or quarterly. These become new parameters that impact daily production. This is untested territory for both the business as well as the production side! The real challenge is now to the system designer.

The architecture required for these roles is being modified along with the technology it requires. Perhaps some day we will see no difference in the architecture, but for the time being one must be concerned with the proper execution times for achieving these different functions as well as the nature of the operator and screen views needed for each of these functions. Keep in mind that any presentation must take into consideration the proper audience.

More Philosophical Issues

An interesting dilemma in developing any control system is the question, "Do system customers and system vendors really know what the application needs?" Many times the excitement over the technology and the clever operational features that can be performed by this technology obscure the actual requirements of the process or the plant. Everyone seems to be caught up with the "gee whiz" of the technology, and they forget what they're supposed to do with it. Technology is not the issue. The issue is commercializing the technology into useful products. We have ten years of technology we're not even using yet for improving product construction and performance, especially in process control. In the operations of a plant, the human is a manager, while the computer or the distributed control system operates the functions. That's different than what happened in control rooms in the past. Keep in mind that all process control is an art, not a science. It is the art of making food, the art of making pharmaceuticals, steel, glass, paper, or cement. The computer merely helps perform the art better makes it more repeatable.

Human Factor Considerations

- Eliminate unnecessary handling of data

  Use a control and data acquisition system to convert, record, store, log, alarm, and trend data

- Minimize the stress caused by of a process upset...

  Use a control and data acquisition system to help identify the problem

- Present current information

  Instantaneous values should be no less than one to two seconds old

- Minimize operator interactions

  Reduce keystrokes, push buttons, display paging, hunt and search

---

Remember:

- The fastest form of input for human: visual
- Provide timely *information*, not data
- Facilitate operator interaction with the process control equipment should become transparent

---

Human Factor Considerations

An important factor in the development of screen views are the actions the operator needs to take in response to the information presented to him or her. The idea is to eliminate the unnecessary handling of data. The data should be converted into information so the operator doesn't have to process the data in his or her head and decide what to do with it. This is exactly the role that a computer can perform admirably. You should use the control and data acquisition system to convert the data, record it, store it, log it, alarm it, and trend it. You should use the functions of a computer to minimize the stress of a process upset and use this control and data acquisition system to help identify the upset problem. You should use the computer system to present current information; an instantaneous value should be no more than one or two seconds old. The system should minimize the number of operator interactions by reducing keystrokes, the amount of display paging, and any required hunt and search for information. Of course, above all you should remember that the fastest input for humans is the visual.

Screen Design & Conflict

- Not enough data-increases the need to search several screens
- Too much data-dilutes the significance of any specific information
- How much can an operator monitor?
- How much can an operator control?

Design Conflicts

I can't emphasize enough that the purpose of this control system or the computer is to provide timely information, not data, and to facilitate the operator's interaction with the process itself. The control equipment should become transparent. Of course, making it transparent presents some interesting dilemmas. The screen design conflict is that if you do not have enough data, it increases the need to search the several screens for this data. If you have too much data, it dilutes the significance of any specific information. So you have to decide how much an operator can monitor and how much an operator can control. Big difference. A shepherd can monitor three hundred sheep, but he or she can only shear one at a time. The age-old problem of trying to determine how much control an operator can manage or how many controllers an operator should try to manipulate probably can be best evaluated by the average person, not from within the plant but by looking at common activities they do everyday.

How Much Can an Operator Control?

Let's examine this question by looking at the art of driving an automobile How many loops can an operator control at the same time? How many parameters can you control while driving your automobile? The controls of an automobile include the following:

1. A steering wheel 2. A brake 3. An accelerator 4. Perhaps a clutch.

Now, picture yourself driving with only those four controls through a nice winding "s" curve in heavy traffic. Midway through the curve, just *try* to also change the radio station! And that's only *five* operations!

Look carefully at your plant and see what you are expecting of the operator, not just in normal operations, but in plant upset conditions.

Moral: A shepherd can monitor three hundred sheep but he can only shear them one at a time!

Menu Structure Guidelines

Serious consideration must be given to how the operators manipulate and maneuver around the process or plant. This certainly is more involved in larger plant structures. The scope and job of an operator doesn't stop with the immediate process but also extends into the things that happen adjacent to that operator. What is happening upstream and downstream from this operation? How do the actions occurring here impact other portions of the process or plant?

The system designer must analyze the task that is required, and the information needed to do it. Having done this, the designer must define the structure that will best provide the tools to do this task. What should be the hierarchy of the menu structure? What are the relationships *between* the tasks and the functions performed in each view? What is the logical movement between these views (tasks and functions)? How do we keep the operator from getting lost in the windowing? What occasions need toolbars, poke points, pulldowns, pop-ups, hot spots, or hot keys? All these different, technically clever features should be done consistently throughout the system, so that every time a specific operation is needed, the actions for performing it well are consistent no matter who is operating!

The most mistreatment comes through the absence of clear labels and the inconsistent layout of all the screen views. Whenever any action is made, there should be immediate feedback on when the request is made that is *separate* from when the action actually occurs. Never, ever, should the operator see on the screen a response to an action that derives from a simulation of that action rather than from the actual occurrence of the result of his action.

Menu and Screen Structure Guidelines

- *Analyze* task required and information needed to do it.
- Determine who will do the task.
- Decide when the task needs to be done (event and/or time-based?)
- Have well-defined objectives to guide content and organization.
- Define *appropriate* access structure to be used:
  — Hierarchical
  — Pulldown
  — Windowing
  — Pop-ups
  — Toolbar
  — Hot spots

— Poke points
— Hot keys

- Navigate *consistently* throughout the system
- Use *clear* labeling.
- Use *consistent* layout.
- Provide *immediate* feedback:
  — When request is made
  — When action occurs
- Provide aesthetic balance!

Often overlooked in menu and screen structure is aesthetic balance! There should be an appropriate blend of colors, and an appearance and use of shapes that it is pleasing enough to not look out of place. We are not talking about just making pretty pictures here! This is more like good page layout in a document. The layout contributes significantly to *conveying* the information from the content on a page to the reader. ("Didn't you get my note?" "I got your note, I just didn't know that's what you said!" Has this ever happened to you?) Poor layout and color combinations will distract the reader from, important information or even hide it altogether.

Display Organization and Content

Based upon ISA-TR77.60.04-1996, the following considerations are offered for general content and layout; emphasizing important items, providing easy recognition for the user, and for grouping, labeling, and coding conventions. Keep in mind that whenever rules are laid down, there will be contradictions in their specific use! Trade-offs will be required, but always consider which option will have the greatest impact upon process/plant performance.

You must consider the general content and layout:

- Provide the necessary content but only what is sufficient to support the display objective.
- Arrange the content so that it is not too dense.

Crowded displays make it difficult to locate information. A rule of thumb is to provide a minimum of 25 percent to 40 percent blank space. For systems with a limited number of monitors, it may be necessary to increase display density to avoid the need for excessive paging between displays. A good effective display design will allow more information to go on a single page without clutter. Careful use of windowing will also help!

- Show the data that is most relevant for the display objective (e.g., capability loss may be more important than resultant low flow).

- Organize elements by the order they will be used (e.g., top to bottom, left to right), with more frequently used elements given more prominence.
- Make comparisons easier by placing those elements to be compared close to one another.
- Match the level of abstraction with the display objective (i.e., summary overviews may need only deviations from intended marks, without absolute values, while detailed process displays will need more concrete values).

You must emphasize important items:

- Establish a consistent focal point for each screen, such as centering the title at the top of the display to serve as a starting point for viewing the display.
- Place those elements that have priority over others in prominent locations.
- Avoid displaying alarm conditions or status conditions that are in normal (unalarmed) condition (i.e., not active, alarm warnings are off) in the regularly used mimic displays. This is not to be confused, however with the need to show normal equipment status (on-off, fill-empty, etc.) which may be needed to monitor plant operations.

Instead of displaying alarm conditions that are in normal, consider alarm *group* summaries instead. These make possible the analysis of alarm *patterns* using certain fixed-layout displays that show all possible alarmed points within a unit process, both in and out of alarm.

- Avoid showing secondary equipment if the current status is satisfactory
- Display limit indications only when the limit is reached, or when knowledge of the limit (and the approach to it) is needed as part of process/plant performance.

You must make the displays easy for the user to recognize:

- Comply with the user's way of thinking about the system
- Take advantage of the physical relationships of the process/plant that are known by the user, such as the locations of equipment involved.
- Maintain consistency in display design with the displays already in use, such as in "legacy" control systems already installed in the plant, especially if the users are rotated about the several systems. This does not mean you should avoid using valuable features of the new system, just make their use, as much as possible an intuitive extension of what has already been learned.
- Take advantage of any existing conventions and practices, particularly if they are well known and accepted. This is particularly important in the seemingly mundane area of plant abbreviations, symbol standards, or color codes.

You must use logical grouping and labeling:

- Make the *grouping* immediately recognizable without the need to read the specific data.
- Use spacing rather than lines to separate groups of data and or equipment, to reduce clutter.
- Group data by functional relationships. Consider the data's user, however, and realize that different occasions will determine whether it will be best to group by importance (priorities), frequency, sequence of use, location, or alphabetical (numerical), or chronological order.
- Make the grouping consistent with all similar type displays.
- Label all data, unless it truly is intuitive and easily inferred from the display layout.
- Make labels short, unique, and distinctive.
- Establish labeling conventions for size, location, and case (upper or lower). Size should be consistent or by some hierarchical standard. Locate labels consistently with respect to data-preferably to the left of or above the data field. (Upper and lowercase lettering is more readable; don't use all upper case).
- Avoid the use of solids to establish boarders; they add to the complexity of the views.
- Place data value "text" that is more important in bright colors (white, yellow, light green, cyan) to make it appear more noticeable.
- Place less important values in lower intensity colors, as much as half as bright.

You must use coding conventions accepted throughout the process and/or plant:

- Establish plant wide (or a least process wide) coding conventions to maintain consistency across the displays. Primary coding should emphasize pattern and shapes over colors.

Shapes are quick and easy to recognize and independent of any color coding. Shapes are especially effective for identifying components and their operational status.

- Code to natural expectations (a larger pump should have a larger symbol).
- Employ codes already known to the users (plant color coding, abbreviations, drawing symbols, etc.).
- Use obvious codes (up arrow as the symbol for "increase," etc.). Avoid ambiguity (PRNT may be better than PR if the system also has functions for Primary, Previous, etc.).
- Establish a "shapes" library to assure uniformity; use standard symbols familiar to the user.
- Make shapes clearly distinct; 10 to 15 are easily distinguishable.

- Use space to ensure the legibility of alphanumeric characters when used in conjunction with a shape. For example, place the label within the shape whenever possible.

Use shapes consistently for the same equipment or to convey the same meaning. Simple shapes should reflect equipment shape as much as possible.

- Provide definitions for special uncommonly used codes, such as using single or short-phrased terms in the appropriate color and if appropriate, a small adjacent color block so this can be referenced by those who see some colors as shades of gray. Use "help" screens for definitions.
- Avoid overusing of codes, which add clutter and require the constant interpretation of the user, which diminishes his or her focus on the task being performed.
- Use a dark or neutral screen background. The *overall* screen background should match ambient conditions, in which 25 percent to 50 percent gray is considered best because it masks glare. The coding of display elements will achieve better contrast if they are set against a darker or black background on their specific field. Examples of this are a small "window" just for text, numerals in yellow on black background, and a green bar chart fill on a black background in an instrument faceplate.
- Use a different background for "pop-up" windows to distinguish them from the main screen and to ensure that the background provides a good contrast with the established color code (such as light gray for a "pop-up").

More discussion on the use of colors can be found in Chapter 15.

You must develop a method to highlight changes:

Highlighting is a way of coding so as to catch the user's attention and should be limited to two or three items on any one display to be effective. Highlighting includes the following:

- *Reverse video*: effective for alarms so as to overcome the low perceived brightness of red.
- *Increased brightness*: increases color intensity or switches to a brighter color when invoked.
- *Flashing*: Extremely useful for attracting attention, but to be effective, it must not be overused. It should be reserved for alarms or for possible target detection in a high-density display. The user should be able to suppress the flashing action.

Flashing text becomes unreadable! The best alarms flash near the text.

Hierarchies of Views

In very large processes, or especially in large plants, not everything is not going to fit on the same screen view. The connection *between* screen views is very critical here. It is imperative that there be some hierarchical concept of how the screen views go together so the operator can intuitively navigate from one view to the other. Display structures provided by vendors of real-time distributed process control systems are most commonly organized in a hierarchical structure. These group displays according to levels of detail, where each display serves as a menu to information above or below its level.

To return to Renzo Dallimonti's original concept form the 1960s and early 1970s, let's, look at the old panel as an overview. Step up to a group of instruments on that panel to observe and manipulate control actions. Slide one of the instruments in that group out of the case to access the control parameters, tuning parameters, or alarm connections so that each loop runs properly. We talked about these three concepts in Chapter 12, which is fine in a process plant in using closed loop control. Let's expand that idea into an overall large plant operation of any kind. Within some plant unit, there could be many small groups of instrumentation clustered in a given process located. Several of these units can be within each of the areas of a plant. The terminology for this scenario will change with every plant, but the concept occurs in nearly all of them.

Our example in Figure 17-2 may be more involved than is needed for a small system. Nevertheless, even a small system needs some logical order. Our example is intended merely to show that there can be many levels. Symmetry is not intended here because most plants are not really symmetrical. Of course all this is "idealistic," but to be *idealistic* is to develop ideas.

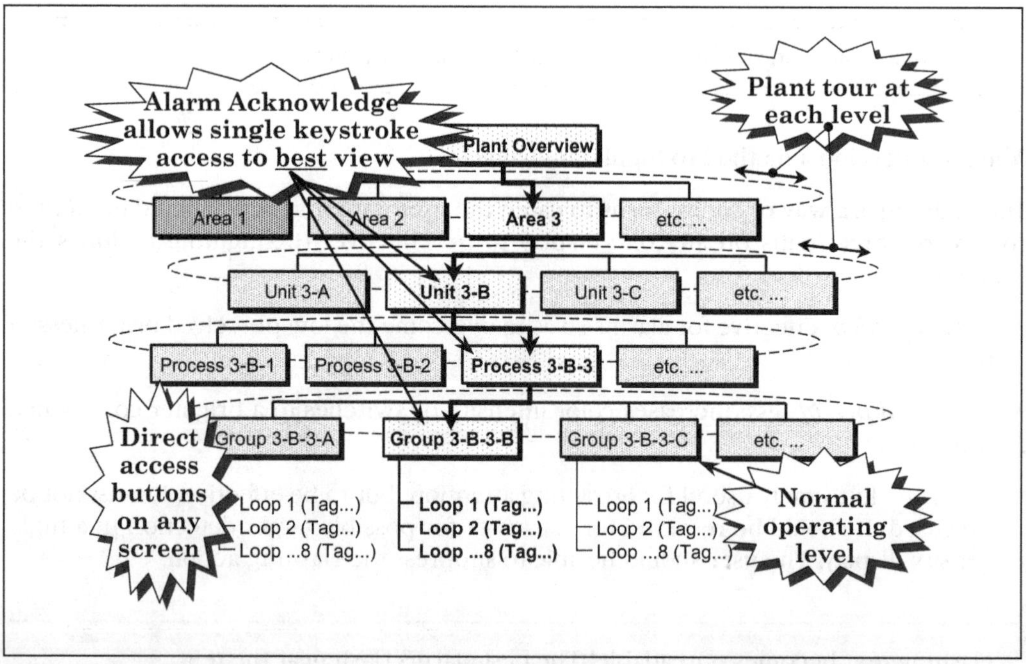

Figure 17- 2. Good Screen Hierarchies are Imperative For Good Navigation

At the top view in Figure 17-2 is an overall understanding of the plant operations, with the focus placed on the general health of each area below it. Besides showing which areas have alarmed conditions, this perspective should assist the viewer in learning where potential problems are developing. Some sort of warning lights or, better, messages are appropriate here. At each level "below," there must be some logical direction toward the next level, perhaps by merely "clicking" on a highlighted area. The pattern is repeated at each level. If an aberration in the plant is being traced, the operator could drill down into the hierarchy by "following the flashing icons."

Keep in mind that movement between screens should be *consistent* but also *appropriate* to the operations of that view!

In addition to drilling through the levels of a hierarchy of views, the operator must also have the ability to "tour the plant" at each level. Sometimes, for example, there are multiple units of the same process, such a boilers in a power utility. This plant tour may easily be accomplished by paging through the screen views at any level. Moving between adjacent views can be done with pointers embedded within the views, such as arrows on process piping, signal "wires," and other parts of the diagram that lead off screen to adjacent views.

Constructing screen hierarchies and navigation are discussed further in Chapter 21, following a necessary discussion of the nature and types of alarms and their handling.

Generally overviews in the upper level(s) of the hierarchy are informational and make possible the monitoring of the general conditions of the different processes within the plant. Rarely would you expect an operating function to occur in one of these views, but they may occur such as to turn a particular process on or off as you do in a start-up condition. In a start-up situation, you ought to consider showing multiple steps as prompts. If some difficulty arises during the procedure you are then led to an adjacent set of procedures to overcome it. The middle level consists of the control displays from which the process/plant is run. The lowest level are the details "within" the controllers and diagnostic displays.

From whatever screen view within any system, the operator must always see the alarm activity and have direct access to any other operating view, alarm analysis view(s), and process tagged point in the system without having to "climb" through any hierarchies of screen views!

Straight hierarchical views are not the only way to organize viewing structures. Two other approaches have also been used successfully:

- **Sequential structure** is where movement from one display to the next is governed by a sequence of procedures. Such a technique is helpful in managing start-up, shutdown, and changeover procedures. Good use of this approach takes advantage of pop-ups in a windowing environment, which were not available in the earlier systems.
- **Spatial structure** is where the video screen structure matches a mental map of the physical layout of the process and/or plant layout. This is an expansion of the fundamental concept of "touring the plant" in some order that is very intuitively logical to the operating crew.

With recently emerging technologies, many new ideas can come from experimentation. Such experimentation requires a rather flexible system that allows the user to start in a simple hierarchical structure, then move easily into some new version as the opportunity presents itself. All these techniques can be embedded into the other structures for a blended "mix and match."

Borrow from Video Games

As the system designer, you will have to have a very good picture of the process in your mind, both functionally and physically. Somehow, you *must* convey that same understanding to *every* operator, no matter their experience level or tenure (this is, after all, the real world). A good model of this challenge are video games, which take the player (new or experienced) through all kinds of mazes toward some goal. Got the idea? Of course, the big difference is that this is no game, and you cannot have any of *your* players *guessing* how to solve the puzzle!

In your overview, you are in the main control room. Look around at all that should be available to enable the operator to understand the plant operations. This could also include a map, either physical or functional or both. To begin any tour(s) you want the operator to take, you must provide "doorways" and directions. There must be doorways, emergency exits, and escape hatches in each screen view for logical progression for and eventuality. Take him or her through well-marked corridors and pathways to each needed operating location. Clearly mark any detours caused by changes in conditions (or even temporarily for maintenance and repairs). "Stairways and elevators" to other levels of the hierarchy must be equally well marked, with no ambiguity.

Within any one of those operational rooms, there should be other "doorways" to step through, and each "doorway" should lead the operator into more details of the equipment for that operation, and perhaps more specific control actions if necessary within that operation. Again, the operator can move around within that area of the plant, finding clearly marked information about that area and what can happen to the process as well as all the controls to cause it to happen or to make corrections. There could be further doorways within this room into other closets, if you will, of specific information and actions, such as the tuning of a controller or the viewing of inputs and outputs and so on, within that other room. Depending on the complexity of the plant, these will depend very much on the levels of the rooms within that plant.

Upon any upset, there must always be clear "emergency exits and escape hatches" (I suppose it will be better to "dematerialize and rematerialize") to allow the operator to instantly either

1. Go *directly* to the location of the upset to make corrective action, or
2. Go to *directly* to some "war room" where a proper analysis of the situation allows the operator to determine what needs to be done, in what order, and how to get to each task (better yet, how to bring each task to the operator).

In both circumstances, there must be prompts, suggestions, and check-off lists for as much information as possible to support the activity.

Remember that the operator just came out of another part of the process or plant. This area may have a parameters and different set of conditions to consider. The more this new area differs, the more important it is to get that operator the correct information, with the tools to make the right response. Proper presentation can take the form of instrument faceplates, dialog boxes, prompts and messages, more complete alarm conditions, and certainly good visuals. Equally important, there must be a route just as direct returning to the interrupted task or specific directions for the next required tasks after the correcting activity.

Alarm Response "Keys" Must Always Be Available:

ACKnowledge, SILence, FILTER, and direct access to go to any alarmed point in context of its most appropriate operating view and also direct access to the alarm summary list for analysis.

Remember the last or back "key." Many users prefer it to toggle, only one "layer."

Remember "utilities" like print (screen), report system (health).

The Operator's Perception Is Reality!

The video game analogy fits most any kind of manufacturing or process control system. More than cute imagery, I present this view to help you to seriously try to perceive what should happen in screen view designs. Recall that in Chapter 10 we discussed "The medium is the message!"

A hierarchy of views must be thought out very carefully! Most systems have a technique for maneuvering between views. Exploit it. Use all of your creativity so the operator is operating as intuitively as possible without having to learning some strange, cryptic function. To do this means that the designer of the plant has to understand the culture of the operators who are going to run that plant. Consider appropriate control room culture; what if operators at two different station make conflicting commands to the same process? This could be the culture of different countries or, more typically, the cultures of different industries. How do people think in a paper plant compared to a power plant or a steel mill? What has been their tradition, which might be centuries old? Then that tradition should be followed as closely as possible.

This doesn't mean you shouldn't introduce new ideas, but the ideas should be introduced within the concepts of those traditions. Now, of course, running a plant well, under normal conditions is relatively easy. It's just like, having once learned to drive an automobile, running on a nice clear day on an open road is relatively easy even if you're on a road you've never traveled before. What's critical, however, is how you respond when a serious accident starts to unfold. What do you do in a critical plant upset? That's the key. So you must look at all the conditions that can happen in a plant and think the way an operator thinks within his or her culture.

What About Control Rooms?

My emphasis has been primarily on the much ignored and abused area of good, workable screen displays. I personally believe this is the area where people have the least experience. This is not to say the control room itself is not important. The uptime and long-term reliability of a computer control system will be the ultimate benefit of initial site planning. Designing as you go, without forethought, can lead to devastating costs and extended installation schedules.

The color schemes on the screen display have to be consistent with the operation of the plant. They should also be pleasant enough so the operator isn't distracted from the operation. The psychology of restful and exciting colors, however, is not as important on the screen as it is in the room itself. A room layout in which the upper portion of the room is lighter and the lower portion darker is standard psychology material that can be investigated in other books. The physical specifications for equipment installation are discussed in Part J, on control system implementation.

Plant Manager/Engineer Requirements:

- Code requirements
- Expected control room functions
- work flow patterns
- Future expansion
- Security (fire, flood, files, foe)

Physically, control rooms must have the proper ergonomic layout. Be concerned about the height of the seats, whether their height can be changed, the position of the operator's arms with respect to the keyboard, and the distance of the operator's eyes from the screen views. Do not overlook the way in which that control room is used. Is the operator continually sitting in front of the screen all day or as in most plants, is he or she merely coming by that operator station to make adjustments to the control system in the midst of doing other duties? Is the operator also required to walk around other parts of the room or for that matter, in other parts of the plant? Pay attention to where the operator sits all day, the layout of the furniture, and the placements of screens and keyboards.

Operator Requirements:

- *Lighting*—Use a mix of incandescent and fluorescent; spotlight certain work spaces; avoid glare; and think of good areas for the monitor and keyboard for writing, for the printer, for the office, for equipment service, and storage, and for the entrance and exit.

- *Noise*—Avoid droning as well as loudness (under STC rating of 52)
- *Color*—Consider in conjunction with lighting—keep them coordinated to reduce fatigue. Need to be appropriate for purpose (cool and relaxing, warm and stimulating), light over dark.
- *Vision*—Consider along with lighting; any wall graphics must be visible from normal operating position (and readable); and screen views must be readable.
- *Ergonomic*—Goes together with all the above; use the proper chair and table heights and styles for the work intended (adjustable); consider accessibility of normal working "tools" (retrieving, reaching, etc.); consider the personnel's with respect to age range for vision, noise, lighting, personal hygiene, and the like.

The operator's performance involves vision, color, noise and lighting. The operator's equipment requirements and the ergonomic demands are part of this design. Other considerations in the room are how the equipment is laid out, the relationship between the kinds of equipment and screens the operator must use, the space required for that equipment, and the access for the maintenance of that equipment. The temperature and other environmental requirements, floor loading, vibrations, and cable restrictions are all integral to the control room layout. From the plant manager's viewpoint; you must view the system; assure appropriate work flow; coordinate the functions of the room itself, plan for future expansion and the code requirements per building, and protect the control room from fire, flood, loss of files, and even interference from outsiders.

Control System Requirements

- Equipment delivery and temporary storage
- Equipment relationships
- Maintenance requirements and accessibility
- Space requirements (footprint, working area needed)
- Floor loading
- Vibration and shock
- Temperature, humidity, altitude if appropriate
- Power
- Air flow
- Noise
- Lighting

Operator Interfaces Outside the Control Room

While an advantage of a distributed control system is in the distribution of the computation, these systems have centralized information going into the control room. Generally, there are databases resident in many places, such as within each controller. The data from these remote locations, however, is gathered so all the information is available at one location so an operator to has an understanding of the overall operations in a plant. This is also the same data to be used in a plant computer. In many systems, there have also been local operator interfaces, often video-based, at specific controller locations. The data within these was only local to that specific operation. Technology is allowing even newer opportunities for change.

The freedom now given us by the expansion of memory capacity and microprocessor power allows these local operating points to have access to whatever information is available to other parts of the system. The operators are no longer limited to some "remote" central console but are able to move closer to the process again. The difference is that they take with them information from all of the plant, not just the central console but also from any computer connected to it or the system!

Transmission techniques now allow a small portable handheld video screen and operator keyboard to be carried with the operator as he or she tours the plant as in days of old. Technology growth is allowing operator to tour the plant again, but with access to all of the console, which changes control room strategies. Now the operator has a first-hand view of the process and can crawl around, smell, feel and hear everything that's going on, all while performing a very thorough link to the actual controls and all the plant information. Returning to the plant floor like in "the old days," he or she is no longer limited to running only some local control point when he or she sees a problem.

Going a step further, because of the technology developed by the military, it is quite practical now to have these field connections linked to helmet devices. Using "heads-up" displays, the operator can see and hear process operations directly from screens suspended from the helmet and microphones attached to them. A small keyboard could be worn at the belt or connected to the shirt, very much as seen in some science fiction shows, except that today it is possible. The practical uses of these helmets probably will first be as a way of tuning a loop or calibrating a remote transmitter, particularly one that's high on a refinery tower or out on a pipeline. Nevertheless, as these tools become economically available, it is quite clear that customers using them will find new and different uses that the vendors could never have imagined.

A major control systems vendor already has a new wireless operator interface. The operator has small "heads-up" view screen in front of one eye and a combination mouse/keyboard mounted on a forearm. This allows the operator to roam the process while still viewing the process data and being able to take corrective action.

Business Views of Processes?

The other direction is to take the control parameters up into the boardroom. This has been touted by many vendors as a wonderful opportunity to display the controls on the screen in the boardroom, perhaps for the purpose of discussing the operating conditions. This would be fine for a management discussion on the operation of the plant, but it would be very dangerous to have that kind of view used to *operate* the plant. The operations of the plant should be left in the hands of the operators. Management screen views of the process should NEVER permit access to operational changes to the process. Process control should never be manipulated by managers sitting in a boardroom who aren't in direct contact with the actual events. Such a boardroom view will certainly be a valuable tool for analyzing the plant in conjunction with the business operations, but never, ever should this capability be used to perform plant controls.

Another advantage of the new technology can be a desktop or briefcase notebook interface. Just as you have notebook computers and briefcase computers for business, so also you could display operations in a plant. Again, this would be not for the manipulation of the plant processes but perhaps for the manipulation of the *information* that goes into the database. In this way, the manager of a plant could show prospective customers how well their plant performing some of the functions for that client, or perhaps the progress of that client's order. In some industries, we are evolving toward having customer-directed custom products. The representative of the factory could actually go to the customer and suggest different changes in the production mix. This could be entered into the enterprise resource management part of the package, but certainly not into the production line itself at that point. Nevertheless, such an option would provide a powerful opportunity for dialogue between the manufacturer and his customer regarding the specific requirements that customer needs.

Part D
Plant Upsets

18 Working With Alarms

The management of alarms is not just about operator displays! The entire system is involved. For this reason, it deserves its own discussion in this book. Nevertheless, because of the strong relationship between the way an operator display is indeed heavily linked to anything that happens within the process, especially during abnormal and emergency conditions, we will address alarm management here.

Architectural Considerations for Alarm Management

The role of the architecture is to swiftly get the data to the operator and just as swiftly respond to the data from the operator. The processor system must allow the operator to respond quickly and appropriately to any changing condition. Included in the issue of the operator station is the performance of the microprocessor circuitry that brings the data to the video screen. That circuitry includes the "build time" (how quickly the view can initially be presented) and how often can it be "refreshed" (how quickly data being presented is updated). For example, it may take seconds for a screen to come up in the first place but perhaps only a half a second between the updates of the data on that screen. The alarm information the operator sees on an existing screen should not be any older than two seconds.

Screen update is not done easily, and there are many systems incapable of bringing update information from the process itself as fast as the operator station can present it. Quite often, if the information must be stored and forwarded in different communication schemes, it slows the speed of the information going to the operator. Some systems have taken to having a history device located near the operator interface so the screen display will build very quickly, but the information displayed may be fifteen or even twenty seconds, sometimes even as much as a minute, old. That delay has more to do with the communication networks of the architecture or with the sorting and prioritizing of the many different levels of information that come over it.

This kind of delay is not as critical in what can be called "business information," as you have between desktop computers running between different offices. Likewise, processes with large thermal capacities move slowly and usually do not present as much of a concern in a process system. When dealing with a fast process, however, such as is found in power stations or chemical plants, then concern with speed is far greater. For this reason, architectures will also have separate subnetworks on the control room side of the system for the management of slower functions such as long-term trends, process history, and report writing.

It is imperative that the operator's attention is called immediately to any new alarm that occurs, regardless of what other display is in use!

Effective alarm management systems are usually built into control system architectures and supplemented by the user's implementation of the system's configuration tools. The operator's instant recognition of an alarm's appearance of an alarm can be accomplished by having a single screen location or a window dedicated to alarms located in only one position that shows the new alarms. These alarms should be filtered, qualified, and prioritized so that only those needing instant attention disrupt the operator from the normal activities (which, if left unattended, could also cause alarms).

State versus Condition

Alarms and events are often used interchangeably in our language. To know what to do with them, how to manage them, it is important to understand their true nature. Although they often go together in the dynamics of a process, they definitely are not the same.

An event is some change of status in the process (Figure 18-1). It is not an alarm. An event can be the start or completion of an operation, the passing of a stage in a sequence operation, the on-off triggering of a pump or motor, or the reaching of a threshold of analog value such as temperature. This change may be used to cause a control action. It probably ought to be recorded in a historical database, which means moving that discrete signal from the controller where the event was either caused or brought into the system through a sensor. From there, the signal may travel over a communication network and into a historian function that may reside in the operator station or a dedicated station. Events do not have to be presented on any screen the operator is viewing, but if one is important enough it should show up on some appropriate screen view. This appearance may not require any action, it may merely let people know of the status of the process.

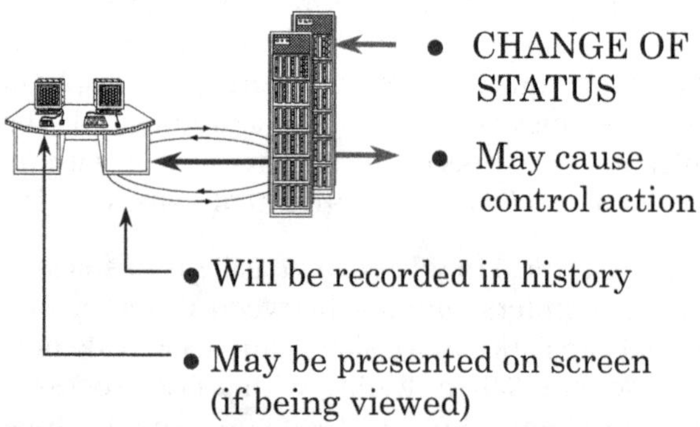

Figure 18-1. Events are Not in Themselves an Alarm

An alarm, on the other hand, is some existing or new status or condition (Figure 18-2). It is not an event. It is a condition that could cause control action and should be recorded in the process history. A new alarm is a condition that must always be presented on the operator's view screen, even if that particular area is not being viewed.

This alarm may result in some flashing icon, red flag, or maybe a line of text coming up on the screen announcing the alarm condition. It could also sound an audible annunciator and even create some automatic corrective control response, or perhaps a shutdown sequence.

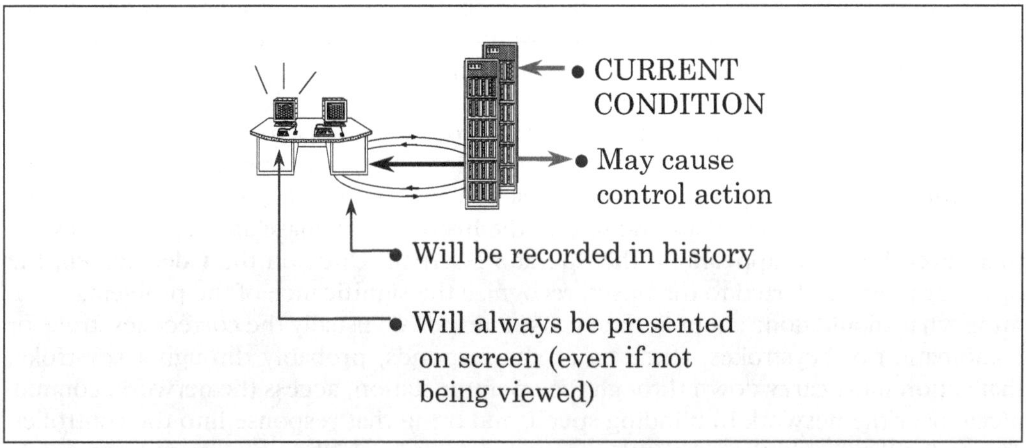

Figure 18-2. Alarms Must Always Be Reported to Video Screen

The alarm shown in Figure 18-2 is a representation of an existing discrete status or condition of an analog value, which is perhaps bad or unacknowledged and *must* be called to the operator's attention. Now, this alarm condition always has two events (Figure 18-3). For this reason many people confuse events with alarms. An event is an occurrence, such as, something running from the normal condition into the abnormal condition. When a signal goes into an abnormal condition, the first event occurs. Another event occurs when that same signal goes out of an alarm condition, such as when the abnormal problem goes away and the process is running normal again.

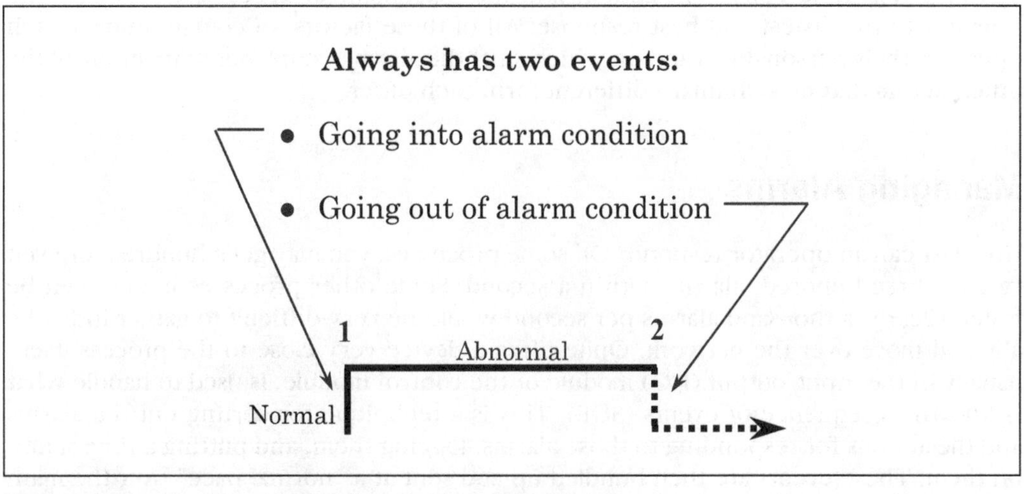

Figure 18-3. An Alarm Will Always Have *Two* Events

Speed of Operator Response

Automatic controllers will respond to a change in a process variable and cause an output without necessarily involving the operator. Only when a manual action from the operator is required does the communication network between the control station and the operator station come into play. The ability of the system to properly present changing conditions will impact operator response time. The operator response time depends on how well he is alerted to the problem.

If a plant upset is involved, the appropriate controller must receive the data, must access the network, and must then convey the information in "blinding speed" to the operator station. The operator station must convert the data from the network to the video screen. The data will also be sent to the historical database and will probably get there even before it appears on the operator's screen. Once on the video screen, the operator must be alerted to the upset, recognize the significance of the problem, determine what should done about it, then cause a response, usually the correct keystroke or combination of keystrokes. Once he or she responds, probably through a keystroke, that action must carry down through the operator station, access the network, communicate over the network in blinding speed, and bring that response into the controller. The controller would then make the corrected action, which in turn must be transmitted back out to the final control element.

Normal automatic control action, input to output, may take only a second or two. Add to that any communication over the network to another station, perhaps another second or two. Where is the slowest part of this "loop?" (Figure 18-4) Clearly, it is the operator's ability to recognize, comprehend, decide, and respond correctly to the problem! Issues of speed when it comes to including the operator interface usually center on the proper presentation of material on the screen itself, along with the appropriate tools for making the correct response. This requires a way of setting priorities, filters, and qualifications in the controller, perhaps on the input/output board itself. In the previous chapters we saw the many issues involved in the proper presentation of data on the screen: providing context to help understand the problem, providing prompts to the operator regarding consistent action, and the placement of access tools to ease the operator to the fastest and best response. All of these factors, of course, impact each operator, their personalities and on which shift the alarm occurs, not to mention all the other factors that make humans different form each other.

Managing Alarms

How fast can an operator respond? On some processes, you may get a hundred, or even two or three hundred, alarms within a second. Some other processes might even be faster. Clearly, a thousand alarms per second would be very difficult to gather individually and move over the network. Quite often a device very close to the process itself, usually in the input/output (I/O) module or the control module, is used to handle what is known as sequence of events (SOE). This is a technique for sorting out the alarms and the actions for responding to those alarms, logging them, and putting a time stamp on them. These events are then bundled up and sent at a "normal pace" over the main network into an operator station, a historical station, or some other computer.

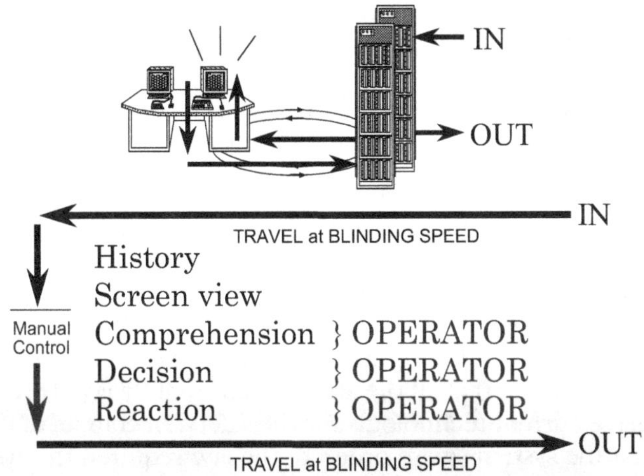

Figure 18-4. Trace the Flow of an Upset Signal into this System; Where is Slowest Point?

No operator can respond in a thousandth of a second, and certainly not to a sudden meaningless list of hundreds of alarms bursting onto the screen. This would be useless even if there existed a system that could communicate that fast from I/O to screen (there isn't such a system). There are, however, SOE techniques that can support the operator. Appropriate design in the remote I/O module, the control station, and the operator station can be used to sort, summarize, prioritize, filter, display with significance, and focus directed action. This design must accommodate natural human delay, not the electronic delay of communication.

Automatic actions are more readily accomplished through comprehensive algorithms having the wide choice of "built-in" alarm selections found in many types of control systems such as:

- Process loop control
- Batch and sequencing control
- Logic control
- Motor control

These allow the easy, on-going development of control and alarm strategies after the system is installed.

In today's control systems, the automatic actions found in the functional blocks of many control systems are quite comprehensive. This is true whether the control system is based on process loop control, batch and sequencing control, logic control, or even motor control. When an event or alarm condition occurs, quite often, the algorithm has enough hooks in it to cause a response to that action and put out a corrective action to resolve that imbalance. Not all conditions, however, should be corrected automatically. Quite often, we need the operator to have input on the appropriate corrective action. This is because the processes we are dealing with are truly an art, not an automatic condition that runs purely on formulas. When automatic correction can happen it should; but don't overlook the operator's interaction with it.

Alarm displays should be more than just a rapid large meaningless list (Figure 18-5). Instead the alarm notification should be sorted, summarized, prioritized, and displayed according to significance and focused for direct action. Remember that the Three Mile Island disaster took two shifts to react to, weeks to know in a limited way, and years to begin to understand fully. (Part of the problem in that incident was that of the ninety-eight failures that they fond in the operation of that system which should never have occurred, at least one set was that all the alarms went red! By law Three Mile Island was not permitted to have current technology- for the safety, of course, of the population. It turns out that when the systems were ordered, the law required the system to have ten years' operational experience. That rather narrowed the number of systems could be used. Furthermore, it took a good dozen years to build the plant, which ran for several years before the incident occurred. So at the time of the incident, the equipment technology was more than a quarter of a century old and, by law, could not have been any newer.) This disastrous experience does not mean we should repeat that action by limiting the technology we use in the system. If we have the technology to properly implement good alarm notification, we should carefully think out how to use that technology.

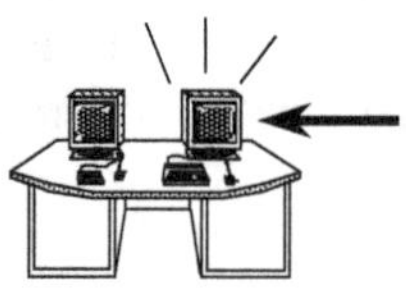

Not just a rapid, large, meaningless, **list** on a screen!

Rather, alarm notification is
- Sorted
- Summarized
- Prioritized
- Displayed with significance
- Focused for directed action

Figure 18-5. Alarm Notification Should Help Guide Operator

Alarm Choices 19

The kinds and types of alarms are important to a control system. Each industry has its own approach to the nature of conditions, which are important to the operation of their kinds of processes. This is an important flexibility, required in any "generic" control system, which is always a challenge to vendors of these systems. The architecture path selected by the system vendors will determine how each vendor will interpret how to implement the needs of those industries that vendor serves. As a user, you must look into these capabilities with some understanding of the alarming needs of your specific process requirements. Below is a discussion on what to consider.

Alarm Priority

Hardware status always overrides process value status!

Consider that anything that gets in the way of signal entry into the system should be annunciated before (in priority) any process alarm. It is scary to be left unaware of process alarms because equipment or control system failures have caused a false sense of security by not seeing the "real" failures.

Order of Overrides

- Input alarms
  - —instrument out of range
  - —open/shorted thermocouple
  - —link fail (remote I/O, to PLC, etc.)
- Controller status
  - —communication error
  - —off scan (reload, backup, etc.)
  - —alarm defeated (maintenance)
- Process values
  - —under/over range
  - —high-high/low-low
  - —high/low

Values can't be trusted if you can't verify that the hardware is operating properly. System diagnostics must therefore override the actual process values in the operation. Following such things as operating system failures and the like, the next order of overrides would include input-out-of-range-alarms, an open/closed thermocouple or similar failure, a link fail to any remote I/O PLC or device externally connected to the controller, and communication loss from or between any controller as well as any device on the communication network would come as a next level of importance.

After that, comes the status-of-controller function, often some monitor of the control action itself. That is, has the alarm been defeated because the loops are shut down for equipment maintenance? Is that alarm off scan because of a reload or back-up, or even off scan during start up?

Only after all of these various equipment failures (and sometime human-caused equipment limitations), should priority should be process values, such as over or under range, or high-high, low-low or high/low, whatever is appropriate to the operation.

Alarm Qualifiers

Qualifications on alarms are typically built with combinations of various alarm types. Used to create a more complete strategy of process management, qualifiers can help pinpoint problems more accurately and alert operators more quickly than simple alarms. Naturally, the focus of these qualifiers requires an understanding of the process so that you know the various relationships of the parameters and can anticipate potential problems. Through the clever use of these qualifiers, specific messages and prompts can be composed to help the operators' responses to upsets be very consistent, regardless of the person, shift, or other circumstances that can impact the thoroughness of the needed actions.

Alarm Qualifiers Build Combinations with

Analog Type

— Limits

— Functions

— Time

— Input

Discrete Type

Reverse/direct variations of

— on-off state

— on-off alarm

— Auto/Man mode upon alarm

By combining analog conditions with discrete states, some very powerful flexibility can be developed. Many times the clever u se of these tools can serve as a more simple replacement for those attempts to implement complex artificial intelligence techniques.

Alarm Cutouts

Cutouts can disable an alarm because an analog threshold has been reached, because of a discrete change in one of the functions (or actions), or because of some logic combinations of both. Because of this capability, cutouts can stop an alarm generation once it has started, so you don't compound the problem with more alarms than you need to determine a problem. For the same reason, cutouts can be used to delete outstanding alarms so you can detect new alarms that occur.

Alarm Cutouts

Can disable:

- Analog threshold
- Discrete change

Logic combinations of both can also:

- Stop alarm generation
- Delete outstanding alarms
- Select which status to cut out

Alarm cutouts can be used to selectively isolate problems. For example, a cutout can choose to disregard a temperature low alarm condition during a partial process shutdown, yet allow an open thermocouple alarm to occur so it can be repaired before the process is again placed into operation. This can save considerable time and expense during the restarting of that process!

Alarm Actions

We will now consider the many alarm functions typically available. In addition to an analog signal reaching some threshold, there could be a need to provide additional alarming as the signal continues to rise. It may be useful to have such an alarm notify at every six percentage points above that threshold so the operator becomes aware of such an absolute threshold, or a single delta, meaning a change in that threshold beyond a worsening condition.

Rapid rate of change, that is, when a signal is rising or falling in say, units per time or in absolute time, can also be a problem, even though a threshold has not been passed. Sometimes, you don't have to wait until a process reaches a critical threshold. An advanced warning can be made before some critical threshold is reached, perhaps giving the operator time for corrective action *before* product is lost or damaged. There could also be situations where a threshold is not involved, but that rapid change itself could cause damage to product or equipment.

Typical Alarm Functions Include:

- Absolute threshold (traditional)
- Single delta (once again, beyond that threshold)
- Repetitive delta (re-alarm at every selected change beyond that first delta)
- Rate of change
  - —Rising or falling (in units per time)
  - —Time (absolute)
- Return to normal (if desired)
- Time delay (to assure condition persists, not a spike)
- "Snooze" alarm
  - —Re-alarms if the condition persists beyond selected time after acknowledging it
  - —Can automatically acknowledge if condition clears
- Hysteresis alarm (has different threshold in return direction)

Some parameters are relatively unstable, or just continually fluctuate, such as pressures and flows. Quite often it is helpful to place some time delay on those alarms to act as a dead band, so that a spike, or "bobbing at the threshold," does not trip an unnecessary alarm. A hysteresis alarm has different thresholds in each direction, up or down. Used much like the time delay, this is a dead band that reduces unnecessary alarms in dynamically active fluids.

Hysteresis—The difference in signal when the point to be measured is first approached with increasing values and then with decreasing values usually expressed in percentage of full scale during any one cycle; a lagging in the response of a unit of a system behind an increase or a decrease in the strength of a signal.

There are also occasions where the operator needs to be notified when a parameter returns to normal, not just when that parameter goes into an alarm. There is also a snooze alarm approach that will re-alarm if the conditions persist beyond some selected time after acknowledging. The operator may acknowledge, and if he or she doesn't get back to it five minutes later, it re-alarms. With some versions, this type of alarm can be set to acknowledge itself if the condition clears.

Alarm Structures and Hierarchies 20

Just as with screen displays, there are alarm hierarchies. These hierarchies must be easy to assemble and modify within your control system. Alarm groupings can be arranged by plant areas, by function, by unit processes, or by equipment. The presentation should permit the operator to cursor on a flashing shape to directly enter a corrective action if at all possible, ideally with a single keystroke. Sometimes, especially when several alarms are involved, the operator must access some view that permits an analysis to determine the best plan of action. Again, this must be in a single, unambiguous keystroke.

Alarm Access

Operators should be able to acknowledge only one of the alarms, in addition to appropriate sets of related alarms. Alarm Acknowledge must be done each time in the identical way. Any "button" must be located in the same location so under the pressure of an upset any operator will be able to respond identically to any other. Alarm access must be direct without the need to go through process tags, names, or lists, and when getting to the alarm, full information should be available to the operator to make a proper decision.

Alarm Hierarchies

- Must be easy to assemble
- Groupings can be arranged by
  - —Plant areas
  - —Functions
  - —Equipment
- Permits operator to cursor on flashing shape to enter
  - —Direct corrective action, if possible
  - —View to analyze conditions
  - —Acknowledge only: single alarms, sets of alarms
- Direct access without process tags, names, lists
- Supply full information when found

Have only one *consistently located* point from which to acknowledge

---

Control system diagnostics schemes should be assembled much as you do alarms. The user should also be able to directly access the source of the problem in a way that is appropriate to the equipment involved. Depending upon the system design, it may be suitable to cursor through hardware layers, through networks, cabinets, controllers, and input/output modules. Ideally the user should then be able to follow the flashing icons. Either way, diagnostics should lead the user to the problem without the need for cryptic codes or even names and without having to search through lists, just as he or she ought to be able to do with alarms.

Diagnostic Hierarchies

- Same as with alarms
- User can create specific hardware map
- User can cursor through hardware layers
  - — Networks
  - — Cabinets
  - — Controllers
  - — I/O modules
  - — etc....
- Follow flashing icons without the need for cryptic codes or even names; no lists (for searching)!

Alarm Management

When an alarm occurs, the operator should be led to it in a simple, quick, decisive way that shows the location of that alarm and the recommended action. The action must be intuitive, from whatever view the operator happens to be at the time. The handling of the alarms should be made easily because the priority setting, annunciation technique, and the act of acknowledging should direct operators to that corrective action.

Techniques should be easily reconfigurable as plant experience is gained. As more is learned about the process itself, it should be easy to make changes to the alarm hierarchies, to operational screen views, and to any presentation of information. Alarm summaries are good, but they should not be *required* to locate alarms. Creative development of the operating views should perform that role. Summaries can, however, be a method to aid in the *analysis* of some emerging set of conditions and serve as a path to directly solve a problem without tedious lookup tactics.

Alarm Management

- Simple alarms to show location and recommended action
- Access to appropriate screen views should be quick, decisive, with minimum keystrokes (one, maybe two)
- Handling techniques:
  - — Priority setting
  - — Annunciating
- Acknowledging should direct operators to corrective action
- Techniques should be easily reconfigurable as plant experience is gained

---

Summary lists ought to be primarily informational, for assessing the extent of conditions at any one time. Information provided should include time and date, point identification, description, location, the current status or value, the warning signal, and the status or value it should be. The purpose of the summary is to give you a list of points in chronological order within the hierarchy of importance, grouped by the priority of those alarms. Depending upon the plant's size, complexity, and expected activity, dedicated video monitor(s) may be helpful for alarming. On small systems, however, using a windowing approach reduces the need for multiple monitors.

Alarm Summaries

- These views should not to be *required* to locate alarms!
- Information to include: time, date, point i.d., description, location, status/value, warning signal, expected status/value.
- Lists points in chronological order within hierarchy of importance.
- Can use dedicated video monitor
  - —Perhaps with alarm support displays until acknowledged.
  - —Split screens and windowing may relieve the need for a dedicated monitor.
- Memory media may preclude the requirement for *dedicated* printers.
- Collect operator actions to help evaluate the sequence of occurrences.

Alarm summary lists are very personal to each process or plant. They should be very carefully thought out. With the easy availability of much larger memory in most systems, as well as robust database managers to "interrogate the data," the need for printers to capture alarms during upset incidents no longer exists. Generally, the hard copy of such lists is not so much an analysis tool but a report of analysis results. A hard copy is helpful after the fact so the operator can read to read printouts rather than scrolling screen views. This is, of course, a matter of preference in each plant.

Alarm Views

In addition to the alarmed areas of the process showing on any active screen view, summary lists do have value in analyzing situations and in indicating how well the process or plant is being brought under control. These are not operating views that allow the manipulation of the process, but they should allow the operator to rapidly reach the appropriate view once that area has been determined. There are at least two types of summary displays that can help this process. One is an Alarm Group display for focusing on all the possible alarmed points in a specific group of "instruments" within a specific unit process. The other is an Alarm Sequence Summary display, which scrolls the entire list of current active alarms in chronological order and some order of priority.

Alarm Group

This group is an improvement over a traditional annunciator panel in that it functions as a view of an alarm annunciator list. This is achieved by showing only those functions within a particular cluster or group that are used in a specific unit process. As a limited list, it presents all of the parameters that have alarms "attached," whether or not they are in an alarm condition. The purpose of this display is to allow the operator to quickly recognize some pattern of what is being alarmed versus what is not. The list is always presented in the same order, pre-configured so the patterns become obvious.

For example, by seeing all of the important parameters in the group, whether in alarm or not, the operator can view any alarm within the context of related possible alarms. If he or she sees three particular parameters in alarm, this may suggest a different response than if he or she saw four alarms in some other parameter combination.

The Alarm Group display contains a Group Acknowledge button that acknowledges all unacknowledged alarms on that page. It also allows the operator to invoke access to any "instrument" in that group with a single keystroke. That "instrument" may possibly be shown in several operating views. In that case the plant engineer had already configured the "button" on this display to take the operator to the specific view appropriate for this circumstance. Each parameter in the list shows process tag, descriptor, status/value, and alarm limit point and provides the ability to access that specific parameter within its assigned operating group.

When showing an alarm descriptor text, never have any of that text flash upon alarm! Flashing text is very difficult to read and could cause misidentification. Instead, flash some adjacent icon.

Alarm Sequence Summary List

This list is also an improvement over the traditional annunciator panel because it provides a "first-out" recognition, which can be a significant aid in the analysis for corrective action. By showing alarms in their order of priority and in their order of occurrence within each priority, this list can help the operator focus on the most important activities needed to bring the process or plant back to normal.

Designed to function in a manner consistent with the Alarm Group, The Alarm Sequence Summary list allows the operator to invoke access to any "instrument" in that group with a single keystroke. Because that "instrument" may possibly be shown in several operating views, this action takes the operator to the specific view appropriate for this circumstance. Each parameter in the list shows process tag, descriptor, status/value, and alarm limit point, and provides the ability to access that specific parameter within its assigned operating group. Ideally, it should also allow the operator to quickly access the alarm group of the selected alarmed parameter for additional analysis, if needed.

Operator Actions

Misunderstood by managers and operators alike, the sensitive area of operator actions must be considered. This function should not really be used to "check up on the operators." Yes, of course, like flight recorders on airplanes, there should be some analysis of the loss of costly product and production time. Many times you want the information *particularly* when the operator did everything according to training. The technique may be better used to determine if the sequence of actions is *always* appropriate or if the information provided to the operator gives the *proper* understanding of the problem. It may even be possible that you want to study the information gathered during normal operations, with no unnatural events, in order to explore more productive ways to accomplish plant goals. Sometimes this provides a closer *understanding* of the process!

Many people may know their process, but few truly *understand* it!

Traditionally, operator actions were gathered on printers blended with alarm summaries. Because unique uses of memory media may preclude the need for dedicated printers, consider reserving the alarm list and all of the information on different memory files. For example, when an alarm occurs, the events, alarms, diagnostics, and operator actions can each be placed in a different part of memory. There is no need to "connect" many different files of data until needed. Later search, recall, and sort using structured query language (SQL) tactics, and then print out very appropriate lists based upon specific requests. This is far better than trying to guess what is needed beforehand or having some printer keep up with the action at the plant at the time of an upset

Evaluating Alarm Structures

Once an alarm structure is established, carefully investigate if all the significant alarms are highlighted. Are less important alarms de-emphasized? As plant alarms occur, some more important alarms should show up over the less important ones, perhaps some that were not even made visible to the operator. Many times when a process goes into upset, there is a significant cause that must be fixed and several resultant alarms that become unimportant once that cause is fixed. When the level drops the temperature will rise, or perhaps the pressure drops off. Did the pressure and temperature change because the level dropped? If so, the alarms for level might be ahead of the alarms for temperature or even pressure. That does not mean the other alarms shouldn't be there. There may be *other* reasons why the pressure is wrong or the temperature is wrong. If level isn't one of them, however, then different reasons can be deduced from this combination.

It may be possible for the plant engineer to determine what combinations of temperature, pressure, and flow about that vessel will give the operator different reasons to react. Using today's technology, it is rather easy to couple these alarm conditions to an IF-THEN-ELSE gate structure, so you can determine which kind of information to present to the operator, and probably even give the operator some suggestions on how to fix it. For example, if the temperature begins to go into a change, the pressure drops, and the floor is wet, it is reasonable to conclude that the vessel ruptured.

Another consideration is the following: Do the related alarms clear when the prime cause is cleared? Or does the operator have to reset all of the individual alarms once he or she fixes the problem? Again, it depends on the plant, the requirements of the process, the necessity for operating safely, and environmental conditions, but suppressed alarms should be considered.

Evaluation of Alarm Structures

- Is the alarm scheme simple?
  - —Are significant alarms highlighted?
  - —Are less important alarms de-emphasized?
  - —Does it avoid more complexity than is needed?
- Do related alarms clear when the prime cause is cleared?
- Is the alarm pattern current and expected? (Cross-coupled process units, etc.)
- Are all expected alarms activated?
- Is the hierarchy based on process cycle?
  - —Enables the operator to orient the analysis of operations
  - —Helps the operator to follow upset through plant

Something else you want to consider in the alarm structure is the following: Is the alarm pattern current and expected? Cross-coupled process units, for example, could have one unit can go down, thus dragging a few other units with it. What kinds of problems can develop in your plant? Try to anticipate these when you construct the alarm structure so the operator doesn't go out of his mind. Remember, because of the microprocessor and the thorough software in function blocks offered by many vendors, it is now possible to alarm many more parameters than it used to be. Don't just throw alarms around indiscriminately, just because you can do it. You will rapidly discover a system clogged with far more alarms than will be useful.

In your alarm scheme, is there a way of knowing that all the expected alarms are actually activated? It would be helpful to have some kind of a signal, a warning if an alarm is deactivated, say, for maintenance, or for partial plant shutdown. Occurring during the start-up procedure, the signal would remind the engineers or operators which alarms have been deactivated and should be returned. Consider an interlock during a shutdown procedure that automatically pulls alarms "off the air," anticipating that they will go out of range during that shutdown. Upon start-up, the interlock can automatically engage the alarms after the normal operating conditions are reached, so the alarms don't go off unnecessarily.

Alarm presentation methods and "ordinary" operator screen views are very personal to each process or plant. There are no formulas that you can use. Each screen and its relationship to all the others must be very carefully thought out.

Is the alarm display hierarchy based on process cycle? If so, this enables the operator to orient the analysis of an operation. The operator can follow upset throughout the plant if the alarm structure fits the approach or technique used by the process itself. Keep in mind that in all screen views, the goal for human-machine interface (HMI) is to provide information, not data, to allow the user to interact with the process, not with just the equipment that he or she is using to operate the process.

Alarm Philosophy and Other Thoughts

A critical aspect of the operator interface is the alarm capability provided by the control system. In panel board systems, the alarm took the form of standard annunciators, which were a set of rear-lit and labeled lamps, each of which would indicate the alarm status of a single point. In typical practice, these annunciators would be mounted on the top of control panels, so they were easily seen from anywhere in the room. All these alarmed points would be clearly visible to the operators at all times.

With the conversion to a video screen-based control system, the alarms were buried the control system and were indicated on the video displays through the use of color, flashing background, and so on. In the earlier distributed control system, the "old" physical annunciators remained part of the control room. More recently, the trend has been to eliminate these annunciators and rely exclusively on the video display. Because of this, some consideration must be given to how these alarms are incorporated in that video display.

One problem with incorporating the alarms into the control system is that with no additional cost per alarm, the user can, and often does, use too many of them. Another rather disturbing aspect of this trend is not the elimination of the panel board annunciators nor is it the total reliance on the screen. The real concern is to fail to realize the full significance of this change in medium! (Remember our comments earlier: the medium is the message!)

Relying totally on the screen presents several challenges. That doesn't mean we shouldn't use the screen only, although there are many who advocate using the alarm annunciator panel as well. However, what you must overcome by incorporating them only in the video screen is that by doing so makes it difficult for the operator to see an alarm *quickly*.

The operator should not have to be the manager of alarms. Computers do that to assist the operator in making decisions.

Usually, the operator will receive an audible alarm, then have to select a target or push a button to bring up the display in order to view that alarm. When several alarms occur at once, as is typically the case, the time required to view them can be excessive. This is in contrast with the alarm annunciator, which is visible at all times. This limitation could be overcome with proper establishment of alarm hierarchies and the creative presentation of alarms in the screen. It also can be overcome by moving the alarm annunciator panel into an adjacent monitor that is dedicated only to alarms. It is all a matter of what is appropriate to the individual plant.

In the situation where the distributed system has too many alarms configured, upon upset the operator is presented with an avalanche of alarms. This large quantity of alarms often overwhelms the operator, and he or she loses sight of the most important ones. The reason for this again is that there is no limit on and no cost for the alarms in the control systems. Often during the configuration, control engineers are presented with choices of alarms for every loop, which requires much psychological effort to leave an alarm off. An annunciator panel, on the other hand, requires the user to carefully choose which points are to be alarms based on space available, number of points, cost, and the difficulty of adding points. This discipline typically keeps the use of the annunciator panel down to a more reasonable level.

Again, the issue is good presentation using video displays. Limiting someone to a piece of hardware is not going to control his or her use of alarms, but using very good discipline in acting *as if* you had to buy each potential line may help determine which alarms are important. There are powerful tools available today for properly deploying alarms with a hardy variation of interactions and interlocks to block out unnecessary alarms. Furthermore, these also afford far more operator notification and information than panel board displays could ever do. Eliminating alarms is not always the answer; the answer is the proper management of alarms.

Overall System Display Structures 21

Many "shrink-wrapped" software packages have been emerging during the 1990s that offer magnificent graphics capabilities for control systems. These packages first emerged for use in PCs connected to PLCs and analytical systems, which needed some data acquisition activity, logging, spreadsheets, and reporting. Very quickly, they added the capability for on-off control switches as well as indicators on the screen for monitoring both analog and discrete values. Because of the initial limitations of PCs, these generally were not suitable for any but the most basic process control. The greater need was for PLC interfaces, which in the past were little understood or rarely deemed necessary by PLC vendors. Keep in mind that over 70 percent of the sales of PLCs during this time were for factory automation, not process control.

Dilemma of Flexibility

The changing capabilities of PLCs along with their more varied uses spurred the vendors of graphics packages into offering many more options and capabilities. As has happened in all products, the asymptotically improving power of microprocessors along with ever larger memory capacities have made possible tremendous changes in these graphics packages. The volume of sales they have enjoyed has been bringing down prices, making them more economical for a wider number of users. In turn, more elaborate graphics icons have been developed, permitting some very thorough and attractive displays.

Be Aware of the Trade-offs

- Graphic density versus screen response time
- Endless flexibility versus solid structure

Because these graphics packages were first used with PLCs, as with PLC vendors they were not provided with structures focused on any particular industry. Thus, application knowledge of any of the process industries has never been the strong suite of PLCs or graphics packages. Pictures of piping and process vessels are not the same as an understanding of the needs of the industry. We talked about the differences between the discrete industries and the process industries in Chapter 1. Circumstances such as those posed by PLCs and graphics packages is where the differences between the two industries come out.

PLCs and their graphic software packages have always been rather "free form" in approach, which accounts for their successes in the industries where they originated. DCSs, on the other hand, come out of a world of controller structures and faceplates both of which have been so necessary for the implementation of many process control needs. The many subtleties of real-time very much impact the process world, and process relationships tend to be complex. (Recall our earlier comments? process control is an art!) For the first DCSs to be accepted, the vendors mimicked the instrumentation hardware used at the time. As a result, the only software designs that were practical to meet those performance and safety requirements had to be quite proprietary.

For this reason, proprietary DCSs for process industries have been highly structured and as the preceding chapters have shown, have some very strict caveats. Process control system users have looked to the many wonders of the graphics software packages with considerable envy. As the proprietary distributed systems become more open and the "shrink-wrapped" capabilities have emerged into these process control systems, some real graphics dilemmas have occurred. So many things to want, and so many traps to fall into! Having such a large toolbox is very much like having pencil, paper, and a dictionary full of words but no lessons about sentence structures or grammar! It is not about telling the user what to write (content) but helping him or her learn how to write (structure). This chapter will at least attempt to consider the "grammar" of the system.

Important Rule for Constructing Display Structures

It is most important in any screen design and multiple screen hierarchies that there should be one overriding rule. We said it in an earlier chapter, but it is important enough to be said again: the operator must always see the alarm activity.

Rule for Constructing Display Structures

From whatever screen view within any system, the operator must always see the alarm activity and have direct access to any other operating view, alarm analysis view(s), and process tagged point in the system without "climbing" through any hierarchies of screen views!

How to achieve this from system to system will usually require some creativity on the part of the system designer. Again, not all systems are alike. There is a trend, however, for features and capabilities that have become popular with users to be made available by several vendors. This process often begins by way of pressures by users through system specifications, which, if seen often enough, influence each vendors' design efforts.

Several ways to achieve this rule have been attempted. Most earlier systems have used dedicated operator keyboards. The disadvantage here is that their relative low volume made them very costly, and they were often a compromise at best. Again, the advent of the many technologies made available by PCs and the software creations that have been a part of that, have opened a few doors.

Use of "Always-on-top" Screens

Using a windowing technology, it is possible to create a "master window" that always stays on "top" of all other activities and can never be suppressed. Sometimes this video screen window takes the form of a bar or banner that can be placed across the top or bottom of the screen. One vendor of custom displays allows a bar to move to the top for one class of actions and to the bottom for another. Nevertheless, the idea of a banner can permit a set of dedicated actions yet allows, choices for the user that would be expensive to offer if they were in hardware form.

The examples shown in Figures 21-1 and 21-2 are two versions of the same banner, both of which permit the user to configure special-function buttons specific to whatever is appropriate to the process or plant the system is running. The user may also switch between them, depending upon the functions needed at the time. (In our discussion, you may also wish to refer to Figure 21-3).

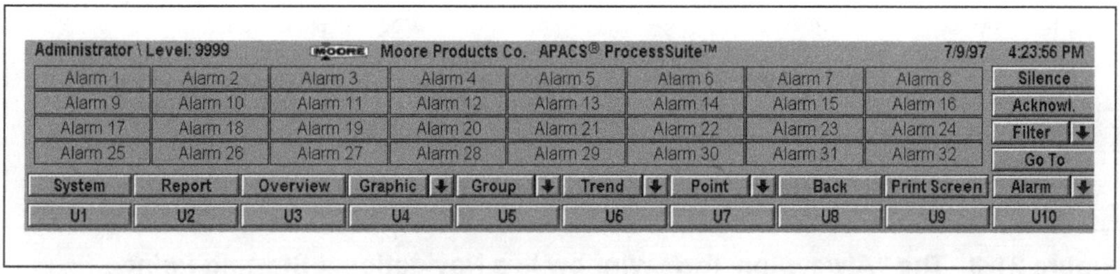

Figure 21-1. "Always-on-Top-of-Screens" Window is Like a Dedicated Keyboard

(Courtesy of Moore Products Co.)

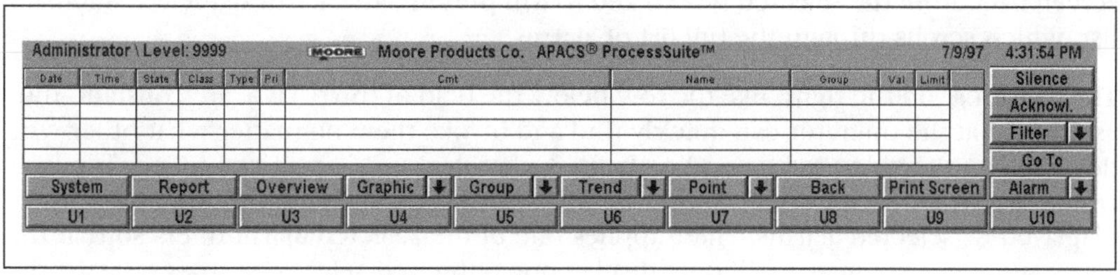

Figure 21-2. "Top-Five-Alarms" Variation of Same "Top-of-Screens" Window

(Courtesy of Moore Products Co.)

In one, there is a bank of thirty-two "rear-lit buttons" that may be configured with whatever message the user wishes, which will be lit when an alarm is active and flash when unacknowledged. They represent an alarm annunciator panel showing the "top" most important groups of "instruments" for which that shift operator has responsibility. When one of these "buttons" is invoked, it presents the most appropriate (preconfigured) alarm group screen display in which that point occurs.

Out of the row of "buttons" below this field, there are Graphic, Group, and Trend. If one of these is invoked just before one of the thirty-two in the field, then the view presented will be the appropriate graphical operating display, group faceplate display, or trend display that this group identity represents. The Overview presents just that, and

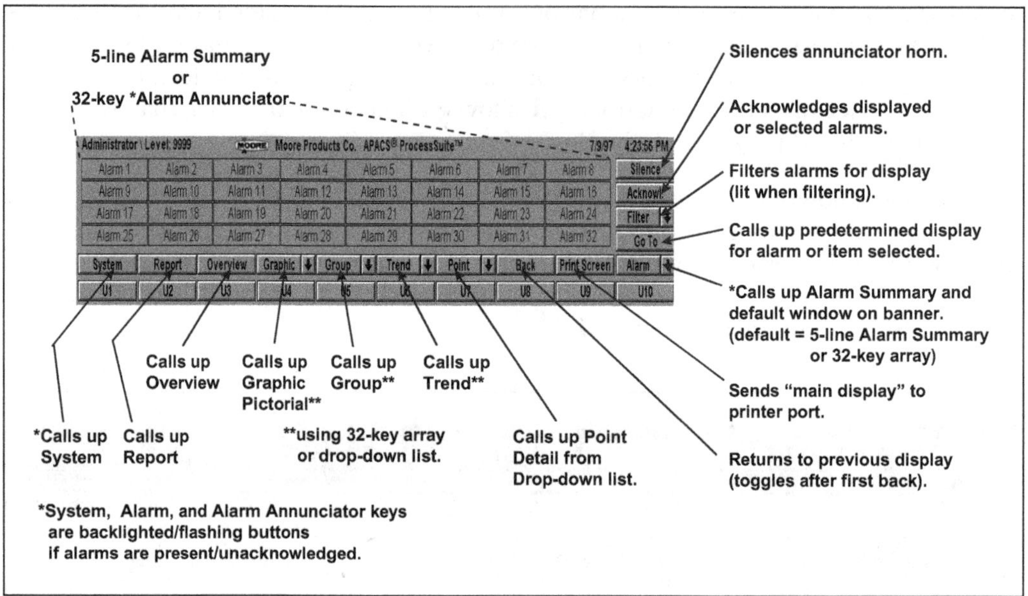

Figure 21-3. The "Always-on-Top" Window Is a Navigational Starting Point

System, which will be lit or will flash if there is a problem anywhere in the control system itself, presents a screen view of diagnostics and performance. Back toggles one screen back from the selected screen and Alarm presents the alarm sequence summary list, which scrolls through the full list of alarms.

The "buttons" on the right, like the row below the field of thirty-two, are constant, thus assuring that the operator can quickly find and invoke them no matter what other windows are on the video screen and no matter what degree of upset emergency is occurring. Silence stops the audio annunciation and Acknowledge stops the flashing of displayed or selected alarms. Filter applies one of the selected alarm filters so that the alarm sequence summary will only display preconfigured selections so as to assist the analysis of situation. The downward arrow causes a "drop-down" display of the available filters that may be selected. The filter "button" is lit when the filter is active.

Graphic, Group, Trend and Alarm all have "drop-down" lists of complete selections available. Highlighting one of the lists will present the appropriate display, allowing complete access to anything in the system, regardless of the hierarchy of views or main field of interest. The remaining ten "buttons" can be configured by the user as needed for any specific function required from this "always-in-view" screen display called a banner.

At the users' option variation of this banner is to present a list of the top five alarms from the alarm sequence summary, which will scroll through the entire list if desired. This is a preferred view for many industries using batch operations, because it allows operator alert messages to be blended into the list to support timely reminders to the operators for selected actions in the proper sequence. This is especially helpful in operations in which long delays exist. The field of annunciator "buttons" will appear for a preconfigured length of time when the operator invokes one of the Graphic,

Group, Trend or Alarm "buttons" described earlier to direct access to any of those views.

It is important to note here that when an operator arrives on shift and enters the assigned password, the assigned "instruments" can be "unlocked" for manipulation to the level cleared for that operator. Also the appropriate banner specific to each operator can be employed if the user desires.

The arrangement shown in Figure 21-3 is but one DCS vendor's approach to providing some structure to a process control system and saving its clients considerable time in implementing screen navigation. That vendor supplies this structure for the clients to use as is and allows the user to later modify it as they see fit with no limitation. It is offered as a "starter kit" just to get the user off the ground and to use for generating ideas. The approach is no different than Microsoft offering "templates" of letters, forms, slide presentations, spreadsheets, and the like. Users are free to build their own versions in whatever format they wish, but by using the supplied templates they can also produce documents on the first day they purchase their computer and software package! Expect to see many more control vendors provide this type of functionality.

The approach shown in Figure 21-3 for banner content and functions and for screen hierarchies shown in Figure 21-4 can also be implemented by the many "shrink-wrapped" packages, but they often must be created from their many individual parts and features. Some vendors may provide a "process control-friendly" structure with their system to speed users' implementation.

Simplified Hierarchy

This screen view hierarchy provides information at summary level, which guides you through various access methods to reach the operating level and detail level appropriate to the needs of the situation. Provision is made for rapid, consistent and unambiguous navigation throughout the hierarchy. Process operators will spend most of their time at the operating level with some use of the Overview (perhaps at the beginning of the shift), System status, Reports, and the Alarm Sequence Summary, which should show the time sequence of alarm occurrence.

In Figure 21-4, the numbers and types of screens are merely arbitrary to show the concept. Large plants and complex processes will, of course, require more, but this arrangement is presented to create ideas not to present "the definitive" approach. The use of group views showing all "faceplates" allow rapid implementation of the system. Once the process is up and operating, appropriate graphical views can be created, their content sometimes significantly improved only after operators become familiar with the expected operations.

Many users very successfully involve operators in the creation of these graphic views. The idea is becoming more and more popular. The use of an operator password makes it possible for each operator to have some views uniquely designed to their preferences, although they may be functionally identical to required operations. The same

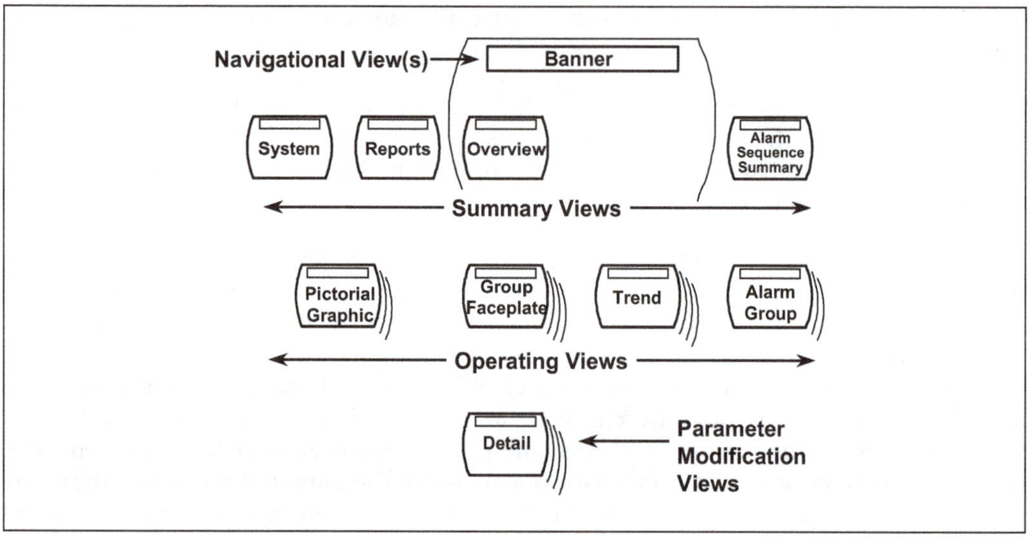

Figure 21-4. Simplified Look at Hierarchy "Layers"

approach can also adjust operating access for assigned portions of the process or plant as well as for job function, skill level, and training.

In Figure 21-4, System is the status of the control system itself, including the condition of each of its components, such as controllers, input modules, output modules, and the like. The Alarm Sequence summary shown in this particular example, displays the sequence of any alarms in the system, when they occur, and when they return to normal. This differs from the Alarm Group views of this particular example, which exist for each Group display and show all of the possible alarms that are identified for (only) that group, whether they are in an alarm condition or not. All of the possible alarms of this group are arranged in a fixed pattern, *functionally* much like the alarm annunciator boards in the past. In this way, the operator can quickly glance at the condition of the alarms, using pattern recognition as one way to analyze any upset.

Navigation through Hierarchies

Consistent access to functions and screen views is assured by having the banner view always automatically "on top" and ensuring that the "button" functions on it are always the same. A dedicated button gives "single keystroke" callup of Alarm Sequence Summary or Alarm Group and two keystroke callup of all-important operating displays (pictorial graphics, faceplate groups, trends). See the discussion under "Use of 'Always On Top' Screens," earlier in this chapter.

In Figure 21-5 we see all the operating displays may also be selected quickly through drop-down lists, without "climb through" hierarchies. Point detail displays can rapidly be invoked by loop tag name and by "hot spot" selection on pictorial graphics and faceplate groups as well as directly through "drop-down" list on banner.

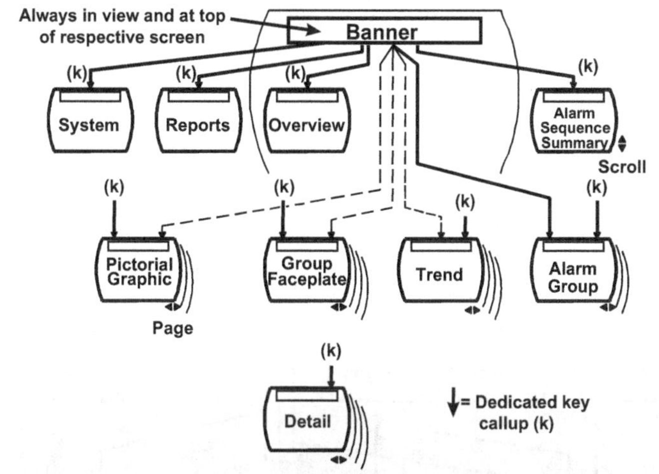

Figure 21-5. Navigation through Displays with Dedicated "Keys" in Banner

Figure 21-6 shows "Hot spots" within the screen view provide rapid navigation directly to the desired pictorial or faceplate display so the operator can take corrective action. "Hot spots" also allow you to rapidly drill down into detail displays for all of the more specific information about any "instrument." Using "hot spots" that are designed into each view can also furnish direct (single keystroke) access to any appropriate related views.

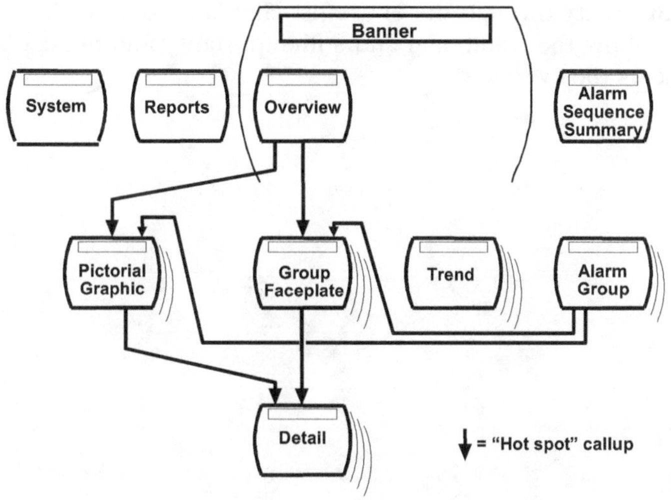

Figure 21-6. Navigation through Displays Using "Hot Spots"

Figure 21-7 shows all navigational methods combined, using all of the navigational approaches to the various displays in a consistent way:

- dedicated keys
- hot spots
- pulldown lists (group names, loop tagnames etc.)

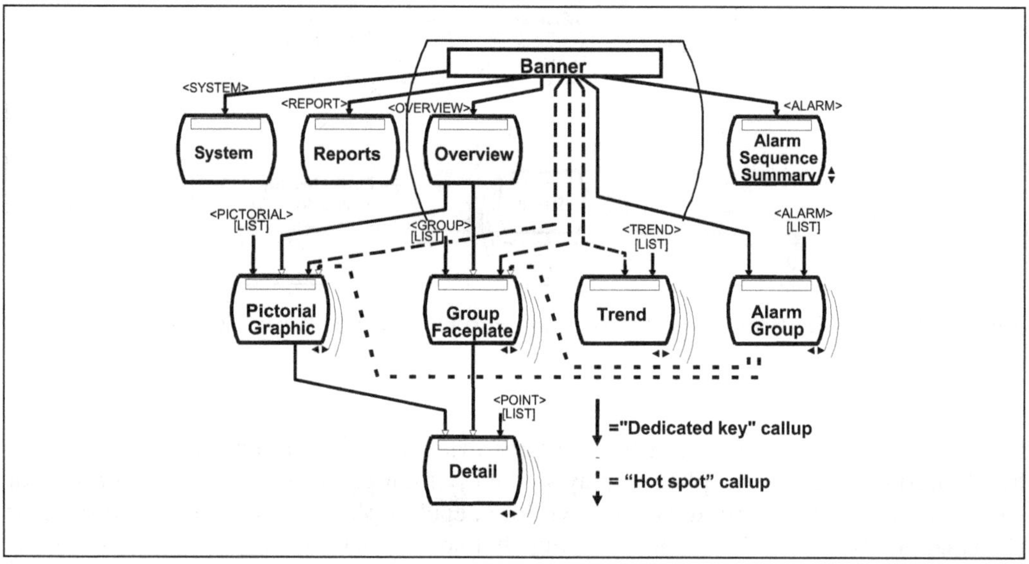

Figure 21-7. Full Navigation through Displays with both "Keys" and "Hot Spots"

Also note the use of small up/down arrows at the Alarm Sequence Summary display to indicate scrolling ability through the entire list. Similar, "back/forth" arrows in all the operating views allow the traditional and still-important "tour-of-the-plant" capability, which supplements the overview.

Part E

Networks

More Nuts and Bolts 22

Before getting into our discussions on topologies, protocols, media access, open systems, and fieldbus, it will be helpful again to brush up on some more nuts and bolts for those not generally exposed to this technology. Those of you who already work in this field can skip this chapter, unless you wish to be amused by my efforts at simple analogies. It is the area in which I get the most curious questions in class.

The Nature of Digital Communication

The concept of using a single wire to communicate data is not new. In fact it goes back to the use of the Morse code, which is really a form of digital communication. In it's early days they called it dots and dashes. Today, we refer to it as "ones and zeros," or two different energy states. Usually "one" is a higher energy level, and "zero" is lower energy level in this application. In the early days of telegraph, long-distance transmissions required a method for tolerating significant drops in energy levels. Even if the energy level (the sound) was weak, one could still determine when the signal was there and when it was not.

In the United States, one of the first uses of the telegraph was to communicate between railway stations along the nation's many hundreds (later thousands) of miles of track. A communication between the stationmasters at each stop along the line would report the status of the flow of traffic along that railroad. The communication between them was a series of short and long signals representing dots and dashes, called Morse code. Using dots and dashes enabled them to distinguish communication from no noise at all, that is, the users could distinguish between the two energy duration's—the dot and the dash—and a complete disconnect or broken wire.

An Example

The letter *C* in international Morse code is "dash-dot-dash-dot" and the letter *K* in Morse Code is "dash-dot-dash". If I were sending the same two in ASCII (American Standard Code for Information Interchange) code, however, I would send "1001011" for a C and "1000011" for a K. This is because in ASCII it takes seven bits to define a character. Other codes include the five-bit Baudot code, IBM's six-bit Correspondence code, and the eight-bit EBCDIC (Extended Binary Coded Decimal Interchange Code). These are just some of the many variations for defining characters, letters, numerals, and punctuation in different fields of endeavor. Of course, the many codes were each developed for different purposes. Their use would determine how large the space had to be to allow the use of more complex characters or combinations of characters.

Let's go back to our railroad communication again. Let us say the station-master in station 3 wants to tell the station-master in station 7 that the train is coming and that it is necessary to go out and prepare the water tower for refilling the locomotive tender with more water. In Morse code, he might send the message, "This is station 3 calling station 7." Everybody along the line would hear this message, but because he addressed station 7 only the stationmaster at station 7 would stop. He might put his lunch aside, lay down his newspaper, go to his telegrapher's key, and respond "This is station 7, what is your message, station 3?" He thus confirmed that he is connected, which in today's terminology is called "handshaking." Then station 3 would send the message "Go outside and check the level of the water in the tank; the train is coming." Station 7 would respond to Station 3, "You asked me to go out and check the water level in the tank; the train is coming". Station 3, having heard this full reply would know the correct message had gone through, and would give station 7 a message to begin the procedure. Today we call this an "echo check." Station 7 could also have said, "I heard your message of 18 words." Station 3, knowing that Station 7 had heard 18 words, and not 17 or 19, would know that statistically it was very likely that he received the correct message, and it was therefore safe to permit station 7 do the job. If he heard station 7 say some other number, then station 3 would resend the original message.

There are many kinds of checks and balances in sending communication, and they all mimic how humans convey information between each other. We humans continually acknowledge the fact that we receive a message from somebody by using some kind of a feedback signal. In the case of Morse code, the feedback has to be in terms of the Morse code technology. In the case of digital codes of any kind, whether it is ASCII or any other method, the feedback has to be in the terms of that code. This is known as "protocol."

For the protocol on this particular railroad, it might have been decided that there are many times for a station to call another station and ask them to check the water. Perhaps instead of keying in all those characters for all those words and sentences, it would be more efficient to reduce this lengthy string to only two characters. Everybody on that railroad would be taught that perhaps the characters CW would stand for "Check the water." This code stood for the entire procedure, yet communication would move much faster and there would still be no ambiguity. Many other "shorthand" codes would also be developed.

Sometime later, the stationmaster left his job and went to work for another railroad where they also had discovered it was easier to send just two letters. The two letters they picked might have been different however. Maybe they used the code LT for "Look at the tank." That would be considered a different protocol, but it would result in the same series of actions. The new stationmaster would have to learn this new protocol for all of the common signals that this new railroad normally sends.

Learning the protocol is what happens when you mix the communications of a Vendor A with the communications of a Vendor B. They're talking a different language. They may be using the same wire, they may be using the same telegraph keys, they may even be using the same (Morse) communication code, but the significance of that code may differ. There are several "layers" of communication involved, and these must be reflected within any type of digital communication technique that we use. In the following paragraphs, let's look for all the variations those differences can take.

Data Highways and Dirt Roads

Digital communications over a single wire, known as a data highway, have saved in excess of 30 percent of installation costs compared with hardwired connections for the same functions. A single consistent cable throughout a plant site, using one consistent connector, can be connected in only one way. It either is connected or it isn't. The only ordering and installation consideration is whether it's long enough. Installers need to know only "that box connects to this." There are no multiple wires to cross, and no surprises at start-up! The real cost is not in all the wire saved, which in itself can be significant. The savings is in all the cost-per-termination charges and the cost in all the checkout time required for each wire to "ring out" each line.

- Digital communications saves installation costs
  - Less wire, **fewer connections**
  - Less error in the wrong connections!
  - But ... avoid narrow bridges, toll booths, and poor road surfaces and capacities.

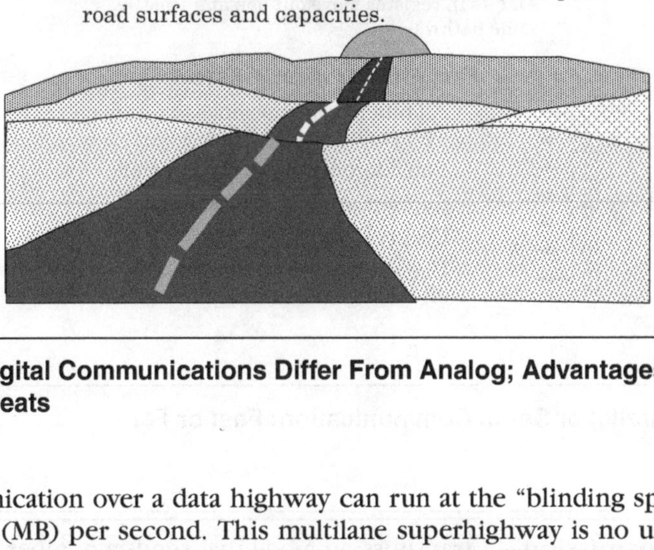

Figure 22-1. Digital Communications Differ From Analog; Advantages, However, Come with Caveats

Digital communication over a data highway can run at the "blinding speed" of 10 and 100 megabytes (MB) per second. This multilane superhighway is no use to you if the only way on or off is through narrow bridges, tollbooths, and poor road surfaces and capacities! Too many routers, bridges, and gateways can impede data flow and be a source of vulnerability. Many recent developments are improving this, but try to avoid sending critical messages through too many links between different networks and protocols. Quite often these networks and protocols must use "store-and-forward" techniques that cause serious delays, and they are not always able to be redundant. These devices will be discussed in more detail in Chapter 25.

Information Transmission

What is being transmitted when one device on a distributed control system (DCS) communicates over a "data highway" (communication cable) with another device? In the final analysis, energy is transmitted. The information exists in the form of binary numbers, a string of ones and zeros. That is the code for a number or a word or a condition. The dots and dashes in the code are actually two different energy durations. Generally, the ones and zeros that are communicated today are actually two different energy levels, such as amplitude differences or frequency differences. These ones and zeros are called "bits," and they are usually stored in-groups of eight or multiples of eight. We now have 16 bit, and 32 bit and even 64 bit transmission.

Energy that at one level defined to represent the one and at another level to represent zero is sent over the communication medium. The form of the message may change several times before it arrives at its destination, but a message always consists of a block of time divided into segments, in each of which there exists a discrete energy level. From now on, we will refer to the transmission of bits but each bit is represented by an energy state. Since time is a factor, there will always be some sort of clock keeping tabs on the message transmission.

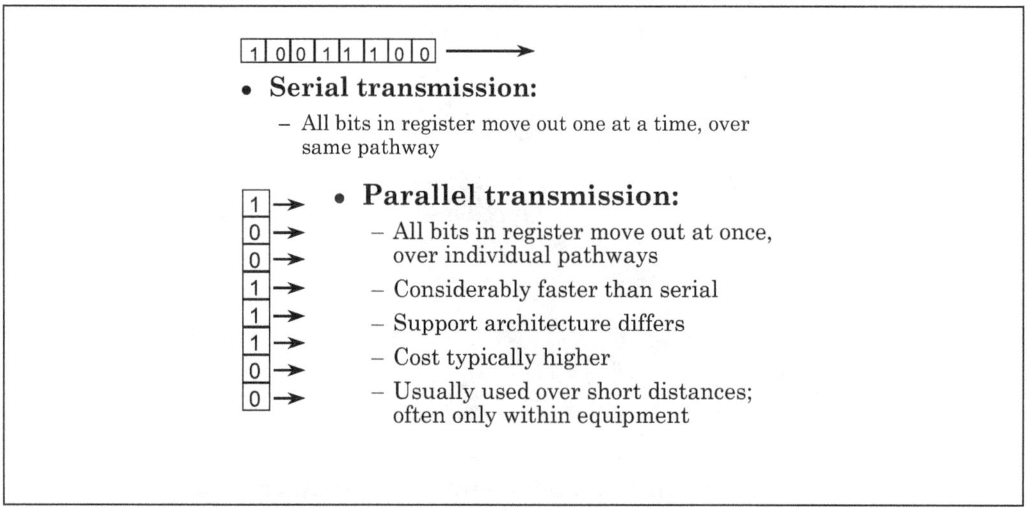

Figure 22-2. Parallel or Serial Communication: Fast or Far

Parallel Transmission—A transmission mode that sends a number of bits simultaneously over separate lines, such as sixteen bits over sixteen lines; usually unidirectional.

Serial Transmission—The most common transmission mode, in which information bits are sent sequentially on a single data channel (wire, radio beam, etc.).

Parallel versus Serial

If the entire sequence of bits can be sent in parallel, the transmission can be very fast. Parallel transmission is often used on printed circuit cards when an entire word is sent over a bus made up of eight (or some multiple of eight) parallel sections. These are usually foils on the printed circuit board, or on the backplane of a controller card cage or other device. Over short distances, ribbon cables, which are flat cables with copper conductors running side by side and insulated from each other with a multipin connector at each end, can carry the signals corresponding to the bits making up a word, in parallel, between devices. For the short distances on a printed circuit card, where so much is happening that time is measured in nanoseconds, parallel transmission is practical and necessary.

Transmission over distances between devices more than a few feet apart becomes prohibitively expensive if a separate wire is used for each bit. Also, there is some loss in energy level as an electrical signal overcomes the resistance of a wire or the conductor, and after a certain distance signals lose strength and must be amplified. The complications involved in amplifying a number of parallel signals and maintaining the relationship between them are great. That is to say, if each of the bits placed into the wire on one side goes a long enough distance, they may not all come out at the other side at the same time. This would impact the significance of that message.

> The complications involved in amplifying a number of parallel signals and maintaining the relationship between them are great. That is to say, if all of the bits are placed into their respective wires on one end of a very long cable of wires the naturally varying individual resistances could easily cause them to reach the other end at different times! This would significantly impact the meaning of the message that is transmitted.

Consequently, most transmission between devices is serial. This means the bits in a register are moved out one at a time sequentially sent on their way, then put back into a register at the other end. For a serial electrical transmission, only two wires are required, one to carry the energy and one to act as a common signal ground. In distributed process control systems (DCS), this has been called the data highway.

Interference with Transmission

Electrical transmission is always subject to the effects of disturbances caused by electrical energy on the wires or near the wires that is not part of the signal being transmitted. In transmission cabling, three types of interference are often encountered. They are magnetic interference, electrostatic interference, and crosstalk.

If a conductor carrying current is near another current-carrying conductor and the current flow in the second conductor changes significantly, there will be a corresponding voltage change in the first conductor. The characteristics of the signal will change because there has been an energy level change. This type of interference is called magnetic interference, because the change in current flow creates a varying magnetic field around the wire. Cables and wire bundles carrying electricity at different power levels or different frequencies should be separated far enough apart to prevent this kind of interference. Some standards call for an eight-inch separation.

An electrical charge resulting from current flow into an inductive device, such as a relay or solenoid coil, or from a welding machine can produce an electrostatic electrical charge on a wire. This introduces spurious signals and can disrupt transmission. Surrounding the wire, or wires, in a cable with conductive shield that can be grounded is one method for reducing this type of interference.

When alternating current (AC) signals or pulsating direct current (DC) signals are transmitted on a pair of multipair cables, it is possible for the signals to be superimposed on other signals carried by adjacent pairs. This is called crosstalk. To help prevent this, each pair in a cable may be twisted and shielded. The twisting will cancel out the unwanted signals, and the shield will carry them to ground.

Another type of problem arises when different points of the circuit are of different ground potentials. When this happens, currents can be circulated from one part of the circuit to another, creating voltages that may be read as significant signals. To eliminate this problem, suppliers require one, and only one, common ground for the electrical system. This is an important requirement and particular attention should be paid to it when equipment from more than one supplier are interconnected in a system. Do not overlook, however, checking equipment from the same supplier as well!

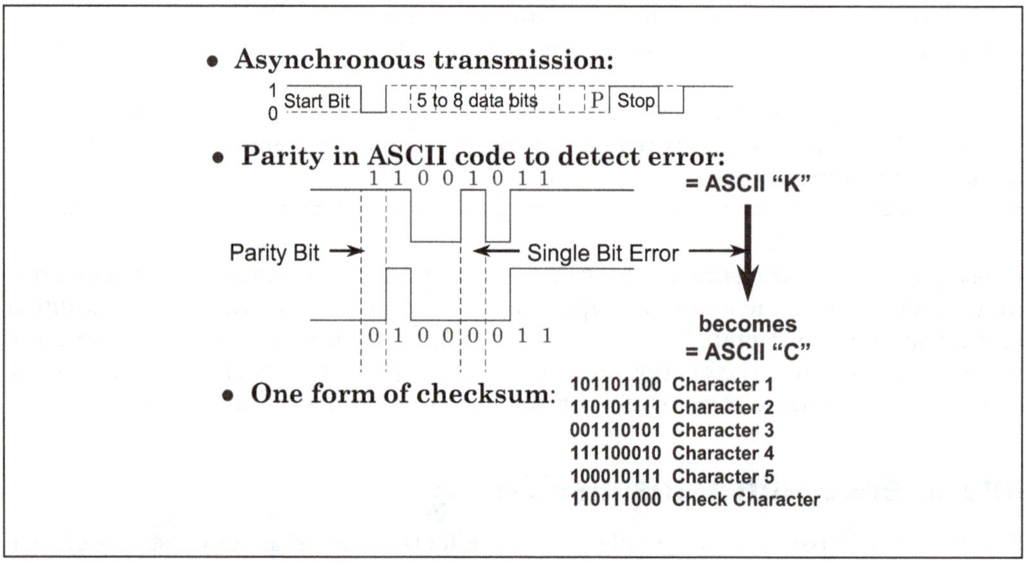

Figure 22-3. Confirming Good Data Transmission

---

asynchronous—Computer logic or communications in which all operations are triggered by a free-running signal not related to specific frequency or timing. Successive stages are triggered by the completion of the preceding stage.

ASCII—[asky] American Standard Code for Information Interchange: Binary character code, each representing a single computer character, to define 128 uppercase and lowercase characters, numerals, punctuation, and special communication control characters. A standard method of encoding characters into seven or eight binary bits, typically 7-bit-plus-parity code, representing alphanumeric data for processing and communication compatibility among various devices. Defined in ANSI X3.4-1986 and normally for asynchronous ransmission.

checksum—The summation of digits or bits according to an arbitrary set of rules used primarily for checking the integrity of data; can detect single bit errors and some multiple bit errors.

parity bit—A bit that is set at "0" or "1" in character to ensure that the total number of 1 bits in the data field is even or odd in digital communication between devices or components.

parity check—The addition of information bits that make up a transmission block to ensure that the number of 1s is always either even (even parity) or odd (odd parity); used to detect digital transmission errors.

Physical Structures 23

Connecting individual devices in the most expedient way is the goal of any network technology. The network should be considered in terms of speed, directness, cost, simplicity, and reliability. Generally, in industrial control systems three popular topologies have been successfully used. They are the star, the bus, and the ring network systems. There are several other network systems used in other industries, but we will not dwell on them, as they are not very common in the current industrial control scene.

In the control of a single industrial process unit, or in a laboratory setting, a network is a system that links a few controllers and perhaps a common operator interface. Different communication requirements are needed to network a plantwide system. There are even different challenges for a system that must reach beyond the plant for long distances, such as you would find in water treatment, power distribution, or gas distribution lines.

Network Topologies

Since the late 1980s, the single loop control networks have been emerging. They, of course, would be the simplest of systems because they were only intended to be used in the laboratory or on an isolated unit process control requirement. In recent times, however, the single loop controllers have been available with multiple loops. More sophisticated control capability is expected on these small systems. They are no longer merely linking a handful of controllers perhaps to a small personal computer (PC) used to manage some reports. In the mid 1990s, this PC has gone beyond report writing to become a local operator station and is even used for configuring other control strategies.

More typical are the network systems associated with traditional distributed control systems (DCSs.) These have generally been designed for large multiunit process control and plantwide control systems. Most of the current topologies have been designed for this scale and grew from systems driven from single mainframe computers. The design of these has had the greatest need for redundancy.

On a larger scale, "traditional" supervisory control and data acquisition (SCADA) systems have been used for control actions and information gathering from *beyond* the plant. For over four decades these "traditional" SCADA systems have not been used in process control but rather in the starting and stopping of remote units, such as those found in remote power transformers or in remote water or gas pumps on pipelines. The communication, quite often, is not through wire, but through radio transmission, phone lines, and even satellites. The time delays on these SCADA systems have usually made it necessary to rely not on monitoring and controlling the details of the process itself from a distance. The "supervisory control" portion of these systems was only expected to merely turn specific units on or off or to bypass units that may have been damaged, for instance, in a storm or in an accident. Any communications of such remote transmissions expected by a SCADA system would have to allow for long time delays between the request for action and the action to happen. This generally precludes any continuous process action, which requires a more responsive operation. As was stated before, do not confuse these comments on SCADA with those on data acquisition and control (DAC) systems used *within* a plant, which some vendors have recently been calling "SCADA."

---

bus—Transmission path or channel; an electrical connection with one or more connectors through which all attached devices receive all transmissions at the same time. In a linear network topology such as Ethernet or token bus, all network nodes "listen" to all transmissions, but each responds only to those addressed to it.

multidrop—A network topology of computing devices or multiple field devices that are connected to one pair of wires, or a coaxial cable, usually attached with "tee-connectors."

ring network—Network topology in which each node is connected to two adjacent nodes, the entire network forming a closed ring; communication between any two points must include the intermediate points.

star—Network topology of computing devices in which each station is connected by communication links radiating out of a central hub that handles all communications.

topology—Logical and/or physical arrangement of stations on a network, such as star, ring, multidrop, tree.

These larger systems, distributed control and SCADA, generally may employ several topology types within the same network. They're generally considered a plant network that is connected by several subnetworks, and these in turn can be connected to other subnetworks. Their structures would depend on the requirements of the environment in which they are to operate. For example, communication between a control room and the rack room, if they are only feet apart as was traditionally the case in older plants with single mainframe computers, would not involve the same requirements as would the more common practice today of having the central control room communicate to distant control stations located in separate rack rooms.

Furthermore, each of the control stations can have a network of input-output (I/O) terminals. Initially, the (I/Os) were analog up through to the controller. Today, with the many smart sensors, transmitters, and final elements, these networks are frequently digital.

Additional links from the control room to a plantwide network of business management computers usually require another network. These do not need the speed of process loops but rather the capacity of a large information-handling system.

As a result, in this plantwide system there are many small local I/Os with relatively low volume of data in each, but response times must be in microseconds. On the other end of the same system, the business management side of the plant requires large volumes of data, but the response time can be in hours or even days or beyond. As a result, the topology, the immediate access technique, and the protocols used will differ on each portion of this system (within each subsystem).

Star Topology

This method, shown in Figure 23-1, is the simplest and therefore the least expensive of the topologies we will be discussing here. In this technique, a single active switching device can be viewed as the center of the system, and it has a link to each of the control system components. This control system component can be an active loop for a discrete control station and/or it can be an operator station. It could be that each of those controllers has an operator interface incorporated in it or it could be that one of the devices is a centralized operator station for managing each of the other controllers. In the latter, quite frequently the operator station is incorporated with the central active switching device.

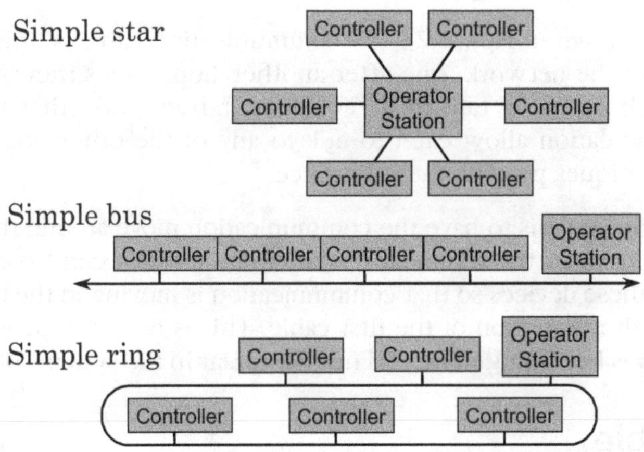

Figure 23-1. Many Control Systems Have Combinations of These Network Topologies

Usually, these systems are not redundant and redundancy starts to increase their price. They are often used so that each of the control elements can operate independently and are not required to communicate all the time. In this way, they can tolerate a loss of communication for a short or even a prolonged period of time. Such a system is probably more suitable for a small laboratory or a single isolated unit process, which normally would not be connected to the rest of the plant. Of course, each of these systems can also be a subnetwork of a larger system. In this case, the larger system would be connected through that central active switching device.

In an attempt to overcome some of the disadvantages of the star topology, a mesh topology has been developed in which each of these devices on the network has its own switching device within and provides communication between every device one to one. This causes a crosshatch of communication, with each box having a single link to each of the other boxes, giving the "mesh" appearance but, of course, increasing the complexity and naturally the cost. The mesh improves the security of the system, but it certainly is not the most expedient way to do this in today's technology, so it is rarely seen in industrial process control.

Bus Topology

In this topology, shown in Figure 23-1, all the messages pass through a common piece of hardware like the star topology, but this common piece of hardware is passive, generally a single wire or a communication cable. The active switching occurs in each of the elements on the bus. There are versions of this which there is a switching device called a traffic director as a separate device on this system, and we'll discuss that when we discuss media access protocols in Chapter 24. As with the star topology, there is a vulnerability should the bus fail. There are methods in this system, however, for a redundant bus that do not involve that cost disadvantage of the redundancy put into the star. Sometimes this bus topology has been called multidrop systems.

Ring or Loop Topology

In this approach, shown in Figure 23-1, a communication cable is linked to each of the control devices on the network, one after another. Sometimes they are daisy chained, meaning that each can only talk to its adjacent station, and other times other techniques of communication allow each to talk to any of the other boxes. Protocols and media access techniques provide the difference.

The simplest arrangement is to have the communication move around the loop in a single direction. Quite often, in the redundant version, an active second communication ring connects each of these devices so that communication is moving in the opposite direction simultaneously with the motion of the first cable. This is not an expensive technique for redundancy and was becoming more and more popular in the systems of the 1990s.

Network Cable

Local and global networks for process control systems are made of electrical wire cable or a fiber optic cable. Electrical wire cables commonly used in the industrial environment include twisted pairs, coaxial, and twinaxial cable (Figure 23-2).

UTP—Unshielded twisted pair: Wiring for signals consisting of at least two conductors twisted together six twists per inch to minimize the effects of electromagnetic radiation between them but without a metal covering to protect it from external EMI or RFI.

STP—Shielded twisted pair: Wiring for signals with at least two conductors twisted together six twists per inch to minimize the effects of electromagnetic radiation between them and covered with metal-backed Mylar, plastic, PVC, or metal-woven sleeve for protection from external EMI and RFI.

coax—Coaxial cable: Popular transmission medium that is formed from two or more coaxial cylindrical conductors insulated from each other. The outermost conductor is usually grounded and encased in either wire mesh or extruded metal sheathing. It is frequently used for television and radio signals as well as digital signals because its design is less likely to cause or be affected by external fields. Many varieties are available depending upon the shielding needed and the voltages/frequencies to be accommodated.

twinax—Twinaxial cable: Uses a twisted pair of conductors within shielding to improve resistance to RFI/EMI over coaxial cable; see coax.

fiber optics—Transmission technology in which modulated light wave signals, generated by laser or LED, are propagated along a (typically) glass or plastic medium, then demodulated to electrical signals by a light-sensitive receiver.

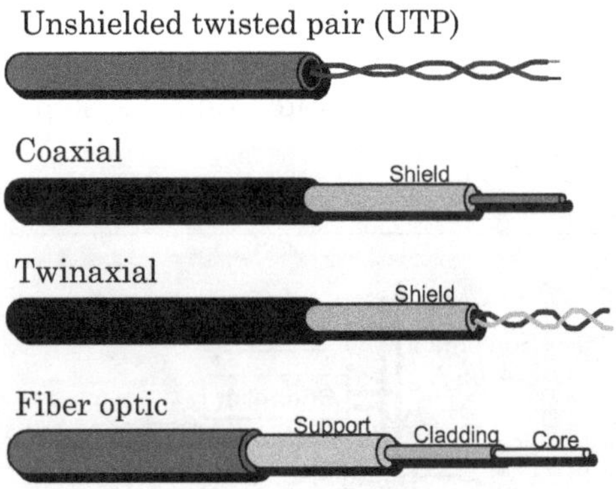

Figure 23-2. Most Popular Cable Types Used in Control Systems

As described earlier, twisted pairs reduce cross-talk and each pair is usually shielded so that magnetic and electrostatic interference is reduced. A shield may be a woven metallic wire or a metallized polyester material. It is usually combined with a drain wire that can be terminated at a ground connection. A number of twisted pairs can be combined into a cable, and it is a good idea to include extra pairs in the cable to accommodate circuits that may have to be added after installation is complete. Twisted pairs are less expensive than the other types of network cable materials, but their range is also less because of attenuation as well as capacitance effects.

Coaxial cable must be handled carefully when it is installed. If the outer tube is bent or crimped, the cable can be changed, degrading the signal.

Coaxial cable has a central conductor surrounded by an outer tube like conductor. The outer conductor, or shield, is used as the common signal ground. It has distinct advantages over twisted-pair conductors when high frequencies and high bandwidth are characteristics of the transmission system. Bandwidth is a function of the number of signals that can be handled by a network in a given period of time. The loading factor of coaxial cable is the attenuation due to conductor loss and dielectric loss. Coaxial cable must be handled carefully when it's installed; if the outer tube is bent or crimped the impedance of the cable can be changed, degrading the signal. Properly installed, it has a long useful life and can carry large amounts of information over long distances. A variation of coaxial cable called Twinax provides two coaxial cables in a single jacket. Twinaxial cable provides more shielding from noise than coaxial cable and is more expensive.

Coaxial cable does a very acceptable job as a communication network media. It is more expensive than twisted pairs but less expensive than a glass cable. Why do fiber optics merit consideration? Significant is the fact that the optical fiber cable does not carry electricity and eliminates all the problems inherent in interference with electrical transmission (Figures 23-3 and 23-4). There are no ground loops or common load voltage problems. Electrical noise is not a problem. There is no inductive pickup, cross-talk or interference from transients. It will not "short out" in puddles and is far more resistant to chemical corrosion than any metal carrier. The cable is lighter and easier to handle than electrical cable, making it far easier to hang on poles and to pull through wire trays and other passages. Under most conditions, there is little possibility of a spark in explosive and inflammable environments (Protection in hazardous areas is governed by energy levels. The energy needed to operate control systems is rarely as high as that needed for interstate phone systems.)

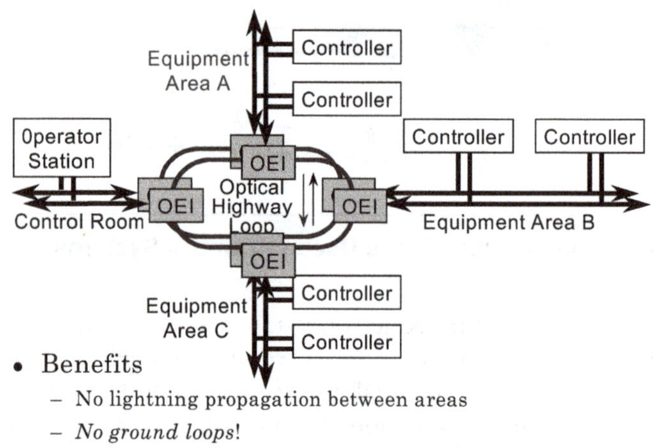

Figure 23-3. Non-Electrical Network Provides Signal Protection

Interestingly enough, because there is no electricity fiber-optic cable is not subject to electrical codes nor must it be installed by electrical crafts. The skill level for installation is very much the same as for coaxial cable. Today, splicing and terminations are done just as easily. Phone companies have laid fiber optic around the world using local labor.

More on Fiber Optics

Fiber-optic communications have been used in control systems since the early 1980s. Glass fibers instead of copper or aluminum wires are the conductor, but energy is still what is being conducted. Instead of electrical energy, light is transmitted in pulses. These pulses can be at different frequencies, and this produces a bit of information. A high frequency, a low frequency, and a neutral frequency (carrier wave) are used to distinguish the bits. Rather than detect absolute voltage levels, the receiving circuit needs only to detect the number of zero crossings in a given time to determine the state of the transmitted bit. Light energy travels at the same speed as electrical energy in this

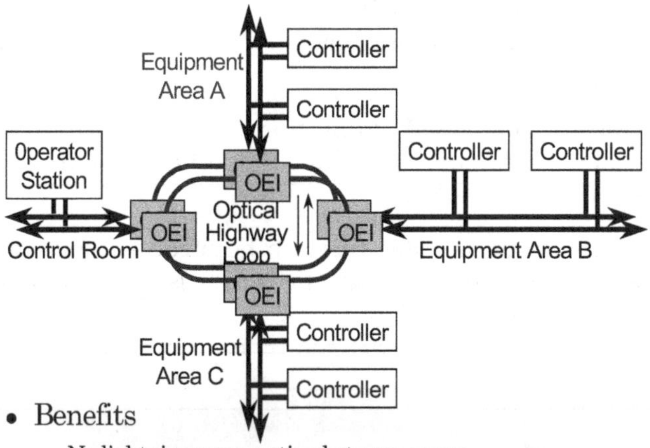

- Benefits
  - No lightning propagation between areas
  - *No ground loops!*

Figure 23-4. Used *Between* Cabinets, Each of Which Has Protection For Their Contents

condition and can represent binary data equally well. (Speed of light is far slower in a medium like glass than in a vacuum, and the more significant limitation in fiber optics is the electronics at either end of the length.)

Once a pulse of light enters a glass fiber, it cannot leave until it gets to the other end. When light travels from one material to another, it bends. A straight rod stuck into clear water appears to bend below the surface of the water because the light carrying the image passes from liquid to air. The bending is a function of a measure called refractive index (Figure 23-5). If the light travels from a material with a high refractive index to one with a low refractive index, it will not pass through the interface, but bounce back, reflected from the surface back into the original material. By making glass fibers with a high-refractive-index inner core, and a low-refractive-index outer sheath, light can effectively be confined in a rod, escaping only at the end. There are many medical applications for this phenomenon.

---

fiber loss—Attenuation (deterioration) of light signal in optical fiber transmission.

graded index fiber—Optical fiber whose core has a non-uniform index of refraction; the core is composed of concentric rings of glass whose refractive indices decrease from the center axis to reduce modal dispersion and thereby increase fiber bandwidth.

refractive index—Ratio of the phase velocity of light in a vacuum to that in a specified medium.

optical fiber—Any filament or fiber made of dielectric materials and consisting of a core to carry the light signal and surrounding cladding that reflects the signal back into the core. A thin glass thread is most commonly used, but plastic fiber can also be chosen.

bend loss—A form of increased attenuation in optical fiber that results from bending fiber around restrictive curvature (microbend) or from minute distortions in that fi**ber (microbends).**

bend radius—Smallest arc in cable that can be made without causing damage; fiber-optic cable is no worse than coax. In fact, it is often superior, depending upon the sheath, not glass or cladding.

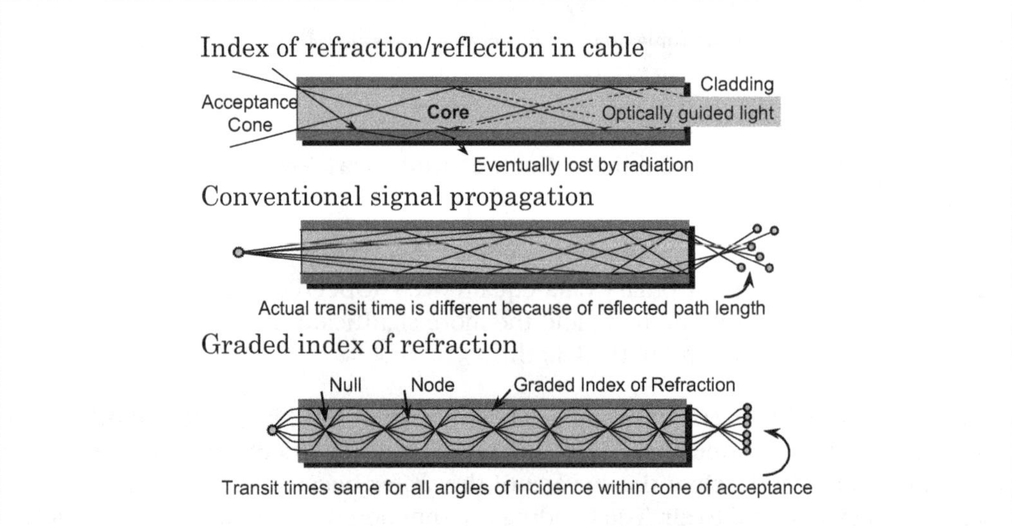

Figure 23-5. Refraction/Reflection Are A Consideration in Fiber Optic Cable, Not Voltage Drops and Current Loss

In the 1950s, when this fiber-optic application was developed, glass was not pure enough for communication transmission. Small imperfections weakened and blurred the signals, so they could travel only short distances before becoming unintelligible. Transmission losses were a thousand decibels per kilometer. Bell Labs and Corning Glass worked on the problem and almost simultaneously developed a process in the 1970s that today produces glass fibers with purity so great that losses are listed as less than ten decibels per kilometer. In the drawing process developed by Bell, a three-foot rod of glass production stock ends up as nine miles of fiber, five-thousands of an inch in diameter. A typical fiber-optic cable suitable for distributed control system network has a diameter of 75 to 100 microns.

The speed of light is far slower in a medium like glass than in a vacuum. The more significant limitation is that of the electronics at either end of the length.

Light travels directly down the center of a fiber-optic cable will emerge faster than light that bounces off the sides. This will cause the signal to break up over a distance as the cable flexes. To overcome this phenomenon, glass layers are deposited around the drawn glass core as it is made. The effect, called multimode (refraction), calls for the resulting cross section to act as a lens that redirects the light toward the center as it migrates outward. Most of the light signal stays intact making longer lengths of cable practical.

At the terminations, an optical/electrical interface (OEI) device will send electrical pulses to a LED, which then converts that electrical signal to optical pulses over the optical cable. On the other side of the cable a PIN diode, which is a light-sensitive device that develops an electrical signal when exposed to light, will take those optical pulses and convert them back to electrical. Of course, there is some circuitry to bring the energy level to the same electrical level as the device requires. These operations are merely energy conversions; they are not a store-and-forward of information and cause no appreciable delay in the signal. The same optical/electrical device can function as an amplifier/relay to extend the cable lengths.

Actually, three different signals are involved in the particular system shown in Figure 23-6.

- The message itself (communication signal); two-directional both send and receive
- The one that disconnects the ring (solid-state switch) during transmission so the signal doesn't go around "forever"
- The one that listens for the signal to return to assure the entire ring is still connected

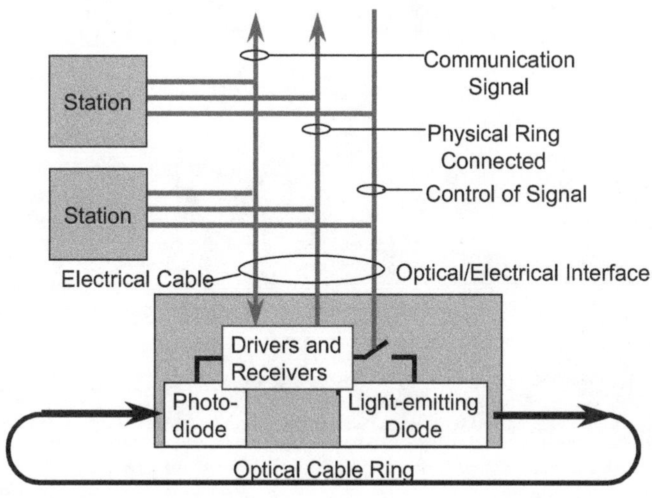

Figure 23-6. One Method of Linking Optical Medium with Electrical

Figure [illegible]. One Method of Linking Optical Medium With Electrical

Logical Structures 24

In the early days of digital communications, there was no question which device was the transmitter and which was the receiver. A computer sent data to a printer, for example. Usually, a single cable connected them, and transmission was simplex, that is, it went in one direction only. In a distributed control system (DCS) today, information must move between operator stations and remote controllers in both directions. This would require two wires in a simplex network. In single-wire systems, communication would occur either as full duplex, a complex technique by which both devices talk at the same time, or half duplex, where each takes turns sending and receiving, very much like a question-and-answer session between people (Figure 24-1).

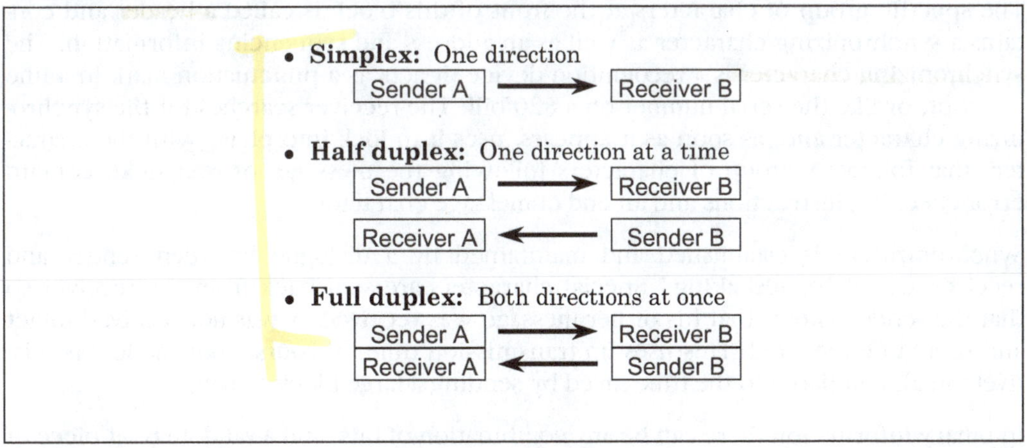

Figure 24-1. People Also Talk This Way: Lecture (Simplex), One-on-One (Half Duplex), and at a Party (Full Duplex)

---

simplex cable—Term sometimes used for a single fiber-optical cable.

simplex mode—The operation of a channel in one direction only with no capability of reversing.

simplex transmission—Transmission in one direction only.

duplex cable—In fiber optics, a two-fiber cable suitable for duplex transmission. With copper wire, a pair of wires insulated from each other and with an outer jacket of insulation around the inner insulated pair.

duplex transmission—Transmission in both directions, either one direction at a time (half duplex) or both directions simultaneously (full duplex).

Message Format

In asynchronous transmission, the sender and receiver use a count of bits to define the transmission interval. A code often used to transmit characters is ASCII. This 7 bit code provides numeric characters, alphabetic characters, uppercase, lowercase, punctuation, and special characters such as carriage return and line feed. These last two are a carryover from the time this code was used with Teletype. (Recall our earlier comment about the ASCII characters for the letters C and K comparable to our Morse code.)

Block-oriented synchronous serial transmission can be more efficient than asynchronous and consequently is used for almost all network use. The transmitter sends an entire block of information at a time, preceding it with specific groups of characters and ending it with another specific group of characters. By using synchronous transmission protocols, efficiency of transmission can be increased as much as 95 percent. On the other hand, if blocks contain only a few characters, this advantage is lost. We will discuss a little later how we can improve the speed of transmission, but for now, let's take a look at how to use synchronous transmission in an efficient way.

The specific group of characters at the front of this block is called a header and contains a synchronizing character as well as an address and sequencing information. The synchronizing character is a recognition device. It acts as a punctuation mark in a line of script, or like the serial number on a $20 bill. The receiver searches for the synchronizing character and, as soon as it appears, uses it to lock into phase with the characters that follow. A group of characters following the message, or text field, contain error-checking instructions and an end-of-message character.

Synchronization is established and maintained by a dialogue between sender and receiver, called "handshaking." Special characters are sent back from the receiver so that the sender knows that his or her message was received or was not received intact and should be repeated. This uses up transmission time, of course, but the loss is relatively small compared to the time saved by sending a large block of data.

In binary information there can be any combination of bits, and a random 8 bit piece of data could have exactly the same bit pattern as that of a control character. It would not do to have the bit pattern correspond to the control character for the termination code "end of message" to show up as a legitimate text character in the middle of a transmission thus causing the receiver to terminate receipt. Each protocol must have a way of transmitting text that may contain bit patterns that look like control characters to the receiver. This is called "transparency." The protocol may call for a control character to be always preceded by another character. In some protocols, this is called a data link escape (DLE) character. Was STX (for "start of transmission") preceded by DLE? If it was not, then it is text. The practice carries over into the data stream itself. Here is a DLE character. Was the preceding character another DLE? If it was, it's legitimate for text. If not, the following character is a control character. Fortunately, the chips have the software for transparency built into them, so all this happens automatically.

A number of synchronous protocols are used by distributed control systems (DCS) suppliers and by computer manufacturers. Commonly used are the following:

BISYNC—binary synchronous communication protocol; developed by IBM.

DDCMP—(Digital Data Communication Message Protocol), which uses a full duplex form of transmission and is compatible with the DEC PDP/11 series of minicomputers.

SDLC—(Synchronous Data Link Control) [Figure 24-2]; bit-oriented standard protocol developed by IBM superseding bisynchronous transmission; uniform discipline for transfer of data between stations in point-to-point, multipoint, or loop arrangement, using synchronous data transmission techniques.

HDLC—(High-level Data Link Control) [Figure 24-4]; international standard communication bit-oriented protocol defined by CCITT for ISO, and used in Open Systems Interconnection (OSI).

ADCCP—(Advanced Data Communication Control Procedures) developed by ANSI (American National Standards Institute).

Some form of SDLC or HDLC is most commonly used in suppliers' specifications.

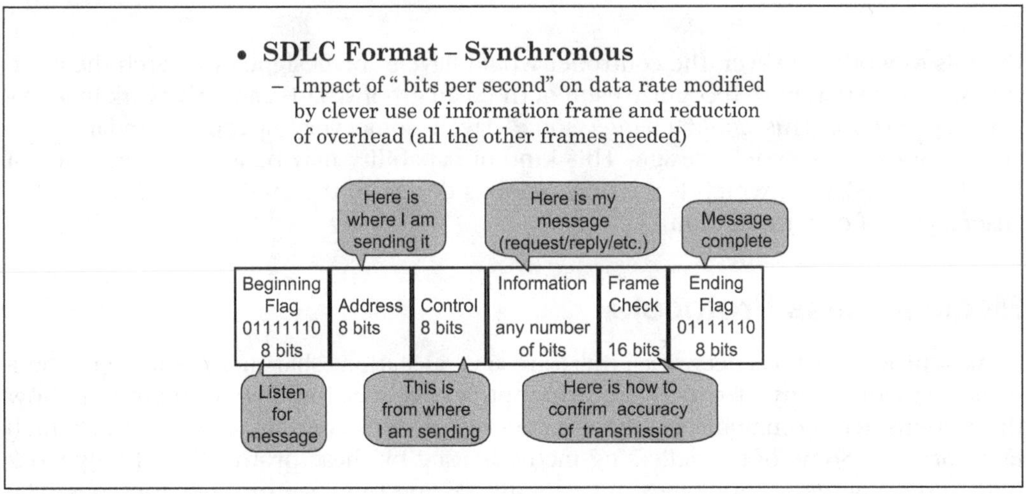

Figure 24-2. Typical Transmission Example

The creative use of scan groups by vendors in proprietary networks helped them achieve the "real" real-time so essential to process control use (Figure 24-3). In this approach, rather than using the same overhead for each parameter, all the needed parameters for the screen view (or other purposes) are clustered into useful scan groups, each group sharing the same overhead. A single scan group could have eighty items, saving eighty times the overhead on a single transmission!

For example, an operator could push a button for information on a screen view. This could result in a different scan group, depending upon what view is being invoked:

- Overview needs only deviation values and alarms for display
- Group view additionally needs "faceplate" data (PV, SP, deviation, alarms, etc.)
- Detail or Point views need to add all the tuning parameters and other settings

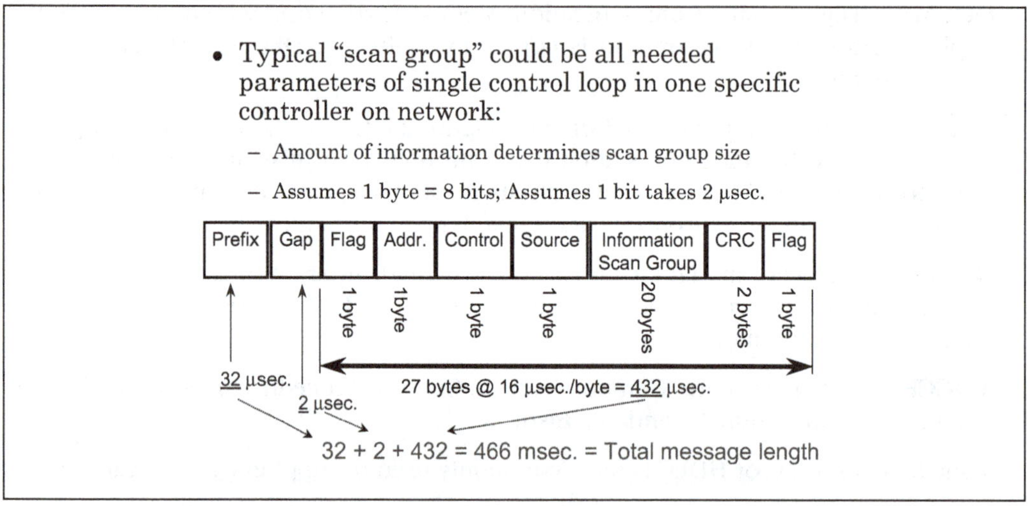

Figure 24-3. Use of Scan Group Can Help Maintain "Real-Time"

For this to work, however, the controller would have to be designed to match the operator station so that both recognize each of the scan groups. This can only work in a proprietary system. This could change some day if some very specific standards can "reach" into every system design. This kind of capability may be a future province of Fieldbus Foundation, which is the only fieldbus design of the 1990s that addresses the "user layer" of communication.

Media Access Protocols

In most process control networks, there are several stations sharing a common communication media, many of which need prompt access. It is imperative to arbitrate how the stations will communicate, the sequence they will communicate in, and which takes priority. Some of the accessing methods used by these protocols will only work with certain network topologies, for example, a ring topology or a bus topology. The purpose of the media access protocol is to control the access of each station to the shared communication media and to structure the format of the messages that go on this network.

When a cable system is shared, a protocol is needed to determine which station is granted access to the medium. If two stations transmit at the same time there is a collision. A protocol is required to minimize collisions.

The media access protocols that are typically used in distributed control systems (DCSs) are as follows:

- **Carrier insertion.** A method whereby a station in the network monitors a message stream of all the messages passing through it until it detects a lull in traffic. At that point it inserts its own message while buffering, and later retransmitting, any additional incoming messages. This is also known as *ring expansion* because the method expands the ring of data by one message until the original message, or the acknowledgment of it by the receiving station, returns back to the sender.

- **Carrier Sense Multiple Access with Collision Detection (CSMA/CD).** A method in which the contention between two or more stations is resolved by detecting any simultaneous transmission and causing each to retry after waiting a predetermined time. The time-out delay is different for each station on the network and is usually several microseconds. This is the method used by Ethernet, which is standard like IEEE 802.3- that is used by Intel, Xerox and Digital Equipment Corporation.

- **Polling.** A method of controlling devices on a bus or a ring (loop) communication network with a single network master, sometimes called *traffic director*. It is the process of inviting another station (node) to transmit data as compared to selecting that station as in TDMA.

- **Time Division Multiplex Access (TDMA).** A method by which a single device or multiplexer accepts multiple channels on a single transmission line. To do this, it connects stations one at a time at regular intervals, interleaving bits (called bit TDM) or characters (called character TDM) from each station. This multiplexer also acts as a traffic director, except that it arbitrarily signals (selects) each device, telling it when to talk.

- **Token passing.** A method for peer-to-peer communication. The right to transmit is passed from device to device, called a token, ideally on a regular schedule, making a throughput and response time predictable (deterministic) so that only one station has the token at any one time. During the time the station has the token, it has complete control of the network. Two versions of this are as follows:

1. The token bus (defined by IEEE 802.4), where the right to transmit is passed from device to device by way of a logical ring on a physical bus configuration, and

2. The Token Ring (defined by IEEE 802.5), where a special data packet is passed from station to station around a physical ring in sequence. When a station wants to transmit, it takes possession of the token, transmits the data, then frees the token after that data has made a complete circuit of the electrical ring.

> Common access methods include Traffic Director, Token-passing and CSMA/CD. Traffic director and token-passing are deterministic, CSMA/CD is non-deterministic. If the network access time for a station can be calculated, the network is called deterministic.

Media Access Analogies

Some analogies of media access methods (Figure 24-4) can be: military (traffic director), a press conference or barbershop (for CSMA/CD), and Robert's Rules of Order at a meeting (for token bus) [versus Pony express rider carrying message packets from station to station (for token ring)].

In the military analogy, the traffic director operates for command headquarters when information is requested from the units. "Fall in and report," commands the leader (traffic director), who then polls who is (which controllers are) available for duty. Requested information from them is then relayed up to command headquarters

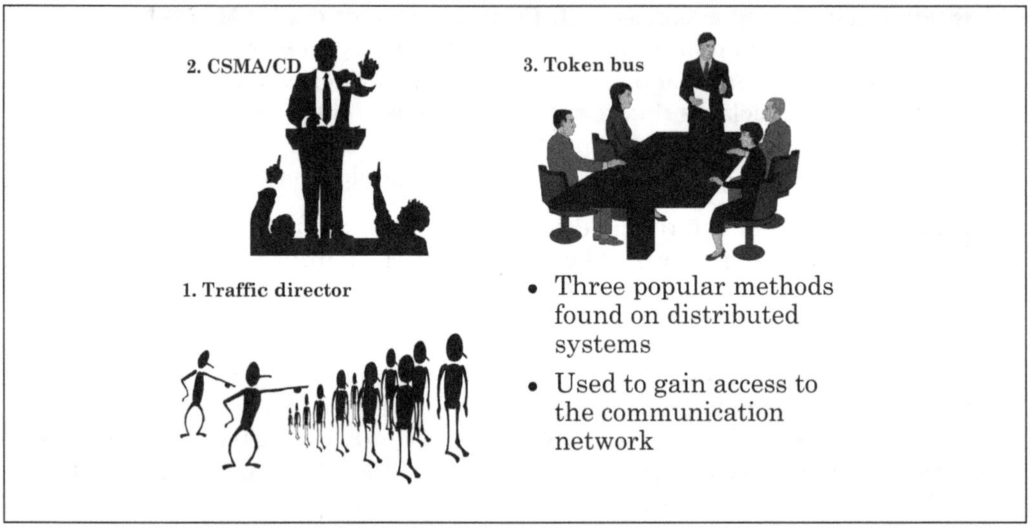

Figure 24-4. Typical Access Methods in Control Systems

(operator station). There is no sharing of data between the troops (no peer-to-peer communication between controllers), but everything must go up the chain of command, where it is then decided what data to disperse and where.

In the press conference analogy, the press corps (controllers) all frantically vie for the speaker's (operator station's) attention. When the speaker selects, only one of the reporters holds a dialogue with the speaker. As soon as there is a pause, everyone again retries for attention. The more prestigious reporters (who have the shorter time-outs) are higher on the list for access to the speaker. In a control system, the critical alarms must be allocated there.

In a token ring system, when a keystroke occurs at an operator station requesting information from various controllers, the Pony Express rider is sent out on a circuit of stations (controllers) with the message in his saddlebag. At each station on the circuit, he must stop, open the pouch, inspected to see if the message is for any activity at that station, add any new mail, close the pouch, and send the rider off to the next stop. This continues around the loop. If there are many stations and/or much more mail (many alarms, for example), then the rider can be slowed or even overburdened. He might end up pulling a wagon of mail, but with the same pony! Sometimes the pony does not live through the ordeal.

The token bus system, however, operates like a business meeting. Perhaps both the president and a vice president are present, along with the employees (controllers). Each has a turn to speak and/or ask questions, but when they "have the floor" they are in full control of the meeting. They could ask for a set point from one, a calculation from another, and a report on any alarms. The others can respond immediately when addressed; they do not have to wait until they have the floor (the transaction is completed right away). The sequence may be by the order of seating (physical ring) or by alphabetical order (logical ring). The managers (operator stations) each have an attendance sheet and make records as each employee takes his or her turn. When each is finished, they "yield the floor" (pass the token) to the next in turn (using a "handshaking routine). If there is no acceptance after a few tries (typically three), the previous speaker will pass over that person and go to the next in order, while the managers mark their attendance sheets (report some diagnostic error code).

Ethernet

CoDeveloped by DEC, Intel, and Xerox in 1973, the Institute of Electrical and Electronics Engineers (IEEE) created Ethernet as their 802.3 standard in 1983 (Figure 24-5). It only handles OSI layers 1 (physical) and 2 (data link). The other five layers are handled with other software.

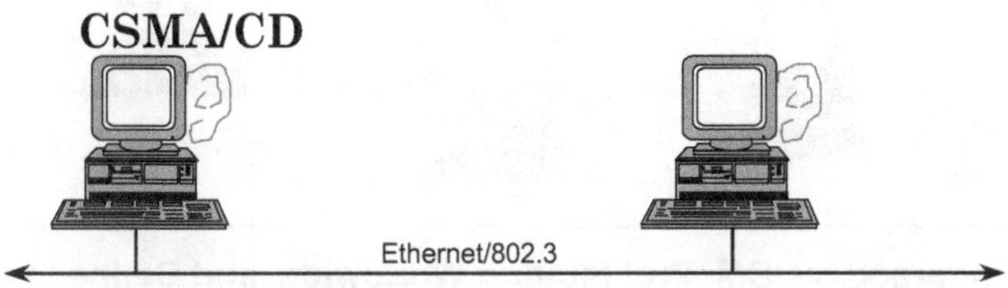

Carrier Sense (CS) – Device listens for clear channel before transmitting. If channel in use (a carrier is sensed), device will delay transmission.

Multiple Access (MA) – Many devices can connect to common cable and have equal access when channel is clear.

Collision Detection (CD) – Two devices can sense clear channel at same time and begin transmitting. Collision will occur and both devices will stop transmitting, wait some random time different from each other, and each will try transmission again.

Figure 24-5. Ethernet is Claimed by Some to Be the Most Widely Used Network in the World

CSMA/CD: Every device has access (Multiple Access), with no traffic director required. A device that wants time on Ethernet first listens (Carrier Sense) until the highway is available. The device then tries to send its data. If another device simultaneously tries to send data, a collision occurs and both devices stop (Collision Detection). They will each retry after different delay times.

Token Passing

One station at a time has the right to transmit (Figure 24-6). That station posses the token. When the token-holding station is through transmitting is sends the token to the next station in the logical ring (Imagine a group of people standing in a circle but taking turns speaking in alphabetical order.) The time it takes for the token to be passed around the logical ring is called the token rotation time. Token-passing networks can be extended to two kilometers (some as high as eight kilometers) with fiber-optic cable.

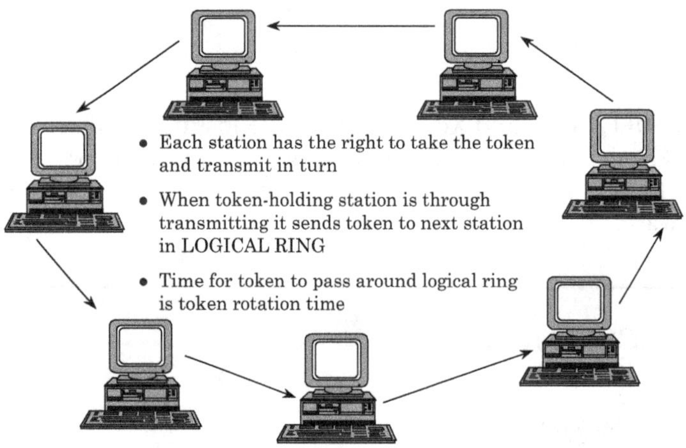

Figure 24-6. Endorsed by IBM, Proliferating Worldwide, and Defined by IEEE 802.5 Standard

---

Token passing—In digital communication, a media access method (ISO data Link layer 2) for peer-to-peer communication bus nodes. The token is passed around to each node on a regular schedule, making throughput and response time predictable (deterministic). Only one node has the token at any one time, and during that time it has complete control of the network.

The Conquest of Speed

A common mistake when measuring the speed of transmission is to be caught up the "specsmanship" game of proclaiming how many bits per second are operating on that network. There are many more factors than merely bits per second. The real test is how much *information flow* can be operated over that network. As an example, we can compare electronics to our analogous telegrapher from the beginning of Chapter 22, who sent every letter of every word of every sentence of every paragraph to communicate an idea or sent two-letter codes that can convey the same idea without having to use all the letters. The example we used was "LT" (look at the tank) or "CW" (check the water). The same thing applies to electronics. There are key "shorthand notes" within the communications structure that can move a lot more information, but that's only part of the story. Another part of it includes how to locate the specific data needed, how to convert that data from electronic processing data into digital signals, and then how to convert it back again in other devices or stations to the form it requires. With the pressure for interchangeability between vendors, this becomes quite a challenge to any attempts at innovation and product differentiation.

- Several factors must be considered in considering transaction time on the network:
  - Request message length
  - Media access time; transit time
  - Turnaround time (find, process reply)
  - Response message length
  - Transit time for return
  - Processing time of originator

Operator Station Request Message	Controller Turnaround	Controller Response Message	Operator Station Processing
200 μsec	80 μsec	466 μsec	320 μsec

Transit = 15 μsec/10,000' Transit = 15 μsec/10,000'

Transaction time = 776 μsec ... Time between transactions = 1.096 μsec

Figure 24-7. Factors in a Complete Transaction

Transaction—In communications, a transaction is a message destined for an application program, usually a computer-processed task that accomplishes a particular action or result and then responds with the result to the initiator.

Turnaround Time

One of the devices needed for communication is a modem, which transforms information from the electronics of the station into the network's needs. Strictly speaking, a modem transforms binary data into an analog form and vise versa. Modems (an acronym for "MOdulate/DEModulate") are usually associated with telephone line transmissions, yet the signal on line has constantly varying values. In distributed control systems (DCSs), bits are transmitted and have either an "on" or "off" state, our good old ones and zeros. However, the interfacing action between the binary information of the controller has some similarity to that performed by a modem, so the term is accepted.

Amplitude. Height of alternating or oscillating signal.

Modulation. Process by which the characteristic of one wave (the carrier) is modified by another wave (the signal), such AM, FM, and PCM. See *AM* and *PCM*.

AM—(Amplitude Modulation). Transmission technique in which the amplitude of the carrier is varied in accordance with the signal. See *PM* and *FSK*.

FM—(Frequency Modulation). Method of transmission in which carrier frequency varies in accordance with signal

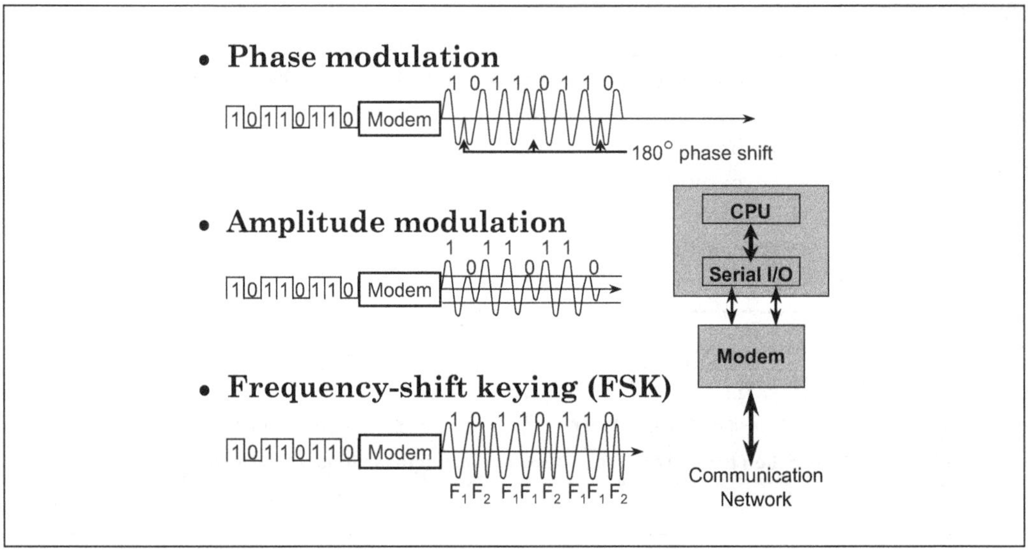

Figure 24-8. Three of the Ways Ones and Zeros Are Transmitted.

FSK—(Frequency Shift Keying). Method of data transmission using frequencies to indicate the state of the bit being transmitted. See *AM* and *PM*.

PCM—(Pulse Coded Modulation). Technique in which an analog signal, such as a process sensor signal or voice, is converted into a digital signal by sampling the signal's amplitude (slicing) and expressing the different amplitudes as binary numbers; the sampling rate must be twice the highest frequency in the signal. See *PM* and *FSK*.

PM—(Phase Modulation). Method of transmission whereby the angle of phase of the carrier wave is varied in accordance with the signal. See *PM* and *FSK*. One of three ways of modifying a sine wave signal to make it "carry" information; the sine wave or "carrier" has its phase changed in accordance with information to be transmitted.

Modems use three basic modulation schemes in general. The names of these schemes are frequency-shift keying (FSK), amplitude modulation (AM), and phase modulation (PM). FSK is a form of frequency modulation. A carrier frequency is changed to one value representing "1" and another representing "0." AM operates the carrier at a constant frequency that changes the value of the amplitude to correspond to the changes in the state. PM shifts a transmitted signal's phase by a specific number of degrees corresponding to an incoming bit pattern. Obviously, all three methods can handle a number of levels of information, not just "on" and "off" (1s and 0s). Distributed control needs only this "simple" data communication, and because FSK has some signal-to-noise advantage, it has become the most commonly acceptable form used for these purposes.

In addition, the carrier can be unchanging when no data is being transmitted at some neutral voltage. When a message is about to be sent, a signal varying from a positive to a negative voltage with respect to a neutral level might be sent at a frequency of, say, 2 MHz. After a predetermined number of variations, the message would follow. To send the message, a carrier would vary its voltage from positive to negative at the rate of maybe a half megahertz for a logical one and a one megahertz for a logical zero. After the transmission is complete, another burst of signal at a different frequency might indicate the end of the message, after which the line would go back to its neutral condition.

To get information out of storage registers and onto the port interfacing on the network, there will be some sort of Serial Input Output (SIO) chip that would change the parallel format of the bits into a serial one. By the mid 1990s the chip probably included a universal asynchronous receiver-transmitter (UART). This device is made up of shift registers into which information comes from a station in parallel form and out of which it is strobed by a clock signal, one bit at a time, to put it into a serial arrangement. Along with this, there is circuitry that packs into the message "packet" bits for start, end, parity, and checking information. At the receiving end the bits that are not part of the message (the "overhead") are stripped out, and the message bits are put back into registers in parallel form. Modems can function as both transmitters and receivers, and they must readjust their circuitry after each transmission to perform the opposite function. All of this activity contributes to the "turnaround time," which is a limitation on the useful information that can be transmitted at any given period. Speed then, involves not just how many bits per second or how efficiently you can frame these bits to communicate more information, but how quickly you can convert these bits into useful information at either end of the message, or the turnaround time. There is, of course, more to our story.

Media Access Time

Probably the least length of time in a transaction is the time it takes for the messages to physically move down the communication media. Picture, if you will, not balls in a pipe, as some physics books render it, but rather flashes of light, as you would see if you were communicating a signal like the Morse code with a flashlight. How quickly can the other side respond to these flashes, and how many of these flashes can you put into the system? One must consider the load of the system, which is how much information or bits are being pushed in, and its ability to respond to that load, which is how well you can recognize the distinction between the energy levels.

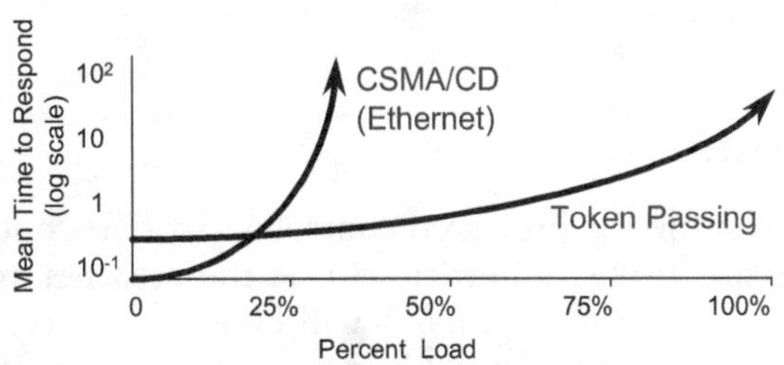

Figure 24-9. Ethernet versus Token Bus

Let us compare two common access protocols. CSMA/CD, or Ethernet, has a very fast mean time to response for the first 25 percent of its load, but then, as the load gets heavier, the curve goes asymptotically high, when it climbs to almost 50 percent of the load, so it cannot respond to real-time needs after it is only half loaded. The trick on an Ethernet system in process control conditions (to maintain "real-enough-time") is to reduce the number of stations or the distance traveled, so that all the messages can be tolerated without being restrictive. A token-passing scheme, however, requires a little more mean time to respond at lower loads, but it is more capable of maintaining a reasonable response time through the entire 100 percent of load. Clearly, it does not have the same time characteristics.

Ethernet is typically nonredundant, nondeterministic, and load dependent. This is overcome by keeping the load under 25 percent by increasing speed, limiting the number of stations, and creative messaging. It runs into the danger of saturation when loading goes over 25 percent. This can happen when traffic suddenly increases, such as during a sudden burst of alarms, which at best will slow down the response time and at worst will cause a crash. One vendor assures its customers that they never exceed 17 percent of load. This means that they only work to 17 percent capacity of the full stated bandwidth of the network [usually stated in Megabits per second (MBPS)]. This is rapidly changing, however; see "Overcoming the Shortcomings," below.

Token bus is deterministic and can manage full load but also needs similar restrictions to stay in the real-time operating realm. Nevertheless, because it cycles at a fixed rate it has a better capability to withstand an alarm burst or similar traffic increase with no loss of performance, or lockup. This system is likely to operate over the full bandwidth specified for the system.

In another example, a communication system could have a higher communication rate in bits per second but much less information flow. A token *ring* requires a sending station to pass its request for information to each of the stations in the ring before the reply returns back to itself. Whereas in a token *bus* arrangement when each station has the token it can talk to any of the other stations and get its reply in a direct response to the transaction without waiting for the token to pass around the entire ring. Both are token passing, but it makes a significant difference in how the communication moves. A carrier insertion protocol access is similar to the token ring, in that while functionally different, and also operating on a bus, it still requires waiting until the signal comes back after visiting each station.

Future of Ethernet

Ethernet is rapidly becoming the preferred control network technology in new systems emerging during the late 1990s. Ethernet will be the area network, the control network, and the I/O network. In five years, it will be everywhere. The Ethernet that is used in these applications, however, will likely be slightly different than the Ethernet of today. Advances like the 1 Gigabyte Ethernet, redundancy, quality of service, and the like will make the future Ethernet much more effective, cheaper, and powerful than

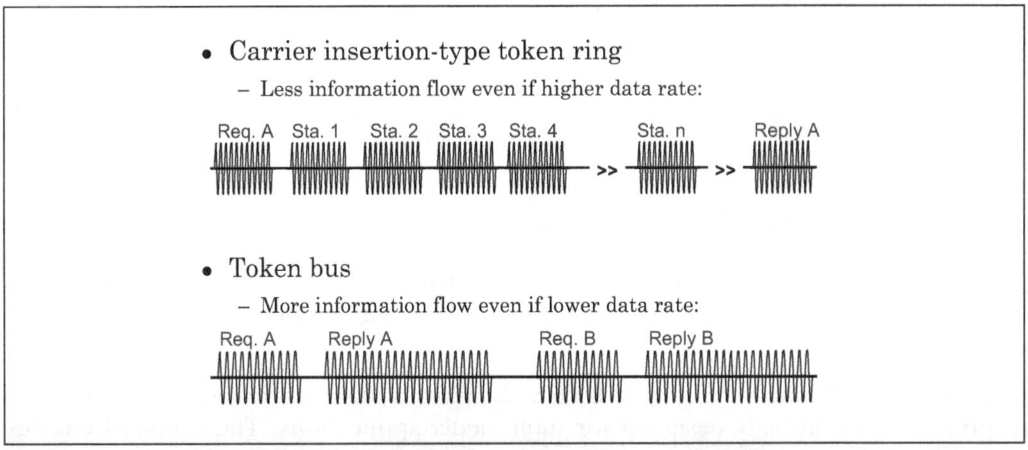

Figure 24-10. Pony Express Rider versus the Business Meeting

any proprietary control or I/O network available today. This is not fully here in1998, but it is coming. Not all the vendors have the newer technology at this point, but some vendors are already trying to cash in on it. The later releases may, however, have newer enhancements.

IEEE (Institute of Electrical and Electronics Engineers). International professional society that issues its own standards and is a member of ANSI and ISO.

IEEE 802.3—Ethernet Local Area Network (LAN) standard except for type field (10 Mbps); physical-layer standard using CSMA/CD access method on bus-topology LAN.

IEEE 802.4—Physical-layer standard using token bus-topology LAN; nearly identical to Manufacturing Automation Protocol (MAP).

IEEE 802.5—Physical-layer standard using token ring-topology LAN.

IEEE 802.6—Metropolitan Area Network (MAN) or High Speed Local Network (HSLN) standard.

IEEE 802.11—Radio and wireless LAN.

IEEE 802.12—Draft standard for 100BASE VG networking.

Ethernet Advantages

This ubiquitous network technology is sold in high volume all over the world. Towards the end of the 1990s, PC boards for this are $50 compared to $900 or more for control or device-network PC boards. For cost-conscious users and the suppliers who must meet their needs there is no contest. The fast growing development of information technology (IT) is causing the abundant use of Windows NT devices and other PCs with Ethernet ports and drivers as standard (no extra cost). The easy connectivity of the Ethernet to the Internet is another factor. The Ethernet is another technology rapidly finding its way into the reality of factory and process automation, working inexorably toward sensor-to-boardroom integration. Expect to see the Ethernet also work its way into fieldbus networks because of its speed and bandwidth in addition to its significant availability and cost advantage.

Overcoming the Shortcomings

Several IEEE Ethernet standards and standard enhancements released during 1997 and 1998 to address three main areas of performance "pucker-points": transmission speed, determinism, and reliability.

- Reducing collisions is the goal of IEEE 802.1 p for traffic class expediting or message prioritization. Initially designed for multimedia applications, The standard enables system designers to prioritize messages, guaranteeing the delivery of time-critical data with deterministic response time and repeatable results. The standard should rapidly replace those control vendors who have made proprietary modifications on their own to achieve this effect.
- Reliability is the goal of IEEE 802.12d for redundant links. Adding redundant links to a network allows the automatic recovery of network connectivity when a link or repeater failure occurs anywhere in the network pathway. As a standard, this should also eliminate the several custom solutions which have been created by different control system vendors.
- The emergence of 100 Mbps bandwidth has been enhanced by two additional specifications to boost performance through increased bandwidth. IEEE 802.3x, for full duplex, allows bi-directional, simultaneous transmission and reception of standard Ethernet frames using separate transmit and receive channels. IEEE 802.3z, for Gigabit Ethernet, will allow a factor of ten-times-faster-transfer of Ethernet format frames while maintaining maximum compatibility with the installed base.

Let's Not Get Carried Away

No one is suggesting that we really connect the business systems *directly* to the plant floor! Not only could this be dangerous, it overlooks the fundamental purposes of a navigational control systems requirements compared to those of the transactional business system. There are significant capacity and speed differences, loading into the battle of "What is real-time?" as opposed to "real-enough time."

Using Ethernet in both realms will be best served by *separating* these domains with the following standard network technologies:

- **Bridges**—which are the simplest technology for this function, connecting network segments which can be different physical layer types, such as Ethernet and FDDI; while they receive all signals, by reading addresses they can selectively determine the appropriate segment to which it will pass a signal (such as not sending it to the originating segment again), thereby increasing network to maximum possible size.
- **Routers**—use logical and physical addressing to connect two or more logically separated networks by organizing a large network into subnetworks with their own

logical address; functioning similar to bridges, they also keep the networks separated, but with access to each other, hence reducing traffic in each.

- **Hubs**—or dumb hubs, can use passive hubs to extend network to longer distances, using the connection of several star topologies, sending all messages to all stations, thereby improving where stations can be located; active hubs act as repeaters, sometimes called multiport repeaters, either amplifying the signals (noise & all) or regenerate signals (replicate signals without the noise). [Figures 24-11 vs. Figure 24-12]

- **Smart Hubs**—also called intelligent hubs, managed hubs, or switched hubs, allow connection of more than two networks by looking at the destination address and forwarding the message to the proper network segment; thus, by limiting the number of signals along each leg, reduces traffic on each, which reduces the potential of collisions, and improves performance [Figures 24-13 and 24-14]. One user's experience changed a 50% collision rate to only 1% by using smart hubs in a large system.

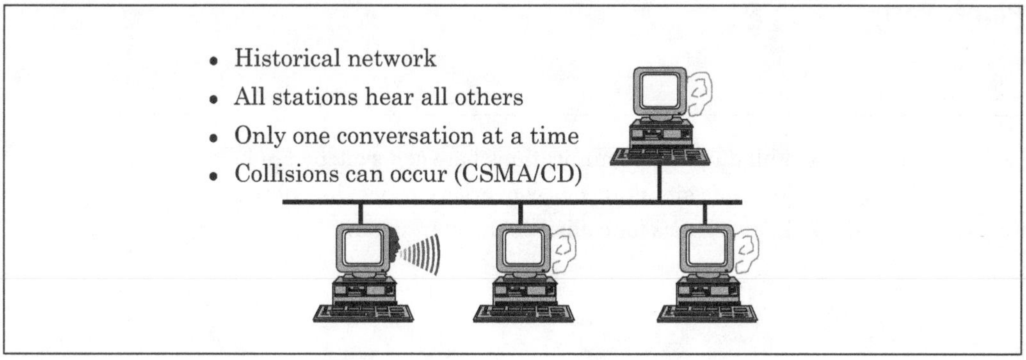

Figure 24-11. Traditional Ethernet

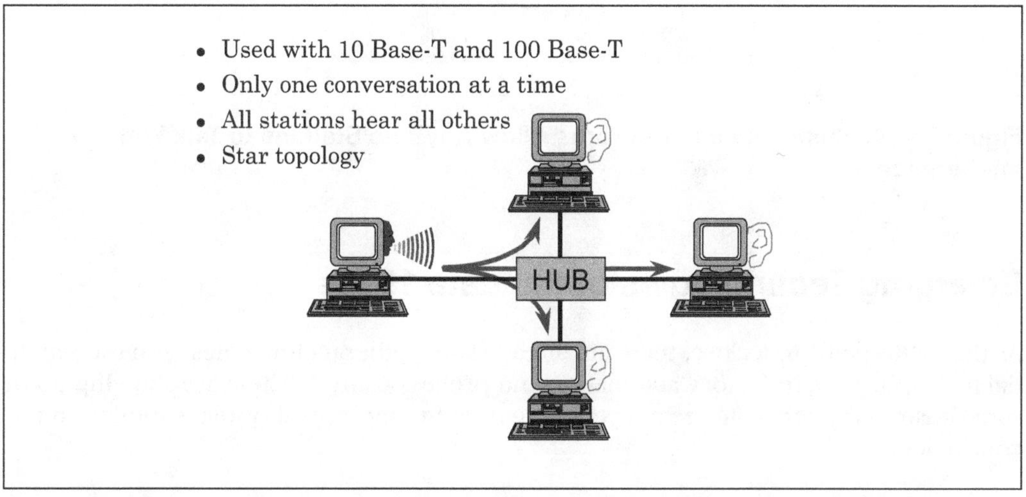

Figure 24-12. Hubs Can Allow Individual Station to be Isolated from Network

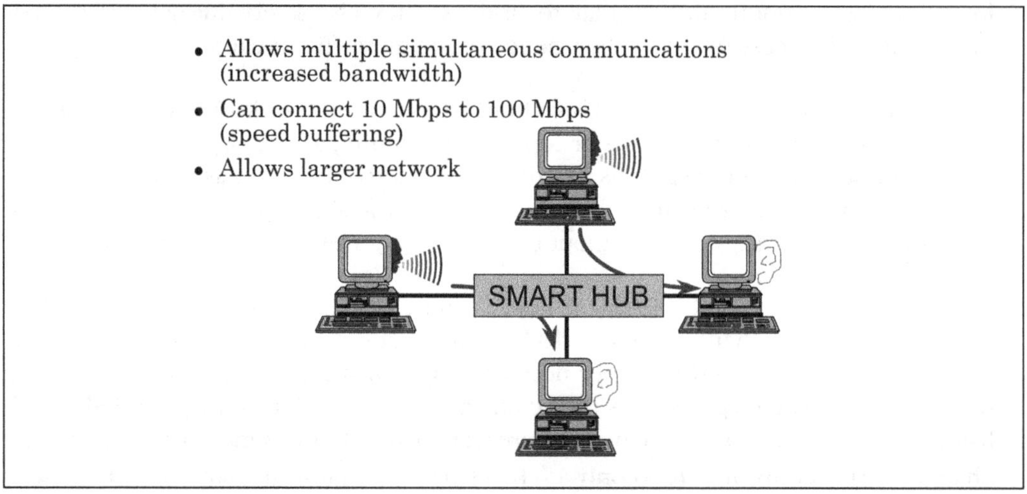

Figure 24-13. Smart Hub "Knows" Network Layout so it can Route Messages to Proper Port

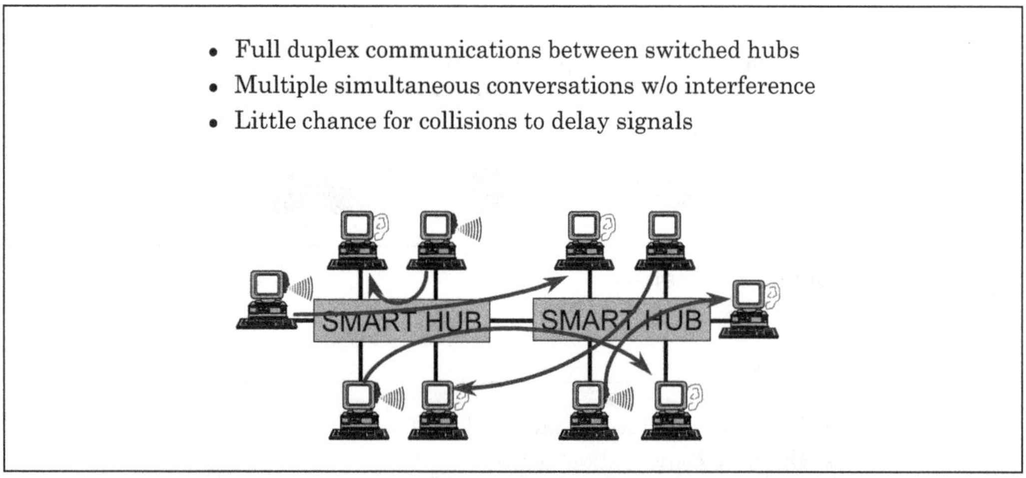

Figure 24-14. Smart Hubs in Networks Allow Any Two Stations to Talk Without Interference

Emerging Technologies of the Late 1990s

As the 1990s come to a close, there are already some other technologies with the potential for application in factory automation and process control. These are showing up in some business systems but are not yet being used by any control system suppliers at the control level:

- **Asynchronous Transfer Mode (ATM).** A physical layer protocol that performs the functions of a network layer protocol, ATM was designed for use in broadband ISDN (Integrated Services Digital Network) systems to carry voice, video, and data simultaneously. Lacking the support structure of Ethernet and somewhat expensive, it could compete with Gigabit Ethernet if volume increases.

- **Universal Serial Bus (USB).** A serial bus protocol developed by a consortium of computer companies as a single replacement for the collection of serial and parallel ports on PCs for the many peripherals (keyboard, mouse, printer, scanner, etc.). Already being shipped in PCs, cost-for-volume, speed (12 Mbps), and deterministic features give it potential.

- **IEEE 1394 (Firewire).** A serial bus protocol with high speed (>100 Mbps) for multimedia peripherals external to the PC chassis, such as digital video camcorders, video conferencing cameras, high-speed disk drives, and the like. Firewire holds promise its the speed and bandwidth, assuming volume brings down the price.

Compatible versus Compliant Standards

Many vendors have confused users in their rush to sound like all things to all people. In discussing their architectures, they frequently declare they are "compatible" with a specific standard. The user hears or thinks that means they are "compliant" to that standard and that the system will work interchangeably with any other system that is "compatible/compliant" with/to the same standard. There is a significant difference.

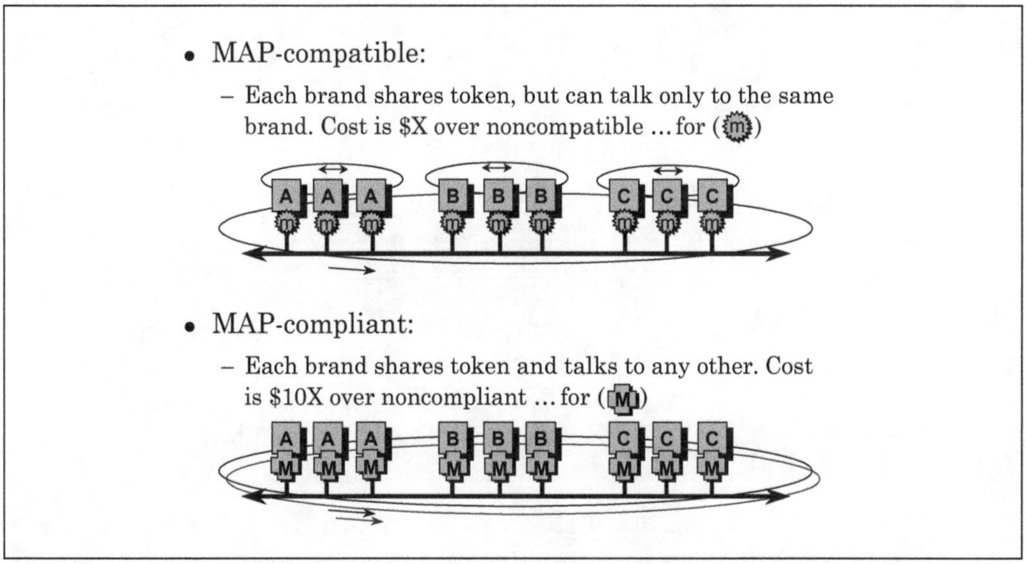

Figure 24-15. Many Have Been Confused by Misuse of This Terminology

Compliant—Conforms exactly with rules of a recognized standard. For example, a specification-*compliant* device will operate on a standard communication system and communicate with all other devices on that system made by any other vendor who is similarly compliant.

Compatible—Can coexist with the rules of a recognized standard, but may not be compliant. For example, a specification-*compatible* device will operate on a standard communication system and communicate with other devices on that system made by the same vendor and will not interfere with devices made by other vendors on that same system, but it will not be able to communicate with those other devices.

MAP (Manufacturing Automation Protocol). Based on IEEE 802.4; General Motors originated this networking protocol which follows seven--layer OSI model (Note: MAP-compliant means it conforms to specifications and will talk with other devices over the system. MAP-compatible means only that it will not interfere (physical and data link layers only) with "foreign" devices, but will only talk with like devices while sharing the timing with those foreign devices.)

MAP/EPA (MAP Extended Performance Architecture). Dual architecture that supports both full MAP seven-layer communication architecture as well as the architecture for time-critical communication that bypasses Layers 3, 4, 5, and 6.

Open Communications Standards 25

"I think standardization encourages creativity! It provides the framework upon which new developments can be conceived and built. For example, without a dictionary and rules of grammar to provide the standards for words and their use, a complex language cannot evolve, without which a complex written literature cannot be cultivated. In the great civilizations, a higher and higher standard of living requires more and more standardization, which produces both brilliant and beautiful improvements...

...which we can all later take for granted, of course!"

Marilyn vos Savant—April 27,1997

Open Systems: What Are They?

Open systems are based upon *widely accepted* industry standards. The question is who makes the standard become standard? To answer this we must consider the two types of standards:

- *Regulatory* or *consensus* standards, which emerge slowly and painfully from technical societies such as ISA (the society), ISO, IEEE, EPRI, ANSI, and hundreds of others. Fortunately, many of these societies are teaming up to avoid confusing and ambiguous overlaps. A strong international effort is at work by many enthusiastic individuals to homogenize many existing and newly required standards. Delays in the emergence of standards in the past came from necessary engineering thoroughness probably more than (from) individual egos. The biggest delaying factor by far, however, is the time for communication of ideas, the time for reviews, the need for many engineers to travel great distances to meet face to face, and the need to convert many good spoken ideas onto paper by people with little spare time. Although supported by industry, this effort itself is done almost exclusively by volunteers! Some exciting efforts using e-mail, the Internet, conference calls, and even "computer conferencing" have significantly reduced communication and publishing delays. Past examples of this include the OSI model from the ISO, POSIX, and FF Fieldbus.
- Often by virtue of *market dominance de facto* standards avoid these messy problems by the fiat of the largest manufacturer, by their sheer popularity with users, or sometimes by the accident a of combination of circumstances. The drawbacks involved in waiting for this seemingly more efficient standards = a creation method include having more inferior products because a company has better marketing than engineering or not having any standards at all because the market is saturated with several equally popular products. Serious delays in regulatory standards will cause impatience in the industry and encourage many vendors to race each other for the de facto prize. Sometimes a user company that is large enough to influence an industry will declare a standard. When General Motors announced the need for MAP, and

refused to purchase anything not fitting that standard, they began to discover that many functions did not fit that standard either! Even though good things came from the effort, the resulting fragmentation of the standard so as to overcome the deficiencies weakened the end result considerably. In fact, it turned many people off of the idea of the possibility of sweeping worldwide standards. Past examples of this type of standard include ISA (the IBM® standard), FORTRAN, MS-DOS, UNIX and SQL.

(Note: actually, MAP is a *specification*, not a standard!)

ANSI—(American National Standards Institute); nonprofit, independent organization supported by trade organizations, industry, and professional societies for standards development and coordination in USA; they represent USA to ISO; they defined ASCII.

EPRI—(Electric Power Research Institute); research consortium of 660 member utilities in U.S.

FF—Fieldbus Foundation, a not-for-profit organization dedicated to developing single, worldwide, interoperable fieldbus... formed from merger of WorldFIP North America and ISP Foundation in 1994.

FORTRAN—FORmula TRANslator; first high level computer language, developed by IBM® (1954); known as scientific language because of its facility for "number crunching," solving engineering, mathematical, and other scientific problems; procedure-oriented and has good array handling features.

IEEE—(Institute of Electrical and Electronic Engineers); international professional society that issues its own standards and is member of ANSI and ISO.

ISA—(Instrument Society of America); organization now formally known as "ISA, the international society for measurement and control," started in1945 in U.S. which is made up of individual volunteers from all aspects of the instrumentation business, representing vendors and users, many types of industries, and nearly every job description; they traditionally provide education and develop international *consensus* standards and practices; BUT also means: Industry Standard Architecture, a *de facto* personal computer 24-bit bus standard used in IBM®PCs and compatibles; developed for extension cards in the first IBM PC, it originally supported only 8-bit wide data path (now called PC/XT bus); subsequently developed to 16-bit for the AT class computers, and called AT bus, supporting both 8- and 16-bit cards.

ISO—(International Standards Organization); international organization for promoting the development of standards for computers.

OSI—Open Systems Interconnect; 7-layer reference model for network operations standardized within ISO to enable any two OSI-Compliant devices to exchange information; the seven layers are Physical, Datalink, Network, Transport, Session, Presentation, Application.

POSIX—Portable Operating System Interface eXchange; originated for computer environments as means of standardizing critical interfaces for the many divergent variations of UNIX® operating system; living under auspices of both IEEE and ISO, it has evolved into an entire family of standard interface definitions, no longer limited to UNIX®; specifies how software applications and operating system software should be implemented so that applications can be ported to other POSIX compliant environments.

MS-DOS®—Microsoft Disk Operating System; developed for IBM® PC and has become a de facto standard; sometimes called PC-DOS designed to control and manage I/O devices and memory for personal computers (PCs).

SQL—Structured Query Language [pronounced "see quill"]; ISO database access standard for communicating (querying, updating, and managing) with various relational data bases; allows client to access only that data required to satisfy a specific request, reducing network traffic and improving performance; derived from an IBM® research project that created Structured English Query Language in the 1970s; now accepted standard in database products.

UNIX®—UNIfied multitasking; time-sharing operating system designed originally by (and trademark of) AT&T for communicating, multi-user, 32-bit minicomputers which has become widely accepted because of its versatility; tradename now belongs to X/Open Corp. Ltd.

Examples of standards in everyday life include automobiles, plumbing supplies, electrical service, audio and videotapes and the like. Many spare parts are interchangeable, but frequently there are several versions in any one industry. Sometimes this is due to the existence of a variety of equally influential manufacturers, sometimes to the need for functional differences, and sometimes because of inaccessibility, such as international distribution.

---

open system—Hardware/software designs in which a degree of interchangeability and connectivity provides the user with choices: the ability to select multiple products from multiple vendors and integrate them seamlessly on powerful networks. Open systems make every resource on the network available to any authorized user who needs it.

Why Are Open Systems Important?

- Why should a company care about openness in a control system? Open systems are important to you for the following reasons:

- You are in a competing global marketplace, and you cannot fall behind your competition. Generally, with the many emerging capabilities of such a variety of different hardware and software products, your company must be nimble enough to add more functions to quickly meet your customers, rapidly changing requirements.

- You must continue to improve your plant operations year after year; otherwise, you will risk falling behind your competition. New methods of production are arising very quickly. How easy is it to add improvements to your way of producing?

- No one vendor can meet all your automation needs, you must rely on multiple vendors. Although the industry has not yet reached the point of "swapping out" a system controller with one from another vendor, there already exist circumstances where one vendor's workstation is capable of residing on a network and operating controllers from several other vendors. (That station, however, cannot *configure* those controllers.)

- To manage your plant operations effectively in response to fluctuating demand for your products, you will have to network all the automation systems together. This will require a degree of interconnectivity through communications standards.

- Computer technology will continue to advance at a breathtaking pace and you cannot afford to avoid using it. It will become even more important to make allowance for regular upgrading, but with no idea, at the time you purchase, *which* parts will need expansion. Your competition will always be adding a growing list of tools.

- You want to preserve your existing investment in computer software as you upgrade your computers. Software will comprise nearly three-quarters of the total cost of automation systems. It better work together.

The Most Common Definition: "My standard is what I have installed"

This definition only works if

- Your vendor can *alone* provide you with cost-effective solutions to your current and future needs.
- Your vendor has the financial resources to be innovative and keep pace with technology in *every area* of process control.
- Your vendor is committed to being compliant with industry standards as they emerge.

It costs vendors hundreds of thousands of dollars to participate in an emerging standard! No vendor "can do it all." Interoperability and the interchangeability of systems are essential for a system user to survive. This may not be entirely possible just yet, and the concept will still be a "journey toward" for some time to come. While there is nothing wrong with the economies provided by "single sourcing," that should never be confused with allowing yourself to be "held hostage" by the vendor.

Advantages and Disadvantages

Open systems preserve user/vendor investment through the following (Figure 25-1):

- **Applications portability.** The ability to use the same application software on computers from different vendors.
- **Vendor independence.** The ability to have computers from different vendors work together.

- **Scalability.** The capability to use the same software environment on all classes of computers, from mainframes to PCs.
- **Personnel portability.** Personnel can be easily trained and moved from one system to another.
- **Evolution of solutions.** User investment is preserved through the planned progression of standards.

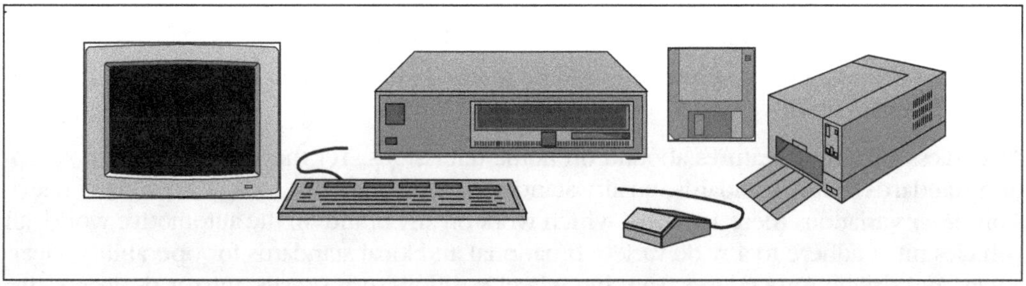

Figure 25-1. Without Standards, Users Would Have No Choices for Equipment, Components, or Supplies for Them

The drawbacks of industry standards include the following:

- Consensus standards can take years before they are fully defined and implemented by the vendors. Pressures from users are real here and have made differences.
- Standards are in general very comprehensive in nature. As a result, products tend to be more expensive, especially in the early stages. Once accepted, however, they can become very cost effective, sometimes not in their actual price but because of the versatility they offer.
- Standards may hold back some technological innovation. The pressure will be on vendors to be creative *within* the requirements of a standard. This has worked in other areas in the past.

Few believed that 4 to 20 mA and 1 to 5 Vdc signals would ever become a standard. By the way, *that* took about a quarter century and was essentially forced by users.

Some of the advantages just described may look quite idealistic. De facto Microsoft standards have opened capabilities in the office world so much that "big-time computing" is now available in the smallest of offices. This same technology is having a similar impact in changing automated control system in ways unheard of even in the recent past. It is moving so fast that readers of this book will probably already have seen examples that the author could only guess about while writing these words.

Fallacy About Standards

A major fallacy surrounding standards is that: "Products based on industry standards are identical." This is a confusion involving the difference between specification and implementation:

- A standard is a commonly accepted *specification* of a set of rules
- *Implementation* is how a specification is made into a reality

The reality behind standards is quite different:

- Products based on an industry standard are not identical.
- Major vendors will continue to implement standards uniquely so as to provide product differentiation.

As endless variety of features abound on home televisions. Yet they must adhere to reception standards, safety standards, quality standards, and so on. Just look at how many television *tuner* variations there are, all of which work on any brand! In the automotive world, all vehicles must adhere to a wide variety if national and local standards for operability, clearances, and driving procedures (steering wheel position, turn signals, mirror positions, tire sizes, and so on). However, most every driver in the world, across incredible culture boundaries, knows "PRND321"! (Look at your automatic gear shift lever).

The use of standards increases competition from smaller vendors, who can supply "niche" products. In the distributed control systems (DCS) market, several systems can consist of parts from different vendors.

Often if one vendor makes a product obsolete, another vendor's product can replace it easily. That second vendor will have reduced design costs, because

1. It does not need to provide the entire solution, only what it does best.
2. It can build on standards; it does not need to reinvent *everything* (e.g., a software vendor does not need to rewrite DOS).
3. Meanwhile, the user can select "best-of-class" equipment from different vendors and integrate the components into a system that is, perhaps, superior to what is available from any one vendor.

Developing Standardized Links: The Ubiquitous RS-232

With regard to interconnecting, that is heterogeneous systems that had computers or microprocessors in them, the RS-232 Serial Link has been the predominant means employed. Although it was a "standard" (from the Electronics Industry Association) it fell short. Even if two vendors touted RS-232 conductivity, they often could not communicate with each other without requiring the development of special software drivers or custom cables. One vendor might support four wires, while the other used seven. (The standard specifies twenty-five signals, many of which are optional.) Each vendor could define its own communications protocol. The problem was that the standard dealt with only one layer of the seven-layer Open System Inter connection (OSI) model. And that was the physical link layer. So, of course, this gets far more complicated when you deal with the other six layers, which compounds the problem far beyond what people anticipated with the so-called openness of the RS-232.

Communications Structure: The Open Systems Interconnect Model

Figure 25-2. The OSI Model Allows Communications Among Computers from Many Different Suppliers Communicate Over Several Different Networks!

Just from our brief discussion so far, you can see that there have been many kinds of protocols used for different circumstances in communication. An effort has been made to organize the hardware and software tasks of networking, through the International Organization for Standardization (ISO), which has developed a reference model for the protocols used in communications. Its formal name is the "International Organization for Standardization Reference Model for Open Systems Interconnection (ISO/OSI)." In their use here, open refers to communication systems that have provisions for interfacing with other nonproprietary systems, using established interface standards (Figure 25-2). The ISO model categorizes the various protocols into seven layers, each of which can be involved in transmitting a message from one system element to another (Figure 25-3). We will attempt to describe these layers will be done with an analogy to the postal system and its equivalent function. Hopefully, this will make it more understandable to the uninitiated. We will describe these layers in reverse order:

- **Layer 7: Application.** This layer really isn't part of the communications protocol structure but rather is part of the application software or firmware that is transmitted *through* these lower layers. In a higher-level language program, for example, it could be a statement that requests information from another system element over this communications media. In a function block structure it could be an input block, for example, that requests that certain process variables be read from another station over the communications system. In our postal system analogy (in Table 25-1), the application is really the contents of a letter inside of an envelope.

- **Layer 6: Presentation.** This restructures the data through some standardized format used within the network. It translates the message formats in the communication system to the information format required by the application layer (layer 7). This allows the application layer to properly interpret the data sent over the system, and, conversely, it puts the information to be transmitted into the proper message format. The postal system equivalent of it is the format and language style of our letter, including the translation of the language that's required, say, from American to German.

- **Layer 5: Session.** This name and address translation acts as security in the synchronized and managed data, which schedules the starting and stopping of communication activity between two elements in a system. It also specifies the quality of transport service required if multiple levels of service are available. The postal system equivalent is the name, address, and zip code of both the receiver and the sender, as well as the postage stamp determining the class (air, land, bulk rate).

- **Layer 4: Transport.** This provides transparent, reliable data transfer from end node to end node. It's the mechanism in each communicating element that ensures that the end-to-end message transmission has been accomplished properly. Services provided by the transport layer include acknowledging messages, detecting end-to-end message errors, retransmitting the messages, prioritizing the messages, and transferring messages to multiple receivers. The postal system equivalent is certified or registered mail, which provide verification to the sender that the letter arrived at the correct destination in good condition.

- **Layer 3: Network.** This performs the message routing for data transfer between stations not in the same network. Within a network having multiple pathways between the elements, this layer handles the routing of messages from one element to another. In a communications system consisting of multiple subnetworks, this layer handles the translation of addresses and routing of information from one of these sub--networks to another. In communications systems consisting of a single network and having only a single pathway between the elements, this layer is generally not required. This is the equivalent in the postal system of the distribution system of transferring a letter outside the postal system to a system in another city or country, instead of within the same postal zone.

- **Layer 2: Data link.** This provides the means to establish, maintain, and release the link between systems, to transferring the data frame between the nodes in the same network, and to detect and correct errors. This layer allows access from one station on a communications network to another, so that it can be determined which station has control of the hardware at any given time and when to transmit its messages or request information from the other. This layer is at the bit level and defines the formatting of the bits and the bytes as well as the message itself so the arrangement makes sense both to the sender and the receiver. It also defines the error-detection and error-correction techniques used and sets up the conventions for defining the start and stop of each message. In the postal system, it's the segment that transfers a letter from a sender to a destination within the same postal system, either a distribution center or a forwarding center to receive the letter in another system. It allows the mail to move within the same zone.

- **Layer 1: Physical.** This includes physically transferring messages between the adjacent stations. It defines the electrical and mechanical characteristics of the interface between the physical communication media and the driver and receiver electronics. This includes the voltage levels, the channel structure, and whether it's parallel or serial transmission, for example. It also includes the signaling and the modulation technique used by the hardware to transmit the data. In the postal system, this is the equivalent of the conveyance, whether it's the postman, the truck, the airplane or whatever.

Different vendors are now able to develop compatible products for any of the seven layers. The seven layers reside in a computer. Layer 1, Physical, is hardware for the physical connection (for example, the Ethernet port); layers 2 through 7 are software "modules."

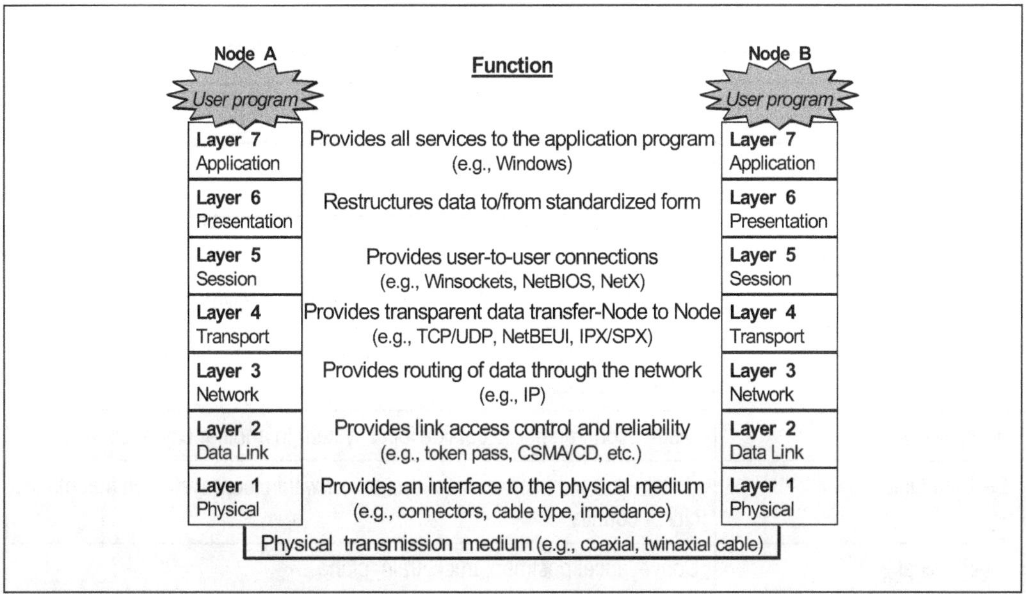

Figure 25-3. International Communications Standard

Brief Summary of the Seven-Layer OSI Reference Model

7—Provides all services directly comprehensible to application programs.

6—Restructures data to/from the standardized format used within the network.

5—Name/address translation to access security and synchronize/manage data.

4—Provides transparent, reliable data transfer from end node to end node.

3—Performs message routing for data transfer between nodes not in the same LAN.

2—Provides a means to establish, maintain and release logical data links between systems; transfers data frames between nodes in same LAN; and detects errors.

1—Encodes and physically transfers messages between adjacent nodes.

Continuing the postal analogy for all the communications layers, we want to send a letter or package to a person in another city or country. We do not need to know any of the intermediate steps; we just put the proper address information ("header") on the package and let the other layers handle the delivery details. We do not care about the tracking numbers, routing, and so on. Likewise, the receiver does not need to understand the routing to receive the letter or package. The user layer, or the program above Layer 7, is the actual information (significance of the words) in the letter content, or the function of the item being sent.

Table 25-1.
All Communications Models Come from Human Activity

OSI Layer	Postal System Equivalent
7—Application	Letter contents within envelope
6—Presentation	Format and language of letter, including proper translation into another language, if needed
5—Session	Name, address, zip code of both sender and receiver
4—Transport	Certified or registered mail; verification to sender that letter arrived at correct destination
3—Network	Distribution transfer to outside local system to another city or country
2—Data Link	Distribution within same local system, or within local system in that other city or country
1—Physical	Conveyance: postman, truck, train, plane...

As the user data moves through the seven layers, each layer adds a piece of addressing information called a header, or footer (Figure 25-4). Each layer does its job independently of the other layers, and different choices are available at each layer. Each layer's header is independent of the other layers' headers. There is no special interface required between layers.

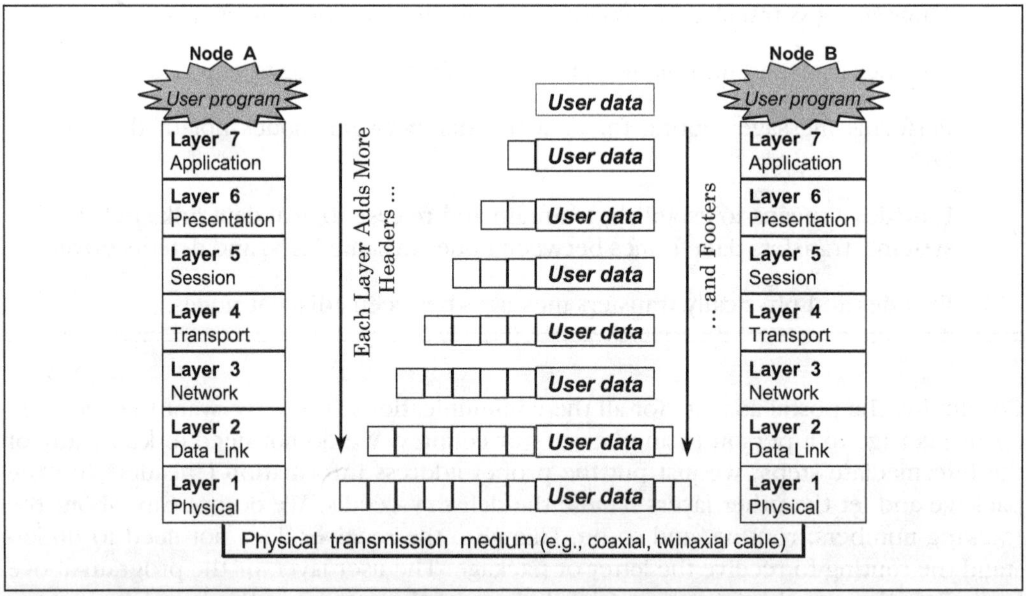

Figure 25-4. Each of the Seven Layers Adds Communications Overhead

Enhanced Performance Architecture (EPA)

EPA is a simplified OSI model for use when the network is not so complex, such as you would find in the fieldbus structure (Figure 25-5). This is divided into three areas:

- **Application services**—which is the application layer, Layer 7;
- **Transport protocol**—which encompasses the network, transport, session, and presentation layers, 3 through 6;
- **Media**—which would be Layers 1 and 2, the physical and the data link layers.

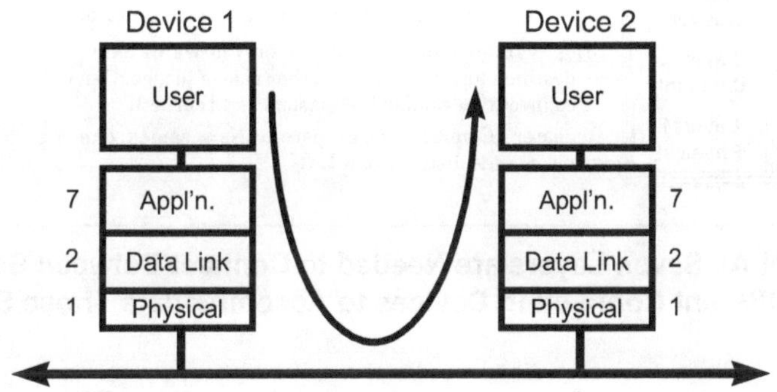

Figure 25-5. EPA Uses Subset of OSI, Cannot Cross to Other Networks, But Must Stay Within its Own

EPA enables some less complex devices on more simple communications links to be more easily defined. It is in this arena that many of the standardizing committees are working to make some accessible standards available without having to define all of seven separate sessions (layers). Most of the fieldbus efforts are here, where only digital input-output (I/O) links are defined.

In this enhanced performance architecture, or EPA, the only concern is with the user "above" the application layer, the data link, and the physical layers. Our post office analogy of the user layer is the information request that is the common language one can read and understand. The application layer is the paper that contains the message, and that is placed into the data link layer which is the envelope that addresses the to and from and carries the stamp. The physical layer is the mailbox that delivers the envelope to the media, and the physical media or the wire is the truck that transports the envelope independently of whatever message was put into it.

Shortcuts Between Networks

Each of the seven layers needs a header of code. All of these individual headers become the overhead, adding to the complexity and hence the expense, vulnerability, and delay of the transmission. Many times, however, it isn't necessary to go through all of the layers if the connected networks already have some of the functions in common (Figure 25-6). Whenever possible, "simple is better."

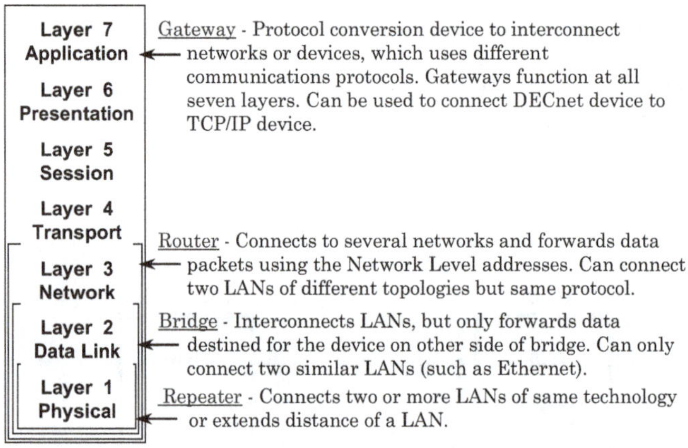

Figure 25-6. Not All Seven Layers are Needed to Connect Between Some Networks So There Are Different Connecting Devices to Accommodate Those Situations

For example, you can "bridge" across the data link layer (Layer 2) so your information only needs to convert through these two layers to reach a network of devices designed to recognize the same level of data organization and structure. A single vendor can provide its own proprietary communications network for much less cost because the bridge is built into all stations designed to operate on it.

To transfer across different networks, it is necessary to use a "router" that interconnects different networks at the transport layer (Layer 4). A "brouter" performs many of the tasks of bridges and routers without the protocol restrictions of a router, which is more expensive, complex, and difficult to install. A "gateway," however, is needed to translate all seven layers so as to move from one system to another (generally between different vendors). Of course, that requires a much more complex (expensive) device.

gateway—A protocol conversion device used to interconnect networks or devices, which uses different communications protocols. Gateways function at all seven layers. A gateway would be used to connect a DECnet device to a TCP/IP device.

router—Connects to several networks and forwards data packets using the Network Level addresses. Can connect two LANs of different topologies but the same protocol.

bridge—Interconnects LANs but only forwards data destined for a device on the other side of the bridge. A bridge can only connect two similar LANs (Ethernet—Ethernet/ token ring—token ring).

repeater—Connects two or more LANs of the same technology or extends the distance of a LAN.

Some Other Communications Standards

- TCP/IP: Transmission Control Protocol/Internet Protocol

  By the way, it is becoming common for CSMACD (a *media access* technique) to be confused with TCP/IP (a *communication* protocol) TCP/IP has the following characteristics:

  — Developed by U.S. Department of Defense in 1974

  — A de facto standard network protocol to connect UNIX systems

  — Does not extend to physical and data link layers, hardware interface is beyond its scope. Since TCP/IP is media independent it has been implemented on variety of media.

  — It is software for Layers 3 (Network) and 4 (Transport). It handles the routing of data to the correct location and error checking to ensure that the data is received intact.

  — It can use Ethernet, token ring, or other standards at Levels 1 and 2.

  — It is the most widely used software at these levels, in large part because it comes as part of UNIX, the most widely used workstation operating system.

  — It is not necessary that the TCP/IP software come from the same vendor (but sometimes it helps).

  — **TCP:** Transport layer (Layer 4). Segments data into packets and verifies that the message got to its destination intact.

  — **IP:** Network layer (Layer 3). Routes data over network to correct LAN address.

  — **UDP** (User Datagram Protocol). Alternative to TCP that does not require the acknowledgment of messages, requires less overhead, and offers higher performance relative to TCP/IP.

- FDDI: Fiber Distributed Data Interface

  — Developed by ANSI in late 1980s

  — Similar to IEEE 802.5 token ring LAN standard

  — Physical and data link layers of OSI model (Layers 1 and 2)

  — Token pass access method at 100 Mbps

  — 200 kilometers (approximately 120 miles)

  — Often used as backbone, with bridges to Ethernet

  — CDDI (copper version) covers shorter distances, but takes advantage of installed cable systems

---

FDDI (Fiber Distributed Data Interface). ANSI standard for fiber-optic links with data rates to 100 Mbps; two 50Mbps counter-rotational token rings, synchronous, prioritized.

FDDI-II—Variant of FDDI that supports isosynchronous traffic.

CDDI (Copper Distribution Data Interface). Unshielded twisted pair, shielded twisted pair, dual-grade twisted-pair options.

isochronous—Equally timed. In data communications, timing information is transmitted on channel along with data, sending asynchronous data by synchronous means. The isochronous method involves synchronously sending asynchronous characters between each pair of start and stop bits.

asynchronous—Computer logic or communications in which all operations are triggered by a free-running signal not related to specific frequency or timing; successive stages are triggered by the completion of the preceding stage.

synchronous—Logic or communications in which all operations are controlled by clock pulses. Synchronous transmission eliminates the need for start and stop bits because everything is sent at a fixed rate.

- NetBEUI: NetBIOS Extended User Interface
  - The primary protocol used by Windows for Workgroups, supported in all of Microsoft's network products.
  - First introduced by IBM in 1985.
  - Small and efficient protocol designed for use on a departmental LAN of twenty to two-hundred workstations.
  - NetBIOS is a network Basic Input/Output System (BIOS), a high-level session-layer interface used by applications to communicate with NetBIOS compliant transports such as NetBEUI.
  - BIOS (Basic Input/Output System). Commands are used to tell the CPU how it will communicate with the rest of the computer. It contains the information typically needed upon start-up.
  - NetBIOS is a communications interface to PC-*DOS* applications.

Communicating Between Software Applications: DDE

In addition to the hardware and software needed to link networks, the actual applications must also be connected. This is especially true now that so many control and operating software packages are being developed to operate in common hardware. Often, the hardware may be common but located in different parts of the plant! Sometimes the hardware does not have all that much in common, but working between similar platforms does make this effort easier.

In Figure 25-7 we see two popular application interface options are Application Program Interface (API) and Dynamic Data Exchange (DDE). Use DDE when simple interfacing is required. DDE needs no programming, just configuration. DDE is only available for Windows but is often used for interfacing to other foreign devices, such as PLCs, when that other device has DDE Server software. No custom programming is required, only the mapping of data points. As the 1990s draw to a close, at least one major supplier of control systems for operating on NT platforms has introduced the much better performing NetDDE, which Microsoft has licensed. A still faster version has been released, and like the NetDDE it will also work with existing equipment designed for DDE.

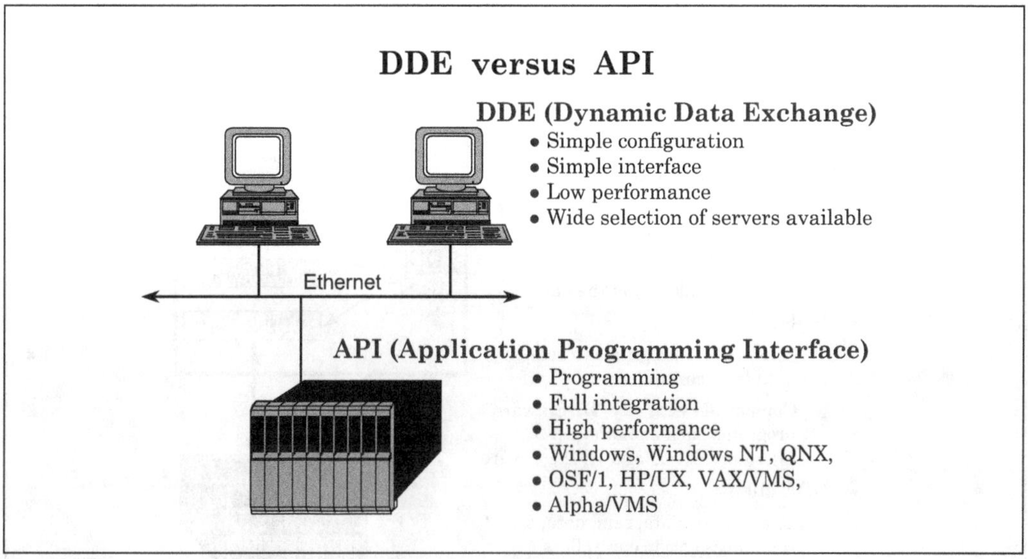

Figure 25-7. Interfacing Between Two Different Applications

An API, on the other hand, gives a more complete interface, has much higher performance, and allows full integration of databases. However, it requires programming. It is available for use with many platforms.

API (Application Program Interface). A set of formalized software calls and routines that can be referenced by some application programs to access underlying network services. Programs that use API-compliant calls can communicate with any others that use that same API. API is an interface between the applications software and the application platform.

DDE (Dynamic Data Exchange). DDE is a Microsoft developed interapplication communications protocol in which data from one program automatically updates another. Originally designed to move data from a spreadsheet to a word processor; DDE is the baseline protocol for OLE 1.0 but not for OLE 2.0 (It is supported there, however, in order to maintain upward compatibility). DDE has become more complex with the advent of Windows and WindowsNT in industrial applications, causing wags to refer to it as "Different Dynamics to Everyone."

DDE is a standard communications protocol that allows several different Windows programs to share data. DDE is a simple connection between applications; it does not understand the data itself. The *application* has the responsibility to understand the data. DDE is included with Windows.

In Figure 25-8 the DDE server is a Windows program that allows other programs to access data from the controller. It is compatible with any "DDE-aware" programs such as Lotus 1-2-3, Microsoft Excel, and Wonderware Intouch (an HMI package). The DDE client can request data, send data, and send messages over a network to the controller through the DDE server.

- **DDE:**
  - Standard communications protocol
  - Allows several programs to share data
  - Simple connection between applications
  - Does not understand the data
- **DDE server:**
  - Allows other programs to access data from controllers
  - Compatible with any "DDE-aware" programs such as Lotus 1-2-3, Microsoft Excel, and HMI software
- **DDE client:**
  - Can request data, send data, and send messages to controllers through DDE server

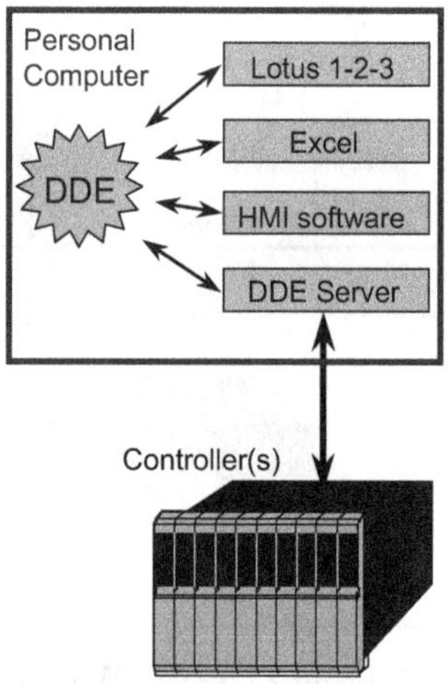

Figure 25-8. Dynamic Data Exchange Flow

Often we wish to get controller data inexpensively to a computer in the manager's office. Purchasing an entire workstation would be too expensive if all that is needed for the manager is data for a spreadsheet but no color graphics and continuous process trend views, which are appropriate for the operator. NetDDE can help expand the data to this additional station (Figure 25-9). It was developed by Wonderware, who established an alliance with Microsoft to ensure that NetDDE is fully compatible with DDE.

In the system shown in Figure 25-8 the computer for Manager 1 gets its controller data from the controller DDE server, and the computer for Manager 2 gets its controller data from Manager 1 via NetDDE.

Communicating Between Software Applications: OPC

Object linking and embedding (OLE) was developed by Microsoft to provide component object models (COMs) that serve as the basis for integrating applications. It is, however, a very broad specification that covers hundreds of ways of sharing information among programs. There is no assurance that programs will work together just because they are listed as OLE-compliant.

A consortium of five vendors drafted a specification in 1995 to define OLE for process control (OPC). This is a standard set of interfaces, properties, and methods that applies

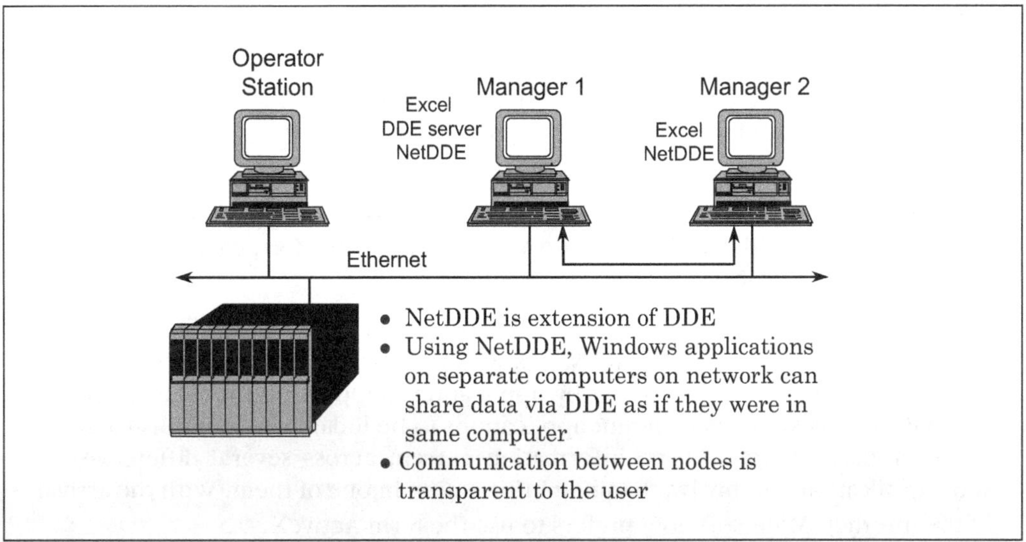

Figure 25-9. Inexpensive Sharing Data with Another Device

OLE and COM technologies to make possible greater interoperability between automation and control applications and the field systems and devices in real-time applications.

ActiveX (Active component eXtension). A Binary reusable software object that plugs into object linking and embedding (OLE) software, allowing different software packages to communicate, and interact with one another in a networked environment thus making possible plant floor integration through the Internet and intranets. Since the advent of the Internet, Microsoft has preferred to use this term over OLE because of its expanded scope (and flashier marketing).

COM (Component Object Model). In computing, a connection mechanism and protocol used to link different applications in object linking and embedding (OLE) environment. Allows the development of independent, interoperable software objects; de facto object standard by Microsoft competing with CORBA*.

CORBA—Common Object Request Broker Architecture; approach to creating open object-oriented system architectures; specifies interoperability of Object Request Brokers (ORBs); this emerging object oriented programming standard is being presented by Object Management Group (OMG); planned by 11 companies including IBM®, H-P®, Sunsoft®; competes with de facto object standard COM* by Microsoft®.

DCOM (Distributed Common Object Model). Extends common object model for the network communication of independent, interoperable software objects.

Java—Software code which can rum on multiple platforms (UNIX, OS/2, NT, MACINTOSH, etc.); originally developed by Sun Microsystems Inc. as a platform for programming on small embedded devices such as cell phones, PDAs and sensors; claimed to be more simple than C++, it has significant implications for use on Internet applications.

Java Beans—Reusable chunks of Java software code that can be assembled as components in larger applications.

OCX (OLE custom controls eXtension). Object-oriented software building blocks that save considerable programming time in the creation of applications. Theoretically, OCX can readily be plugged into Visual Basic, Visual C++, databases, spreadsheets, and word processors.

OLE (object linking and embedding). In computers, an application integration feature of Microsoft Windows and WindowsNT environments that treats data as a collection of objects to be shared by applications supporting the OLE specification. OLE enables several different applications to be linked to accomplish a given task and allows them to keep information current across several different software applications simply by changing information in one of them. With the arrival of the Internet, Microsoft now prefers to use the term ActiveX.

OLE-PC (object linking and embedding for process control). OLE extensions to improve interoperability among different industrial automation devices and software. Now frequently called OPC. See *OPC.*

OPC (OLE-PC; object linking and embedding for process control). The task force of a consortium created to rapidly develop an OLE-based interface standard for manufacturing automation to improve interoperability among industrial devices and software. Includes AEG Schneider, Applied Automation, Aspen Technology, Fisher-Rosemount, Fluke, Gensym, Hewlett-Packard, Honeywell, Hitachi, Intellution, Intuitive Technology, Moore Products, National Instruments, Rockwell Software, Siemens, USDATA, and Wonderware.

*See table comparing COM with CORBA.

Being an OPC server in a distributed control system (DCS) is only part of the communication issue. The OPC client needs to use these interfaces to push or pull data from the running system. OPC is commonly used in human machine interfaces, alarm managers, and historians. In the late 1990s the question arose about how fast OPC really is and if it can be used across a *network* connection. While OPC is adequate for communicating with servers running on the same machine as the client, most people like to distribute OPC servers in their own PCs. When an OPC server is located on a separate machine than the client, DCOM needs to be used to transfer data. If the communication transactions are based upon standard marshaling, then OPC servers tend to be slow. There are those at the end of the 1990s who see great promise in this technology but at the same time felt that if a DCS is using OPC for client and server communication for all real-time data, then significant performance considerations arise as the size of the system grows.

Competing Objects to Link Applications

If you began reading the definitions in the sidebar-box, you may have picked up on two different software object oriented programming standards. One uses Common Object

Models (COM) to link applications, the other uses the Common Object Request Broker Architecture (CORBA). It is, of course, a difference between Microsoft®, who uses the former, and the Object Management Group (OMG), a consortium of companies who use the latter. The table compares these two approaches:

Comparing COM with CORBA—COM only rules wherever Microsoft rules, and is extremely platform restricted. CORBA, however, is really the only platform-independent object standard:

COM	CORBA
Advantages	
Supports scripting languages, which makes for simpler development	Platform independent
Native integration with Windows environment	Fast developing synergy between CORBA and Java standards
Has an object component container model	Supports multiple instances
Free with Windows and Microsoft products	
Disadvantages	
Extremely platform restricted (Windows only)	Requires sophisticated programming skills
Outside Windows environment COM is as complex to use as CORBA	Little support for scripting languages
Does not support multiple instance	Lacks a component container model
	Not free, CORBA ORBs must be purchased from a vendor

Communication from Afar

There are times where it is convenient to view the process from somewhere away from the plant site. The blue-sky people could say these could be when salesmen need to view the progress of the order or a manager needs to look into the health of the operation. More realistically such remote process viewing is for the plant engineer troubleshooting control configurations or for a vendor who has permission to look in on some new innovation, or perhaps review a particularly obstinate service problem (they do happen, you know, even in the best of systems).

Never do you ever want to *control* blindly from afar, except for some very simple actions, like turning a specific piece of equipment on or off!

The standard workstations and networks used in some control systems have made applications such as remote dial-in a simple solution. By connecting a modem to one of the communication ports, you can access the controller data from anywhere in the world that has a telephone (Figure 25-10). From a remote location, you can display and manipulate any program that could be displayed and manipulated at the plant site: operator interface, controller configuration, and the like. Dial-in from a remote site provides benefits such as off-site process and system troubleshooting and allows applications such as unmanned sites. This architecture can be accomplished in a few ways. Dial-in access can be password-protected.

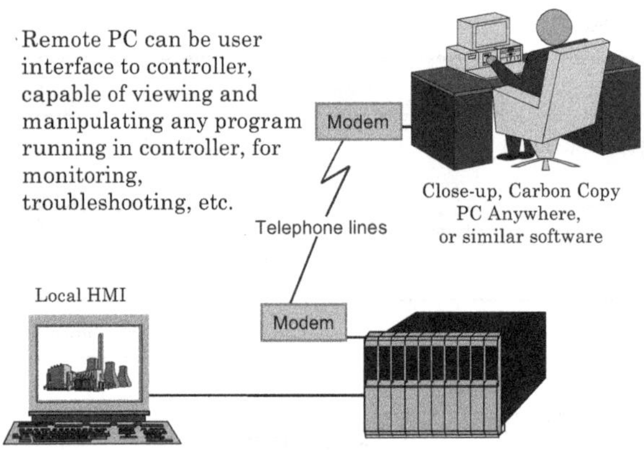

Figure 25-10. Reconfiguration from Distant Engineering Location

In the PC architecture, dial-in can come from a remote PC to the operator interface PC using one of several commercial software packages (Figure 25-11). The monitor, keyboard, and mouse signals are being sent over the phone lines through phone modems at each end. In this architecture, the host PC has the necessary software for its normal function along with the remote software package, while the remote PC only needs the remote software. The software mimics the host PC on the remote PC, allowing the remote user to have full control of the host PC while the user of the host PC watches and vice versa. In some systems, you only need to purchase controller software for the plant site; the remote computer actually manipulates the software that resides in the controller access port.

The second method uses a communications protocol called SLIP (Serial Line Internet Protocol). In the SLIP architecture the appropriate software must be on the remote PC, and only data is transferred over the phone lines. In this architecture, the local modem is connected to the serial port of the controller. In the workstation architecture a remote workstation or X terminal can access a workstation over the phone lines using the X windows protocol and PPP (Point-to-Point Protocol). This option gives the remote station all the functions that are available on a local X terminal.

Spread Spectrum Radio Technology

There are many emerging needs for wireless communications for linking the remote areas of an operation. Off shore oilrigs, pipelines, and even large water plants have this

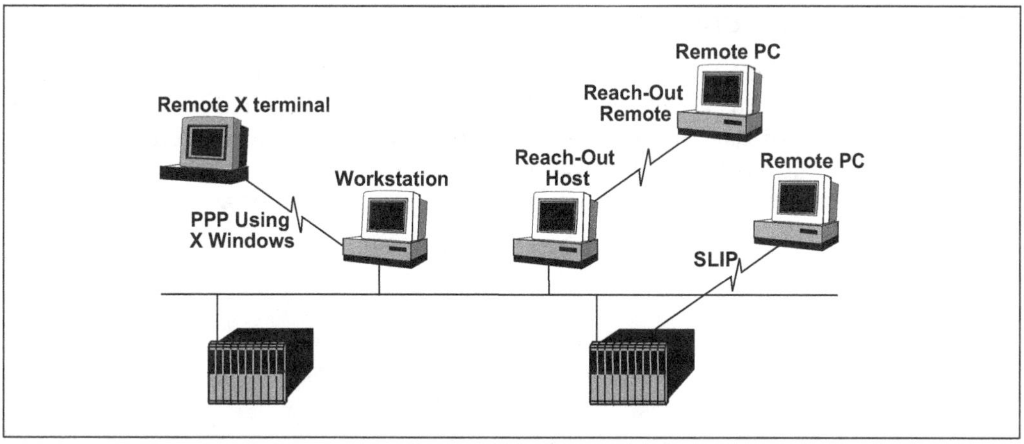

Figure 25-11. Remote Dial-in for Monitoring and Troubleshooting

need. There can be severe limitations to this approach, so it is better to operate as a "true" SCADA system. (As we said earlier, many people erroneously refer to a simple data acquisition and control (DAC) system as a SCADA system). In such a system, there must be very carefully thought out control strategies to allow for frequent, sudden interruptions. "Check-before-execute" routines must be thoroughly understood and implemented.

Several methods of communication can be used, including microwave, satellite, and radio. One radio technology to reduce the impact of interference is spread spectrum signals (Figure 25-12). The spread spectrum signal is created by modulating the radio frequency signal with a spreading sequence code or by "hopping" the frequency of the carrier signal. This was originally developed for the U.S. military to prevent jamming.

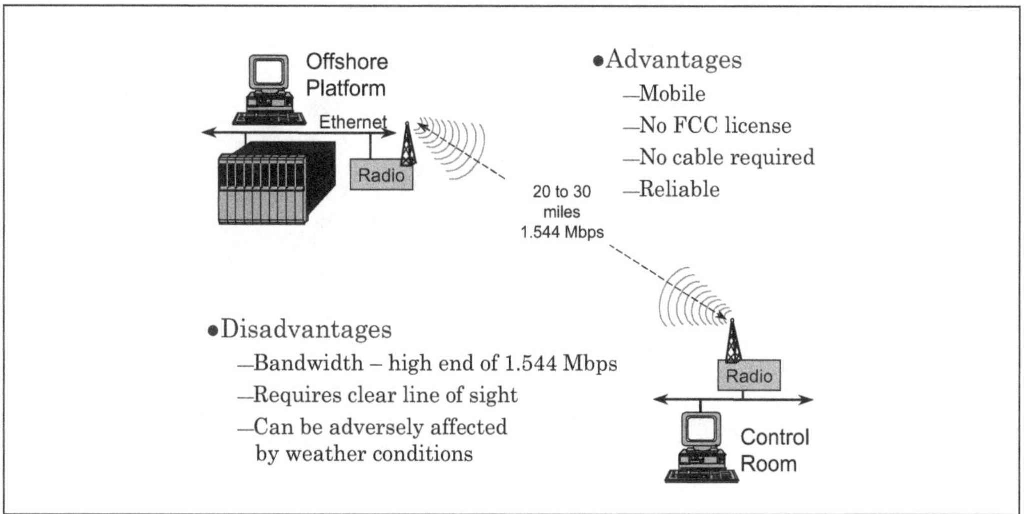

Figure 25-12. Spread Spectrum Radio

Cellular Phone Technology

An emerging wireless digital communications technology in the late 1990s that is useful for "true" SCADA systems is Cellular Digital Packet Data (CDPD). This uses a technique that sends packets of data using existing cellular communications technology for a given region. While cost is a constraining factor with CDPD, this technology has proved effective for regions without direct telephone or leased lines.

Digital Field Communications 26

In the previous four chapters, we discussed systemwide networks. There are also digital networks between controllers and their inputs and outputs. Several "standard" digital networks have been devised, many of which have been encouraged by the vendors who designed them and who hoped for de facto acceptance. There is nothing wrong with this multiple approach, because these designs have been created to fill product gaps left by the lack of any standards to meet specific communication needs!

All of the various network designs have serious merit for their intended use, and many have been innovative enough to be expanded to more comprehensive uses. The one we have selected for discussion here is only one of those that was *not* selected; however, it was an ISA development and this book is published by ISA. Fieldbus Foundation (FF) fieldbus has been picked because it is the first one that has addressed the user layer and, as such, represents the most comprehensive such design to date.

Fieldbus—A digital, serial, multidrop, two-way communication path among industrial field equipment such as sensors, actuators, controllers, and even control room devices. Fieldbus is a specific ISA SP50 (Fieldbus Foundation) standard for digital communications operating at the lowest level of data communications (I/Os) in automation systems. It allows for communication and interoperability among "smart" field devices and control system devices from multiple vendors; it also supports information access for monitoring, control, and alarm tasks during plant start-up, operation, and maintenance. As this standard is developing and gaining interest, two versions are emerging: H1 for linking sensors and actuators to control devices, and H2 for functioning as a full blown data highway on a more sophisticated scale.

Fieldbus Communication Services (FCS)—In the context of the Fieldbus Foundation, FCS is a messaging sublayer that the application layer provides to access remote application process objects and their object directory descriptions.

Why Digital Field Communications?

The problem is that we have had microprocessor-based transmitters, instruments and actuators, using digital technology for years now, but up through the 1990s we are still communicating using an analog technology for communication (Figure 26-1). This limits the information that can already come into the control system as well as the information that can go to the various field devices!

The conventional signal links a transmitter to a device that requires the signal. Typically, this is done using an analog representation of the primary value (Figure 26-2).

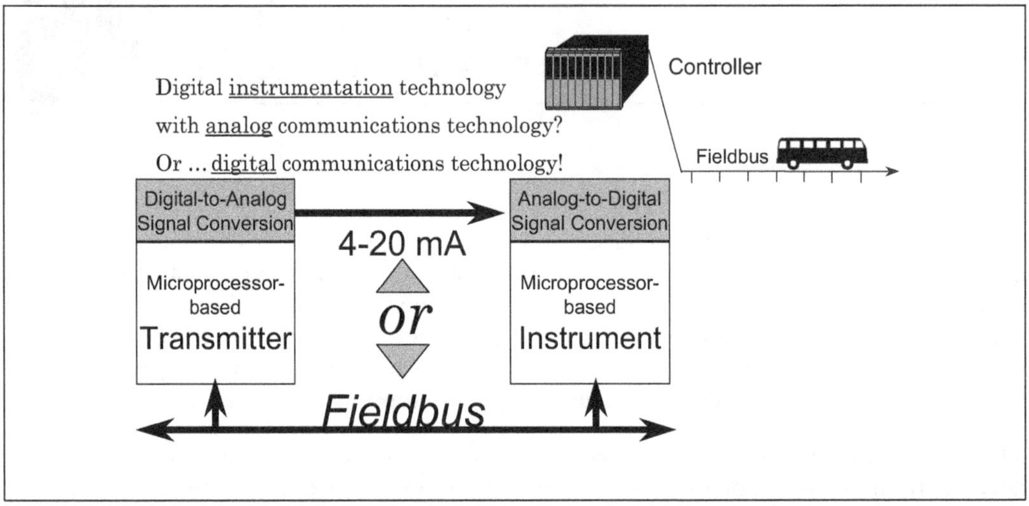

Figure 26-1. Which Is Better. . .Analog or Digital Field Communications?

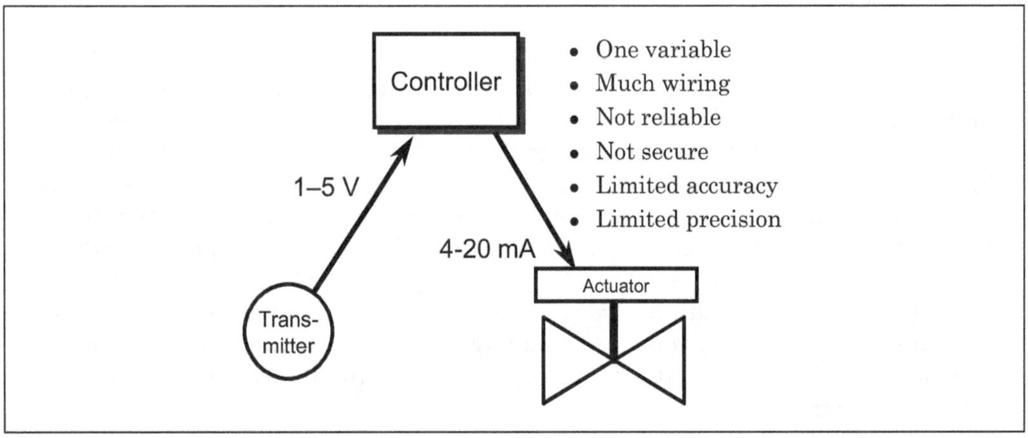

Figure 26-2. Traditional Analog Technology

For actuators, the process is the same. These shortcomings limit the very advantages offered by the remainder of the digital control system.

The basic problem is that microprocessor-based devices are converting their digital values to analog signals, transmitting them and then converting them back to digital signals (Figure 26-3). What is needed is a standard digital communications protocol that allows intelligent devices to share much information and permits a multidrop instrumentation network! (Figure 26-4)

To better understand the evolution of fieldbus, we should first look at the evolution of control and monitoring. In the beginning, there was LOCAL control and monitoring (Figure 26-5).

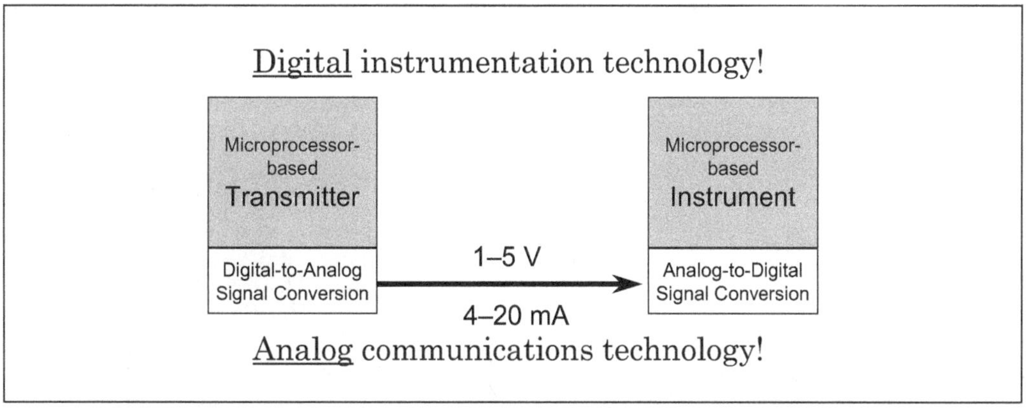

Figure 26-3. Much Wasteful Conversion Exists Today with Conventional Signals

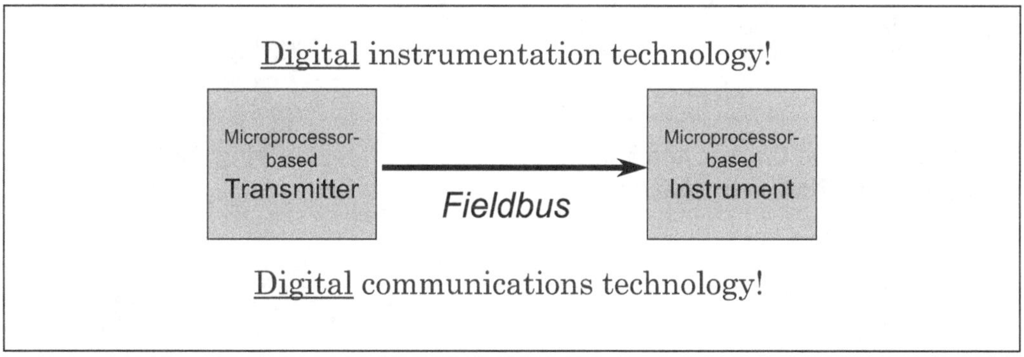

Figure 26-4. Fieldbus Is Specifically Designed For Digital Communication Among Digital Instrumentation

There were advantages:

- Not much wiring

And also disadvantages:

- Not much control
- Not much monitoring
- Not much alarming.

Then, with the advent of the minicomputer the local equipment was replaced with computer equipment at the control room, and all the points were wired to the control room. We called it centralized control and monitoring (Figure 26-6).

This increased the advantages:

- Central view of process
- Flexible control
- Flexible alarming
- History, events

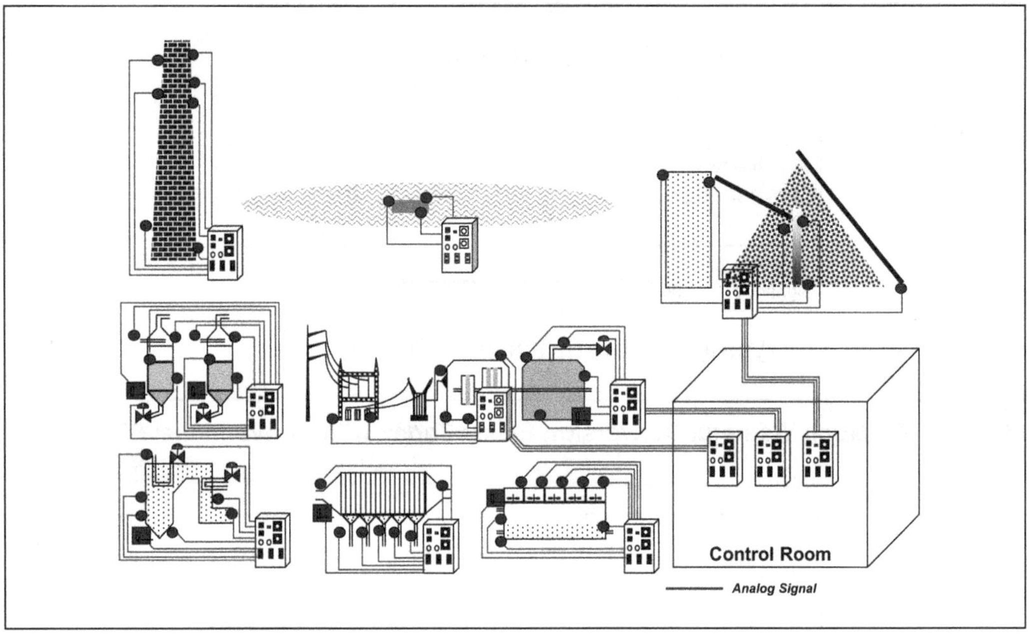

Figure 26-5. When Control and Monitoring Were Local and Analog; Not All Control Panels Were in the Control Room

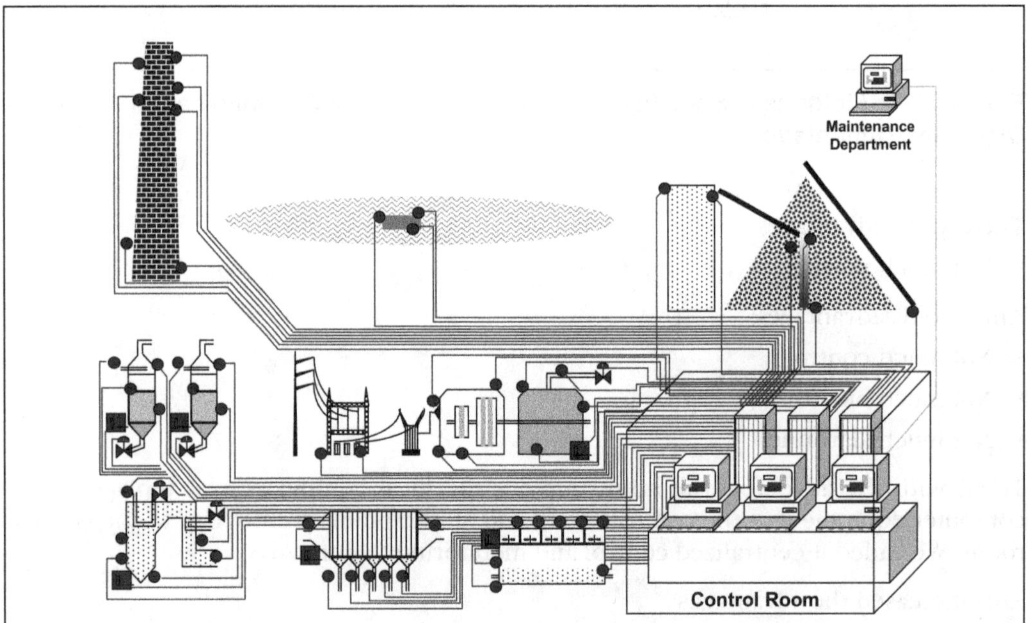

Figure 26-6. Direct Digital Control (DDC) and Monitoring in Mainframe Computer Brought About Central Control From a Single Control Room

But still left with disadvantages:

- Wiring costs
- Risk of losing all control
- Not scalable.

Next, with the advent of the microprocessor the massive wiring was no longer necessary, the I/O equipment was distributed throughout the plant, proprietary digital data highways were added to interconnect the distributed processing units, and we called it DISTRIBUTED control and monitoring (Figure 26-7).

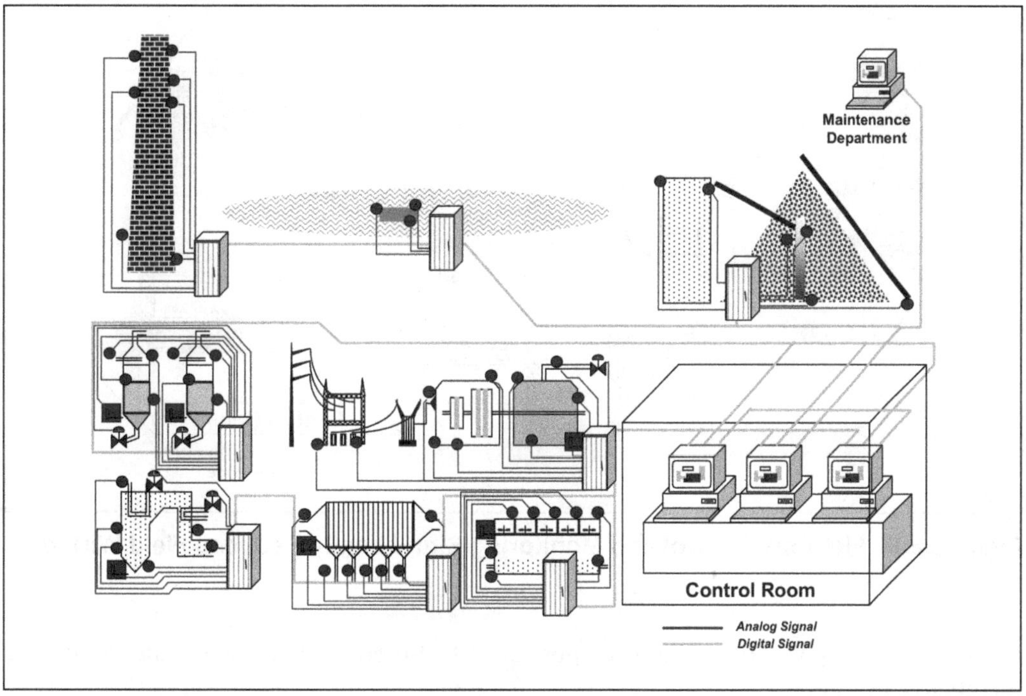

Figure 26-7. Microprocessor Allowed the Design of Distributed Control and Monitoring to Happen

This added to the central computer's advantages:

- Shorter wire runs
- More scalability
- Far less risk of losing all of the process or plant through a simple computer failure.

However, it still retained some disadvantages:

- Still had significant wiring, and
- It could only be made possible through proprietary systems, causing vendor interconnection problems.

Then, however, came a two-way, multidrop, digital communications standard *designed* for control and monitoring rather than modifying a design from another purpose. This approach permitted digital communications lines directly to the transmitters and actuators and allowed the devices to fully exploit their digital capabilities. It was called "FIELDBUS control and monitoring" (Figure 26-8).

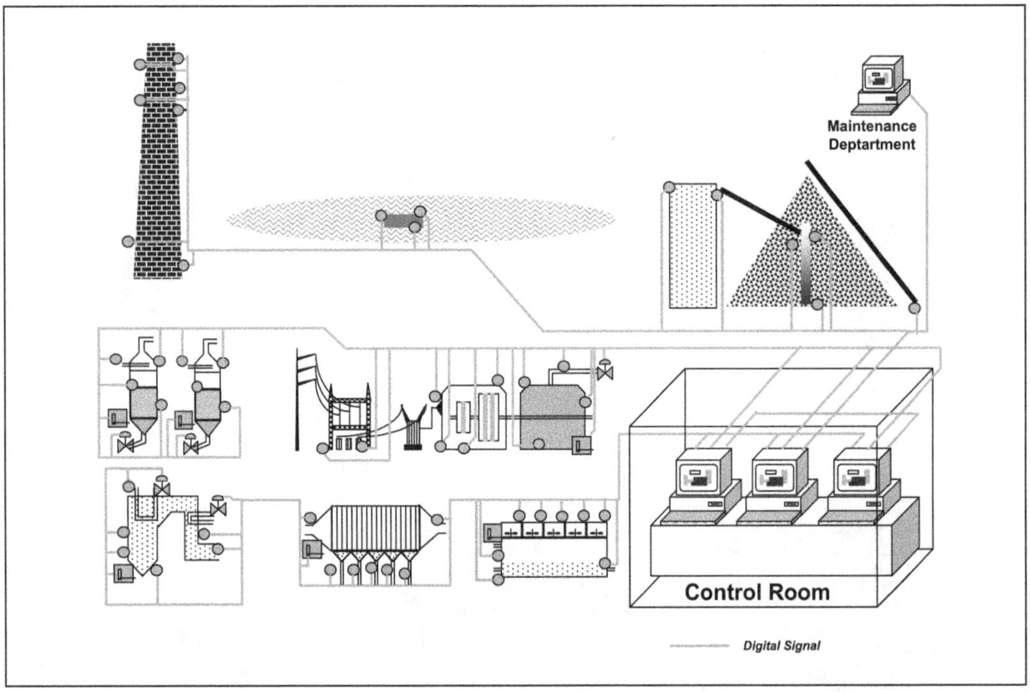

Figure 26-8. Fieldbus Control and Monitoring Significantly Reduces Field Wiring

Fieldbus has expanded the advantages of distributed control with the following features:

- Greatly reduced *wiring*
- Even more *scalability*
- Still less *risk*
- Multivendor *interoperability* (due to an open global standard)
- Can interconnect *DCSs and PLCs*
- Control can be *local* (again!)
- *New opportunities* for advanced features for the manufacturers and the users (e.g., self-tune, fuzzy logic, neural networks).

Advantages of Fieldbus

These architectural advantages to Fieldbus (Figure 26-9), lead us to a list of the benefits of fieldbus which can be placed into three categories: installation, operation, and maintenance.

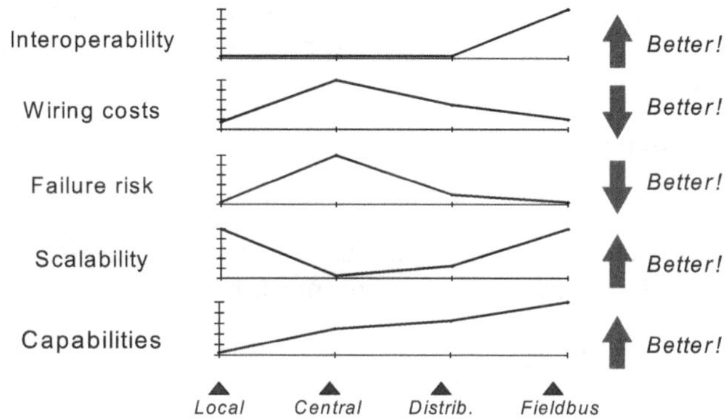

Figure 26-9. Architectural Changes in Control Systems Changed Benefits Picture

Installation benefits include:

- Fieldbus is multidrop, which reduces the amount of wiring and the costs, not just of the wire, but also of the terminations and testing of all this wiring.
- Fieldbus provides standardized access methods to the device parameters of both sensors and end elements over the wire, thereby enabling remote configuration. This improves the accessibility of those devices, especially those mounted in outside environments. The use of digital signals will also increase the accuracy of calibration. Incorrect model numbers, for example, which can "report back" when digitally accessed, will show up before start-ups, saving considerable time and expense.
- Fieldbus defines enough user services to provide interoperability so that users *may select* from multiple suppliers. A single supplier cannot supply *all* of a user's needs! Why should the user have to compromise? (Shouldn't the user be able to take advantage of specialized products?)

Operating benefits include:

- The use of digital floating-point representation permits the transmission of numeric information with no chance of the degradation that can happen with an analog signal. Inaccuracies are not introduced in the transmission step.
- That same seven-digit digital floating-point representation also provides far more precision than its analog counterpart.

- Digital signals eliminate the worry over bad control actions as a result of bad signals. Digital transmission ensures better control, which leads to less wasted product and energy both of which directly improve profit.
- More information will be made available from fieldbus devices because it is so easy to gather information at essentially no extra cost. For example, a transmitter that has temperature compensation for its pH or conductivity calculation will be able to transmit the temperature in addition to the pH or conductivity.
- Digital signals are more secure because they have the safeguards needed to detect errors and degradation of signal due for any reason; whereas analog signals have little or no safeguards. Reliability reduces downtime.

Maintenance benefits include:

- Less maintenance because of the increased reliability of digital technology.
- Faster maintenance because digital diagnostics can be specific, leading to faster correction and complete, automatic documentation.
- Access to numerous parameters within smart devices makes *remote* diagnostics possible (Figure 26-10) and sometimes maintenance as well.
- An open standard of this depth permits the *interchangeability* of similarly functioning products. Therefore, at replacement time the user again can select the most appropriate vendor.

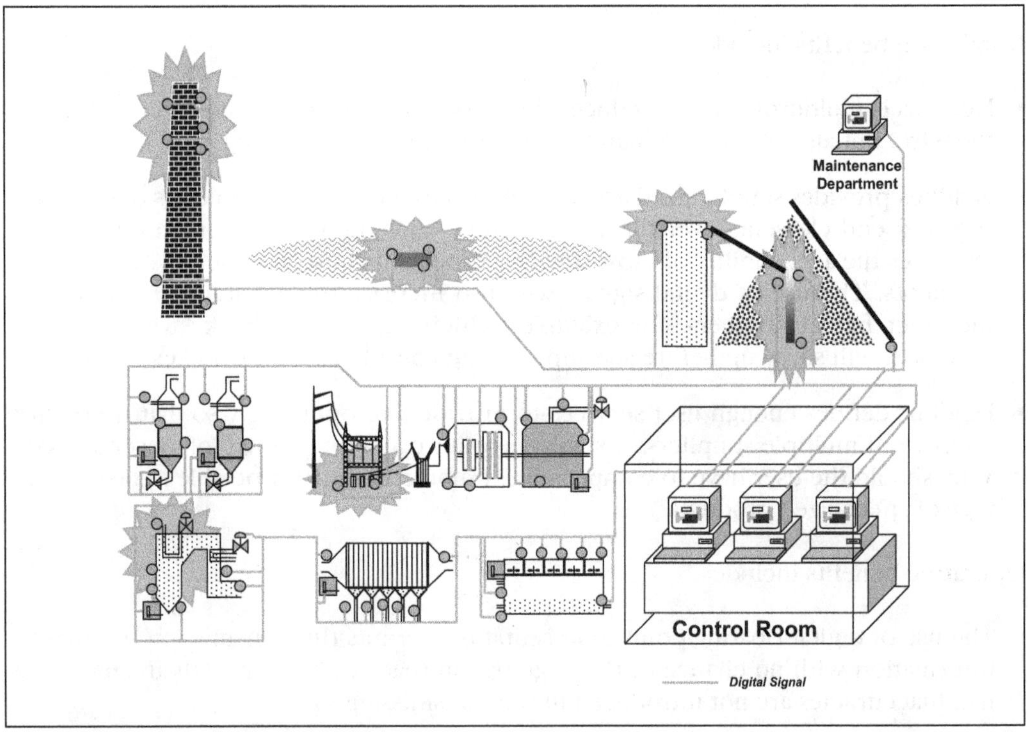

Figure 26-10. Fieldbus Allows Remote Diagnostics Through Standard Access to Calibration and Maintenance Attributes

Consider those devices that are high, hot, wet, located in dangerous places, and hard to access. Fieldbus permits standardized access to calibration and maintenance attributes as well as to the information provided by the vendor. A disk from the vendor can be used to load appropriate information into the user's workstation to allow access to any of the features provided by that vendor, including calibration and diagnostic information.

Interoperability and Interchangeability

What do these two terms mean? Interchangeability permits you to replace a device from one vender with that of a similarly functioning product from another. They will each have the same complete access to other devices on the same network. For example, no "reprogramming" of other devices by the user will be necessary to accept the change.

Interoperability, on the other hand, is the ability to tightly interconnect devices from two different vendors. They will operate together both properly and closely, sharing status and all parameters.

Fieldbus provides interoperability by defining the following:

- Electrical signal
- Media access protocol
- Communications handshaking protocol
- Supported data types
- The method to describe the device over the wire
- Comprehensive function blocks
- Modes and status
- Cascade initialization, fail-safe propagation
- The alarm and event reporting mechanism

Differentiating Fieldbus Vendors

A common fear regarding standards that are detailed enough to ensure interoperability is that they will prohibit innovation by holding vendors to the functions in the standard. However, vendors have plenty of room to show product differentiation and innovation:

- Quality of sales, training, delivery, documentation, service, and support
- Quality of the product, accuracy, precision, and robustness, maintainability
- Superior measurement/actuator technology
- Functions beyond the standard
- Application expertise, both through added features and assistance to user
- Value, ruggedness, features included

None of these are addressed by the standard.

How Fieldbus Works

Fieldbus uses a subset of the ISO's OSI Reference called Enhanced Performance Architecture (EPA) model which omits Layers 3 through 6:

3: Network 4: Transport 5: Session 6: Presentation

Fieldbus uses the other three layers (Figure 26-11):

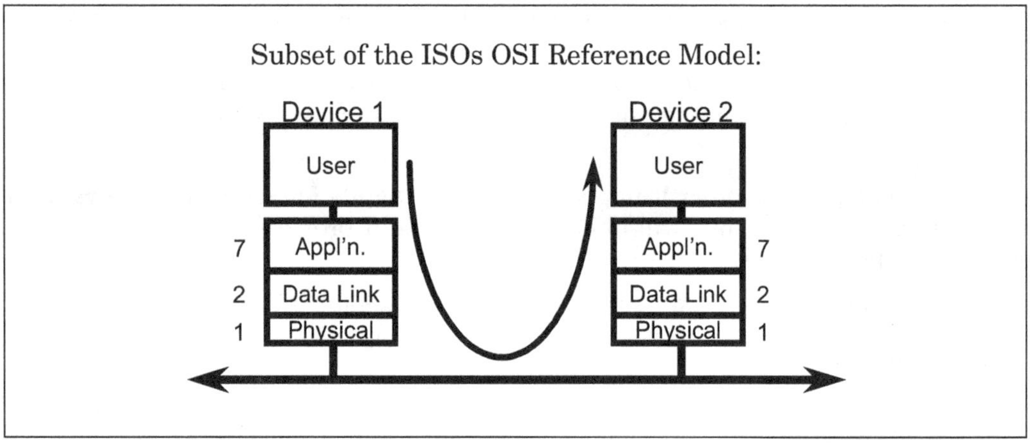

Figure 26-11. Fieldbus Uses the Enhanced Performance Architecture (EPA) Model

1: Physical Layer

—Signal characteristics, preamble/postamble, frame check sequence

2: Data Link Layer

—Media access protocol, reliable message transfer, cyclic and acyclic services

7: Application Layer

—Naming and addressing, variable access, uploading and downloading

In addition, Fieldbus uniquely has included a user layer. This layer defines the function blocks with mode and status, events and alarms, and device descriptions (Figure 26-12). The user layer is device oriented and database oriented and is not considered a communication layer. The application layer that is the highest layer is message oriented.

Because the user layer defines the behavior of the device, it is the most important layer.

A **function block** is:

- An algorithm
- Set of defined inputs, user-connected
- Set of defined outputs, user-connectable

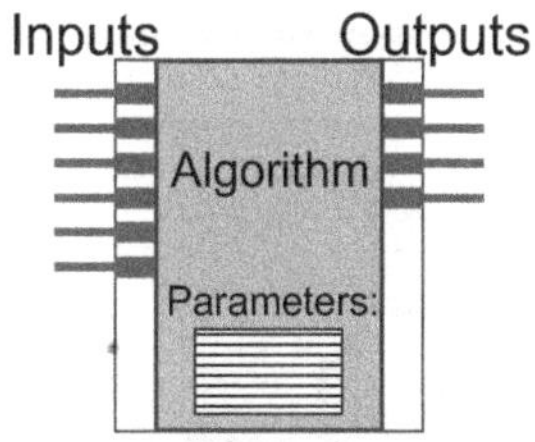

- Analog input
- Analog output
- Discrete input
- Discrete output
- Pulse input
- PID
- Step PID
- Manual loader
- Ratio station
- Bias/gain station
- Control selector
- Lead/lag
- Dead time
- Set point generator
- Signal characterizer
- Signal selector
- Device controller
- Timer/counter
- Arithmetic
- Calculator
- Integrator
- Complex analog out
- Complex discrete out
- Analog alarm
- Discrete alarm
- Analog human I/F
- Discrete human I/F

Figure 26-12. Fieldbus User Layer Defines Function Blocks for Many Elements of Control

- Set of attributes:
  - —Limits
  - —Tuning Parameters
  - —Constants
  - —Miscellaneous specifications and parameters

The analog input function block (Figure 26-13) includes process variable and scale, signal output scale, linearization, alarm limits, and alarm priorities.

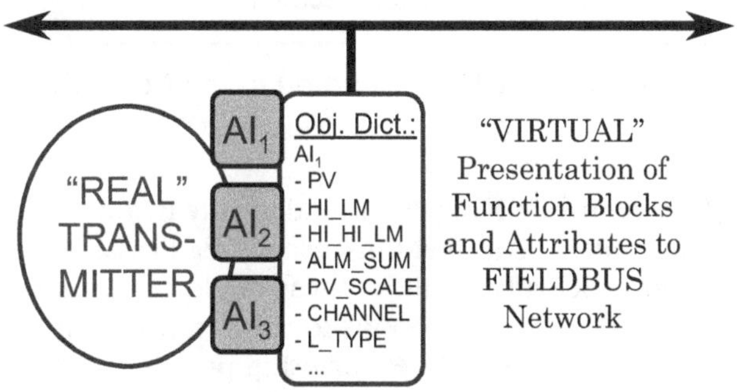

Figure 26-13. Analog Input Function Block is Like a Virtual Fieldbus Device

Virtual three-mode (PID) controllers on the fieldbus (Figure 26-14) network through the object dictionary give access to tuning constants, gain, reset, rate, feedforward gain, mode, alarm limits, description, and units of measure.

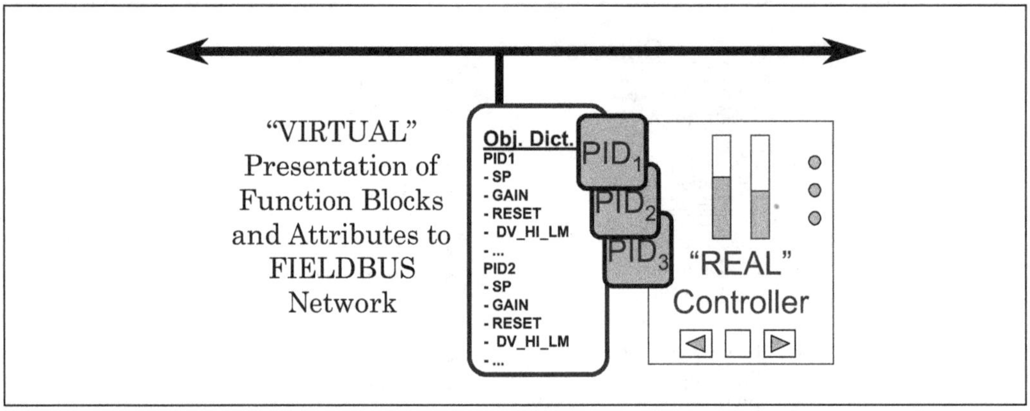

Figure 26-14. Fieldbus Object Directory May Present One or More PID Controllers

An end element such as a valve (Figure 26-15) can also be presented to the fieldbus network through the object dictionary and includes cascade input, output range limits and units, as well as fail-safe condition and action.

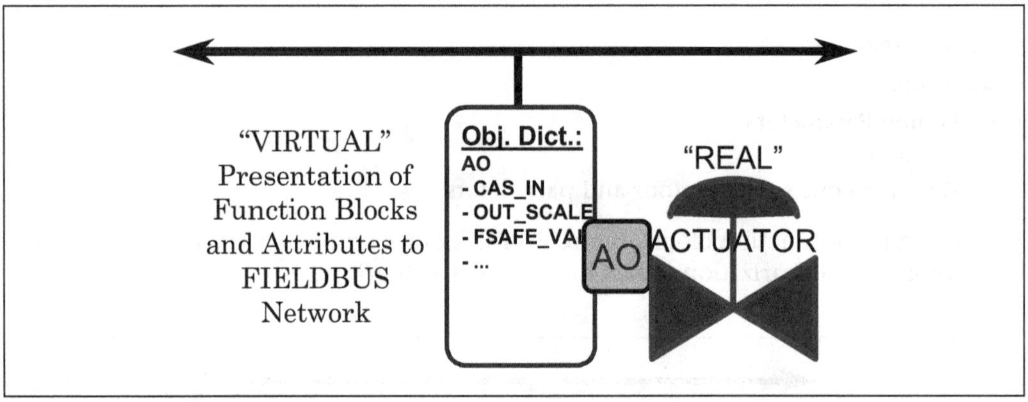

Figure 26-15. End Elements Are Also Presented to the Network

Today three-mode (PID) controllers may be found locally in any input or output device, such as a valve or transmitter. The Fieldbus user layer has already been designed to accommodate these and especially to allow these "field controllers" (Figure 26-16) to couple tightly to other parts of control loops located in products from other vendors. This will dramatically alter the possibilities for using process control strategies.

A control loop can be configured directly over the fieldbus (Figure 26-17). For example, the connection between the analog inputs and the three-mode (PID) controller is provided with automatic cyclic updates of their values, including the status of the input variable.

Typical fieldbus devices today include transmitters, actuators, controllers, indicators, and recorders. Consider, however, the impact Fieldbus will have on the use of handheld

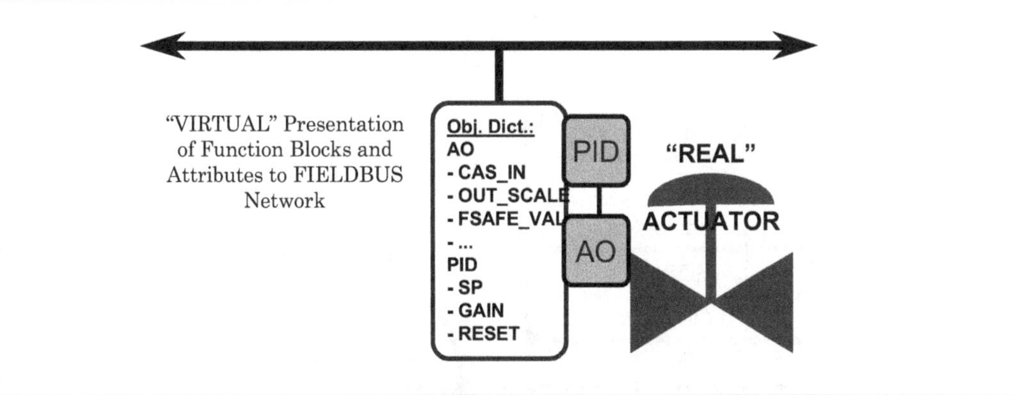

Figure 26-16. Fieldbus Allows for "Smart" Transmitters and End Elements

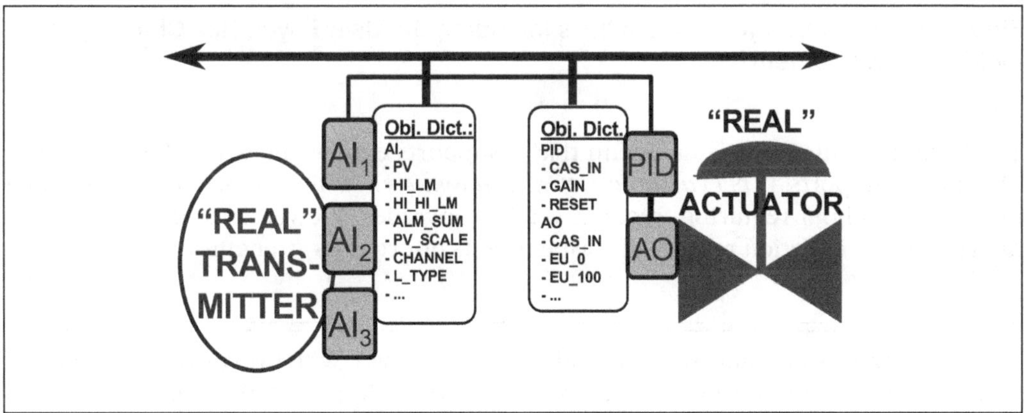

Figure 26-17. Control Loops Can Be "Spread Out" over Fieldbus

devices, local graphical user interfaces (GUIs) rather than only central control rooms, the role of PCs, and the entire architectures of distributed control systems (DCSs) and programmable logic systems (PLSs).

The Fieldbus Foundation

The fieldbus Foundation (FF) is a group of companies cooperating to accelerate a single international fieldbus. They banded together (quite painfully) because the development of the IEC/ISA SP50 standard had been taking too long (well over a decade). They saw the concept of fieldbus as too valuable to ignore but felt that most of the needed technology already existed to accelerate the pace. They also felt that an expedient compromise was necessary to provide desperate users with real products (Figure 26-18). Those compromises, however, have been made in such a way as to support future work.

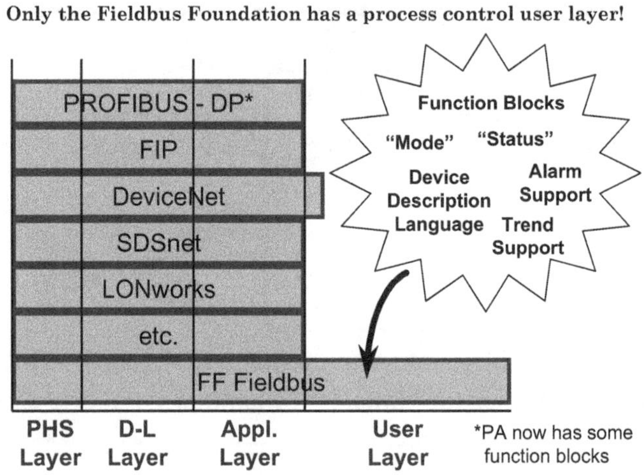

Figure 26-18. Thoroughness, Such As Including the User Layer, Has Challenged Fieldbus Development

The Fieldbus Foundation is unique in that it supports extensions *beyond* the standard. The group supports *VDS (Variable Definition Syntax)*, which is essential to enabling innovation without requiring frequent version upgrades. Viewed as quixotic by some, the Fieldbus Foundation regards this aspect of its effort as its strength!

VDS (Variable Definition Syntax)—This is DDL renamed, with the copyright granted to the SP50 Committee by the Interoperable Systems Project (ISP) Foundation.

DDL—Device Description Language from Highway Addressable Remote Transducer (HART), and now called VDS (not to be confused with data definition language, used in database management systems).

---

27 Architectural Issues

Rarely does a control system function in isolation from other computer systems in a plant. Several situations call for supplementing the control actions with data from other operations in the plant, gathering data from the control system to provide other operations in the plant, or both. Connecting these, of course, alter the architecture of the system. The nature of the impact depends upon the frequency, quantity, and speed of communication needed for the functions involved.

Impact of Control Strategy on Architecture

A collection of loops, sometimes in separate controllers, used in either a small laboratory or on a unit process that is a stand-alone needs only a simple structure. It may have a simple bus interconnecting each of the stations, and perhaps one of the stations might control the communication and in effect be a central operator interface, such as you would find in a personal computer (PC). This communication link would not need, as fast a response as would be required on larger systems because these small systems rarely require sophisticated multivariable control. Any multivariable control is likely to be limited to a cascade pair of loops, and those probably will be done within a single control station.

A more complex situation is having multivariable control in a larger processing plant. Here, the impact of multiple processors, linked together from different areas of the plant, may very likely control the performance, speed, and/or quality of the other processes within the plant. An example is a complex chemical operation in which batching and continuous operations are blended together within the same plant.

The use of advanced control techniques so far has usually been limited to unit processes. Optimizing a control loop is often a question of modifying the gain and/or reset action of a control loop from some influence outside the loop itself but within the same process unit. If such an automatic function had to come from the other end of the plant within a critical response time, then a very sophisticated network would indeed be required. For managing sophisticated loop optimization a good input/output (I/O) network is generally needed. If the I/O is from a digital network, then it should be very local, perhaps only to that particular controller and very likely a parallel link.

Impact of Advanced Control

More advanced control techniques are now emerging, such as model-based control, as well as more advanced control strategies based upon fuzzy logic, neural networks, generic algorithms, and chaos theory. These technologies generally require a tremendous amount of computation, and in process control these computations must occur essentially in real-time. The practicality of these methods will increase as microprocessors become faster and more powerful and local memory becomes larger, requiring much smaller space.

These advanced strategies, which are often used in combination, are becoming practical in overall plantwide strategies. As a result, advanced control has been relegated to an "external" computer that gathers data from a very large number of variables. In such a role, the advanced strategies are designed for suggesting guidelines or creating long-term adjustments to operations. Nevertheless, this "independent" computer may indeed reside on the same network. As advanced control techniques become faster, communication response times of the differing applications on the network must be matched and not limited by protocols and connections.

Subsets of fuzzy logic and neural networks are now being used within local controllers. They are nearly always a supplement to the use of traditional three-mode (PID) control technology for obtaining functional completeness. As newer technologies are able to migrate into local controllers, the "strain" will also be removed from the communications system. Remember, however, these new technologies are for multivariable strategies, not single loops involving the matching of process variable (PV) with set point (SP). Much depends upon where these variables come from!

Dilemma of Multiple Vendors

There are many kinds of control function blocks, such as PID or three-mode control, sequential control, logic control, motor control, and variations of these. Quite often, there are products that do logic control without very sophisticated process control, other products that do very sophisticated process control and are very skimpy on sequence control, and so on. The degrees of control function block sophistication will vary with each vendor's experience with that type of control.

Motor control, for example, requires the use of many interlocking blocks and overrides and often is relegated to programmable logic controllers (PLCs). Few vendors experienced in process work have a complete function block for this capability built into their product. Yet the PLC vendor may not have a single function block with all the sophisticated features built in. Some PLC vendors do not use a function block approach. This results in the need for the user to create the features upon each use of that function. Even with "cut and paste" techniques, upon reconfiguring, the user may inadvertently omit portions or develop time-consuming procedures governing on how to maintain consistency.

Frequently, when several of these functions are brought together in a common system, such as motor control and process control, there is a need to link different products together. Interlinking controller blocks between different vendors but on the same network presents problems in the way they communicate between each other. If these blocks are separate devices, they're quite often required to have peer-to-peer communication, meaning that one box can talk directly to one of the others on a common network. Often this becomes some direct "external" link to one of the stations as a subnetwork

Connection to External Hardware

Many systems allow external devices to be connected directly onto the network. Although these will generally communicate using the same protocol, this is not sufficient to ensure that no loss of performance is incurred. Because many external devices have different data processing requirements and different database update rates, they may need to communicate at different rates.

Therefore, a computer connected directly to the network may tie up a disproportionate amount of bandwidth for communication that has nothing to do with the direct process control application. In a similar way, the device performing high-speed logic required in detection of sequence-of-events may need to off-load large amounts of data in a relatively short time period. In such systems, the basic performance of the control system suffers, and in some cases the data highway or communication network can stall as a result of the integration of these peripheral devices.

One solution is to provide a separate subnetwork for these external devices, but this has two main drawbacks. The first is that the incorporation of these devices under a separate network means that true integration into the control network database is difficult, and many of the advantages of the so-called open architecture are lost. The second is that adding separate hardware and additional communication software modules for the networks adds to the complexity of the system and thus reduces its overall availability by adding disproportionately to the total component count.

In Figure 27-1(A), the computer is connected directly to the data highway, perhaps for control optimization. In Figure 27-1(B), the connection to the computer is through the operator's station, such as would happen for gathering history. In either case, the external device links should never impede the control performance!

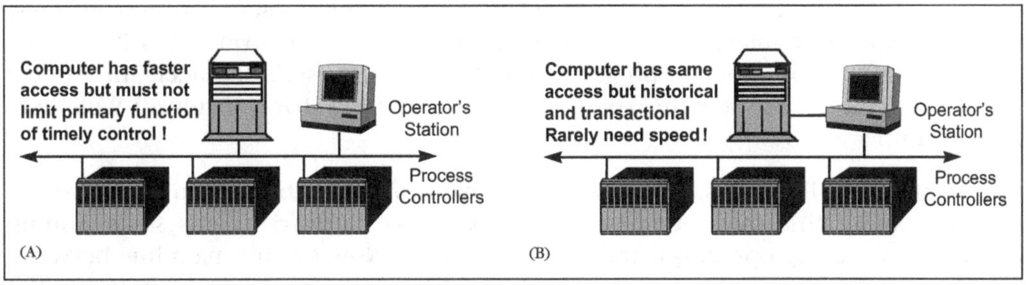

Figure 27-1. External Device Links Must Not Impede Process Performance!

There are systems offering "open architecture" that are combinations of totally different hardware communicating through multiple layers of networks, gateways, repeaters, and the like and yet purporting to be integrated systems. Do not confuse integration with interfacing.

Interfacing External Devices—More Nuts and Bolts

Business structure is significantly different than plant control structure, and as a result the two require different database types, different memory capacities, and different processing speeds. Therefore, they need different kinds of computers with different kinds of databases. Although these machines may talk to each other, they certainly make it very difficult to have one common computer with both navigational and transactional activities within it. As a result, there needs to be an interface between these two kinds of computer systems. This is no different than the links between any two different computing devices that were not specifically designed to communicate with each other. The extent of the interface depends upon how different the devices are.

When number-one son was in kindergarten, he asked one night to have a "Show and Tell" project for the next day. Not to be outdone by other parents, I showed him the old cup-and-string telephone (By the end of the week that school was awash with cups and strings. They hated me there for months). Excitedly, he took it in and demonstrated with a friend as I had showed him. At first, both kids placed their cups to their ears to listen. Nothing happened, of course. Onlookers were confused.

It was just like two people discovering they both have an RS-232 port on their computers. "Hey," says one, "let's plug them into each other, and they'll work together!" Surprise! They don't. They just sit there and listen and listen. Of course, our kids realized what was happening, so they both turned and began to talk. Realizing that didn't work so well either, they devised a signal to notify each other when to talk and when to listen. Hardly unique, that signal quickly reduced to the word over, which evolved from them saying, "now switch over." How original. They had discovered a protocol, and *they* were the "driver package."

When two devices are interconnected, the first requirement is to determine if the driver package resides in either of them or in some separate device connected between them (Figure 27-2). When deciding what external computers or other networks to use, this is one of the requirements. Others include what kind of data (information) must pass between, how much of it, how frequently, and in what form. Then it must be decided who is responsible for programming that link, the user's engineers, the system vendor's engineers, or some third-party system integrator. What is involved? Well, here comes another analogy.

Picture if you will a railroad system with a main line stretching from New York to Chicago. Along this route, there are many kinds of industries, let's say a mining operation, a logging operation, and some steel mills. Now on this main line between New York and Chicago, there are standards to be met, such as the width between the rails. Various railway cars from many different railroads, from Canada down through Mexico, must be able to operate over the same lines. Among the standards to be determined are the kinds of couplers between the cars, standards to the dimensions of the cars for handling the weight across the bridges, the dimensions within tunnels, and so on. All these standards would be made to operate according to the normal function of transporting goods and people from the one point to the other.

Now, one of the industries along the line is a mine. It would be very impractical to take an 85-foot-long passenger car and stuff it down a hole on the line to get the miners to the mine face, or for that matter to take large vehicles and try to haul the ore or coal

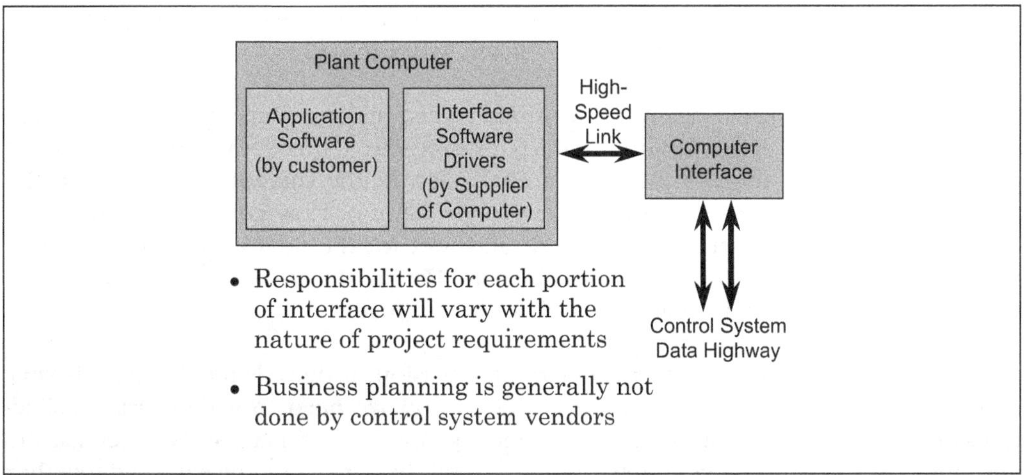

Figure 27-2. Every Computer Interface Needs a "Driver Package"

from the mine face back to the surface. As a result, specialized vehicles to carry people or the coal or ore mined would be designed to fit the space and relevant requirements.

Another industry on our line is a lumbering operation, which requires that you have lightweight rail with the rail closer together than is standard, usually two feet apart. This is so the track can easily be relocated as the trees in a given area are cut. The operation also needs a different-shaped car that can easily navigate the very rough terrain, quickly laid track, and narrow winding curves, and yet support those heavy logs.

The same thing occurs with the needs of a steel mill, another customer on this line. There, different shapes of vehicles are needed to carry molten steel around, something you don't deliver over the main line. The owner will want to move product throughout the plant according to the schedule of the steel mill's production, not the schedule of the main-line railroad.

So whether it be for the speed, or flexibility, the timetable or capacity, or the track dimensions, each of these customers requires different standards than the main-line railroad. The same is true in computers. Different kinds of computers used for different functions take on different dimensions of capacity and speed. And all dimensions capacities and speeds do not fit every circumstance.

There remains a need; however, to connect all these efforts so they can work together. In the case of the railroads, you have railway depots that are between the two systems. The size of this station or depot depends on the varying numbers of people or goods that need to be transported from one system to the other. Everything must be unloaded from one car with one set of dimensions and repackaged to be loaded on a car with different dimensions. The frequency of connections will determine how big the depot has to be to provide service for the different railroads. For example, the size of the depot will increase as the amount of time people or goods wait at the station increases.

So also in every computer interface: there must be sufficient capacity, and processing speed, and the communications link on either side must match. The one side must be sized for the amount of data it carries and the speed at which it arrives, and the other side must match its capacity, speed and packaging requirements. This brings us to the various ways in which computers communicate with each other.

There are some occasions where the computer must make a single query to the other side. In a distributed control system (DCS), for example, the request is for a calculated piece of data out of the computer for a controller. In the case of the computer, the request is for some parameter or temperature, pressure or flow coming from the DCS. This single query must go to the "station" and wait for the next train along the main line, then get off at the correct stop for the data. Having the answer, it must wait again for the correct train to take that data back to the originator.

Although a single query may be necessary on occasion, if there is much data it is very inefficient. Regular "pickups" and deliveries can be arranged to gather larger collections of similar data. The railroad would typically "spot" several cars to be loaded at the customer's site as product becomes available. Then the cars would be gathered together and moved all at the same time, using the same locomotive (communications overhead). In the same way, data can be transported in large blocks of preconfigured data, which would be transported as a single package; when possible, it is far more efficient to move many blocks of data with same overhead (same locomotive) than to move each block individually (one locomotive for each railway car)

The railroad would call this a "unit train."

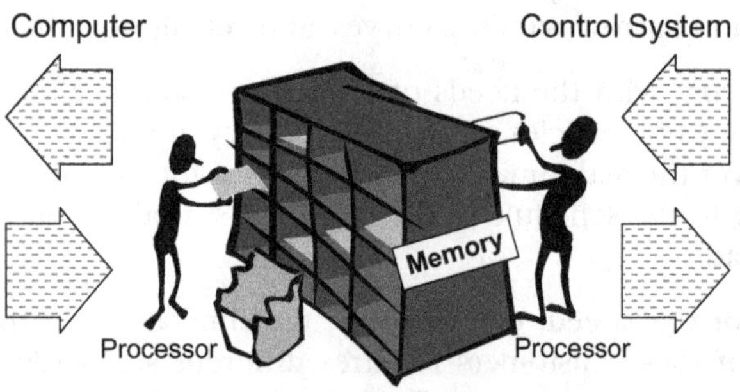

Figure 27-3. Connecting Computers through "Mailboxes"

There is another method for connecting known as a *mailbox*, used for a variety of messages coming in and being sorted at the depot into different categories to be picked up by the "other side" for the specific requests or answers being searched (Figure 27-3). In this scenario, enough memory would be needed for the appropriate number of mailboxes and their respective sizes to allow for delivery cycle. Traffic will come from the computer for inquiries made of the control system and vice versa. Answers would be located in an appropriate spot within the depot for pick-up during the normal delivery cycle used by the control system and/or the computer. The role of the computer interface would be to manage the traffic flow, whether it is of large group, single queries, or the "mailboxing" function that occurs between the two disparate systems.

Integrating External Hardware into the Data Base

The best solution for incorporating external hardware is to provide clearly defined methods and locations for the connection and to supply a data base location specifically for the purpose of making that connection. When other process-level devices are connected, such as programmable controllers, analyzers, data acquisition systems, single loop controllers, and the like, this link is achieved directly at that process level using the control station as a gateway. Every control station can be equipped with a serial interface and a relevant protocol for the external device can to installed within it.

The communications to the external device is handled by a dedicated microprocessor within that control station, so no other system functions will slow it down as a result of the connection. The data received by an external device is placed directly into this control station database, and can be used directly in graphics, trending, reports, and calculations. In a similar way, the data to be written to the external device also comes from the control station's own database, which has its own collection of process variables and set points, and the data may come from a calculation, a control action, an operator input, or an applications program running at any level.

It is therefore possible to connect external process-level devices to the control system network to provide a completely integrated database without degrading the system performance.

Links to Integrate with Plantwide System

The operator station link can also have a dedicated serial interface, again supported by its own processor. This link can support standard protocols such as DDCMP, or HDLC, or X3.28, which are commonly supported by various computer manufacturers. This link provides access to the operator station process tags and display database as well as to the historical data being trended on the system. Real-time data is available across the control network from the various control stations to the operator stations, and available to the computers only through those operator stations (Figure 27-4). The important thing is that this control network access by the computer is controlled and limited by the operator station and that it's therefore impossible to overburden the control network with most computer requests for data. Using this technique, it is still possible to obtain several hundred data values a second.

Consequently, the operator station in this network would be the logical conduit for data moving to the plantwide system. By using separate processors for each of the links, there is no speed delay in moving the data about and in particular no speed delay in the operator functions, which of course must never be impeded. Separate processors also provide the plantwide system with all of the information that resides in the operator station itself and the database of the operator station. Generally, on a plantwide system the information gathered within the operator station is essentially the same information as needed by the plant wide system. Rarely does the plant wide system need any information beyond what has already been reported to the operator station.

The link from the operator station to the plantwide system certainly does not need to have the speed. Rather, it needs to be able to handle the volume of data coming from this one operator station along with many other operator stations. This link provides

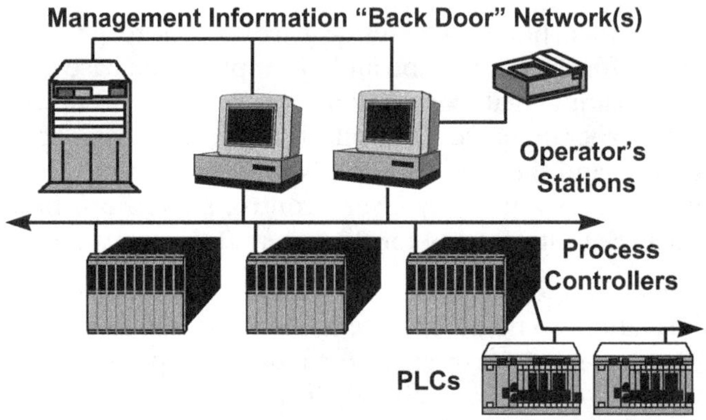

Figure 27-4. "Back Door" Network(s) Reduces Load on Real-time Process Networks

another layer of networking, but its performance and capacity requirements would be far different from those needed for the control system itself. The link also provides a logical division between the two networks. This prevents the network that has the need and desire for information from different parts of the plant from interfering with and delaying the actual control actions of the process itself. A very important buffer is provided here, which is probably a good reason never to allow a "business computer," to be connected directly to the process control network.

The main point to emphasize is that the external devices need access to the system *data* and not to the system itself. By using a dedicated processor to support these links, and by using these processors to allow controlled access to the system's own integrated database, fast, secure access can be granted without degrading the control system's response to standard tasks.

Part F

Connecting the Enterprise

Succeeding in the Business 28

To be successful in a very competitive marketplace, corporations must think more about making improvements to their entire enterprise. Such thinking must go well beyond the production lines. All corporations must adapt to changing business conditions, improve quality and productivity, strengthen internal controls, and manage costs. Solid business planning is essential to making this all actually happen.

Managing the Enterprise

For a number of years, computers have been used to help implement the planning process. Typically, however, these computers have been disjointed tools used in separate departments and often connected by monthly, quarterly, and even annual reports on paper. Once analyzed, some of the interpreted data may be manually entered into the other computers. Only recently have these business computers been linked together, and true integration of information is just emerging.

ERP—enterprise resource planning; computer based corporate planning system defined by GartnerGroup, linked through Manufacturing Operations Management system to plant controls; counterpart to COMMS by Advanced Manufacturing Research (AMR).

GEMS—global enterprise-wide management system; beyond enterprise resource planning, this includes connectivity from a corporation to the companies of suppliers as well as customers, often over the Internet, to manage the flow of business requirements and products among all of them, as defined by Automation Research Corporation (ARC).

MES—manufacturing execution system; software packages for such functions as plant management, supervisory control and monitoring, plant engineering, and quality management; model concept developed by Advanced Manufacturing Research (AMR), in late 1980s with intention to describe system which, rather than focusing on measurements of material usage or process control, "centers on product itself as it moves through plant on way to customer;" intended to bridge real-time information gap between planning (MIS) and controls (PCS) to link operators and managers with current views of all processing resources; counterpart of MOM model developed by Gartner Group.

MIP—middleware integration platform; provides capability to connect multiple control systems to multiple manufacturing &/or business applications; integration functionality includes event handling, messaging, workflow transactions, systems management, dynamic configuration, some form of database management, etc., as defined by Automation Research Corporation

MOM(S)—manufacturing operations management (system); software packages for such functions as plant management, supervisory control and monitoring, plant engineering, and quality management; model concept developed by Gartner Group, Stamford, CT, USA, intended to bridge real-time information gap between planning (MIS) and controls (PCS) to link operators and managers with current views of all processing resources; counterpart of MES model developed by Advanced Manufacturing Research (AMR).

MIS—management information system; computer network which allows managers to track performance of plant at close to real-time without excessive need for paper based systems; primarily used for planning and scheduling of resources.

OCS—open control system; term used by some for next generation of DCS where ideally hardware and software is not proprietary.

PCS—process control system; responsible for manufacturing of product, as compared to MIS, context being used by vendors of PLC systems (and some market research firms) as equivalent to DCS.

Much talk has been circulating about actually connecting the plant floor to the business operations (Figure 28-1). With enough programming, this can be done, of course. Nevertheless, it requires both scarce time and significant amounts of money.

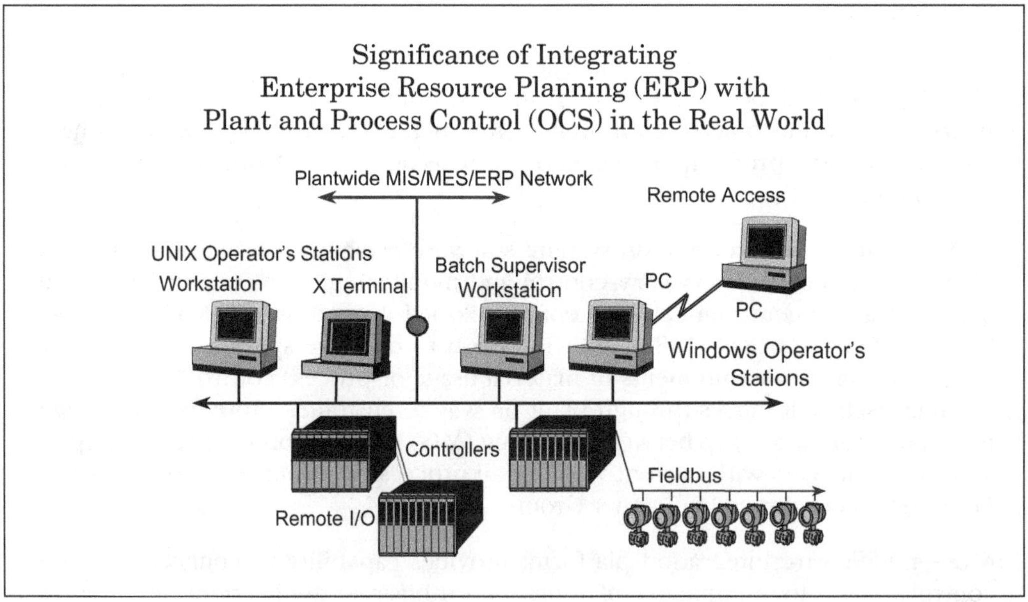

Figure 28-1. Communication Must Exist between the Plant Floor and the Business

---

Corporations Must Reengineer Continuously to

- Respond to market changes
- Respond to technology changes
- Reduce internal fear of change
- Reduce business perturbations
- Manage costs (margins)

When corporations reengineer as a response to changes in market conditions, it is usually a strategy to regain their market losses. All change is disruptive! It will always initially cause some loss in business. The underlying concept is that the effects of the change will more than recover the losses caused to bring it about. During change, the flow of business is disrupted, causing customer uncertainties. Employees also become uncertain as changes in techniques and skills cause them to lose productivity and experience morale problems.

Ideally, a corporation will make changes proactively rather than reactively. Change should be constant and gradual rather than a traumatic bump:

- Customers fear your change because they may no longer count on the consistent product or service that they have become comfortable with.
- Employees fear your change because they are forced to question their skills and their own abilities to suddenly change their existing ways, which they understand and do well.
- Both of these reactions apply to everyone at all levels, especially the managers, if they are honest with themselves.

All of this creates considerable difficulty for a corporation trying to manage costs and margins!

Managed, Continual Change

- Customers see managed as *positive* because it leads to continual change

— Product growth and improvement
— Service growth and improvement
— Company growth and improvement

- Employees see managed as positive because it leads to continual change

  — Personal growth and improvement

Managed, continual change, is a very positive strategy:

- Customers see this as product, service, and company growth and improvement.
- Employees see such change as leading to growth and improvement for products, service, and the company itself.
- Management also sees such change as an opportunity for growth and improvement.

So we have:

- Sudden traumatic change(s) = fear, uncertainty, initial loss of business
- Continual, managed change = enthusiasm, control of destiny, improvement of business

Corporations require both people and equipment to survive. Change impacts both upgrading and involvement. Equipment will sometimes reach a limit to in its ability to be upgraded. As long as the right tools are used, people reach that limit and usually go well beyond it.

Properly directed change, that uses the appropriate tools and allows on line training without loss of productivity and will improve on-the-job performance. The more gradual the change, the healthier the results, and the traumatic bumps that cause employee unease and business perturbations will be avoided.

Properly Directed Continual Change *without* Traumatic Bumps Needs

- Proper business parameters
- Continually updated information from
  - — Process control systems
  - — Factory automation systems
- Continual planning
- Acceptance by plant personnel
  - — Focus on production
  - — Focus on quality

To come closer to achieving this ideal change, proper planning is imperative. Inputs require a continual flow of changing business parameters, blended with a continual flow of current information from the actual operations. All of these however, must be practical!

The control system should be well qualified to provide a continual flow of both process control and factory automation information. Along with a good flow of business information, such information makes possible the continual planning that is so essential to this dynamic paradigm.

The control system provides the visibility needed for the operator to properly understand the operations. As a conduit to the business plan, the link between that plan and the control system exposes the operator to appropriate portions of the business side of the change requirements. This will shift the operator's role from "running the stuff" to focusing on production optimization and product quality. The operator's job begins to become that of a business manager! (Figure 28-2)

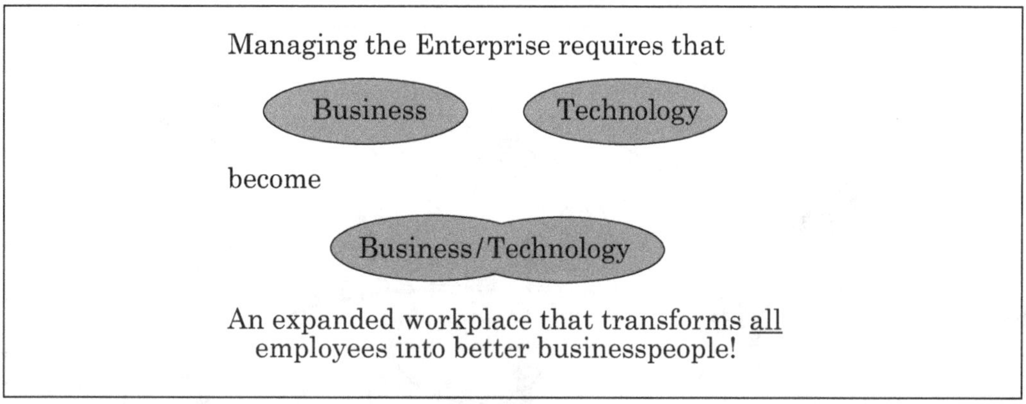

Figure 28-2. Technology is Changing Business!

Running a business, like operating a process, is an art!

There are no magic formulas that apply in every situation! Owners and operators alike must continually make judgments on when to apply known practices and when to be innovative. Both need tools to help decide what is the proper decision and when to apply that decision.

Computers cannot run a process or plant.

They are merely *tools* that help one perform the *art* of running a process or plant and do it *consistently.*

Good management of the whole enterprise requires an understanding of the business and the technology of that business. These two worlds have traditionally been separate for a variety of reasons. Today, however, successful corporations have been able to take advantage of the merger of both business and technology as the two become one. Because of this blending of business and technology, more information (not just data) is available to all parties involved, thereby expanding the workplace. This capability is truly empowering all employees, at all levels, transforming them into better business people.

Defining functions

A good typical example of any business is the batch operation (Figure 28-3). This is true in both the discrete and the process worlds. It is a matter of "scale." Simplistically, a continuous process is just a very long batch run. All of the elements of the batch operation are there. In fact, several "supporting" functions of the primary continuous operation are usually very much like traditional batches.

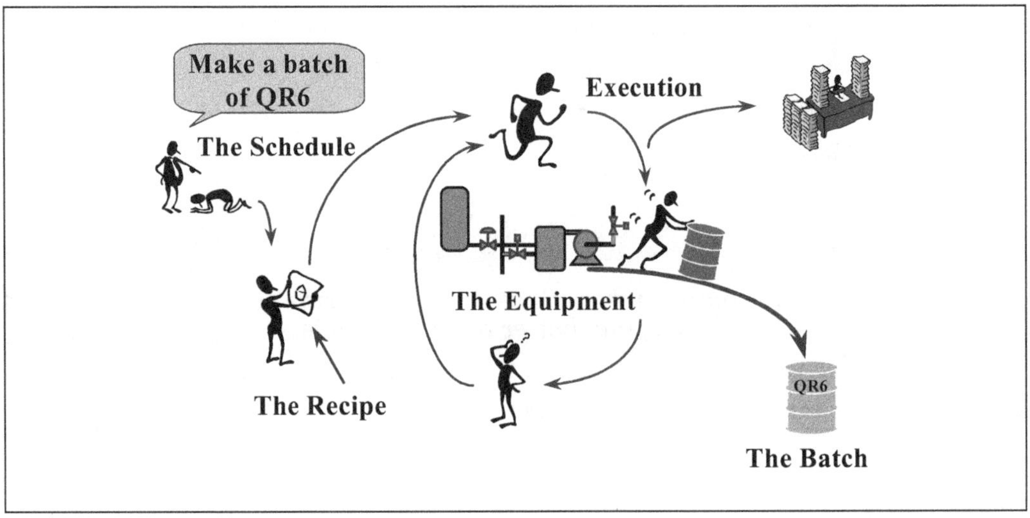

Figure 28-3. Components of a Typical Batch Operation Reflect Most Processes

Boiler constraint limiting control packages for large power utilities are every bit as complex as any chemical batch. This is also true of any metal heat-treating operation. Batch examples are found in steel mills, water treatment operations, paper mills, cement plants, glass making, and manufacturing. If you translate the terminologies, you discover the same problems. Of course, there are significant differences from one type of operation to another and from one type of plant to another. Usually, however, the differences are only in the degree of complexity.

Without going through the details of the emerging ISA standard S88 there are now formal definitions of every aspect of possible plant production (Figure 28-4) from the sensing and final elements up to (but not including) the enterprise (more precisely, the corporate business plan for the enterprise). There has been tremendous effort made to provide a modular product and process framework for the plant floor.

Many, however, see S88 as "just a batch control standard" instead of a general modular automation standard. There is no question that there is more that must be addressed quickly, now! At the ISA'96 Chicago Conference, the inaugural meeting of Committee S95 began to define enterprise/plant floor practices which must include explicit support all those issues in linking the business plan to batch, continuous, discrete, and hybrid plants.

Keep in mind, this link may extend remotely from corporate headquarters to all types of plants around the world (hence, "Enterprise"). It sounds so wonderful on paper, but it involves so many tortuous details!

The SP95 effort to cover enterprise/control functions has been motivated by the S88 "batch" standard, but it is most certainly very different:

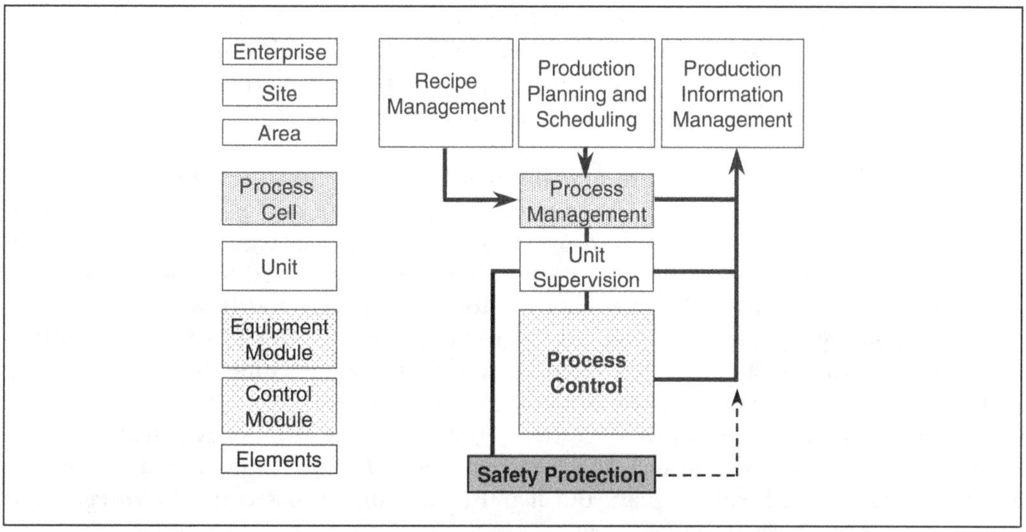

Figure 28-4. Batch Operations are Not Unlike all Continuous and Discrete Functions

S88 leverages *product* knowledge.

S95 leverages *business* knowledge.

Simplistically, one can envision a business plan being executed by providing explicit instructions to the plant floor and receiving back into the plan the results of each action. Of course, as the process becomes more complex and the number of connections increases, this approach becomes extremely impractical (Figure 28-5). Not the least of the problems is the "business computer" concept of "real-time" compared to the process concept of "real-time."

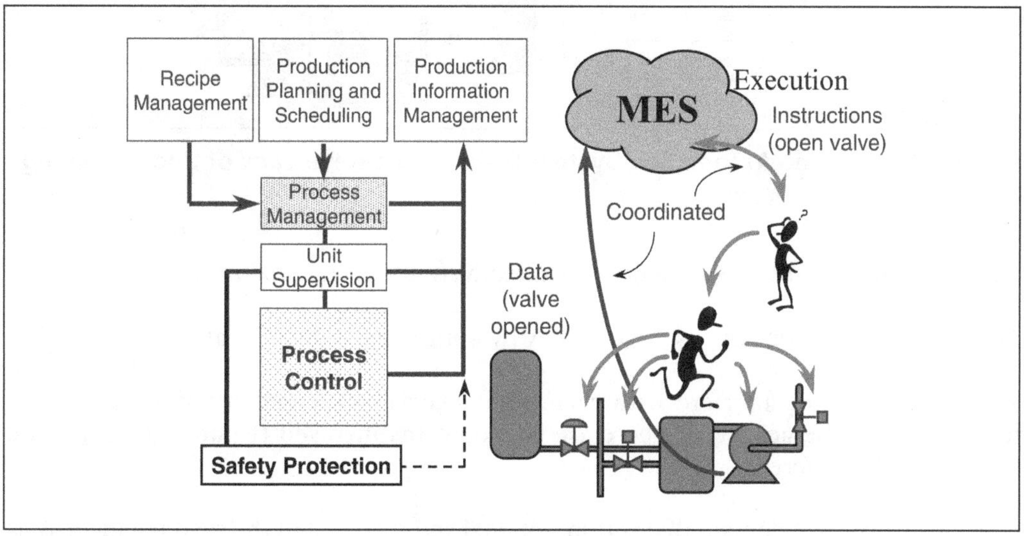

Figure 28-5. Business Plan Cannot Operate Each Device in the Process

It is just as simplistic to presume that an automation system improves conditions. Connecting the control system to the plant computer is nothing new, but currently *information* exchange is nearly always paper-based and then interpreted by individuals so as to meet the significance of the task at hand.

Where electronic connections are actually made, the solutions are very customized, and/or they are point-to-point links of specific data. Cause and effect are frequently mismatched, compared with the *real* needs of the enterprise (Figure 28-6). For example, the business plan doesn't really care which valves are opened or closed but rather is concerned with what is the current inventory of product and how is it changing. "Business computers" are not designed to rapidly shift priorities in response to plant upsets and to quickly analyze alarm spurts. Alarm spurts in a nine-story utility boiler control system at a power generation plant, for example, can come in at one thousand per second! Through appropriate control strategies that use today's technologies, savings occur within the automation system and *outside* the business plan, some may argue *instead* of the business plan. But it must be realized that control *strategies* are *different* than business plan *objectives*.

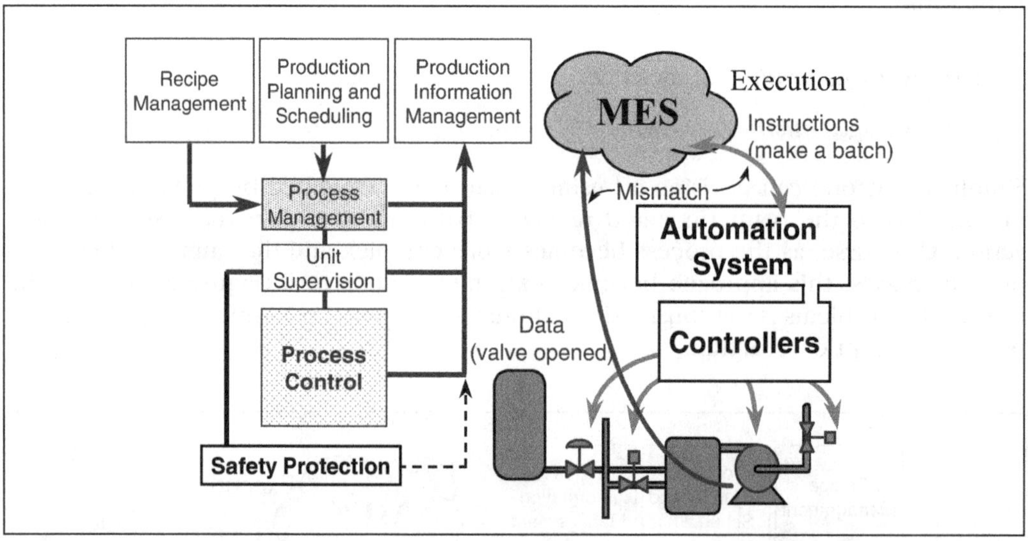

Figure 28-6. Adding Automation System Does Not Resolve Lack of Understanding

Business plan objectives: Save money by effectively allocating resources.

Automation system objectives: Save money by optimizing control strategies.

The two should not interfere with each other's goals, and creativity must be used so these goals can be achieved. There are two domains involved (Figure 28-7), that are fundamentally different:

- An informational domain that is transactional and involved in the search and analysis of information

- A control domain that is navigational and involved in causing action and observing the results

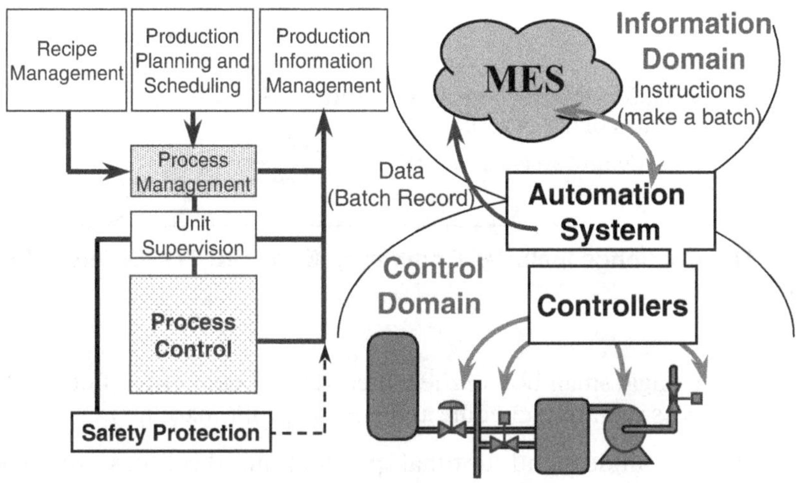

Figure 28-7. Boundary between Information and Control is *Not* Smooth!

During the past two decades, distributed control systems (DCSs) in the process world have evolved because of the increasing memory capacity and the increasing performance capability. This has resulted in a dichotomy of automation system. This system shares both control and no small amount of information (versus just data). Some rather sophisticated relational databases employ search techniques to allow us to analyze sort, compare, filter, qualify, and simplify raw data into information within the control system itself. Some of the results are already redirected to manage advanced control systems, with built-in constraints appropriate to the art of performing that particular process.

As a result, there is no easy demarcation between control and information domains but rather a "gray area." For example, the batch record is full of data, but it can be presented in such a way as to be information (i.e., data already predigested to reduce the search). This is the current battlefield of the many "middleware" vendors.

The Challenge of Two Computing Communities

All of this has set up some significant challenges to the SP95, not the least of which is bringing together two very different computing communities (Figure 28-8).

The businesspeople understand the complex interaction between such concerns as order entry, inventories, material procurement, scheduling, distribution, warehouse management, invoicing, and even (especially?) profit margin. They need copious record correlations that involve the annual, quarterly, monthly, daily, down to hourly tabulation of corporate-wide conditions of the equipment, personnel, and product. The

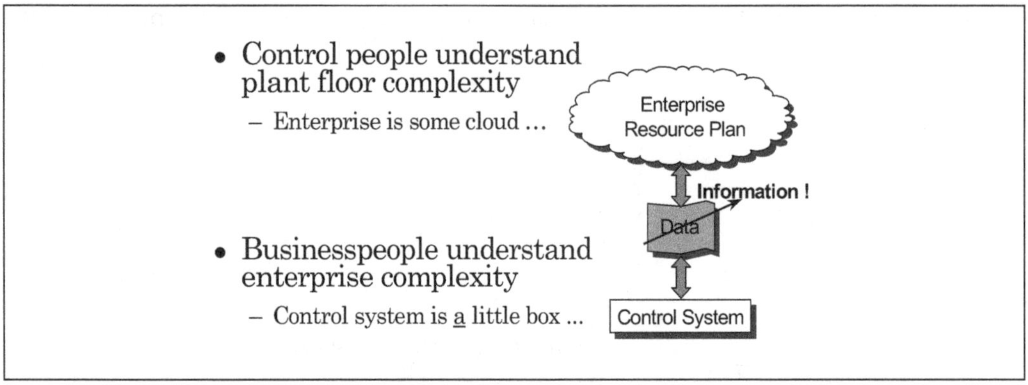

Figure 28-8. The Challenge Includes Combining Efforts of Two Different Computing Communities

control system is a single small box in their hierarchy of concerns. (But "no blockhead bit-nerd is gonna mess with my schedule and cost us profit margin.")

The control people understand optimal production, deadlines, the strategy of creating product under continually changing conditions, dynamic regulatory agencies, environmental considerations, managing plant upsets, and analyzing alarm conditions while maintaining the safety of equipment, product, and personnel. They routinely need to respond to change within hours, minutes, seconds, milliseconds, and microseconds. The enterprise plan is some vague cloud that connects with their activities. (But "no stinking bean counter better mess with my set point and blow this plant to kingdom come.")

Challenge of S95

The tasks of Committee SP95 are as follows:

- Establish common vocabulary
- Find a common view of Problems
- Build a common model
- Define data structures

These tasks must be usable for both process and discrete manufacturing and unlike the years it has taken for so many other specifications this one must be completed promptly but thoroughly! S95 must allow the enterprise to become one with both the business process and the production process! Flexible production is a an increasing requirement of industry. Enterprise integration is extremely challenging. Dynamic requests that come from ERP must be accommodated by the control system. This is not just data mapping!

Just as S88 terminology, definitions, and concepts are slowly becoming known and useful outside the traditional batch industries, so S95 must also be applicable in all industries. The need for it is already overdue in continuous and batch processes as well as discrete manufacturing.

To properly operate any business, there needs to be good planning, appropriate tools for the execution of that plan, and correct controls for the implementation of that execution (Figure 28-9). A good control system must have proper feedback through out the operation to improve both the execution and the planning. As with any control system, the better this dynamic can be made to function, the better appropriate corrections can be made at all levels. It needs to be a *continuous* adjustment.

- **Business** Needs:
  - Planning [ERP]
  - Execution [MES]
  - Control [OCS]

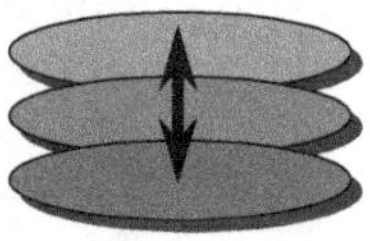

- **Control System** Contribution:
  - Right information needed for business plan
  - Right timing when needed
  - Right context to be properly used
  - Right response to planning requirements

Figure 28-9. Successful Management of Business Requires Good Control of Production

The role of the control system is to provide the right information needed for the business plan at the exact time it is needed in the right context for it to be properly be used and with the right response to the requirements of the business plan! Without these essential ingredients, a viable business plan is not workable. Having the information (not just data) in the control system layer is not enough. There must be an easy and quick way to move this information to the other needed areas. The easier and more simple that link can be, the more likely it is that the correct information will be located and transported.

All of this requires a system that is readily altered to meet the changing needs in the plan and allows the plan to be easily changed to meet the marketing and distribution needs of the corporation.

Combining Business and Control Architectures

There are many corporate consultants offering methods for structuring businesses today. They frequently include several highly integrated business modules to meet the customized needs of many unique corporations in different industries. These business modules include tools for sales and distribution, purchasing, production, plant maintenance, financial accounting, human resources, customers, vendors, and so on. Are interconnected so that changes in any one function are correctly reflected in all the others to the appropriate scale.

One of these modules relates to process production; others include plant management, and so on. Connected to each of these is a powerful "point-and-click" link to the control system. This link is more than just data mapping but also includes diagnostics and memory (remember, the connection may be to other countries over phone, microwave, and the like).

Ideally, the workstation uses the same development tools as the link, so the link is *embedded* (Figure 28-10). This provides a completely integrated open control system (OCS) with *direct communication* to the planning software normal engineering, and with no added software beyond what customers need for their business applications. An additional benefit would be controllers that can act as a DCS, PLC, or both and a legally separated safety system that configures the same way as the controllers and can inherently communicate with the rest of the overall system.

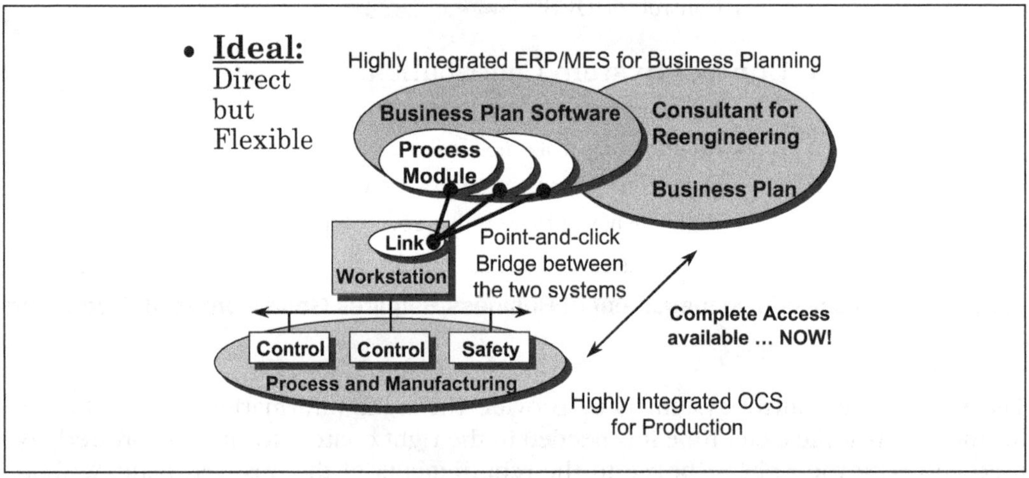

Figure 28-10. Creative Interconnection is Possible, but It Needs Disciplined Structure to Properly Manage the Enterprise

The business planning software vendor has invested its expertise in building the tools needed to efficiently run the business (Figure 28-11). These tools help to do the following:

- Manage *all* the resources the company has to do its job: machines and equipment, personnel, sales force, physical plant.
- Manage all the needed inventory: raw materials, storage, suppliers, finished-product handling.
- Manage the sequence and amounts of production: size of production runs, length of production runs, product mix, quality assurance.
- Manage all the scheduling activities: determining amounts and timing of deliveries from various suppliers, optimizing production with customer requests, providing "just-in-time" deliveries.
- Manage financial requirements: invoicing customers, paying suppliers, payrolls, performing cost analysis.

- Track business performance *with suggestions for change*: asset management, cost accounting, plant maintenance.

It is important to add here that the tools described here are best recommended by professional business consultants.

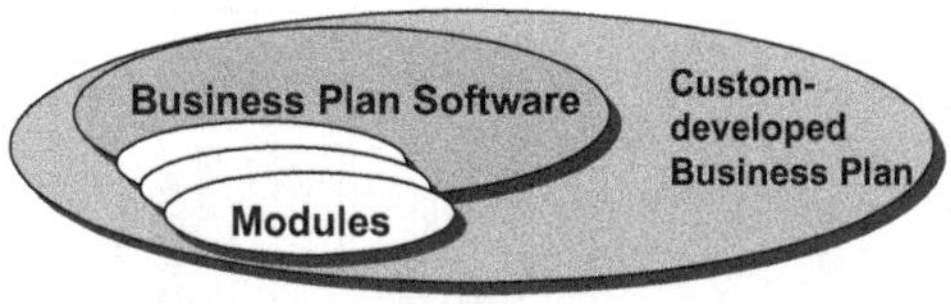

Role of Business Planning Vendor:
Managing the Business

- Resource management
- Inventory management
- Recipe management
- Scheduling

Figure 28-11. The Business Plan Needs Good Software Modules

The graphical mapping method presents side-by-side tree views of both the control system and the process module within the business plan (Figure 28-12). To map data, the user simply selects a process module field and visually attaches it to corresponding control tag variables. In a trigger window, the user defines the prompt conditions for the link to move data. These conditions can include any combination of time, events, ad hoc requests, or business plan requests.

This graphical mapping capability eliminates the time and expense of writing custom code by directly connecting the business plan to the plant floor. Because the software development tools are also the *foundation* for the workstation of the control system, no custom coding is needed to unite the control system with the link to the enterprise. The link is embedded.

Thus, the information flow between the control system and the process module of the business plan can begin in the early phases of an installation. In addition, if the business plan requires different information later, the control system can be easily reconfigured without requiring any hard-coded changes to the link itself, so the business plan can receive new data in minutes rather than months. In this way, the package permits faster start-up time, simplifies modifications, and removes roadblocks to responding to continuous changes of either the business plan or the control system.

For those interested in the technical implementation, note that:

In one approach to develop the link uses the business plan's remote function calls (RFC) to communicate to each of the business plan modules (Figure 28-13). RFCs can be used to communicate to any of the business plan modules, but the link certification currently covers only two. The shaded areas in Figure 28-14 represent the direct

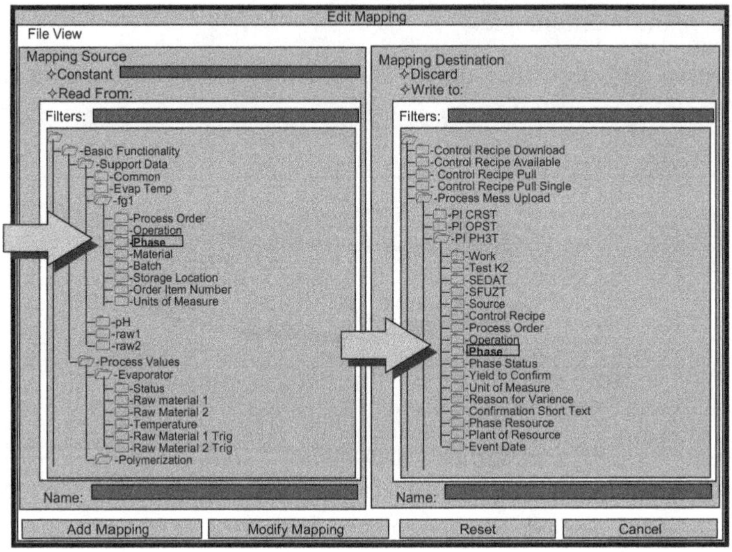

Figure 28-12. The Interconnection Requires Good Tools, Such as "Point-and-Click" Mapping, to Be Practical

connections made through the link to the open control system. The business plan software, which can be a very tightly integrated system, will already allow information to pass between other modules as needed by the enterprise.

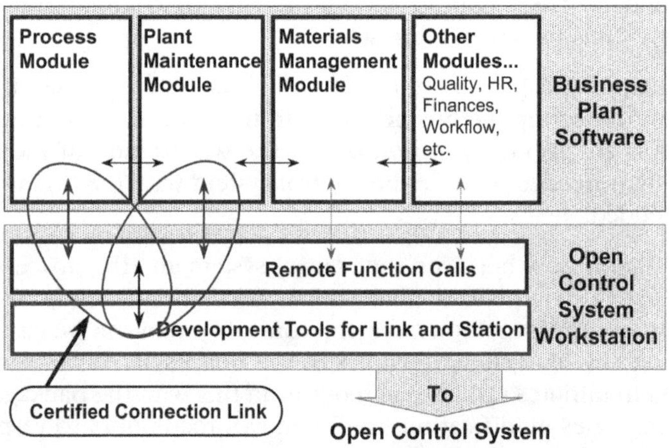

Figure 28-13. Software Components In One Approach to Implement the Coupling

The vendor of this middleware product integrates the business system with the control system (Figure 28-14). The object-oriented design reduces work and risk. It allows a visual mapping of the data between the process module within the business system and

Role of Link Application
Platform Vendor:
Connectivity

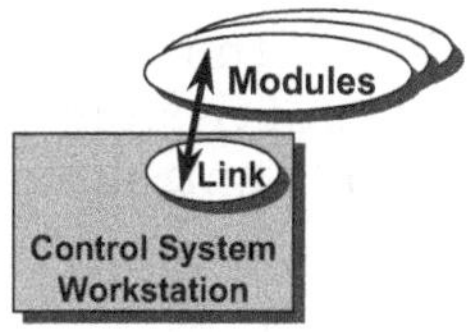

- Point-and-click mapping
- Mapping audit (import/export)
- Automatic event-driven messaging
- Simplification of module data structures
- Process data upload/recipe download

Figure 28-14. "Middleware" Products Ease the Pain of Integration

the control system, configuring a run-time server that uploads process data into the business plan and downloads recipes into the plant control system.

- This particular link provides the following:
- Point-and-click mapping between business modules and plant control systems.
- Flexible message triggering for process uploads and recipe downloads (Operation State, Phase State, Resource State, Material Consumption, etc.).
- A data server that automatically links business modules to plants.
- Data protection from network problems.
- Persistent data store for the information that the business module needs.
- Communication object that encapsulates business module and simplifies complex data structures.
- Communication object for software development tool supervisory software already within the control system vendor's product line.
- Interactive tracing and testing tools.

The control system must contribute to the productivity of the enterprise in many subtle ways (Figure 28-15). The control paradigm was established by control system suppliers at the interception of microprocessor-based control systems. Traditionally, two types of control systems are available: a DCS (distributed control system) and a PLC (programmable logic controller). The DCS was traditionally very good at controlling continuous processes that had very few discrete requirements, and the PLC was very good at logic-intensive control. Unfortunately, user applications are not split as cleanly as the suppliers' so-called solutions. Many applications have a mix of continuous requirements and discrete requirements if not on the application level then at least on the plantwide level. This presented the users with a dilemma when they were considering process automation. The following choices were available to the user:

1. A DCS in which *inexpensive* discrete functionality would have to be sacrificed.
2. A PLC in which *sophisticated* continuous functionality would have to be sacrificed.

Role of the
Control System Vendor:
Plant Control/Safety

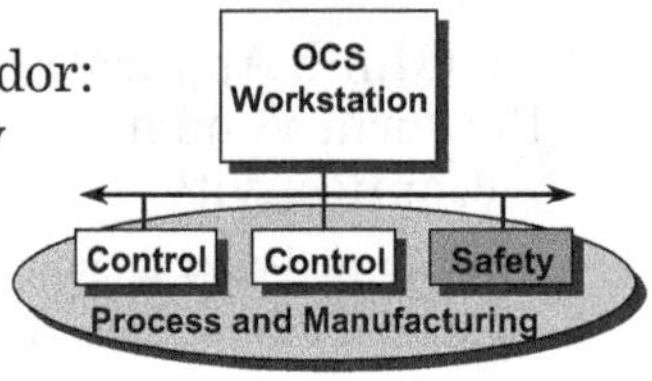

- Saves time
  - Less configuration
  - No links to create
- Reduces costs
  - Less hardware to buy and install
  - Simple architecture to learn and maintain
  - Protects investment and avoids liabilities

Figure 28-15. The Control System Must Provide "Bottom-Line" Advantages

3. A Safety System, that is required to be separate from either option 1or 2.
4. A hybrid integration of these combinations which required implementing expensive interfaces.

Control systems emerged in the mid 1990s in which all of these functions were built in. Some can also configure all of these functions with any blend of the same languages as the IEC standard IEC #1131-3. This saves both time and expense.

OCS Requires More Productive Results

- Plant and Operator data is available from the beginning of project, for faster analysis into the business plan
- Can re-configure control to fit needs as they are discovered during start-up and operation
- Provides security of equipment, product, and personnel, specifically where needed without penaltyof installation and learning costs

More importantly, the control system provides more product results. It allows a faster start-up, enabling the control system to come online much faster. No additional cost and time for the engineering is needed to link the flow of information to the business system. Because of this faster availability, information can flow into the business system earlier. Analysis will always suggest some changes to be made in the control strategies (that is why the system was purchased!). As these needs are discovered, they can easily be incorporated into the control system. Ongoing business analysis will continue to study the plant's performance, and suggestions for modifications will continue. The flexibility of the control system enables it to always embrace new improvements as they present themselves.

As we mentioned earlier, for a business to be viable, it needs (Figure 28-16) planning, execution and control:

Planning is done using the business planning software packages with the highly integrated modules that are appropriate to your plant(s), and by communicating through the process module of that software.

Execution occurs through the simple, highly integrated "point-and-click" interface within the control system workstation.

Control is achieved through the highly integrated open control system and managed through the same control system workstation.

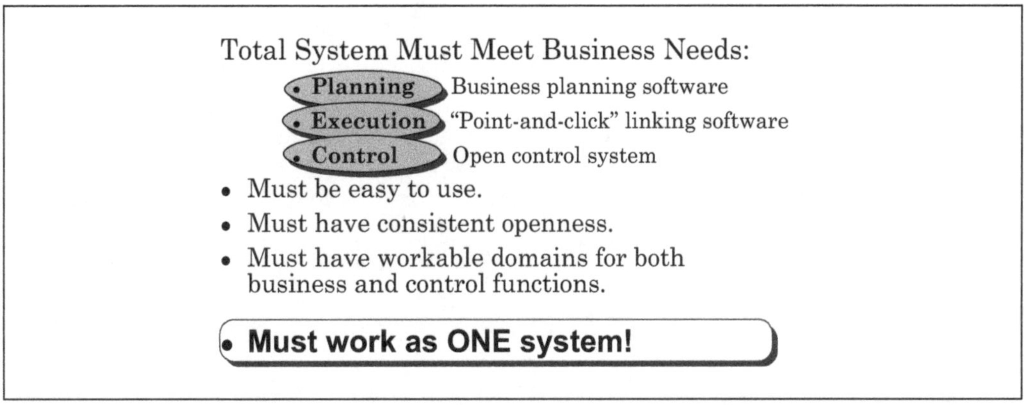

Figure 28-16. Requirements for Good Enterprise Resource Planning (ERP) System

This permits a system that is unified with the business plan and capable of being responsive to it but also capable of implementing the emerging requirements of S95. All of these ideas are useless, however, unless all the effort and capabilities are blended to bring about a system that performs as one!

Plant Information 29

One of the business dilemmas is optimizing the making of a product and determining the costs of that optimization. On the plant floor, the concern is how you manage the operation and stay within temperature, pressure, and flow limits and how you relate those limits to the quality of the product. This is an entirely whole different type of report and a whole different kind of a concern for control room operators on the one hand and the plant managers on the other. Now, it's a fact that the business's information needs require data from the plant floor for some of the calculations, such as energy consumption and inventories of raw materials or finished product. On the plant floor the concern is information that's dealt with in a matter of minutes, or seconds or even microseconds, whereas on the business side you're dealing with information that is gathered over weeks and months and quarters or even a year or so.

Flow of Data

Corporate objectives must be transmitted through the plant level operations down to the plant floor and ultimately to the controllers and final elements (Figure 29-1). Sensors in the unit processes transmit data back up through the structure and the results are analyzed to determine the results of that planning. Each of these layers of computing functions needs access to databases in each of the other realms. These functions do not reside in neat little compartments, nor are they located within their own computers. In the real world, most plants "just grew" with now outdated concepts, plans, and computers. They were correct at the time, it's just that the changing technology has allowed so many more considerations to come into play. Nevertheless, databases of data need to be addressed.

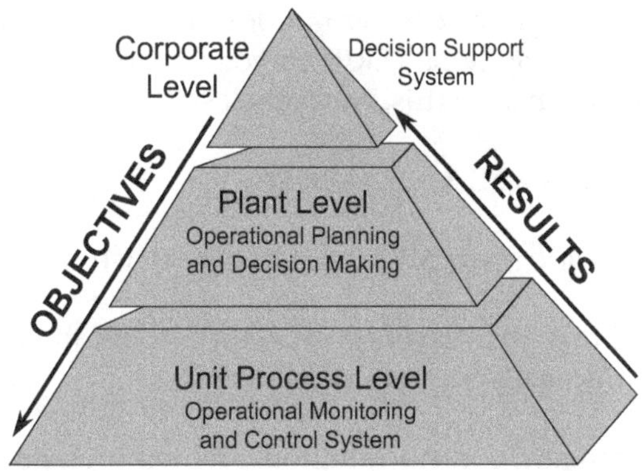

Figure 29-1. Computing Layers of Process Information Flow

Here we are with our hierarchies again, but now with new terminologies (Figure 29-2). These realms, shown in Figure 29-2, have been defined by the Gartner Group, a market research firm. They are generally accepted by most people in the late 1990s, but exactly which functions reside in each is open to a variety of opinions. For other definitions in this field, see boxed sidebar at the beginning of Chapter 28.

- ERP
  - Enterprise resource planning systems
- MES
  - Manufacturing execution systems
- OCS
  - Open control systems

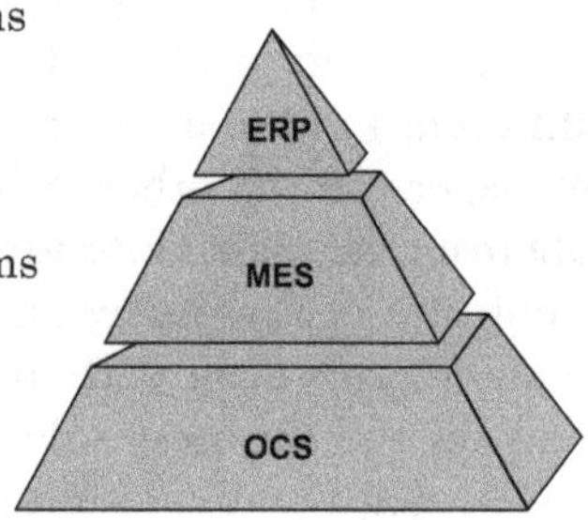

Figure 29-2. Gartner Group Definitions of System Layers

- Enterprise Resource Planning Systems (ERP)—Top-level software that contains Forecasting, Planning, Sales Order, Receiving.
- Manufacturing Execution Systems (MES)—This is the Middleware that contains Scheduling, Reporting, Document Management.
- Open Control Systems (OCS)—OCS is a general term for any open control system including DCSs, PLCs, or PCs (Personal Computers). The implication is their complete connectivity of controls with all other networked devices, which for most control systems in the 1990s is quite optimistic.

MES is a buzzword created a few years ago to describe the nebulous layer of software that connects your business systems (ERP) to your control systems (OCS). There are may independent packages that do this. Nevertheless:

1. Many ERP vendors provide MES functionality.
2. OCS vendors also provide some MES functionality (Dispatching, Reporting).

There are some that feel this MES "layer" will disappear, but in fact the FUNCTION will remain, wherever it is physically located.

OCS is the realm of automatic control functions, which include supervision, continuous and discrete control, monitoring, and alarming. The real challenge in this realm is working with real-time data manipulation.

Timing is Everything

Computers were never real-time at best, some are "real-enough time."

As we see in Figure 29-3, memory capacity, processing speeds, functions needed, all vary with the "level" in the hierarchy of the plant. In the past, this has required many different computers, some connected with others, many requiring that the data be reentered by some clerk after it was analyzed for the function involved. We also see, however, that

- The typical business database manager system has high levels of human transactional access requirements by users; for example, a relatively large slow-changing volume of money in a bank but continually accessed by many hundreds of tellers (operators).
- The typical control database manager system has very low levels of human access requirements by users; for example, one or a few operators accessing a large database of hundreds of rapidly changing sensors and final elements in a process.

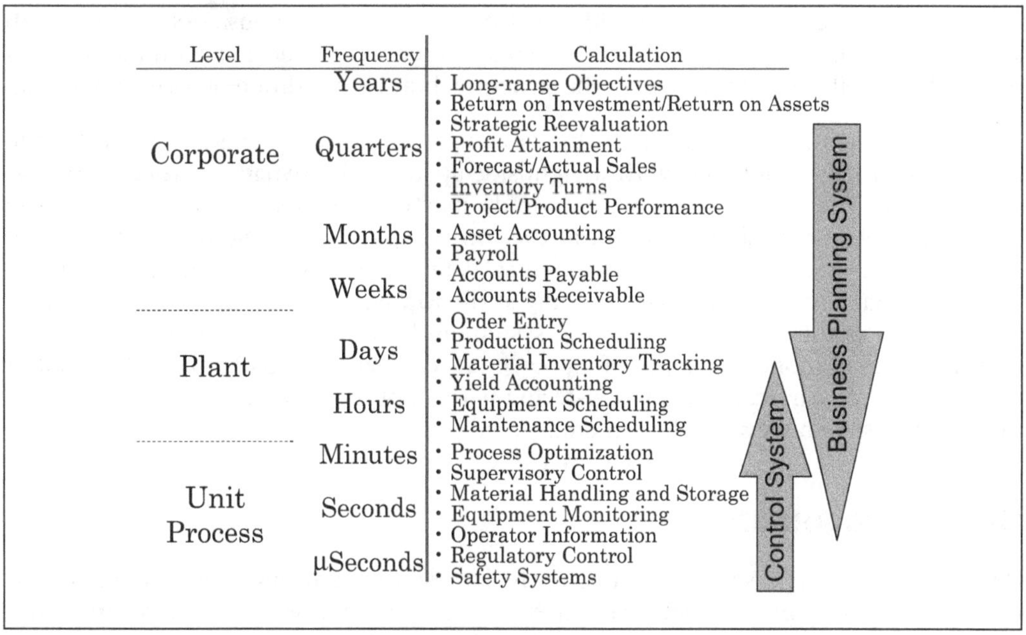

Figure 29-3. There is an Overlap of System Functions; No Clear Line of Separation

So we then see in Figure 29-4 that the database manager systems (DBMS) for business and for process control have totally different orientations. From a software standpoint, they would not seem merely upside down, but even inside out.

These two distinct types of databases—one of speed and rapid manipulation on the plant floor and the other of capacity of data with a much slower need to know—require different kinds of database structures and different kinds of data manipulation. The

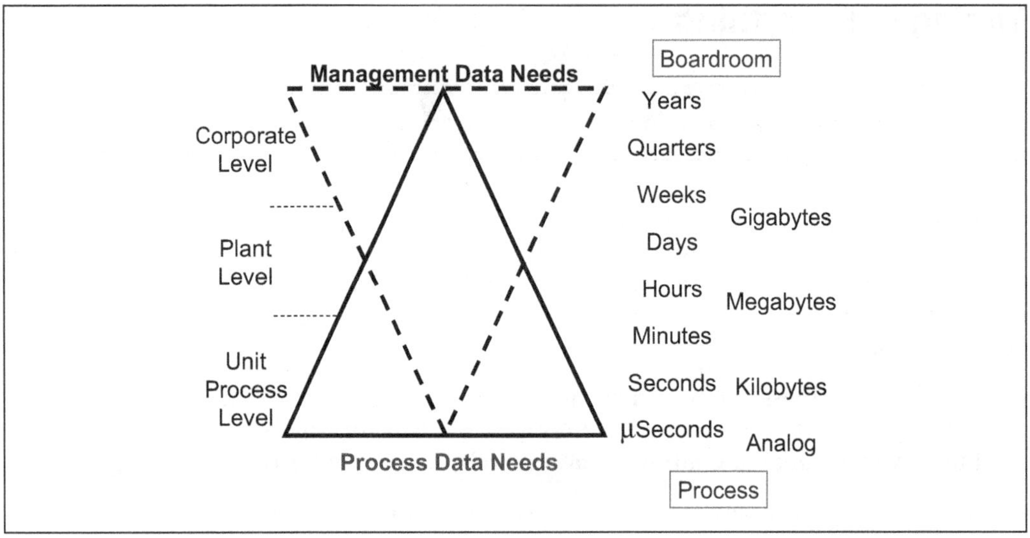

Figure 29-4. DBMS for Process and for Business Have Very Different Orientations

differences are between working with transactional data on the business side and with analytical data on the plant floor. Now, of course, there is analytical data on the business plant side as well as the upper side of the structure, but it is of a different form and timing.

The easiest way to contrast these, is by viewing an inverted pyramid or delta, for the transactional data compared with a right-side-up delta for dynamic process analysis (Figure 29-4). The base of a delta has hundreds, maybe thousands, of inputs and outputs to the control system, and the point at the top is typically a single or small group of operators managing and manipulating that data. In a business structure, it is an inverted delta, and the broad base is really at the top where you may have many, many people such as the tellers of a banking system and the point is at the bottom where there is a core of money. This pot of money changes relatively slowly in size but a lot of daily transactions are continually registering with all of the teller machines, tellers, and people with screen views at the top end.

Data Management

Database management software is one of the largest software categories. Today, almost every user of a computer, whether it is a PC, a minicomputer or a main frame, make use of this kind of software to some degree. From keeping lists of events and alarms, entering batch recipes, and analyzing trends of operations to the modeling of an entire business strategy or enterprise, the data required for these operations is typically stored in and accessed from a database management system (DBMS).

Two main areas of business are online transaction processing and online analytical processing. The latter is colloquially referred to as "end user computing." For most online processing applications today, a DBMS based on a relational model is often used. Nevertheless, online analytical processing has a distinct requirement different from the traditional relational database manager. As a result, a multidimensional model is emerging.

Many users of the relational type of DBMS find that it handles some problems rather poorly. During dynamic events in process operations, for example, users need to analyze the situation. This involves more than just recording and retrieving large amounts of information about the process and production. It also differs from order entries or marketing, sales, and financial data. Because of this, other types of DBMS's are gaining popularity, especially multidimensional DBMS products. In an era where computers are proliferating and end users want to use them as effectively as possible, a single DBMS approach is impractical. It cannot satisfy all the computing needs of an entire business.

Using the wrong kind of DBMS raises the cost of performing a task and slows the retrieval of information (rather than data). The DBMS may also require several layers of add-on software before it can work the way users want it too. In some cases, it may not even be possible for the DBMS to perform the task desired. The reason it is hard for a single data base system to perform all the tasks now required of it stems from the differences between transaction and analytical process applications.

In Figure 29-5 we see the parent-child relationship of a hierarchical database, which requires that the system trace its way from one leg to another, which consumes time and processing power. Queries must be made in the same way data was stored, more suitable for fixed transactions. Transactional applications are concerned with current, ongoing data. The record of an order is often deleted soon after product is shipped in some industries, for example. Exceptions include pharmaceuticals and heat treating. Marketing departments may keep portions of the records as historical data for future projected. Data may be kept back for two or more years so it may be inspected for trends and forecasts. Transaction applications are generally static, whereas plant control applications are dynamic. For instance, once an accounting system has been designed and implemented, the files or fields are rarely changed, and the transactions and screens used to enter them rarely change either. In control applications, however, it's harder to plan the data structures ahead of time and predict all the ways in which the data will be used.

Users in process control operations need maximum flexibility, good presentation of the data from every imaginable perspective, and the option to create new screens on the fly. Transaction applications are usually flat or file oriented and consists of linear lists of related values, each describing an employee, customer, dates, product and similar entities. Most of the time, this data is accessed by single key value and is viewed as simple list on the screen or a page. The flat relational database management system (RDMS) of Figure 29-6 acts more like a lookup table, allowing queries from the database to be different from the way the data was stored. Dynamic changes are difficult, and all parameters must always be available for every situation. Process control situations, in contrast, are best viewed in a multidimensional format because the user needs to look at all the possible combinations and interrelationships.

Although most end-user applications are done at the overview level, they also require the ability to drill down into the detailed data from which that overview was derived. This "drill down" may follow a hierarchical order that unfolds more and more detail as needed. All told, the differences between transaction and end-user applications are so many and so large that the effects of a specific DBMS software approach on performance and user satisfaction can be quite dramatic. To be effective, the DBMS software should fit the job. To do this, the design should focus on three areas: data model, data access and manipulation language, and implementation strategy.

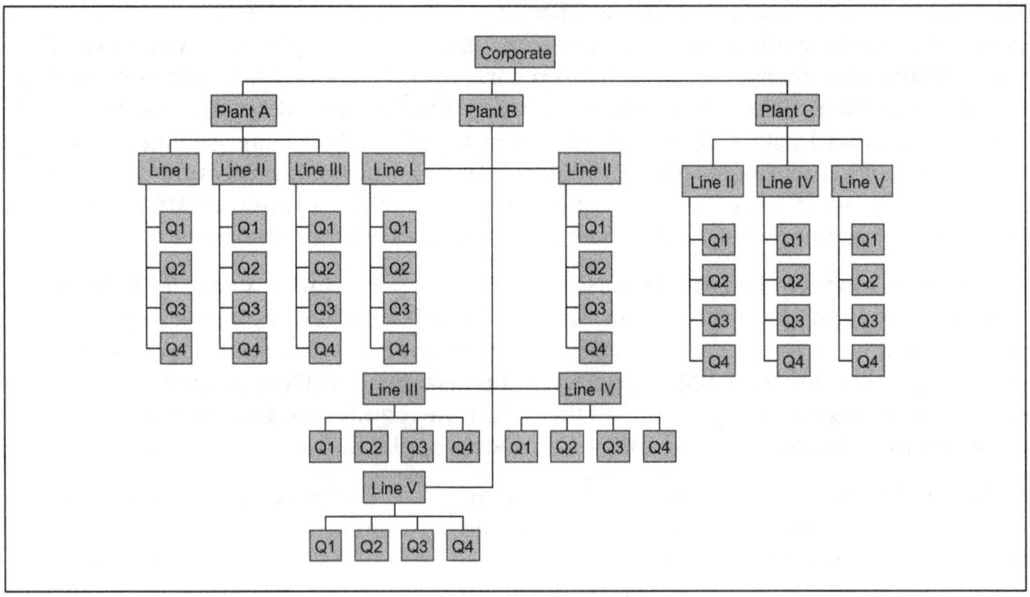

Figure 29-5. The Parent-Child Relationship of the Hierarchical Database

Plant	Line	Quarter	Production......
A	I	1	
A	I	2	
A	I	3	
A	I	4	
A	II	1	
A	II	2	
A	II	3	
A	II	4	
A	III	1	
A	III	2	
A	III	3	
A	III	4	
B	I	1	
B	I	2	
B	I	3	
B	I	4	
B	II	1	

Figure 29-6. Flat RDMS Acts More Like a Lookup Table

The DBMS data model is the logical representation of how the data is structured and how operations will be performed on it. It is the principal determinate of how the user will have to look at the data. The so-called single file data model of record sharing the same structure is still widely used. Data models of greater sophistication are also widely used for transactional applications. The hierarchical model is based on a parent-child relationship between different record types. Some of the current popular relational models are really an extension of the single file data model. It gives a database of many single files the ability to dynamically combine the data across different files. This ability is important because of the types of data that need to be combined frequently.

The data model of Figure 29-7, in which data is viewed in multidimensional arrays, shares some features with the relational data model but is oriented much more toward the data interrelationships. In the relational model, these are rarely explicit and so must be defined in some way by the end user. It is these interrelationships that give the multidimensional data model its power to support end-user applications, most of which are concerned precisely with understanding those relationships. In this data model the basic unit is dimension. Essentially, a dimension is a set of similar entities, such as the set of all of the alarms associated with a single unit or all of the temperature profiles of a particular device. The data is structured by these dimensions into arrays with a vertical dimension, a horizontal dimension, a page dimension, and so on. The contents of these arrays are actual values.

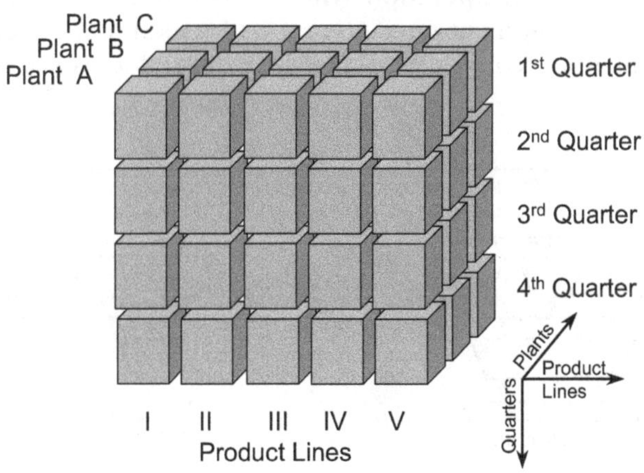

Figure 29-7. Flexible Multidimensional Database Provides Better Views of Relationships

This more flexible multidimensional database uses less memory, has faster access, and provides better views of relationships that were not anticipated when gathered.

Operators typically want to know what the data represents then its record structure. That is, an operator wants to know what is happening in a process or, more importantly, what is happening in the yield of the product, but rarely wants to know all the temperatures over the last shift. More likely, he or she wants to know the interrelationships between temperatures, pressures and flows, particularly at times when different operations occur rather than just a straight-line calculation of everything that happens in that shift.

When analyzing a process yield, for example, the engineer will want to know all of the common things that happened on the different times that this particular product was put together. He or she may want to trace the half-hour prior to the end of the product in each of five different occasions, each of which may have been spread out over the past three months. This will give the engineer a pattern from which to determine what the parameters are influencing the quality of the product. A pure list of temperatures would not give him or her this answer.

An interesting component of the multidimensional model is the singularity of dimension; that is, the product dimension exists once, and only once, for the whole database, no matter how many arrays there are that the product participates in. Each entity, or item, in a different dimension is identified by a unique alphanumeric key. The key lets the user automatically access all the information about an item through the entire database not just within a single file, as it would in a relational database.

Multidimensional views reduce storage requirements. Since data in a relational database is combined only through the matching of common keys across many files, keys can proliferate, greatly increasing storage needs. Multidimensional databases reduce the control data redundancy because keys are stored in single central lists, the dimension itself. For example, let's take a plant in which there are many, many pieces of equipment used in various combinations to make a wide range of different products (Figure 29-8). This could be a batch operation where it is often just as important to know which portions of the equipment have no data and which do. A user could determine that piece of equipment in which a particular type of product is *not* being made as well as that in which it is.

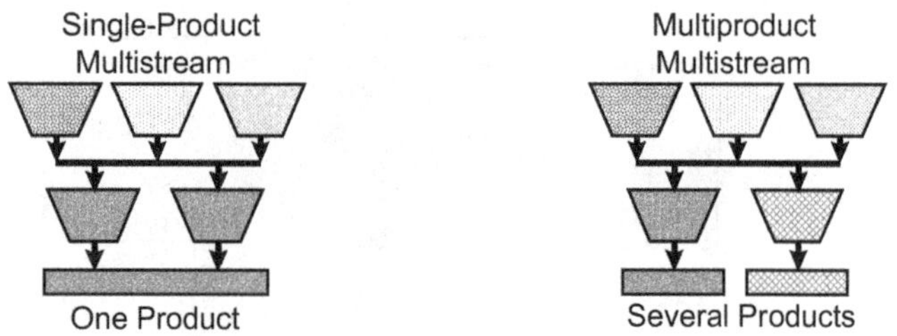

Figure 29-8. Database Parameters Are Continually Changing in Some Processes

In a batch operation, there are often many kinds of product passing through many different vessels. This can vary based on which vessels are being cleaned, which are being used for other production cycles, and so on. All the different product do not need the same parameters measured. If a vessel is empty, there are no temperatures, pressures, and flows, so there is no need to store all of the information that is not there. Now, many implementations of a relational system cannot readily change what is being saved in an active way while production is running. In these systems, it is difficult to refine or add attributes or parameters that become apparent after you create the product.

The multidimensional approach, on the other hand, allows dimensions to be maintained independently, making it easier to visualize what is missing. In other words, some products may need temperatures and pressures to be monitored, while others may need pressures and pH monitored. Still others may need flows and temperature combinations monitored. To retain data on all those parameters of temperatures, pressures, and flows, and pH would be a waste of memory. What is needed is to be able to save the parameters necessary for each product, and selectively save them and to make a new product that needs to measure different parameters, like consistency or weight. This requires a system that can add these parameters without losing or changing the data that went before it. We can combine the impact of alarm handling across all of these situations. Particularly useful is using this approach in circumstances where alarms are not likely to occur but later using a combination of equipment and product where alarms do occur. Furthermore, alarms do occur, you need to know to what extent and in what parameters.

Manipulating Data

The data manipulation language (DML) is the means by which the database manager system (DBMS) is instructed to store, retrieve, subset, match, calculate, or otherwise manipulate the data. You may wish to use a manipulation language to ask a DBMS to find all the products whose total temperatures have exceeded a certain value. Not surprisingly, the DML employed by a multidimensional database differs markedly from the standard query language (SQL) of a relational database. Record-oriented languages, such as an SQL involves specifying the attributes to be retrieved and the tables or files to be searched. Records are identified by means of search predicates for example all the temperatures over 100° C. That will filter the data so you can determine which individual records are returned by your query. In operation, a record-oriented query often causes the system to scan many or even all the records in the participating database tables.

A multidimensional DML, on the other hand, is a domain-oriented language. The domain is synonymous with dimension in this context. In this case, the emphasis is on selecting the parameters of interest, such as the products, their various temperatures, or the time periods involved, without regard to the files in which they appear. The idea is that the DMBS scans the various components in the indicated domains or dimensions, pulling together on the fly whatever information is needed. A case in point might be the yield point of a product over a period of history as compared with the quality yield over the next quarter of operations.

The differences in the need for business management-type software as opposed to data collection and reporting are a matter of trying to determine the many relationships between the following:

1. The amount of inventory that must be stored to create a product,
2. The amount of inventory that must be stored after creating the product before delivery,
3. The amount of energy consumed in the process of creating the product, and
4. The ideal implementation of various control strategies for determining the best methods for developing a high-quality product.

More Reality

We said earlier that in real-time processing, unlike typical business processes, in real-time processing, you have some requirements for speed and capacity that are far different than what occurs in the business world. Instead of large data tables, you have a lot of instantaneous actions from the various sensors that must be processed. And, at the same time, you have to manage the calculation of the totals, inventories, and quality that must go into the larger computer system "above" this activity to manage the business and develop a business plan. Because of all these different requirements, you require different strategies, which gets us back to the multidimensional databases versus the relational databases.

In either case, there is no free lunch. The strategies for updating a multidimensional database are much more expensive than for updating a typical relational system. This is because a large number of arrays must be searched for individual entries in order to update a transaction record. It is generally not realistic to use a multidimensional database manager system (DMBS) to perform a function for which it was never intended, namely on-line *transactional* processing on the plant floor. Likewise, relational databases though successful at many transactions and simple query applications on the plant floor have not proved themselves in many end-user computer applications on the business plan side. So when deciding which database manager technology to employ, the potential user should not ask simply which database is best, but rather, which is best suited for the type of applications that must be created.

Part G

The Process

Continuous Processing 30

There are many challenges to good configuration. Among these is the ability to take advantage of the many new sensor types and their characteristics as well as the many new final element types and their characteristics. Advancing technologies will continually alter these devices, and whatever you do, you do not want to exclude any opportunity to improve operations as a result of the inability to "change with the times." Changing that which connects to the system should mean the ability to change control strategies as well. Companies can no longer afford to change *technology*; they must use that technology to change *solutions*!

Change is a journey, not a destination!

Change is a move from the status quo to higher performance.

Change is unsettling, painful work.

Change is not the issue, journey management is!

Moving Toward Configuration

A major part of implementing a system is the importance, not just of easy configuration, but especially of the ease of *re*configuration of that system as new requirements are imposed upon the process. This may be a result of new discoveries in best operation, changing market pressures, new laws for pollution control, and, as we discussed earlier, adjusting to a changing business plan. The ability to change configuration must exist both offline and online.

The critical need is for simplicity in developing changes (Figure 30-1). The design engineer must be free to focus on the needs of the process, not to have to figure out some vendor's configuration package. Otherwise, these needed changes will not happen! Configuration should be as near intuitive, and consistent as possible. Even better, it should be similar across several different vendor systems. We will discuss more on this last thought in Chapter 32.

In the past traditional control hardware as well as complex programming has stifled most changes in industry, which has led frequently led to obsolescence. Many industries barely understand the full role of the simple three-mode (PID) control loop in improving operations. It has only been in the past two to three decades since many plant engineers have been using the very creative process control strategies developed and published a half-a-century ago. It isn't that these ideas were ignored; it is just that they were so difficult to implement in field conditions. There was no easy way to "play around" with them without overrunning the budget. That is because of the hardware.

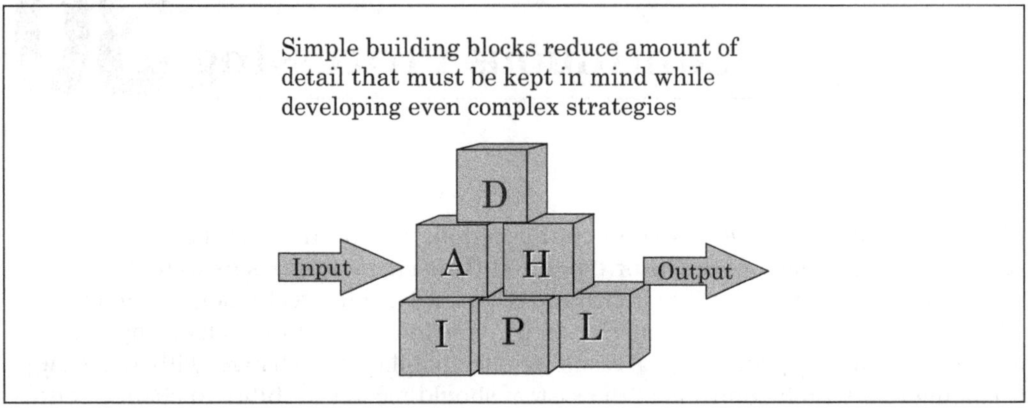

Figure 30-1. Control Strategies Must Be Easy to Configure and Especially to Later Change as Needs Change

Three-mode (PID) Control Is Very Much Like Driving Your Automobile: (Figure 30-2)

There is a relationship between your gas pedal position and speed of the vehicle. Perhaps in your auto, halfway to the floor (50 percent signal) is forty miles per hour on a flat road. Any change of that pedal position will change the speed in proportion (P). The range over which you can operate (as an operator of this process) would be called the proportional band. An engineer would see this as the gain of the system because he or she sees an equation with output/input, the inverse of your view.

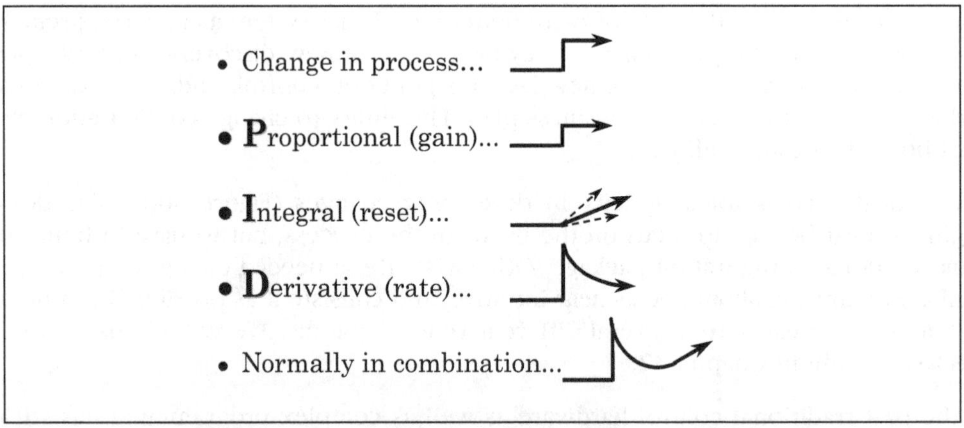

Figure 30-2. Not Everyone Was Able to Easily Take Full Advantage of PID Control Actions in Combination Until the Microprocessor Made Selection of Capabilities Simple to Accomplish

When you come to a hill, the load changes, and you slow down. To just maintain speed, you must reset the pedal position to increase the flow of fuel to the engine (increases the signal). How much depends on how steep the hill is. An engineer would describe this mathematically as the integral (I) of some appalling equation again, the inverse of your view.

Now you come to the entrance ramp of an expressway, which is posted at twenty-five miles per hour. The highway, however, has traffic that is moving at sixty. What to do? You "floor" the pedal, your auto gathers itself up and somewhat leaps forward toward the roadway. But you cannot hold the pedal there! In the all-too-short acceleration lane you quickly "let up on the pedal" to adjust to the velocity of the traffic and pull into the space between two other cars at their speed. You have just experienced a rapid change in your rate of acceleration to overcome quickly changing conditions. Our engineer friend would define it as the derivative (D) of his preposterous equation, and again it is the mathematical inverse of your view.

In real life, you have learned to drive with all three control mode's (PID) operating simultaneously, just as the controller operates using whatever amounts of each action is necessary. Next time you drive, remember, you are the PID controller. Pay attention and you will develop a "controller sense" that will help you walk through your plant and "feel" the process, just like those old-timers who "toured the plant."

Three Modes?

Few even understand how to tune a loop. This is not because of ignorance but because in the "old days" each mode fully interacted with the other's, which sometimes made tuning very difficult in some loops and near impossible in others. Furthermore, if you suspected you needed three modes and you only had a controller with two, you had to go out and buy another chassis. If you then decided only one mode was best, you had to go out and buy the one-mode-chassis because with the interactive components you could not just "turn off one mode"!

Limits to Creating Good Control

Physical design restrictions significantly limited the duplication the of control equation. Pneumatic, electromechanical, electric, and electronic designs all required separate chassis, or chassis modules, to achieve different mode combination in a controller (Figure 30-3). Think of the innovation that is discouraged when to change mode you have to specify a new controller, obtain a purchase requisition, place an order, wait for delivery, create a work order to install it when it finally arrives, test it *then*, try it to see if you guessed correctly! The microprocessor has significantly changed much of this. Because of the phenomenal processing power in every chip, people get "all three modes in every controller." Changing from one-mode to two-mode to three-mode is merely a question of selection!

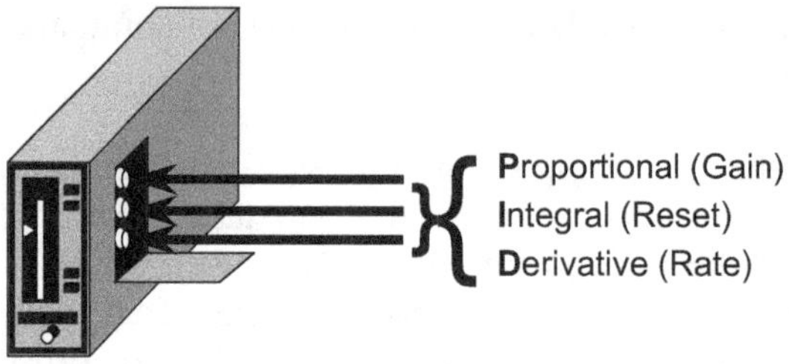

- Principles were the same for pneumatic, electro-mechanical, electric, electronic—until the microprocessor!
- Equations differed with each vendor
- Each mode interacted with the others
- Required different chassis for P, PI, PD, PID
- Change from one to another costly, so was rarely done!

Figure 30-3. Accurate Tuning Was More Difficult Before the Microprocessor

It is claimed by some that before microprocessors became available only 10 to 15 percent of "automatic" control loops really ran in automatic for very long after they were installed. It is also claimed that the number has increased to about 40 percent among loops operated through microprocessor controllers. It is expected that that number will double through the use of advanced control techniques, such as multivariable predictive control, and its combination with fuzzy logic, neural networks, genetic algorithms, and chaos theory.

[Yes, "genetic algorithms" is correct, not generic–still yet another advanced computing technology]

This is the reason few people in the recent past were able to use the many control strategies published so long ago. Just in the simple matter of controller selection the past two decades have made an unbelievable difference! Remember, even simple cascaded control was exotic for many industries. When it was discovered that both discrete and analog values of various control loops resided in the same microprocessor-based "box," the interconnectability of those control loops changed the way control strategies could be made more practical.

Many of these control strategies existed in the old days of the 1940s and 1950s and were not very easily implemented. Now they are easier to do. Many of these strategies were developed in theory only or tried in one or two installations where money was available. The economical availability of the "magic microprocessor" allows greater experimentation to determine the best combinations of loops, which was simply not possible in the past. It also leads to better opportunities to develop control strategies, which are much more effective than a mere loop in many processes.

Management Disturbs Control

The *role* of the controller in a process loop is changing as well. In the past, you considered the disturbance on a process. Today, expect the controller to get disturbances! (Figure 30-4)

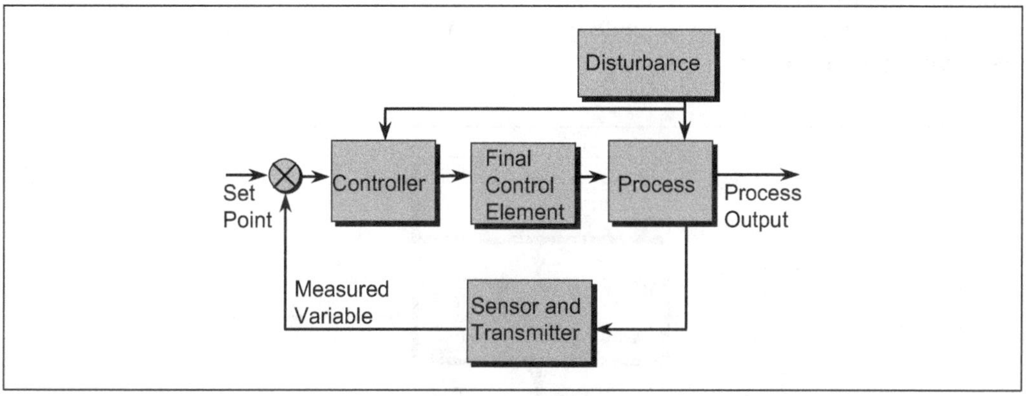

Figure 30-4. Notice the Disturbances Impacting the Controller, Not Just the Process

We spent the last few chapters discussing how corporations need to change with their market pressures. This pressure gets transmitted down the hierarchy of the corporation, altering the needs of each plant and process (Figure 30-5). This not only changes control loops but entire control strategies. The response to this pressure on the plant floor must include an easily reconfigurable control strategy in a system.

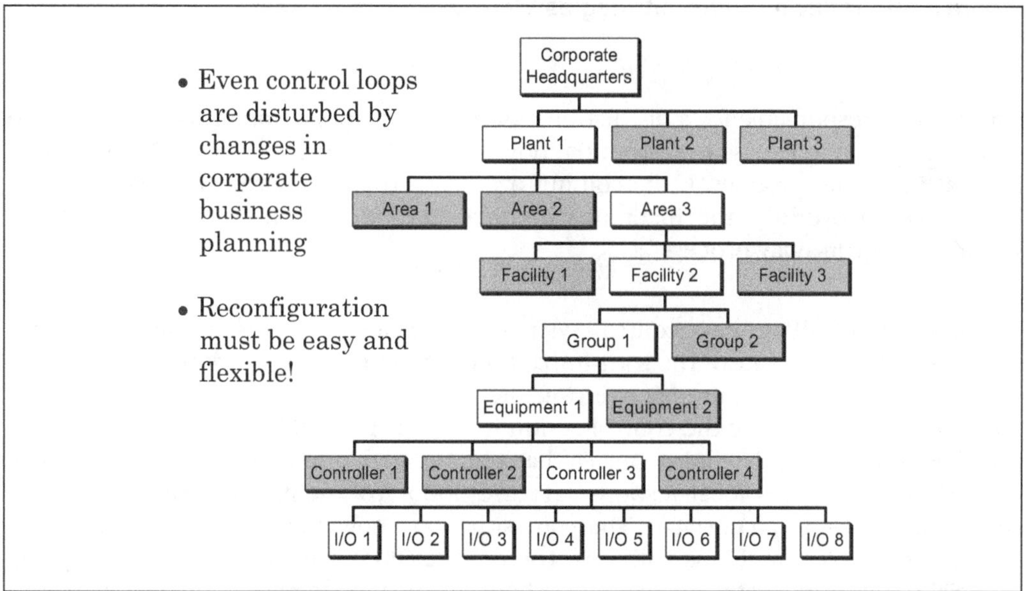

Figure 30-5. Controller Disturbances Trickle Down Subtlety through Corporate Hierarchy

Feedforward control, for example, is an extremely powerful tool, but it has traditionally been very hard to manage in most circumstances (Figure 30-6). It was really not for the faint of heart! This is because there is so much interaction among many variables on most processes, and feedforward by itself is not self correcting like feedback. A strong advantage of feedforward is that it can resolve a change in some input and cancel its effect on the product. A disadvantage of the far more prevalent feedback loop is that it cannot act until the product does change, and is moving (or has already gone) out of tolerance. The wrong tuning of feedback can also cause the loop to slip into oscillation, also ruining the product.

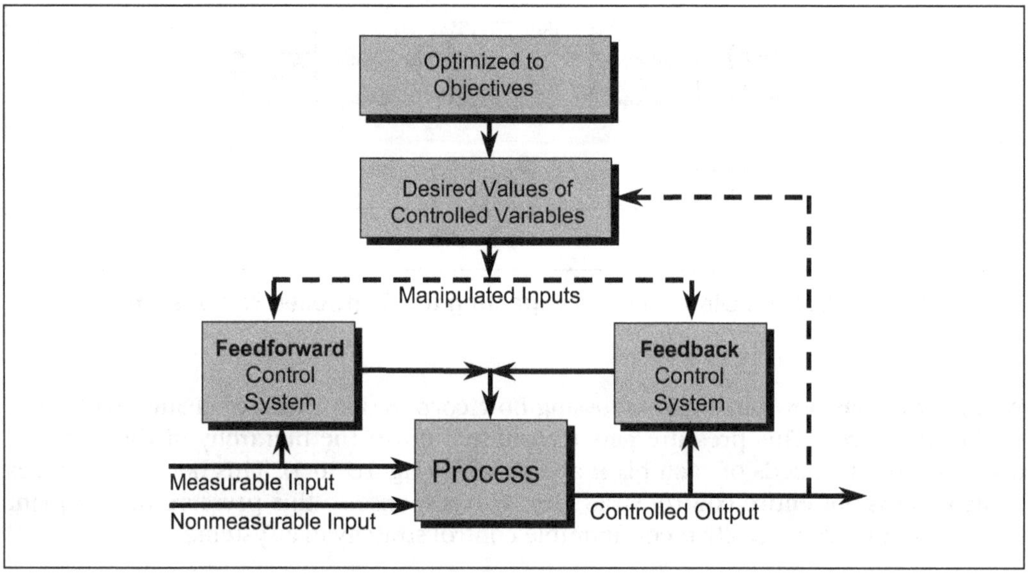

Figure 30-6. Today's Control Strategies Were Daring in the Past

An engineer responsible for a distillation column, for example, might have a request to save energy, so the excess heat from the downstream heat exchangers could be used to preheat incoming product. If the column overheats, there is more excess heat, which in turn could overheat the incoming product, and...well without tight control you would have a run-away process!

The purpose of all process control systems is to manage all disturbances within a system in a way that causes the least impact on production of good product. A flexible control strategy is a requirement during the discovery process of each alteration of conditions. The object of the control action is to return to stable conditions as soon as possible. Ziegler and Nichols suggest that the "quarter amplitude decay" curve can roughly represent this ideal response (Figure 30-7). To attempt to return faster will cause the process to go unstable. There are situations, however, where the time it takes to return to stable conditions with only three-mode (PID) control is unacceptably long, especially if it is imperative to avoid overshoot. Instead of merely a controller, a control *strategy* is needed.

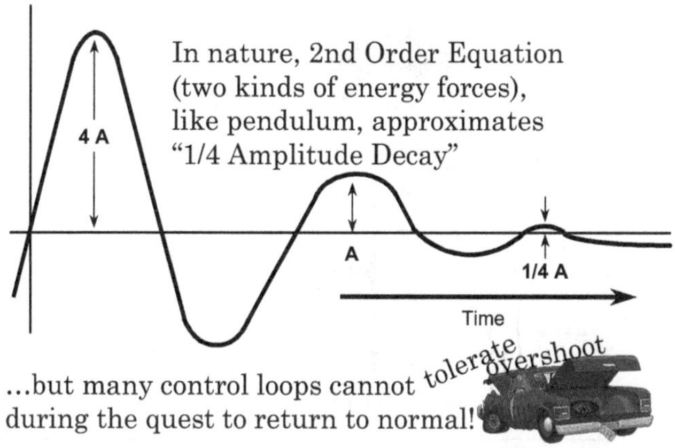

Figure 30-7. Every Process Change Results in Some Response Curve; the Ideal Is to Return to Stable Condition as Quickly as Possible

---

Please note that this simplistic discussion is to show the need for easy re-configurability. IN NO WAY do I intend to show here any method of tuning a loop! My friend Tom Keyser, of Moore Process Automation Solutions, reminds me that even John Ziegler was upset with the myth developed around their arbitrary assumption of the "quarter amplitude decay" concept, which became some kind of golden rule in tuning. There are too many variable conditions in any loop to do that. For example, many times ANY overshoot is unacceptable. In the developed example here, you will notice that the evolving "improvements" actually move AWAY from that so-called rule of thumb!

Building Control Strategy

As an example of developing a control strategy, as opposed to a control loop, let us explore a saga of change in a simple unit process (Figure 30-8) through discovery from a growing set of requests.

In a new effort to save energy, management has observed that toxic gasses in another part of the plant are rendered safe by burning them off. The heat is wasted, so they request to have that gas pumped into this process that needs heat. Everything goes well with a simple temperature control loop (Figure 30-9) until changes in the *other* process alter the flow of gasses in this one. Our product goes out of tolerance during upset of the other unit, and our simple temperature feedback loop, with all three modes in correct action, cannot maintain proper control.

Our intrepid engineer adds a flow controller as a cascade *strategy* to regulate fuel flow and maintain temperature tolerance (Figure 30-10) but notice that upset still takes *time* to settle.

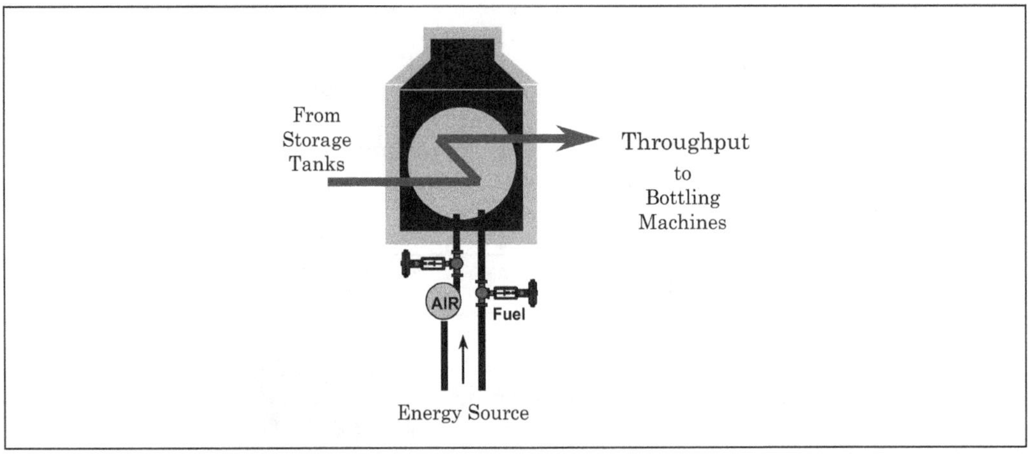

Figure 30-8. A Simple "Unit Process" Heater as a Configuration Example

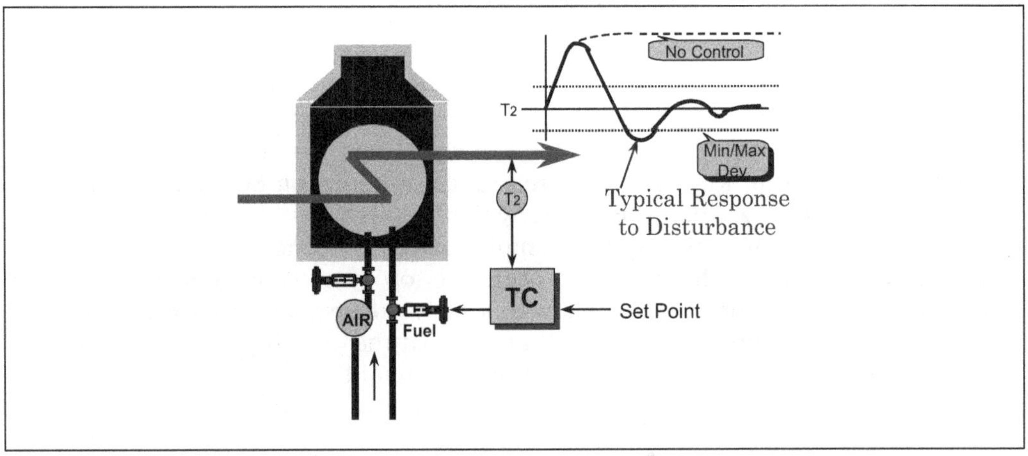

Figure 30-9. Simple Temperature Feedback Loop for Control

The company now and then gets a very large cluster of orders, and management adds extra bottling machines downstream to allow for this. When the additional machines are turned on, the product moves through faster, therefore is not exposed to the heat for as long, and temperature drops below tolerance. By adding a measurement to the input, the feed*forward* signal can anticipate flow change (Figure 30-11). It could also anticipate pressure change if the level of the one of the upstream storage tanks changes.

In our case, however, the input piping passes through the outside so there are periods of sudden changes in temperature due to the weather. Feed*forward* signals from another temperature sensor can help anticipate these changes in the product entering our heater, to help offset this problem. Those immediate signals reaching the summing block make the change too soon, however, and the control first opens the valve to add heat but changes the product already in the heater! Now the feedback slams the valve shut to compensate, but it's too much too soon, especially if circumstances sent only a

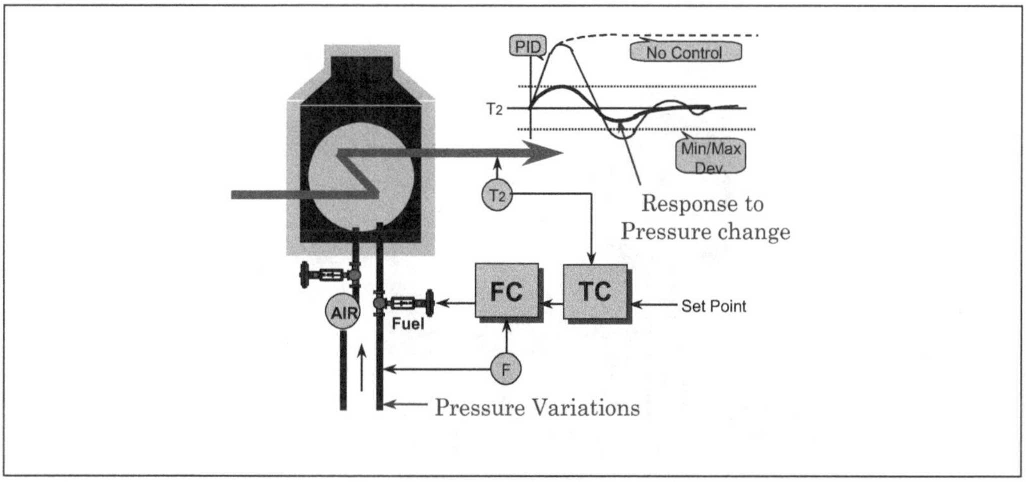

Figure 30-10. Second Loop Added For Cascaded Control with Temperature Driving Flow

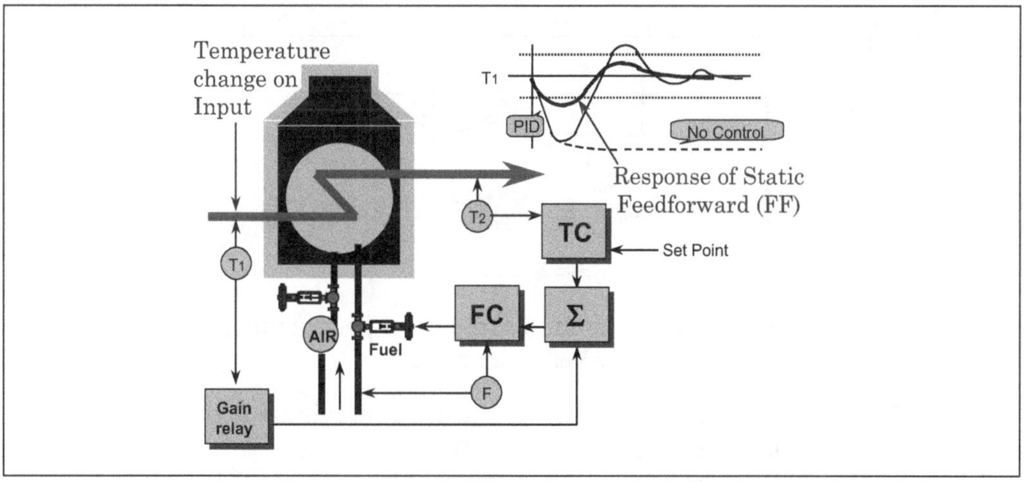

Figure 30-11. Feedforward Coupled with Cascade Control

"short slug" of cold (or hot) product through, and the product temperature is already moving rapidly in the same direction as the correction. The result is to make the control far worse than no help!

Creative Control Saves Money

Our undaunted engineer has added a time delay to match the flow so the correct action on the valve occurs! (Figure 30-12) Notice the curves! It seems with this more sophisticated control strategy he has improved the process and can make corrections in far less time than with the original single feedback loop (Figure 30-13).

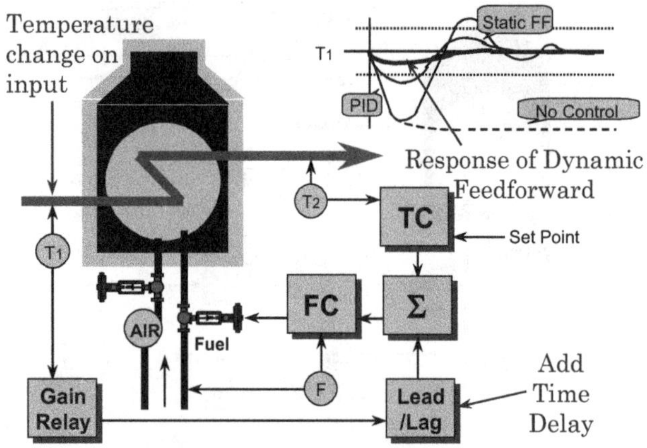

Figure 30-12. Adding a Time Delay to Feedforward Signal

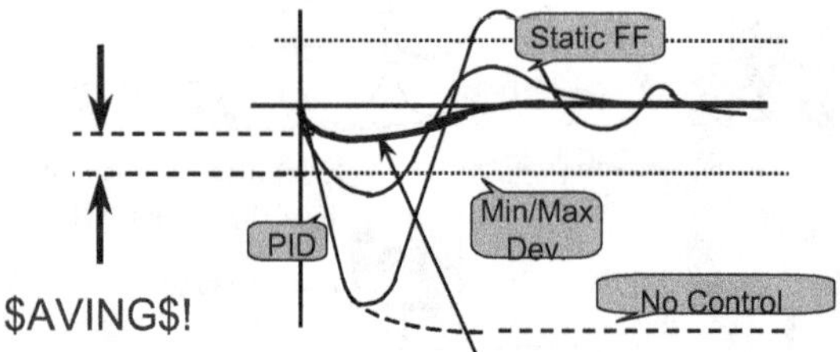

- Easy to experiment for improved performance because of easy **re**configuration!
- Savings from resetting the deviation limits and lowering set point can be from less energy, waste (treatment), reagents, raw stock, etc.

Figure 30-13. Ability to "Play Around" with Strategy Can Save Money!

Also notice the savings brought about by the use of a creative control strategy rather than just a control loop. If that tight control is repeatable, then the temperature set point can be lowered, using less energy in the process. Savings can come from using similar strategies in many processes. These curves could represent reduced need for as much raw material, a less expensive reagent to adjust pH, and so on. In a configurable system, the "instruments" are really function blocks already within the software of the same "controller," all connected with "soft wiring." All that was needed in this scenario were some new sensors. By the way, throughout the whole scheme there has only been the same single valve! What we developed is called multivariable control. Simple as it looks here, it was very difficult to achieve only a few short years ago.

Many more control possibilities could have easily been added into this example. Remember, none of this is using hardware, but rather function blocks within a single microprocessor controller! We didn't even explore ratio control, in our example... or the effects of online analyzers, or any of the many interesting advanced control techniques that have become much more economical than in the very recent past. Nevertheless, it is now possible to do significantly more with "plain ordinary" control function blocks, in fascinating combinations, to continue to build on plant optimization for quite some time to come. The limit is only the engineer's imagination. Many of the control systems of today will additionally allow you to create your own function blocks, easily add your own equations, and develop strategies using many of the same "cut and paste" and other computer application functions now available in word processors and graphic packages.

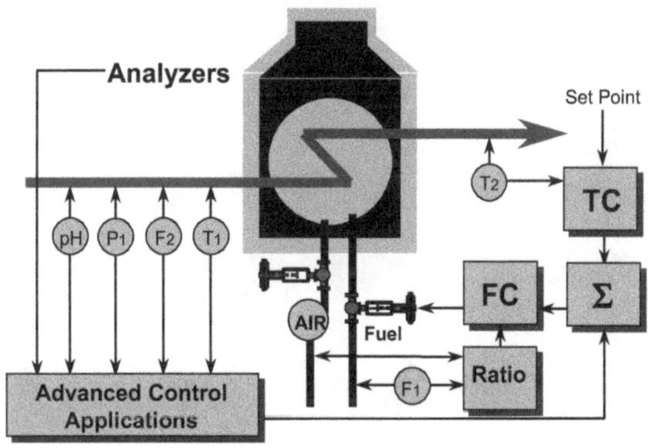

Figure 30-14. Many Other Strategies Could Easily Be Added With Microprocessor System

---

The purists among us may be wondering why I chose to not use the traditional ISA standard "bubbles" in this example. The "bubbles" provide more information, and reduce ambiguity, but I wished to instead call attention to another facet. All of those "boxes" are really function blocks, which could reside in a single controller, or eventually reside in various sensors and end elements, communicating along a fieldbus as if the entire strategy was in a single controller. That will happen as control systems become more distributed!

---

31 Discontinuous Processing

Prior to the middle 1980s, batch control systems were expensively assembled using various combinations of minicomputers, distributed control systems, and programmable controllers. From the middle 1970s to that time most batch control systems were done by process controls system vendors for millions of dollars. There were no standards. Since the middle 1980s, smaller and less expensive batch control systems became available, some for as much as a tenth of the cost of the earlier systems.

About that same time, because of the significant increase of less expensive systems, many users began to push for standards. In the U.S. a committee called TC4 was formed at the Purdue Workshop, and in Europe an organization of German, Dutch, and Swiss chemical industries formed a working group of Norman Ausschultz Für Messung Und Regelung (NAMUR) focused on developing batch standards. In 1989 ISA formed the SP88 committee to build on the work of these two groups, and in 1995 released the first part, ANSI/ISA standard S88.01 defining models and terminology. This is not a compliance standard, with rules or procedures that must be followed to ensure that a batch control product follows all of the terminology. By the end of 1990s, however, virtually every batch software vendor has base their products on S88.01, using terms like "S88-consistent."

What Sets Batch Manufacturing Apart?

Batch processes differ in several ways from continuous process (Table 31-1). Nevertheless, it can be argued that continuous is just a very long batch. Most systems are not exclusively "only batch" or "only continuous." Batch operations may take different forms, but they occur in nearly all industries, such as the following (Figure 31-1):

- Working with solids in heat treating
- Blending of powders in cement
- Mixing liquids in chemical and pharmaceuticals
- Unique, meticulous start-up, shutdown, and switchover procedures in power utilities.

Because of the many steps usually required in most batch operations and the nature of some of those steps, automatic control has been difficult and, until recently, made these operations to rather labor-intensive. There are several characteristics that distinguish batch operations:

- They are usually non-continuous operations, often because of to small product orders that are highly individualized

Table 31-1. There Are Some Clear Distinctions Between Batch and Continuous Operations, Between Control and Other Considerations

	Batch	Continuous
Control	Recipe driven	Set point driven
Product grade changes	Frequent	Occasional
Operations	Transient state	Usually steady state
Product volume	Smaller	Larger
Production life cycle	Shorter	Longer
Process equipment	Shared	Dedicated
Product chemistry	Not clearly known	More clearly known
Operator involvement	High	High when abnormal
Analog control loops	Few	Many
Interlocks	Large number	Smaller number
Sequential control	Complex	Simpler
Tracking and scheduling	Complex	Simpler
Operations management	Complex	Simpler

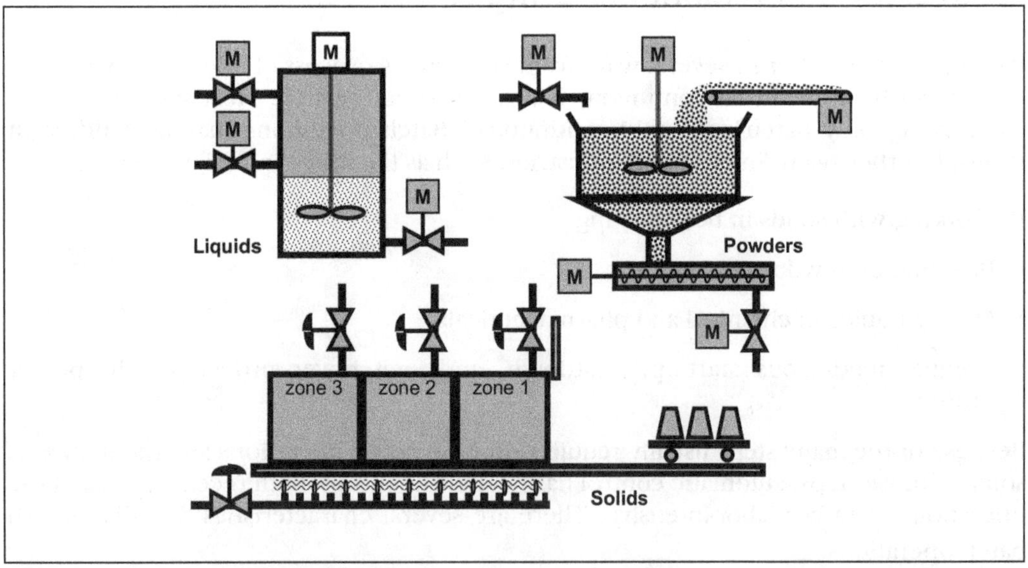

Figure 31-1. Typical Batch Processes Include Liquids (Chemicals), Powders (Cement), Solids (Heat Treating)

- Multipath, multiproduct configurations are often necessary to allow the cleaning of vessels between products so as to eliminate contamination
- Frequent and quick product changeovers are required to meet the needs of a variety of different orders and the specifications for each order
- Process control variability from batch to batch is based on ingredient quality and the ambient conditions needed for each different production run
- Manual and automatic operations are common because of controller limitations and the highly unique nature of the actions required
- They are under close scrutiny by regulatory agencies, not just in the food and pharmaceuticals industries but also in the metals industry, for tractability of stress analysis.

Batch Operations Challenge

A complete control system must be able to accommodate both batch and continuous processes to optimize the whole business plan. To do this, a plant's batch processing operations ought to be integral with the balance of the many continuous portions of that plant. This is not as easy as it sounds. Some of the challenges of batch and hybrid systems include the need to

- reduce the life-cycle engineering costs of automated and integrated systems
- reduce the time needed to bring new products to market
- enhance management's decision support with precise and timely information
- bind planning systems to execution systems
- reduce the dependence on system experts
- provide common terminology and structure

To help overcome these limitations, we must refer to the reasons for developing SP88 for batch control include the following:

- There was no universal model for batch control, which caused problems when dealing with recipes.
- It was difficult for users to communicate their batch control requirements to vendors because of the terminology problem.
- Batch control was difficult to configure because of the many different languages used by vendors.
- The integration of devices from different vendors was difficult in batch control because of the proprietary communication protocols used.

A Standard Helps to Overcome Needs

In the mid 1990s, the SP88 committee took on the near impossible task of organizing all the requirements of users *internationally* and addressed many of these needs. This was necessary before any vendor could hope to provide end users with complete sets of

Table 31-2. Batch Operations Have Many Unlike Requirements, Unique to Specific Industries

Application	Industry
Small quantities of product; different grades in small quantity	Dyestuffs and specialty chemicals
Slow-reacting process; reactant held in vessel long time	Food industry; fermentation of beer and wine
Complex reaction not easy to control	Chemical resins manufacturing
Chemical reaction does not take place immediately	Pulp and paper industry; batch digester
Large number of shades or grades	House paints
Products or feedstock that cannot be handled continuously	Solids or highly viscous materials in iron ore beneficiation and wax separation
Precise quality control in dispensing raw materials; production practices and historical documentation	Pharmaceuticals

tools for configuring both continuous and batch operations. This SP88 batch control standard addresses the following:

1. Reduces life-cycle engineering

   —Process modeling eliminates the need to write custom code for batch management

   —Graphical mapping of data between control and management systems eliminates the need for custom interface code

2. Reduces dependence on system experts

   —Modular automation allows reuse of standard phase and control module library elements

3. Reduces time to market

   —Simulation of recipes in a pilot facility using the process models of various production areas helps determine the best site for making a new product

   —Validation of the process model allows quick and easy creation of new recipes without re-validating the lower-level control logic

4. Enhances decision support with precise and timely information

   —Material utilization and tracking functions provide complete material genealogy and electronic batch recording

5. Binds planning systems to execution systems

   —Standard applications that provide graphical mapping of data between control and management systems eliminate the need for custom interface code

Model for S88 Process Automation Model for Batch Operations

Developing a model for batch operations, the committee realized that its implications would impact all industries, including continuous control. Already, as they investigate it, many industries are beginning to see this effort in the same way. This is not a comprehensive discussion (little in this book can be). Like all the other topics in this book, however, it should help move you a little closer to *understanding*.

Physical Model

The (Figure 31-2) section of the S88 standard defines the "vessels and plumbing" and all other equipment needed in the batch operation. This definition can "climb" as far into the business as is appropriate for the plant and process involved. Included in it of course, is the control system.

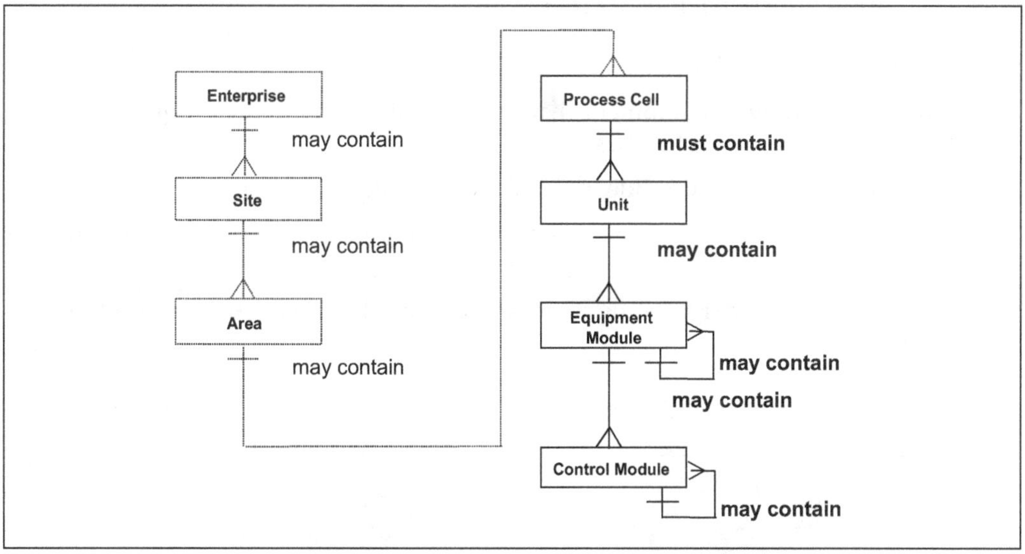

Figure 31-2. The "Batch" (Process Automation) Physical Model Appreciates the Whole Business

- Control Module
  - The lowest-level grouping of equipment in the SP88 physical model that can carry out basic control
  - Control modules implement basic control
  - Basic control may include regulatory control, monitoring, exception handling, and discrete or sequential control
- Equipment Module
  - A functional group of equipment that can carry out a finite number of specific processing activities
  - Usually centered around a piece of process equipment such as a process heater or weigh tank

—Consists of control modules and may contain other equipment modules

—Contains all equipment and control functions needed to perform its process function

—Contains a fixed amount of equipment

- Unit

—A collection of associated control modules and/or equipment modules and other process equipment in which one or more major processing activities can be conducted

—May contain a flexible amount of equipment, equipment modules, and control modules

—Frequently operates on all or part of the batch but only on one batch at a time

—Cannot contain another unit

—May operate independently of other units

- Process Cell (Figure 31-3)

—A logical grouping of equipment that includes all the equipment required for production of one or more batches

—A frequently recognized subdivision of a process cell is a *train*

—A train is composed of all units and other equipment that may be utilized by a specific batch

—The *path* is the order of equipment actually used or expected to be used by a specific batch

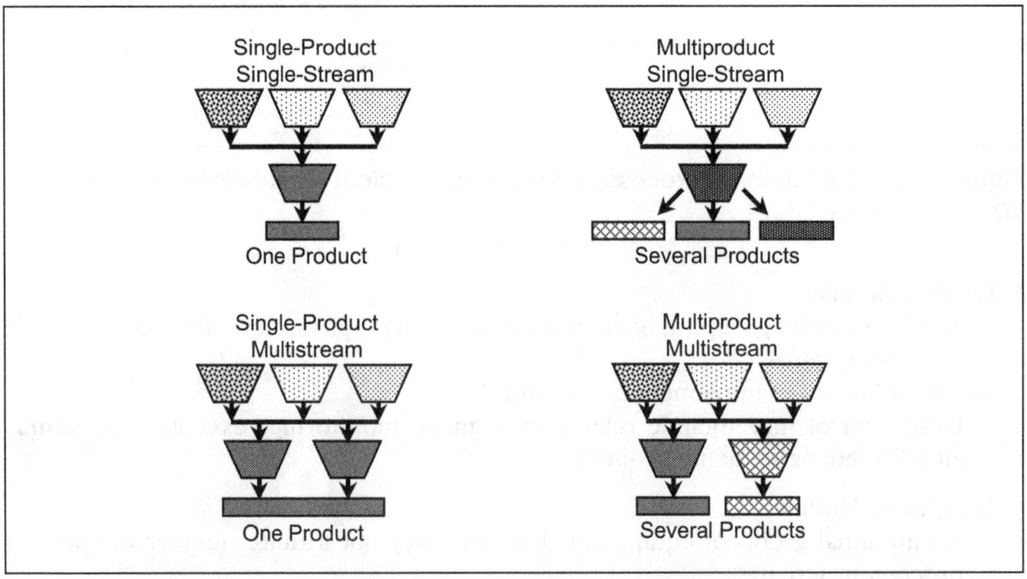

Figure 31-3. Batch Streams Within a Process Cell Can Be Very Complex, Requiring Intricate Scheduling

Procedural Control Model

The procedural control model (Figure 31-4) of the SP88 defines what equipment to use, and when to use it. It involves the methods of production, the sequence of operations, the control strategies, and the safety overrides necessary to protect personnel, equipment, and product.

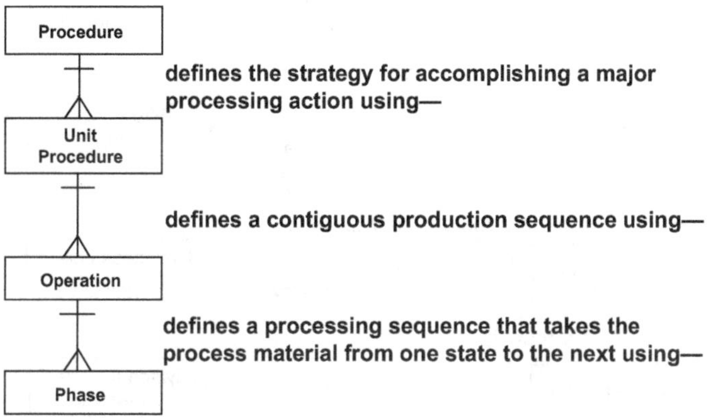

Figure 31-4. The Procedural Control Model Defines How to Use the Equipment

- Phase
  - —The lowest level of procedural element in the procedural control model. It provides an interface to basic control
  - —The point of connection between supervisory control and the process--connected device
  - —Phases can operate in a parallel or sequential manner
  - —Phases always end in a "safe" state
- Operation
  - —A procedural element defining an independent processing activity that consists of the algorithm necessary for the initiation, organization, and control of phases
  - —Only one operation may be active in a unit at any time
  - —Operations are carried to completion in a single unit
- Unit Procedure
  - —A strategy for carrying out a contiguous process within a unit. It consists of contiguous operations and the algorithm necessary for the initiation, organization, and control of those operations
- Procedure
  - —The strategy for carrying out a process. In general, it refers to the strategy for making a batch within a process cell
  - —It may also refer to a process that does not result in the production of product, such as a clean-in-place (CIP) procedure

Recipe Model

The recipe model (Figure 31-5) portion of the SP88 standard involves everything about the product being made through all the procedures and use of equipment. The recipe is the orchestration of the other model components and the direct driving force behind the control system.

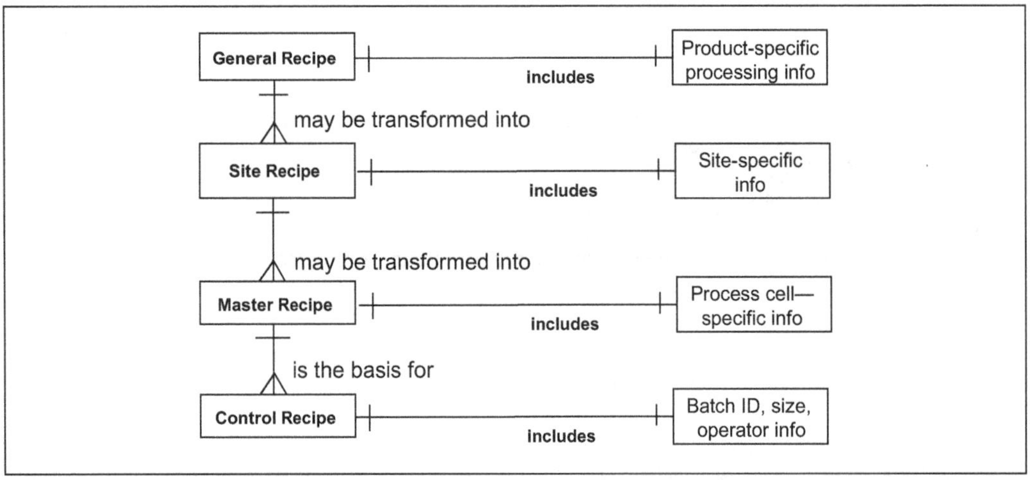

Figure 31-5. The Recipe Model is Everything Orchestrated to Making the Product Itself

- Header
  - —Administrative information including recipe and product ID, version number, originator, issue date, approvals, status
- Formula
  - —Process inputs
  - —Raw materials or other resources required to make the product
  - —Process parameters
  - —Information such as temperature, pressure, or time that is pertinent to the product but is neither an input nor an output.
  - —Process outputs
  - —Material and/or energy expected to result from one execution of the recipe
- Equipment Requirements
  - —Constrains the choice of equipment that will eventually be used to implement a specific part of the procedure (trains, paths, etc.)
- Procedure
  - —Procedure
  - —The strategy for carrying out a process
- Other Requirements
  - —Other information that may include regulatory compliance information, process flow diagrams, and packaging/labeling information

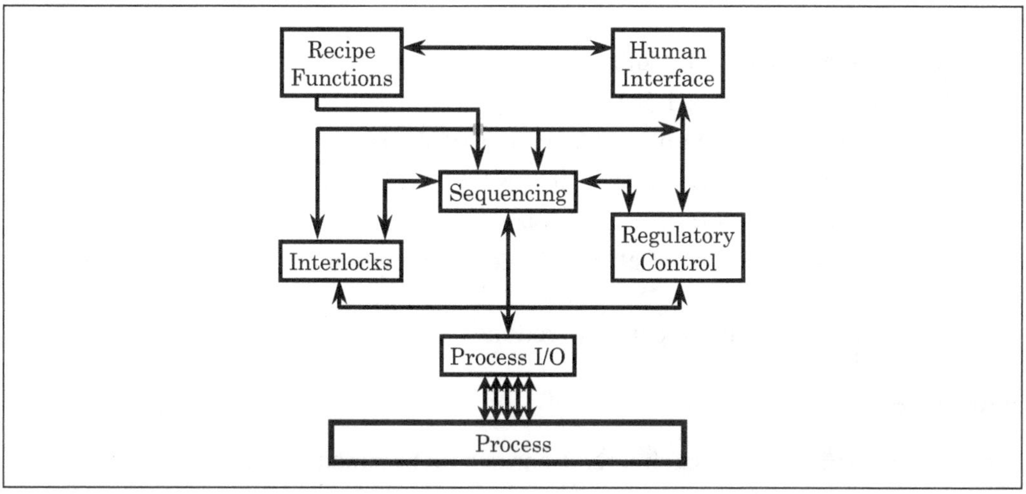

Figure 31-6. Recipe Drives the Controls

Crossing the Line between Enterprise and Process Control

More dilemmas continue to arise. There is no easy place to put some of the "control" of the batch process. Two very important areas must be considered, but each has a "foot" in both worlds. When viewing the plant as a whole, be concerned with the function not with "purity of specification." Just be consistent within the corporation. The suggestions presented in the following section will benefit the cost controls of the enterprise, but are often implemented through the controls system.

- **Scheduling is Important**
  - — Meet market demand
  - — Eliminate vessel idle time
  - — Share constrained resources
  - — Reduce the need for equipment change-out
  - — Reduce disruption in product cycles by scheduling clean-in-place (CIP) and line flushing operations
  - — Provide alternate paths and optimized equipment reallocation in the event of process or equipment failures
  - — Make the most use of equipment and reduce the use of inefficient equipment, such as by eliminating of intermediate storage from processing units to downstream units
  - — Assist operators in making product transfer, recipe management, and equipment allocation choices
  - — Eliminate unplanned overtime
  - — Improve turn-around time and shutdown planning
  - — Reduce maintenance costs with the balanced use of equipment and predictive maintenance techniques

- **Reasons to Track Batches**
  - —More efficient batch scheduling
  - —Monitor the status of each batch in the process
  - —Keep a permanent and updated inventory of all goods
  - —Track the quality status of raw materials and finished products
  - —Locate all products throughout the plant
  - —Keep historical records of all production parameters associated by batch or lot number
  - – Learn and improve upon plant operations

More Information:

Further information about batch operations can be obtained from:

World Batch Forum, 3239 E. Cottonwood Lane, Suite 100, Phoenix, AZ 85044-7857
Phone: [602] 759-WB4M; Fax: [602 759-6700; Email: 71713.217@compuserve.com
web site: http://www.cyboard.com/wbf/index/html

Toward Standardizing Configuration 32

Remember the controller "blocks" we used in the illustrations of the heater example in Chapter 30? If you could assemble them as a control strategy diagram, and "soft-wire" them together to show the signal flows from one function to another, you would have what is called the "configuration" (arrangement) of control strategy. In Chapter 5 we compared that with programming, and discussed the march from "traditional" programming code to object oriented graphical configuration. Because of the distrust of early users of computer-based controllers of the middle 1970s, the word "programming" was a red flag! Vendors also appreciated the need to allow users to focus on the need to intuitively configure their system so the effort would be on the application, not on the programming. Since the release of the Macintosh computer, users expect application-oriented configuration, not programming, to develop their applications. (I don't want to design a light bulb every time I walk into a room that needs light).

Each control system vendor, having nothing but various programming languages available, began to develop some form of non-programming way to assemble control strategy. In the United States, PLC vendors had their own ways to develop ladder logic, because the users were typically electricians. Control system users tended to develop "function blocks" which carried the features of the hardware controllers they already manufactured. All developed techniques based upon the industries they served, and of course, no two were alike! Many very creative functions and methods of configuring them did emerge. The only thing agreed upon by everyone was that the user should not have to "do programming."

Benefits of Configuration Standard

An international standard has been established that, for the first time, offers the promise of resolving the proliferation of configuration techniques that have buried the users of control systems. The history of the standard, which emerged from European PLC vendors and reflected their preferences, created a combination of languages so as not to favor any one of them. Although it was a slight step backwards from the very creative (but proprietary) methods developed by the many process control vendors, the standard at least organized a consistent approach which is the same for all the vendors who use it.

Why Was IEC 61131-3 Created?

- Structured methodology
- Hierarchical design
- Program portability
- Reduce training time
- Reduce support costs
- Modern programming concepts applied to process control

Although originally developed for PLCs, IEC 61131-3 is becoming available on several new distributed control system (DCS) designs from traditional vendors. The advantages of using IEC 61131-3 as the control standard are as follows:

1. Allows for multiple language
   — User has the option to select the best tool for the application at hand
2. Has uniform programming
   — Easier to learn
   — Once learned, training can be used on several different vendors
   — All control can be documented in a consistent manner, including continuous, discrete, sequential batch, etc.
   — One ideal goal is for the user to pick multiple venders and port applications
3. Supplies structured organization
   — Provides much greater maintainability
   — Reusable configuration/program objects—this minimizes the need to develop new software, reduces cost, and speeds up development
4. Covers wider range of applications
   — No need to use DCS and PLC combined architectures since most applications can be covered by a single IEC-compliant controller
5. Standardizing on a common configuration language is to
   — Focus on new concepts
   Structure
   Mixed language capabilities
   Sequential function charts (SFCs) and actions

   — Gain compliance
   Defined feature by feature
   Allows various levels of implementation

PLC controllers have been and are changing as rapidly as DCS controllers. Traditionally, they were programmed very much like computers, and there were many companies that offered configuration conversion packages for all the popular brands. Most sold in the United States are configured in ladder logic. In other parts of the world they follow the European approach, which favors instruction list or structured text of one form or another.

Who Is the IEC?

The IEC (International Electrotechnical Commission) was established in 1906 to facilitate the coordination and unification of standards among member nations focusing on electrical and electronic products. In 1994 it consisted of forty-four national committees that collectively represent 80 percent of world's population and produces and consumes 95 percent of its electricity. Examples of IEC standards include the following:

- **IEC 6617-12**—Graphical symbols standard for diagrams and binary logic elements
- **IEC 6617-13**—Graphical symbols standard for diagrams and analog elements
- **IEC 6848**—Standard for the preparation of sequential function charts for control systems (SFCs)
- **IEC 61131**—Standard (initially) for programmable controllers

There are five parts to this standard:

Part 1 General Information

Part 2 Equipment and Test Requirements

Part 3 Programming Languages (the only focus of the discussion in this chapter)

Part 4 User Guidelines

Part 5 Messaging Service

PLCopen, "a vendor- and product-independent worldwide association that brings greater value to users of Programmable Controllers through the pursuit of the IEC 61131-3 open software development standard", also supports IEC 61131 standard.

Founded in June 1992 in the Netherlands, has over sixty corporate members. Its offices are located in Zaltbommel, the Netherlands; Scottsdale, Arizona; and Tokyo, Japan.

The standard is also supported by ANSI. See IEC1131-3, "Programmable Controllers—Part 3: Programming Languages"

American National Standards Institute (ANSI), 11 West 42nd St., New York, NY 10036 Phone: (212) 642-4900; Fax: (212) 302-1286.

Also see "Programming Industrial Control Systems Using IEC 61131-3," by R. W. Lewis, available from IEEE/INSPEC Department c/o IEEE Service Center, 445 Hoes Lane, Box 1331, Piscataway, NJ 08855-1331. Phone: (908) 562-5553; Fax: (908) 562- 8737).

Standard IEC 61131-3 Languages

During the early stages of the IEC 61131-3 standard's development program, the task force found such a large number of programmable controller language (PLC) dialects that it was impossible to choose just one of them as a common language. Therefore, the team set out to develop a new common language by applying modern software engineering principles to the best existing practice. The IEC 61131-3 standard defines two graphical languages, two text-based languages, and a fifth-language invented to provide a high-level of syntax. The two graphical languages are ladder diagram (LD), a typical PLC logic (continuous or sequential) language, and function block diagram (FBD), a mostly continuous execution model (PID, math, continuous control). The two text-based languages are instruction list (IL), a low level (like assembler or machine code) language, and structured text (ST), a Pascal-like program language. The fifth language was invented to provide a high-level syntax—sequential function charts (SFC).

SFC performs sequential control, parallel sequences, transition logic, and the like. It includes structured programming, abstract data types, and data and procedural encapsulation, while maintaining a close relationship to the classical programmable controller languages. In addition, the IEC 61131-3 standard allows different parts of an application to be programmed in different languages that are linked into a single executable program.

Standard IEC 61131-3 Languages

- Function block
  - Mostly continuous execution model
  - PID, math, continuous control
- Ladder logic
  - Typical PLC logic
  - Continuous or sequential
- Sequential function charts
  - Sequential control
  - Parallel sequences, transition logic, etc.
- Structured text
  - Pascal-like program language
- Instruction list
  - Low-level, like assembler or machine code

We will not go into the details of these languages, but a brief explanation of standard languages, language constructs, mixing languages, derived function blocks, sequential function charts, and actions is in order. Several language constructs used for consistency include programs, derived function blocks, global variables, local variables, variable types, arrays, structures, actions, I/O references, and access paths.

System Model Diagram

The system model illustrated in Figure 32-1 depicts relationships among the following elements within an IEC configuration:

- **Resource.** The highest level, one per controller module; controls tasks.
- **Program.** A logical grouping of functions with one task assignment; scope is user-defined; may encompass the control of a process cell.
- **Task.** An element of a program that provides for the periodic or event-triggered execution of the program's content (i.e., how the program is executed). It may be prioritized and allow for preemptive or nonpreemptive operation; it may also be specified for an individual program with its own scan rate settings, etc.
- **Declaration.** The mechanism for establishing variables and functionality. Examples include variable declaration dialog boxes, declare statements in structured text, and declaring a new derived function block.

- **I/O references.** This includes not only direct references to screw terminals but also to alias point tags.
- **Access paths.** Provide single-name access to variables or groupings of functionality.
- **Function blocks** (and other languages). Each have inputs, outputs and state information, with internal data retained, and each instance (copy) is unique, for instance, timer, flip-flop, PID, mass flow, etc.
- **Derived blocks.** Used to organize the program further (specific to user's needs) and includes other languages, just as with function blocks.

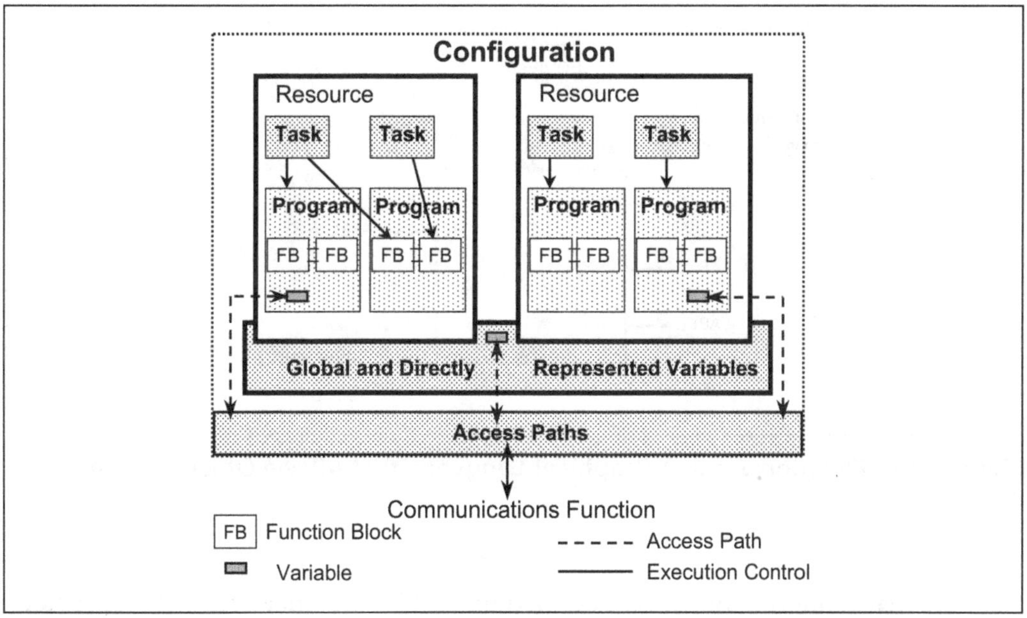

Figure 32-1. Relationships among Elements within an IEC Configuration System Model

Function Block Diagrams

A function block diagram (Figure 32-2) is a graphical language that allows program elements to be viewed as blocks that "soft wire" together. This can easily provide a network like graphical showing the signal flow between functions. These blocks execute algorithms that remain hidden, so the user can use object-oriented programming techniques to configure a system. They are controlled using external parameters appropriate to each function (algorithm). The IEC standard ensures that these are defined using a standard methodology. There can be three types of function blocks:

1. Standard blocks

   —Math, logic, trig, string, etc.

   —Exact functionality is specified by IEC

2. Vendor-supplied blocks

   —PID, cascade, majority voter, lead/lag, dead time
   —Vendors may implement them differently

3. User-defined blocks

   —Definition may be in any IEC language

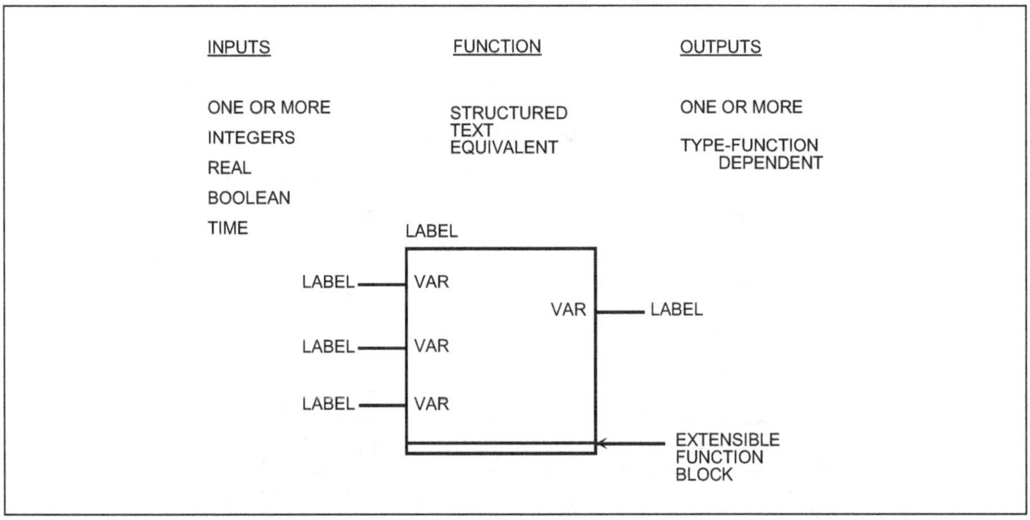

Figure 32-2. Function Blocks: Graphical Language that Allows Objects to Be "Soft Wired"

Many standard function blocks are defined in the IEC specification, which provides a commonality of functions and appearance among IEC-based products. These standard blocks are fundamentally PLC-type functions. Technically, the IEC only defines one class of block that can be created by the user. That is the derived block. One vendor provides a user-defined block that organizes the user-created blocks into those that are meant for single use (derived) versus those that are meant for reuse (user-defined).

The IEC specification does not limit implementation to only the defined programming languages or elements. It is open to enhancements and supersets of functionality. A prime example of this is that the IEC did not define PID functionality. Therefore, vendors could implement standard PID functionality as a superset of the function block language without violating the intention of the specification.

Function blocks may be connected using "wires" or by using the "name" of another function, such as the output of a tank level (Figure 32-3). These connections can be made with any data type: Booleans, integers, real values, arrays, and so on. (An array is a multidimensional variable consisting of elements of the same data type that are individually addressable through numeric subscripts). By using stub connectors, an unambiguous link can readily be made

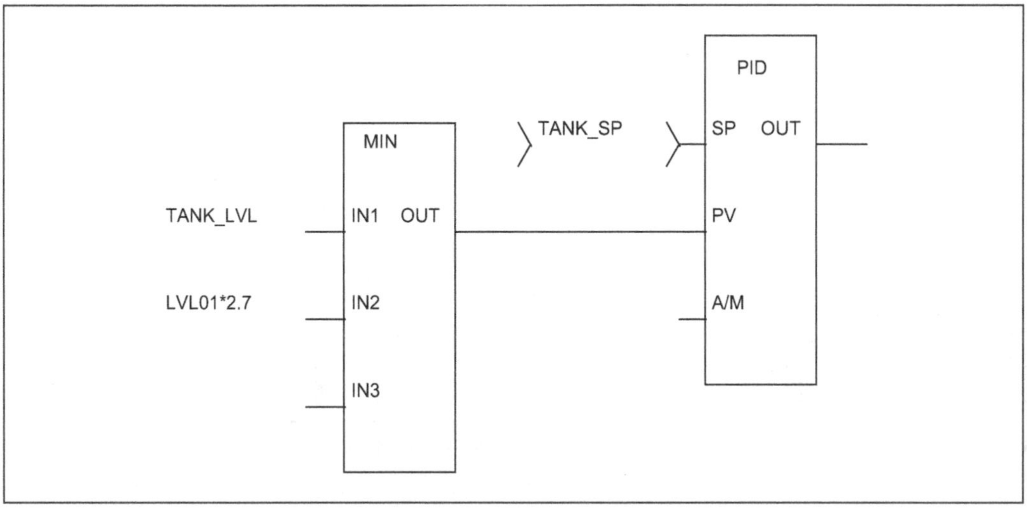

Figure 32-3. "Soft Wiring" of Function Blocks Shows Intuitive Signal Flow

Global variables can reside on any IEC language "sheet" and hence can be used as a vehicle for interaction between languages. Single elements can be local to one resource (the controller, for example) or global, making it available to several resources (controllers, residing in other locations on the network). Direct variables are vendor-defined (I/O, registers, etc.). Arrays are multi dimensional, for example, temperature profiles.

Passed variables provide object-oriented functionality so data can be moved between languages. Expressions may be placed on diagrams, and on some systems can become a part of them by that action. Expressions are, in reality, single-line structured text equations that are compact and intuitive when sitting on a function block diagram, and can interact with it. Derived Function Blocks (Figure 32-4) allow the user to create their own custom function blocks, which can then be placed in a library to be reused in any other strategy.

Ladder Logic Diagrams

Ladder logic is the traditional language of programmable controllers. It originated with electricians and electrical maintenance operations. In the IEC 61131-3 standard, ladder logic, although adopted, still uses a standard set of symbols from that discipline to represent electrical sequences of operations. For those familiar with ladder, it is a concise and easy way to troubleshoot if online data can be depicted (with color indicating power).

Ladder logic diagrams (Figure 32-5) are used to represent the intersections of field devices in such a way that the activation of one device could turn on another according to a predetermined sequence of events. The structure is like a ladder in that it starts at the top of a sequence of actions, then moves down in steps. Once complete, it can either repeat the whole sequence or wait for another initiation signal.

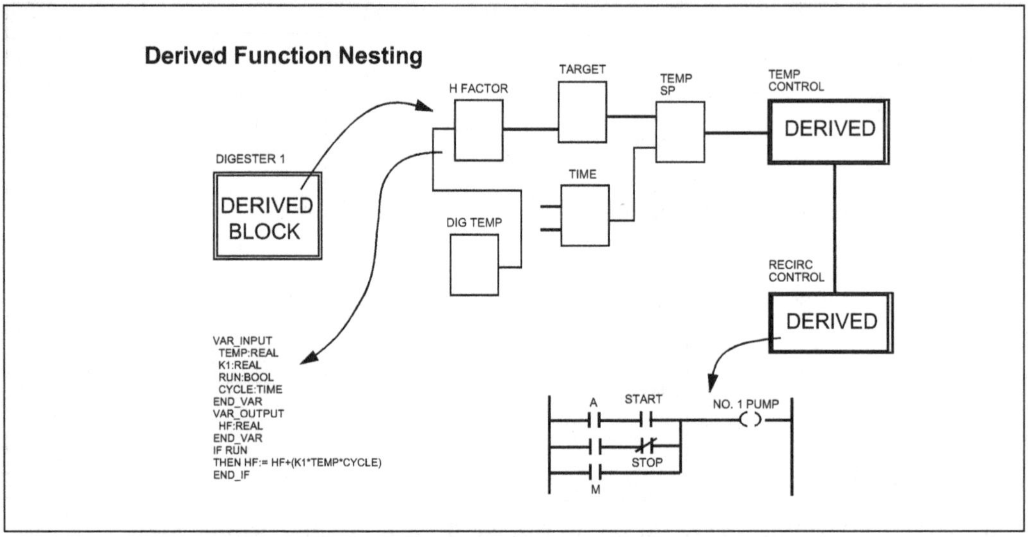

Figure 32-4. Derived Function Block Organizes User's Creation into Single Function

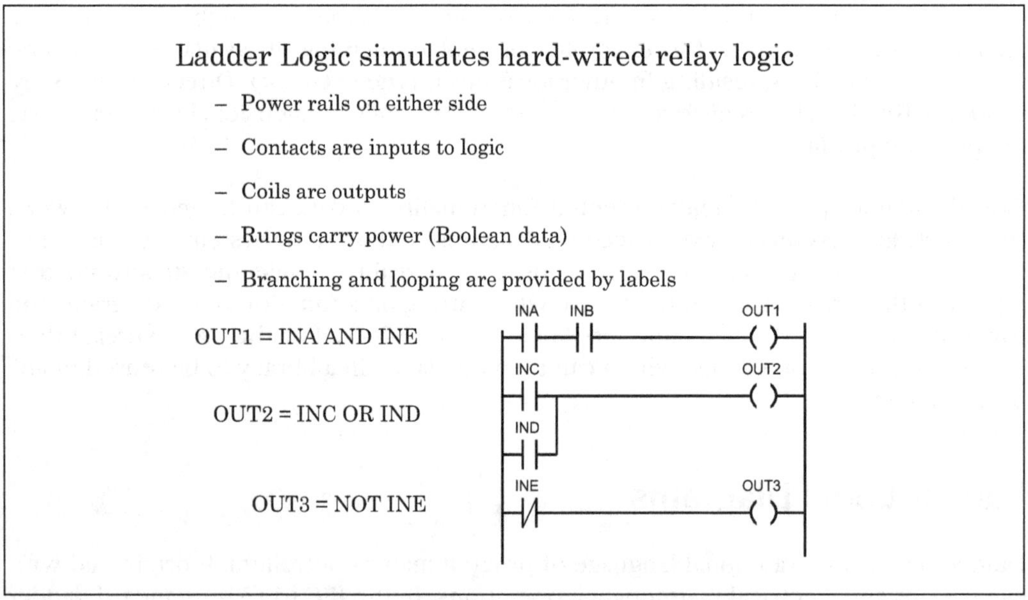

Figure 32-5. Structured Text Compared to Same Expression in Ladder Logic

Sequential Function Charts (SFCs)

Another set of programming elements defined by IEC 61131-3 are the sequential function chart (SFCs) elements—steps, transitions, and action blocks—which can be used to organize programs written in the other languages for the purpose of accomplishing sequential control. It is not a stand-alone language, but one that pervades the other four. The SFC elements are based upon the IEC 6848 standard, which is the international version of Grafcet, a well-known French standard. They act as building blocks in programs and can be used inside function blocks or as other parts of programs. While often represented as graphical elements, these elements can be written in any language, including text-based ones. Figures 32-6 through 32-12 are intended to be merely a quick graphical tutorial of the concepts behind Sequential Function charts, demonstrating how intuitive this very powerful language can be. Well, a little help might be appropriate in Figure 32-8,

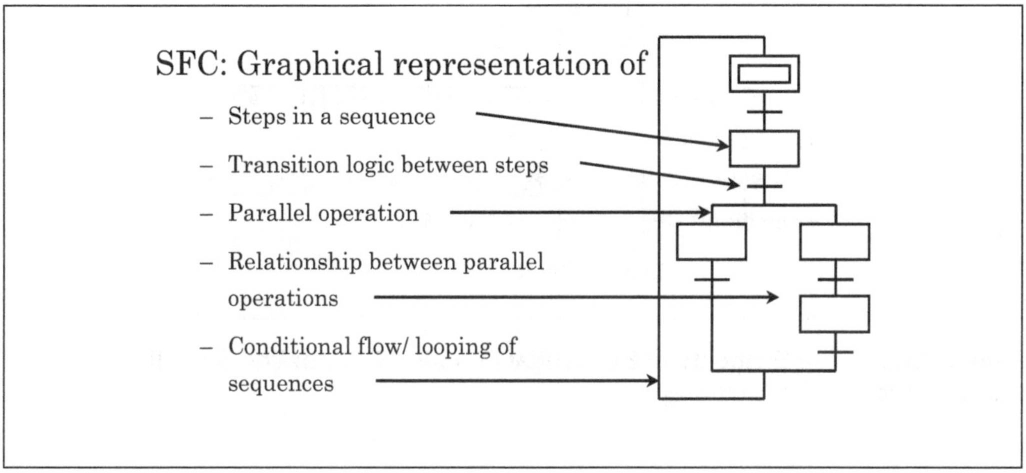

Figure 32-6. Sequential Function Charts: A Relatively New Language, but Simple to Learn

where "intuitive" use of convergence and divergence may not be so intuitive (convergence and divergence should always be in matched pairs—what diverges must always converge):

- Divergence of Sequence (lower right inset of Figure 32-8)
  - —Single horizontal line
  - —Branch to one sequence of many
  - —Transitions below horizontal line
  - —Step 2 or Step 3 will execute, **not** both
- Convergence of sequence (lower right inset of Figure 32-8)
  - —Single horizontal line
  - —Convergence will occur only when transition below active step is true
- *Simultaneous* divergence of sequence (main view on Figure 32-8)
  - —Double horizontal line
  - —Branch to multiple parallel sequences
  - —Transition above horizontal line
  - —Step 2 and step 3 will execute
- *Simultaneous* convergence of sequence (main view on Figure 32-8)
  - —Double horizontal line

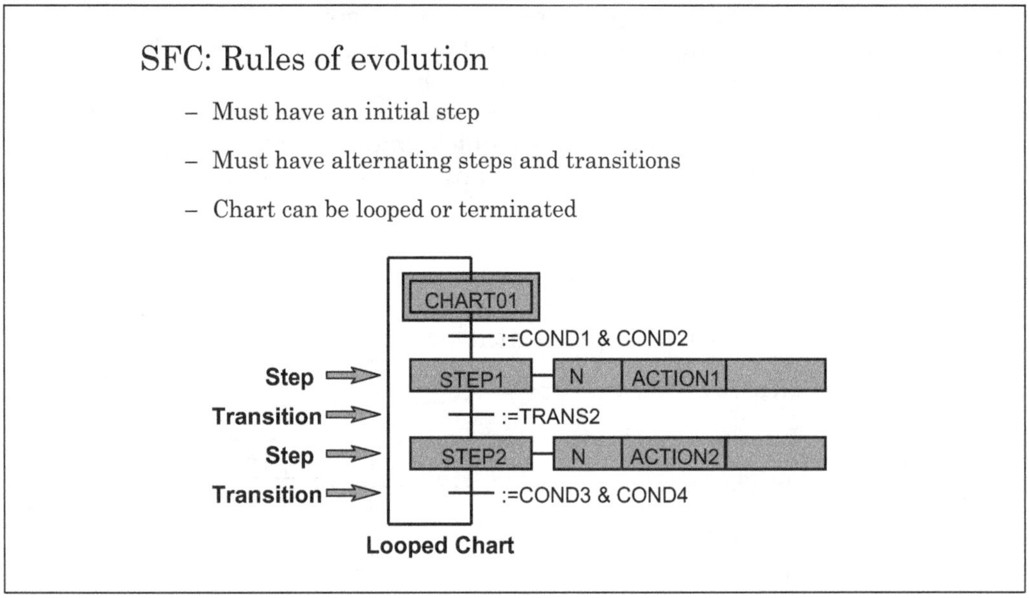

Figure 32-7. Three Elements of Sequential Function Charts: The Step, the Action, the Transition to the Next Step

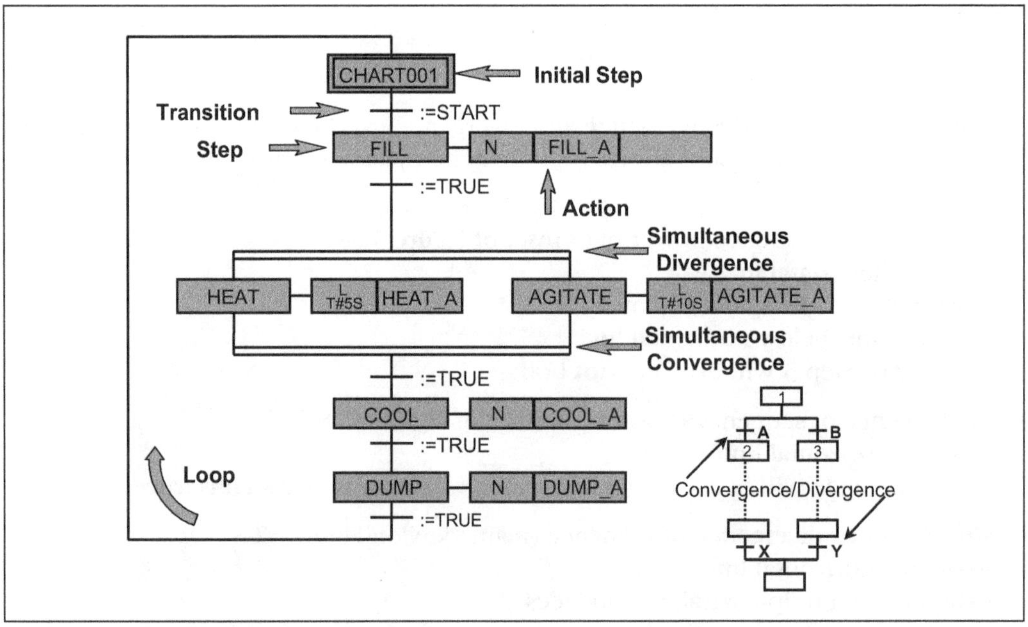

Figure 32-8. Divergence and Simultaneous Divergence in Sequential Function Charts

- **Skip sequence**
  - Divergence of sequence, one branch has no steps
  - If transition D becomes true before A step 20 and step 21 will be skipped.
- **Loop sequence**
  - Step 20 and step 21 will be executed as long as transition C becomes true before D

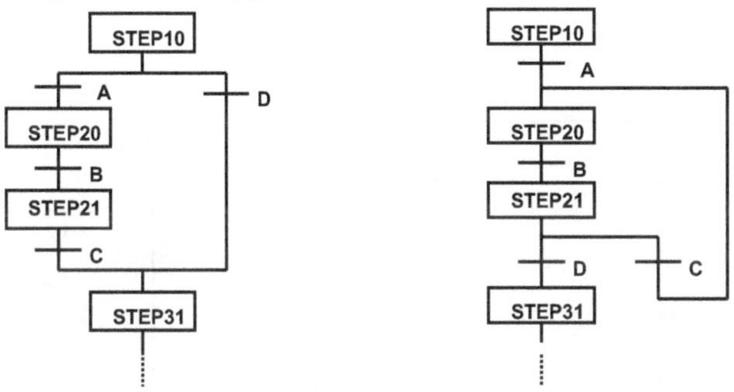

Figure 32-9. Graphic Representation Aids the Understanding of Control Actions in Sequential Charts

Action comprised of
- Action qualifier
- Action body
- Feedback variable

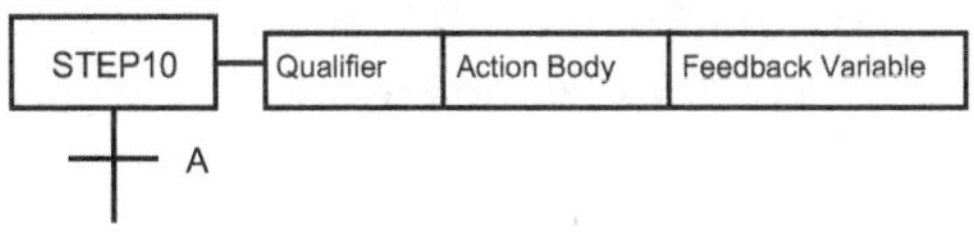

Boolean action
- Controls only one variable

Action with action body
- Body may be defined with FBD, ST, LL, SFC, IL

Action with action body and feedback variable

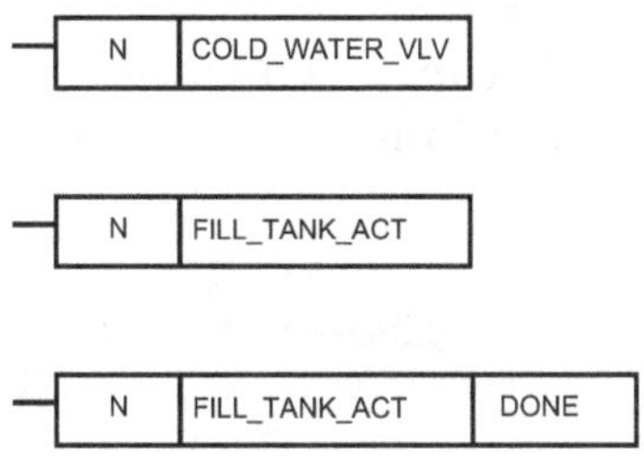

Figure 32-10. Actions Can Be Very Flexible in Their Use

— Transition below horizontal line

— Convergence will occur when transition below the horizontal line is true

Oh yes, there are some things to keep in mind about the many uses of actions within Sequential Function Charts:

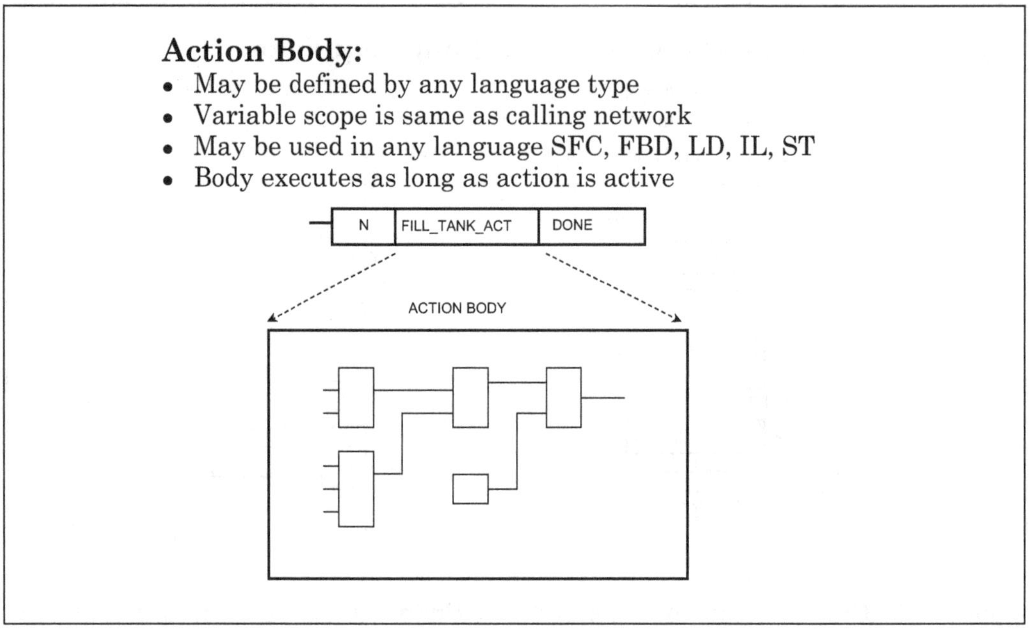

Figure 32-11. Any Language Can Be Used within an Action Body

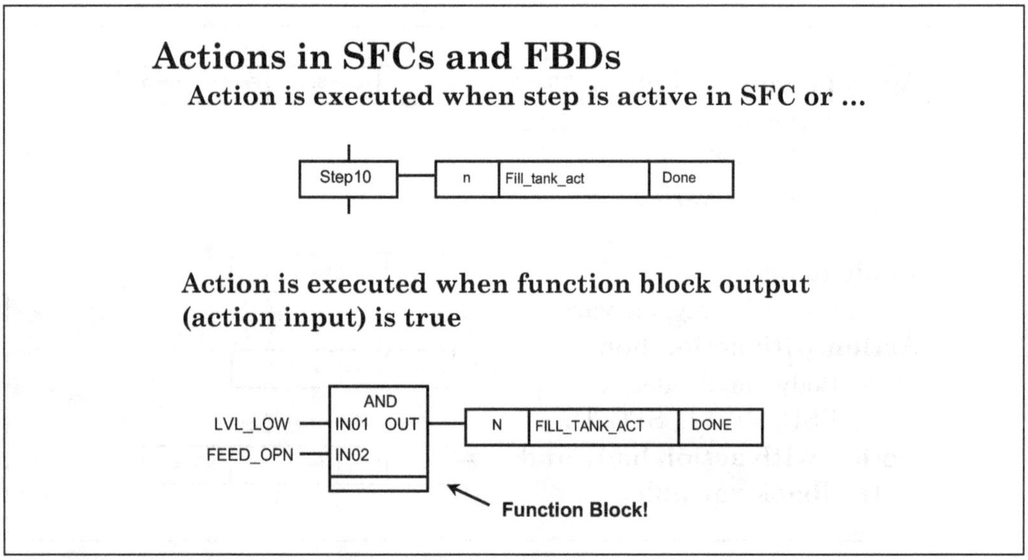

Figure 32-12. Another Language Can Be a Step

1. Actions are controlled by the following "action qualifiers"

N Nonstored—Action only executes while input is true.

S Stored (set)—Action executes from when it is set...

R Reset—until it is reset

P Pulse
L Time limited
SL Stored and time limited
D Time delayed
SD Stored and time delayed
DS Delayed and stored

2. A single action may have multiple action qualifiers
3. Action qualifiers can be thought of as "minitasks" run "as needed"

Structured Text

Structured Text (Figure 32-13) is a high-level block structure language that has a compact and easy-to-follow syntax that resembles Pascal. It can be used to express complex statements involving variables that represent a wide range of different types of data, including analog and digital values. There also are specific data types for the management of time, dates and durations, which are important to batch processing applications. The language has support for iteration loops such as, "repeat ...until ..," "while ....do ..."; conditional execution using "case of," "IF-THEN-ELSE" constructs; and various Boolean and arithmetic replacement statements. Text-based languages provide significant benefits when they are used in conjunction with the graphical languages because they allow the flexibility to combine special and often proprietary "formulas" as well as unique instructions to the control strategy.

Structured Text:

- Pascal like
- Assignments :=
- Arithmetic and Logic
  - Plus, minus, multi, OR, AND, etc.
- Conditionals
  - IF, ELSE, ELSEIF, THEN
- Multitest case
  - CASE OF, ELSE
- Looping
  - FOR, WHILE ... DO, REPEAT ... UNTIL

```
EXAMPLE

VAR
   P, PC, T, TC : REAL ;
END_VAR

(* Convert Pressures to psia *)
P := [PRESS] + 14.696 ;
PC := [P_CAL] + 14.696 ;

(* Convert Temperatures to Rankine *)
T := [TEMP] + 459.67 ;
TC := [T_CAL] + 459.67 ;
(* Orifice Calculation *)
[FLOW] := [F_CAL] * ( ([HEAD]/[H_CAL])
            * (P/PC) * (TC/T) ) ** 0.5 ;
```

Figure 32-13. Structured Text Is Very Useful for Blending Equations into Strategy

Instruction List

Instruction List (Figure 32-14) is a low-level language similar to assembler language whose origins lie in the early days of PLCs when memory was at a premium. It is based upon the German standard "Anweisungsliste." In today's new controllers, it is unlikely most users will revert to this kind of implementation for any involved strategy. Nevertheless, it is included in the specification, and has use for small refinements of function, generally in PLC-type actions.

Instruction List has low-level assembler-like instructions

• LD Load	• ADD
• ST Store	• SUB
• S Set	• MUL
• R Reset	• etc.
• AND	• JMP Jump to label
• OR	• CAL Call function block
• XOR	• RET Return

Figure 32-14. Early Programming Language from When Memory Was Scarce

Mixing Languages

Any or all languages can be used within a single controller. Derived blocks, for example, are used to encapsulate each application of a programming language, which also helps to organize the entire program. The various languages communicate or pass information to each other by "soft wires," variables, or tag names.

Languages are intended to coexist *within* each other! That is, function blocks can exist in ladder diagrams, structured text within function block diagrams, and any of the languages as a sequence function chart action. The major advantage lies in the ability to *BLEND* languages based upon user familiarity as well as selecting that which is most effective in terms of the time and effort needed to express the required function, execution time, memory needs, any combination of these, or even the whim of the implementers.

The structured methodology and hierarchical design of these languages furnish modern programming concepts that are refined and standardized. Working with a combination of these languages permits the user to apply the best tool for the task at hand and quite literally "slip in and out of" each and any of the languages as needed, thus greatly reducing programming time. All of this also makes it easier to understand and troubleshoot another person's program, regardless of which vendor's hardware is used.

With a standardized system, competitive advantage will be based upon price, performance, and capability rather than on proprietary languages.

Contrary to what many people believe, exchanging programs from one vendor's controller to another is neither defined by the standard, nor was ever intended to become a part of the standard. The purpose defined by the standard is to provide a uniform programming environment so users can reduce training costs. The difficulty with portability stems from practice. Then, hardware design was done first, and any facilities for programming were tightly linked to the hardware design. The two major difficulties with incompatibility are differences in physical addressing and different names and functions for the function blocks. As time goes on, expect this to change. As vendors adapt good software engineering principles, programs will become portable in time. Physical addressing might be approached by a symbol notation that separates basic functionality from the uniqueness of a vendor's architecture.

For More Information on PLCopen, contact—

PLCopen
P.O. Box 2077
NL 5300 CB Zaltbommel
The Netherlands
+31-4180-41139 (Tel)
+31-4180-15115 (Fax)

PLCopen USA
10229 North Scottsdale Road, Ste. B
Scottsdale, AZ 85253-1437
USA
+1-602-951-1107 (Tel)
+1-602-951-0720 (Fax)

Part H

System Security

Risk of Failure 33

Failure can come about due to imperfections of design, physical flaws from the manufacturing process, weakness from environmental stress, or damage from human error. To overcome these we must look to several methods to prevent the cause, correct the problem as it occurs, provide an alternate path to the functions, or limit the impact of the defect. One of the significant advantages of a system with distributed processors is the distribution of risk of failure.

Dependability

Discussions of the dependability of distributed processor systems are often based on a comparison of the dependability of the large mainframe computers used in process control. This is not the only comparison that should be made. Distributed processors for control also replaced centralized analog control installations, and the dependability of these latter systems is rated differently than the dependability of digital computer installations. The analog installation has a single loop integrity. Each loop is independent of all the others. The failure of one loop might degrade the overall process effectiveness but will not shut down production. The failure of the mainframe computer, on the other hand, inevitably results in a total process shutdown.

System Security

- Increased safety
- Improved reliability
- Higher system availability
- Reduced start-up time
- Minimum downtime
- Reduced configuration time
- Increased security
- Open communication

The dependability of the distributed processors in control is somewhere between individual loop failure and failure of the entire process represented by mainframes and centralized analog control installation. The degree of dependability depends upon the design by the supplier of the equipment. In all cases, remote units have their own processors and memories and will keep on operating if the central operator station fails. The operator will no longer have visual information about the condition of the instrumentation and the condition of the process. Operators can no longer make changes, but automatic control will continue. If one remote unit fails, none of the others will be affected; the operation will continue as before. The difference in dependability between various suppliers' equipment is more a function of the amount of redundancy built into the equipment, or supplied optionally, and the amount of multiplexing of input and output signals. A dependable system is one that's available for use by the proper user (security) and does what it's supposed to do (integrity). Thus, we can say that system dependability is made up of operator security, integrity, and availability. Operating security allows only authorized actions by authorized people. This is usually controlled at the operator interface and can involve the use of such tools as physical key locks, software key locks, and passwords or key sequences or code words or limited restrictions on screen hot spots and windows.

System Integrity

Simplistically, system integrity does what it should, when it should. That means all the components function the way that you expect them to function. They use such things as check-before-execute (CBE), Bose-Chandhuri-Hocquendhem (BCH), Cyclic Redundancy Check (CRC), parity checking, bus checks, self-checking routines, subordinate checking, and confirmed outputs. Availability means a high percentage of uptime. It is often defined by the equation of mean time to failure (MTTF) divided by mean time to failure plus mean time to repair (MTTR). Availability assumes components that are both reliable and maintainable; reliability is the mean time to failure (MTTF); and maintainability is mean time to repair (MTTR). Maintainability is established through error detection and correction (EDAC). EDAC sounds like *real* magic, but actually comes from once-expensive technology in critical computers that is now becoming commonplace in most small computers. If the diagnostic checks discover, for example, that one of a number of PROMs has failed, the stored information can be "reconstructed" by EDAC in the remaining PROMs, based on how it was used.

Diagnostics help identify where to maintain and service the device. The modularity of components makes them easy to replace. A service philosophy should support graphic maintenance, the availability of spares, the use of hot spares (which are already on line), and the ability to do live insertions of components without turning the power off. Reliability that contributes to improved mean time between failure involves fault prevention, fault limiting, and fault tolerance.

Fault Prevention

Fault prevention, or Fault Avoidance (Figure 33-1), is brought about by the use of robust integrated circuits through high reliability testing of components. Designing to high-temperature specifications usually assures that components will operate over a longer life in normal temperatures and environmental conditions. Preconditioning and burn-in tests are designed to remove any "infant mortality" probabilities by prestressing components, modules, and subassemblies. This is done by running modules in a hot/cold room, cycling the ambient temperature the full excursion through the limits every few hours for two or three days. Gold-plated connectors reduce the effects of corrosion, as do fully lubricating connecting surfaces. Various gripping techniques are frequently used on the hardware to assure good contact at all conditions. Fault limiting involves proper fusing and annunciation of fuse conditions through the diagnostic system as well as the LEDs on the equipment itself. These work together for quick and sure maintenance.

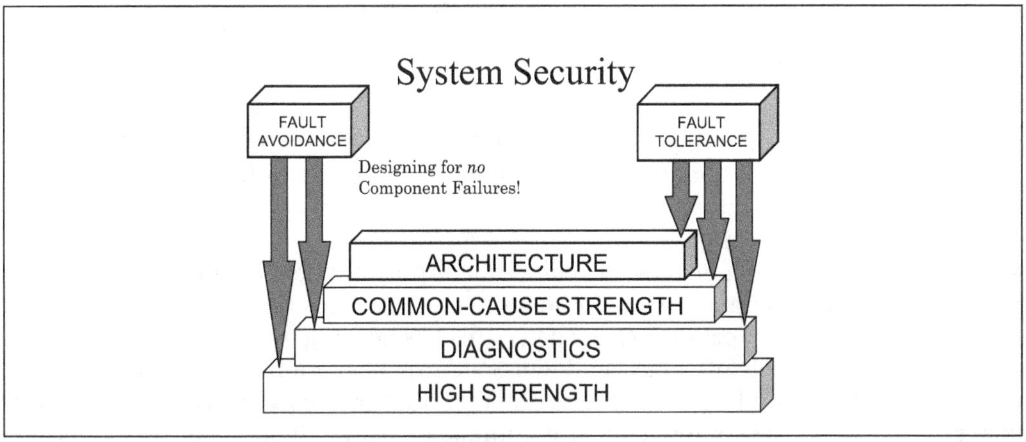

Figure 33-1. Four Important Building Blocks for System Availability

---

HALT—Highly Accelerated Life Test. Typically, this involves the rapid ramp-soak cycling of electronic equipment between the extremes of its temperature rating over two to three days to quickly identify failures that would otherwise take years to surface.

Thorough noninteractive fault design affirms that a particular problem or stress on the system does not impact other components on the same system. The functional distribution of both processing and memory as well as physical distribution prevent environmental events from affecting the entire system. Watchdog timers and time-out gates confirm performance and make possible early detection of nonperformance. Used in combination, many of these techniques go into producing a design that reduces the possibility that a single failure will be common to several components of the system, thus causing multiple devices to stop performing when a single mishap occurs.

Fault Tolerance

Tolerating fault is the ability of a system to operate successfully even in the presence of one or more failures. Fault tolerance is achieved through the use of redundant architecture, extensive diagnostics, and high common-cause strength (Figure 33-1).

Redundant control strategies take over in the same phase of operation, transparent to both process and operator, if the strategy within the initial controller fails. This has been discussed in Chapter 6 on controller redundancy and redundant inputs and outputs (I/O). Redundant I/O can be somewhat tricky in switching groups of signals, especially those with 1 to n (shared) redundant controllers. An uninterruptable power supply assures that if there is any loss of power, there is an alternate path for additional power to keep the control system operating. Battery-backed power provides power to the control functions for some limited length of time. Digital communications paths may require those signals to be switched over to some other route, or to continuing using two paths and absorbing the "traffic" load with one of them if the other quits.

Switchover "mechanisms" themselves are vulnerable. This will be discussed further in a later chapter.

A formula for achieving high reliability *and* high availability involves techniques of fault avoidance (for high reliability), and fault tolerance (for high availability).

Another approach to redundancy has been called "graceful degradation," in which the plant continues to operate during the loss of some modules but the system may lose some performance or capability. (No, Scotty, this has nothing to do with two dowagers sitting on the verandah of some rundown Southern plantation house sipping sherry while gracefully degrading from the aristocracy to "tobacco road"!) Less expensive than duplicating all the components, this approach must be thought out very carefully. Be sure to exercise all the "what ifs" that can be conceived of for the specific operation involved and the impact each potential failure will have on the process.

Redundant architectures have long been equated with fault tolerance, but redundancy alone can be useless without good diagnostics and high common-cause strength. Without diagnostics a system cannot tolerate faults because it doesn't know about them. Without common-cause strength a system cannot tolerate faults because individual stressors can cause the simultaneous failure of redundant resources.

Task Partitioning

One of the problems with the single computer is that it has to do all the work. Besides acting as a process controller for a large number of variables, it has to also scan all the variables, move around all the data, check all the limits for alarm conditions, keep track of the status of all its registers, and print out log sheets. All the tasks reside in one mainframe. The centralized analog control system is on the other extreme, of course. Its tasks are distributed among many individual controllers, each one operating independently of the others.

Distributed control is somewhere in between (Figure 33-2). The remote control unit performs for a number of loops those tasks that involve scanning, conditioning, and storing input variables; tasks that involve performing the control and computational operations; tasks that involve checking alarms; and tasks that involve developing output signals. The tasks that involve displaying, logging, and sending signals to the operator and to the process are assigned to a centrally located computer, but a much smaller one than is required by traditional mainframes. The remote stations are also microcomputers, and there is a further task of partitioning involved in their design. A number of microprocessors share the jobs of moving around data, scanning, controlling the function generation, and interfacing with the communication networks, as we described in Chapter 4 on controller hardware structures.

Because of the microprocessor chips, both the central operator units and the remote controlling units are smaller, more reliable, less expensive, and use much less power than their predecessors of a decade or two ago. The number of variable inputs and control outputs that are associated with the remote unit is a further extension of task partitioning. The number varies with the supplier and is a function of how much multi-

Figure 33-2. Partitioning of Tasks Among Several Processors within a Controller

plexing is done in the input and output circuits. The number is varied from one up to thirty, but eight or a multiple of eight is most often the number used. So while it is true that input and output signals may be partitioned between a number of remotes, it is also true that a failure of a remote may result in a loss of more than one output signal. If a critical move happens to be in the remote that failed or several loops that were interconnected or configured into that remote unit, the effects on production may be quite serious.

Redundancy

When selecting a control system, the effects of component failure should be assessed in the context of the process to which the control will be applied, and redundancy should be included accordingly. Suppliers recognize the importance of redundancy and make it available but in varying degrees. Some follow the philosophy that sooner or later there will be a failure, and there had better be something ready to replace the failed part. In the equipment that these suppliers offer, redundancy is standard. Others supply redundant parts as an option at additional cost. In some cases, adding redundant parts requires the use of construction ports, or communication capabilities, so the total capacity of the system is reduced. Some feel strongly that the standard redundant controller design should include separate cabinetry, power supplies, data highways, and even remote control unit electronics (so-called hand stations). In systems where these parts are not redundant as standard, the supplier again will usually offer them as options for redundant backup at additional cost. Additional discussion of controller redundancy is found in Chapter 6.

UPS (Uninterruptable Power Supply). Used to ameliorate the effects of poor electrical power quality, including voltage anomalies, high-frequency noise, or ground loops; especially applicable where power outages of over half a second duration are possible.

Redundancy. Duplicate equipment or a duplicate transmission path to prevent the failure of a function (versus *fault tolerant*).

Fault tolerant. The ability of a system to continue executing tasks regardless of the strategic component failure but perhaps with somewhat diminished effectiveness, performance, and/or functionality.

Graceful degradation. A method for keeping a process running, though component failures may degrade the degree of automation and sophistication.

In addition, suppliers recommend purchasing multiple operator stations, which will more likely be "dual-operating." That is, every view and function is identical in both, so that if one station fails the operator merely moves to the other. This is not as transparent as "electronic redundancy" but is certainly effective in keeping the plant running. Consider, for example, if the cathode ray tube (CRT) itself or its direct support electronics fail, the view goes blank, and there is no choice but to move to another station.

Redundancy is most useful when the transfer to it is automatic, that is, indicating the change by some alarm display but otherwise transparent to the operator and process. This is generally the case, but in some designs transfer must be made manually after a diagnostic alarm has indicated a failure. These systems are becoming less common.

Single Loop Integrity Myth

This was discussed in detail in Chapter 6 on controller redundancy.

Software Backup

Actually, software backup is a variation of hardware backup in that the control functions, which are located in the software, are replaced by software in other devices. This might be called functional redundancy and is differentiated from hardware redundancy because sometimes only part of the total number of functions of a controller rack is backed up or because one of the backup devices may be shared among several other controllers. There are designs that have a pair of cards (modules) along the backplane within the control unit, each of which is a complete controller. When one of these cards fail, it is backed up by the other card on that same backplane. In some other designs, several controller cards (modules) reside along the same backplane. One of these cards is left available (empty) as a backup to any one of the other cards. When this shared backup design is used, the control strategy configuration is frequently saved earlier in some separate memory location and downloaded into the shared controller. For both of these design approaches, there are some who are made comfortable by the fact that the backplane is "passive," that is, it has no components to fail. However, there are others who feel that this card is still a "single point of failure." This is also discussed in Chapter 6.

In addition to having shared backup among controller cards on a common backplane, there are also designs that share the backup of entire control units, where one unit is left "empty" and can be used in reserve to several other units. That is the style or the explanation used in the table "Effect of MTTF on Redundant Backup with 1 to n Configuration" found in the section titled "Measure of Reliability" in Chapter 34. This controller unit can be used to back up one, two, four, six, or eight other controllers, with varying levels of security and effects on Mean Time Between Failures (MTBF). A number of suppliers also provide a one-for-one backup controller rack with an automatic transfer from the primary to the secondary unit. In this arrangement, the database of the backup controller is partially updated every scan period, so during the backup there is very little loss of data, usually in the microseconds.

Hardware Backup

Another level of reliability assurance is to provide an extra piece of equipment that can be used to take over the operation of the control loop if the distributed processor equipment system fails. This is usually called a manual station, or a hand station, and gives a local operator the ability to manipulate the final control device directly. It can also be an analog controller that can be switched into the circuit to take the place of the digitally produced control signal for the distributed control file.

Both of these systems are rapidly disappearing from the scene, although many thousands of them have been implemented in the past and are still out there. Some manual station designs operate in parallel with the digital controller, and the output signals are developed by the manipulation of dials or switches on the manual unit, but their effect is produced through the digital circuitry of the controller rack itself. These are not truly backup devices since they give the operator the ability to take over control as long as the controller rack has not failed. But if that controller rack fails, it no longer is operable. This is not control backup but operator interface backup. This approach was frequently taken as an alternative to having the video screen and keyboard, which in earlier days were always considered to be the most unreliable portion of the system.

There are other manual stations, called *hard manual* stations, that are completely divorced from the controller rack, except that their outputs are routed back through the controller circuitry so their signal can be tracked. Though now fading from the scene as microprocessor reliability dramatically improves, tracking with hard manual stations provides a bumpless, balanceless transfer of the automatic control if that mode is selected after manual operation. The output signals developed in some hard manual designs are supported from independent power supplies to assure complete autonomy. In that way, if the rack in which the controller resides should fail, the operator can switch to manual control and continue the process operation or at least shut down the process in a safe and orderly manner.

The safest alternative is to operate the manual station from a completely separate power supply. "Bumpless" transfer between manual and automatic modes of control assures that the process will not be upset by a step change in the control signal. To achieve the "bumplessness," it is desirable to be able to perform the transfer without having to balance the output of the manual unit and the output of the automatic unit before making the transfer. This is not difficult when going from manual to automatic because the digital circuitry of the controller rack can be designed to track the output of the manual station. However, going in the other direction is more difficult because the manually operated device cannot readily follow the automatic output unless there's some sort of motorized servo that continuously positions the manual setter. Consequently, balancing so as to avoid a bump when going from automatic to manual is a necessary evil in most of these type of units. These manual stations will have at least two indicating meters with a knob or a switch for developing increase or decrease signals. One meter may display the value of the process variable being adjusted from the manual station so that the operator can determine the amount of adjustment to make. The other meter will show an output signal value and percentage of full scale.

Manual stations that are used parallel to the action of the digital control include a means for changing the set point, but this adjustment will not be found on those used only for backup. Since the function of backup is to take over the output signal when the regular controller has failed, there is little point in being able to change the set point value of the controller for which it is substituting. A better alternative is to back up the digitally derived control signal with a complete analog controller. With the reliability of today's digital microprocessors, however, this method seems to be completely unnecessary and is rarely sold as a new unit. All of the complexity of relays and circuitry and the expense of duplicating all of the controls in each of these loops make these techniques very much obsolete. Because most of the controllers today involve multiple loops that are highly interactive, the far better solution is to back up an entire control strategy with a one-to-one backup system using an entire control module. This is not a very expensive proposition anymore, now that the reliability of the systems has gotten to the point where the prices of multiple loop controllers are actually cheaper than the original mechanical controllers of the past.

Power Sources

There are at least three different varieties of power supply within a distributed system. There is a main power supply, which is probably 24 volts dc with fairly wide specifications. Then there are a number of well-regulated supplies, the most common being 5 volts dc. And, finally, there may be small storage batteries used to retain the memory of the database in case of a loss of main power so the entire configuration does not have to be reloaded. Each of these levels has its own considerations with regard to reliability. The main power supply in many cases is not supplied where the redundant unit is standard, but the purchaser is strongly encouraged to buy a redundant supply. This can usually be supplied optionally from the vendor. In most cases, it will be installed so that the outputs of all the main DC supplies are backed by diodes. If all put out the same level of voltage, they will share the load, but if one is higher than the others only its output diode will pass the current, and the others are truly backed up. Only the highest output level will be active. This is sometimes called "auctioning." Many suppliers include redundant regulated power supplies as standard design. If not, redundancy should be optionally available.

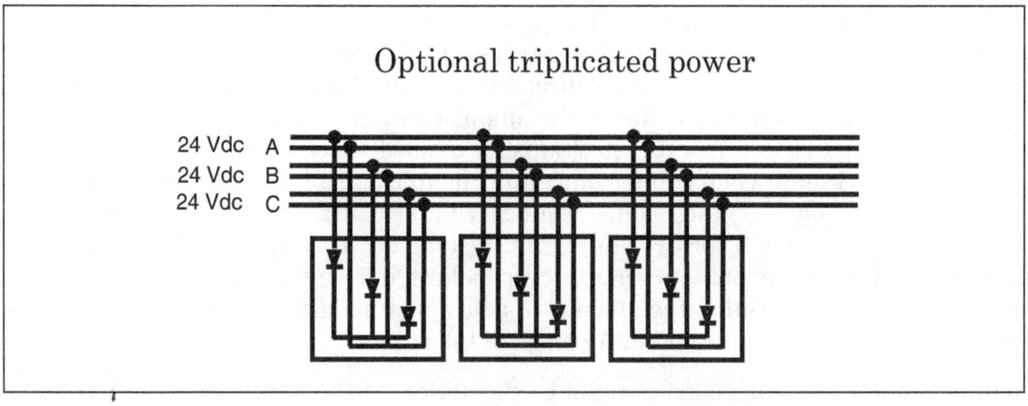

Figure 33-3. Example of Triple Redundant Power Sources (Two Power Lines Plus Battery)

The batteries used to back up the memory in the database perform to many different specifications. In some suppliers' systems, they will retain the information in the database for an hour—time enough to survive the normal power outage. Others last longer, with one supplier advertising a two-year period. This allows units to be shipped long before installation and start-up, as is often needed with systems supplied to meet the specifications of architectural engineering firms. They are likely to still have active databases holding the configuration that was put into the controllers at the vendor's factory when the equipment was staged and checked out in the system. In any event, there should be some sort of diagnostic to indicate when these backup batteries begin to loose their charge, as they must eventually do. Since the operation of all parts of the system is dependent on having an operating DC power supply, and indeed the diagnostics and backups depend on this as well, an installation in which continuous operation is absolutely vital should either have battery backup, or an uninterruptable power supply.

Power Loss

Control systems on critical processes, such as burner management systems, should always include dual- or triple-redundant power supplies to protect against power failures.

Spare Parts

The key to ensuring a small value for the mean time to repair (MTTR) factor is to have spare parts on hand with trained service personnel who know what to do with them. Faults in distributed control system (DCS) equipment are most quickly rectified by replacing the circuit cards or modules. First the diagnostics are used to locate the probable source of the fault. Then a series of substitutions with known good cards can quickly isolate the problem. Today, most of these diagnostics are backed up by light-emitting diodes (LEDs) physically located on the edge of those cards or modules, which correspond to the diagnostics shown in the operator's screen views. In this way, it's very simple to replace the existing card—the exact card—rather than have to hunt with a series of substitutions. The modules or cards themselves are usually far too complex for the average service department to make detailed repairs. Sometimes it's easy enough to replace chips, but if the problem goes further it is far easier to replace the entire module with a replacement spare and send the damaged module back to the vendor.

Of course, more things to stock would be fuses and lamps. These are parts that a service person can replace quickly. Sometimes the simple substitution of a fuse will put a failed system back on line. Generally, solid-state parts are very reliable. Their smallness reduces temperature problems that were once the major source of trouble with earlier electronics. Usually, if equipment survives the first three days of operation after start-up without any failures, it will go on and on indefinitely until the wear factor occurs, as we talked about earlier. Thanks to the stringent requirements of the nuclear programs, all suppliers have become very conscious of quality assurance and do a great deal of preshipment testing, so they are able to back up the specifications listed in their literature. Most suppliers subject their electronic equipment to lengthy burning procedures, cycling to high and low temperatures in excess of published limits for a number of days. During the burn-in, the system of equipment is operated with various parts cabled together. Parts that have deficiencies will fail and be weeded out during the burn-in testing.

Cost of Failure

In figuring how much redundancy is required in a system or how many failure techniques are required, one has to consider the cost of the plant being down and how long it will be down. The cost of the process not operating and product not being manufactured could very well dictate how much the redundant system or the fault-tolerant capabilities are worth. These must be considered in the overall life cycle cost of the system. When you design a control system to last, say, five years, you must consider the cost of engineering, installation, and start-up along with all the other variables involved at the time of purchase. Then you must also add in maintenance costs and the downtime cost over the lifetime of the control system. This can result in a far different figure, which may be developed to justify some fairly sophisticated fault-tolerant and redundant capabilities in a system. For a far more complete treatment of the fault tolerance and reliability of control systems, I would highly recommend the textbook *Evaluating Control Systems Reliability: Techniques and Applications* by William M. Goble, published by ISA.

A major design feature is the support of 100 percent redundancy at all critical levels within the control network. The proper use of full redundancy techniques *can provide in excess of a 200-fold improvement* in the system's mean time between failures (MTBF).

---

34 Measuring Deficiency

Measurement of deficiency has been an evolving art along with so many other developments using microprocessors. I suppose it goes with working on "bleeding edge" technology! One of these changing areas is the terminology, causing confusion even in such phrases as "mean time *before* failure," or "mean time *between* failure" or mean time *to* failure," depending upon WHEN you talked of the topic. Some discussion on this topic is in order, especially if you are the one who must create system requirements when developing a request for a quote from several vendors.

Time Dependent Behavior

Typically a failure rate curve, sometimes known as a "bathtub curve" (Figure 34-1), can be computed for most systems. There are three phases: a decreasing failure rate, a constant failure rate, and an increasing failure rate. Decreasing failure rate is a characteristic of the fault-removal process we spoke of earlier, in which a portion of the initial set of modules have manufacturing faults. If the entire collection of modules is placed on an accelerated task, manufacturing faults reduce the strength of the module and modules with faults will fail in a relatively short period of time. Failed modules are removed from the tests. After a period of time, no modules that have manufacturing faults will remain in the collection. The failure rate due to manufacturing faults will have dropped to zero.

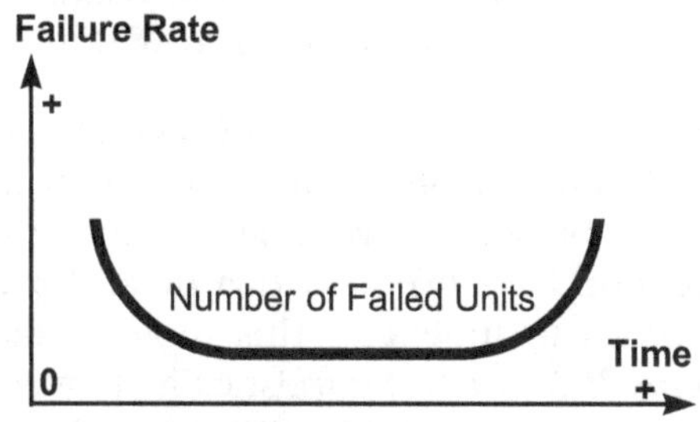

Figure 34-1. "Bathtub Curve" of Unit Failures

Now if the failures in a collection of modules are due to stresses from the environment, the failure rate from a large collection tends to be constant. Stresses are of many different types, and they may appear to come at random times and appear to have random magnitudes. In some cases, specific reasons why a stress is generated may be determined. But for the most part, the specific stress events that cause failure are not really understood or recorded and are treated as random in time. Design faults will also tend to cause a constant failure rate among a large collection of modules. As each module is used differently, it will eventually use that piece of hardware or software in which the design fault exists, and the module will fail. Since the usage is quite varied, it can be considered random. As long as the number of units in use is large, the rate of failure will appear constant.

In the increasing stage, some components have consumable resources, and when that resource is gone the component is worn out. For example, the chemical that will wear out in a battery or the bearings that will wear out in a motor. Because these components do not wear out at the same rate, they do not fail at the same time. However, as a group of components approach wear-out, the failure rate increases. The process of wear can be thought of as a gradual increase in susceptibility and eventually the susceptibility, increases above that required for normal use. Some of these failures are caused by repeated stress events. Each stress event increases the components' susceptibility. One example is electrostatic discharge. Each time that a component receives an electrostatic strike, it is damaged and its susceptibility is increased. After a number of these hits, the component's susceptibility rises above that required for normal operation and the component fails. Any susceptibility-building process will result in increasing failure rate.

Measure of Reliability

Reliability may be defined as an assurance that something will be available when it's needed and perform the function that was intended, especially within certain design limits. Reliability is really a measure of success, and as we said earlier, must be considered in terms of time. In the context of distributed processor systems, reliability measurement has been defined for resource-sharing systems as well as for redundant systems. An automobile is an example of a resource-sharing system: it becomes inoperative if there's a failure in the battery or if the fuel line becomes clogged or if a tire loses its air. The direct comparison in this case is to the mainframe computer system in which any computer failure will shut down the entire system.

We could perhaps picture the path of a signal entering one side of a control system and passing through a series of components on its way out to the final element (Figure 34-2). In actuality, there may be some parts that are not in direct series, depending upon the design of the vendor. Let's overlook that detail for now for our simplifying example. For a more rigorous treatment of this topic, I again recommend Goble's *Evaluating Control Systems Reliability*. Simplistically, however, the reliability of this resource sharing system is the product of the reliability of its parts.

We show this in the equation

$$R^t = R^1 \times R^2 \times R^3,$$

where R^t is the reliability of the total system, and R^1, R^2 and R^3 equal the reliability of the components 1, 2, and 3.

If the reliability of each of three components making up a critical chain of parts is 0.95, then $R^t = 0.95 \times 0.95 \times 0.95$, which equals 0.857

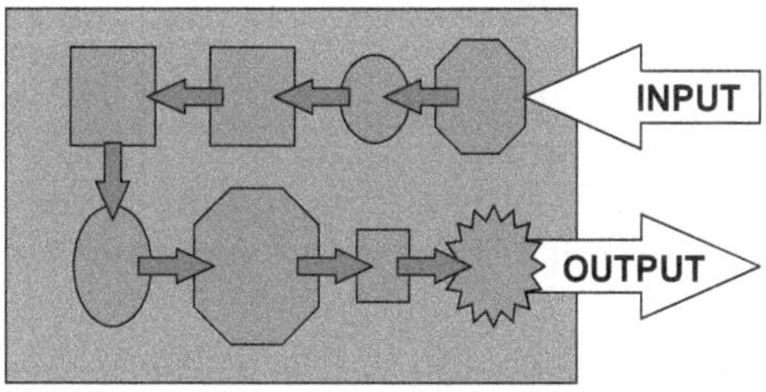

Figure 34-2. Each Component in Signal Path Must Be Calculated for MTTF

Now suppose one is in the enviable position of having two automobiles, each with the reliability of 0.857, and where one is always available if the other is not. The reliability would now be the equation

$R^t = 1 - (1\text{-}R^i)_2$,

where R^t is the total system reliability, and R^i is the individual system reliability.

Then $R^t = 1 - (1\text{-}0.857)_2$, which equals 0.9795, which is a significant improvement.

This illustrates the importance of redundancy. Availability, however, has different dimensions, expressed in real time: Availability = MTTF/(MTTF+MTTR). The concern here is the amount of time that the process will actually be under control, and the factors are the mean time to failure (MTTF), which is the function of reliability and the mean time to repair (MTTR). So the best availability will exist when the system is very reliable, that is, a high MTTF, and can be repaired or replaced very quickly, or a low MTTR. The figures relating predicted MTTF to the number of controller racks backed up by another rack are shown in the following table:

Table 34-1. Effects of MTTF

Effect of MTTF on Redundant Backup with 1 to n Configuration	
Number of Backup Units per Number of Controllers	**Predicted System MTTF in Years**
No backup	1
1 backup per 8 controllers	36
1 backup per 6 controllers	59
1 backup per 4 controllers	118
1 backup per 2 controllers	349
1 backup per 1 controllers	939

Some of the factors that contribute to satisfactory liability and availability of system are functions of the design, while others depend upon the needs and budget of the user.

Mean-Time-Before-Failure Myth

Prior to 1962, by the military specifications that were in use at the time the concept of availability was calculated to be equal to the mean time before failure, divided by the sum of the mean time before failure plus the mean time to repair (MTTR). The concept in process control is the calculation of what is in *the path of the control signal* from the input through to the output that could contribute to the failure of that loop. The operative word here is mean time before failure. It's the arithmetical mean (Figure 34-3) from all the failure probabilities of all the components in the path of that circuit. This number is a calculated number, *not a tested* number!

Availability = MTTF/(MTTF + MTTR)

Ratio: Time system is operating correctly to total hours of scheduled operation.

- **MTBF**—Mean Time Between Failures
  = **MTTF + MTTR**

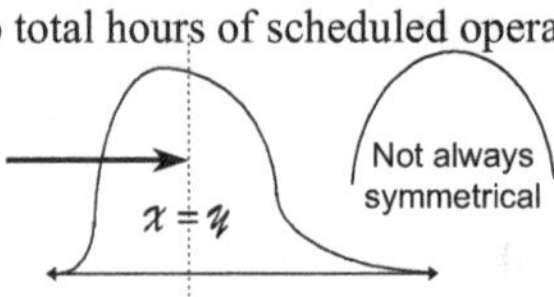

  Stated or published period of time for which user may expect device or system to operate before failure occurs; computed arithmetical mean of time, … not a tested value! Value will drop by about 50% for every 10°C increase; all other ambient factors will have similar impact.
- **MTTF**—Mean Time To Failure; calculated measure of overall reliability.
- **MTTFD**—Mean Time To Failure (to) Dangerous condition.
- **MTTFS**—Mean Time To Failure (to) Safe condition.
- **MTTR**—Mean Time To Repair; average time required to perform corrective maintenance on failed device or system.

Figure 34-3. Mean Time Between Failure, and Other Definitions

It is important to know what the typical probability of failure is for every resistor, capacitor, transistor, processor, and other component in that signal path. This probability would be calculated for all of those components on a circuit board, then for all those circuit boards in this path, and then for all of the other modules of circuit boards that were in the path. So it is calculating all of the "boxes" from the input on through to the output as the signal passes through connectors, wires, circuit cards, and components on those cards and so on. It is a very difficult computation that some companies will compute for vendors for several thousand dollars.

Many buyers of distributed control systems who ask for this MTBF number do not realize that the intention of this calculation has been to ensure the signal path integrity. They frequently request the MTBF for all the hardware in a system. All the hardware in a system includes communication paths over the data highways and all the electronics in the operator stations and then all of the communications to plant computers. In a complex communications network, this gets to be a very complicated and expensive affair to study. No two systems are ever alike, even those from the same vendor. There is no way an MTBF can have meaning in many of those attempts to look for system security and availability. Vendors have generally done their best in trying to come up with numbers, but there are many factors and many ways to look at the statistics involved. For this reason, to compare a MTBF figure for a *system* from one vendor to another is a rather fruitless exercise. It is far better to understand the nature of their system structure, and something of the vendor's reputation for quality, than try to come up with a definitive number that has meaning.

FMEA Failure Mode and Effects Analysis. A procedure by which every individual component is ranked with percentage failure values for each failure mode (i.e., transistor short, open, drift, etc.) to determine their respective failures in time (FIT). An overall impact is then calculated for the device in which all of these components are used. FMEA is used in developing MTTF.

Change in Availability and MTBF Definitions

Many of the calculations made during the evolution of computer systems did not occur using the formula mentioned in Figure 34-3. Rather, they calculated the availability as MTBF over MTBF plus MTTR. Since 1962, however, the official military specs have been modified somewhat. The current formula is "availability equals mean time to failure, divided by mean time to failure plus mean time to repair." And the mean time between failure equals mean time to failure, plus mean time to repair. Notice that the terminology has also changed; MTBF now means mean time *between* failure, instead of *before* failure, and the latter is given in turn a definition relating to mean time *to* failure.

To understand the subtleties of this seemingly nitpicking arrangement, one must study more completely the military specs that define it. For our purposes here, however, we should understand that there are many *additional* factors that impinge as well. For example, these statistics very much depend upon the environmental conditions of temperature, pressure, vibration, shock, and so on, that can affect these components during their normal life span.

The MTBF will drop about 50 percent for every ten degrees centigrade increase. The actual amount varies, depending on where you are along the scale.

All other environmental conditions will have an impact similar to that of temperature (box), so there is not only a factor of time involved in calculating availability but also a factor of environment. Rarely will any of these show in a manufacturer's listed numbers. Quite often, the very ambitious numbers that a manufacturer will provide you could very well come from ignorance as much as from deceit.

Nature of Failures 35

In the very complex issue of defining the kind and types of failures, two types appear—those that are physical failures and those that are functional failures. Physical failures are usually the ones that are considered by manufacturers that happens when a component or components within a module fail. Physical failures are typically studied extensively, but there are other failures to be considered, such as functional failures. Those are the ones which occur in a system that's *capable* of operating but does not perform its intended function.

An example of functional failure is a common software crash. A piece of data is entered into the computer, but then the computer simply quits. The computer has failed to accomplish its intended function, but no component has failed. No physical failure has occurred. The computer is restarted; it will often operate after being reset. The failure may, or may not, reappear, depending on the data entered.

Physical failures are almost always permanent and are usually caused by a component or module that wore out, burned out, or physically broke because of vibration or shock. If all the physical components in a system are working, and the system still fails to perform its function, the failure is classified as "functional." Functional failures have the same attributes as physical failures. Each failure has a failure source, which is almost always a design fault, although sometimes a maintenance or installation error will also cause a functional failure. The exact source of a functional failure can be terribly obscure. Often, the failure will occur when the system is asked to perform some little-used or unusual function, or perhaps the system receives some combination of input data that was never tested.

Types of Faults

Faults that can be detected and remedied will fall into two major categories. The most obvious is a change in component parameters. Normal environmental stress over time can cause components to change parameters or can cause the component to stop working completely. This can show up as a calibration shift in an analog amplifier or as a short or the opening of a component, like a diode, a transistor, or a capacitor. When this type of fault is detected, some sort of redundant hardware must take over to continue the operation.

The other type of fault takes the form of short disruptions of component function. This is most often caused by a noise transient and creates a disruption of the communication between subsystems. An example of this type of fault is an "alpha hit" to a memory system. Ionizing alpha particles can change the memory cell charge in semiconductors with high impedance nodes, causing a "soft" error in the memory. These faults have a limited duration and cause no permanent damage to hardware. If time permits, it is preferable to attempt to retry the operation. If this is unsuccessful, backup hardware should be put in service. If the retry is successful, however, the primary hardware should be kept in service so as not to "use up" the system redundancy before it is necessary.

Attributes of Failure

Both physical and functional failures have three attributes that are important to the analysis of control system reliability: that is, a failure source, an effect on the controller function, and some time-dependent behavior. The term failure source is used to represent the cause of a failure, the combination of stressors that exceeds the susceptibility of a component. Failures occur when some form of stress exceeds the susceptibility of the product or component. Total stress is composed of many stressors applied in combinations. Stressors can take many forms, including chemical corrosion, electrical voltage and current, mechanical vibration or shock, temperature, humidity, and even human error. Susceptibility is the result of the design. The choice of various design parameters and protection components dictates the susceptibility of the product. Stronger modules with higher safety factors in their design have lower susceptibility.

Effects on the controller function are the second attribute. This means that as a result of this failure the controller may go to no output, go to a full on output, or hold at some safe value, depending upon its design and the design of the components around it. Sometimes the most important thing in looking at failure analysis and the reliability of systems is to arrange for the effects on the controller, so that in spite of a failure, the process itself is not damaged or the people are not hurt. This will be achieved by trying various combinations of the components and modules and responses to the system that are wrapped around the part that failed.

The third attribute is time-dependent behavior, which refers to a large collection of components, modules, or systems. This collection is operated continuously. The number of units that fail in each time period is counted. This number, or failure rate, may increase, decrease, or remain constant depending on the stressor-susceptibility interaction. Any discussion on reliability must include the element of time. A statement such as "The system reliability is 0.95" is meaningless because the time interval is not known. The statement "The reliability equals 0.98 for over a period of 100 hours" makes perfect sense.

All parts and components degrade over time. That is why you might consider using components designed to a much higher temperature specification than your application requires. In that way, the *normal* operation of your system is less likely to degrade because the system is designed to operate at a higher temperature. The effect of temperature is less likely to cause a failure over a period of time.

Failure Sources

Many different things individually or in combination can cause failure. Therefore it is always important to take a broad, open look at these things. Failures are caused by a wide spectrum of stressors. For example, if we looked at the effects of humidity, even though the components are operating well within the humidity-designed range, higher humidity will accelerate the chemical process of corrosion. A badly corroded electrical contact will eventually fail. Was the humidity the cause of the failure? No, the corrosion was the cause of the failure, but the humidity accelerated the process. In a similar way, exceeding the rated specification so that the humidity condenses will cause water to drip onto the electronic controller, and when it fails humidity is considered the source.

Failure sources are both internal and external to the system. Internal failure sources, which can be very subtle and far more difficult to ascertain, typically result in increased susceptibility. Internal sources can include design faults in a product as well as manufacturing faults in the creation of the product. The faults can occur at any level: the components, the modules, or the system. External failure sources typically result in increased stress. External failure sources include environmental sources, maintenance faults, and operational faults.

Design Faults

Design faults can cause system-wide failures; in fact, they are the major source of functional failures. For example, if a designer does not understand the environment or the stressor levels and the intended usage of the system, design faults or high susceptibility are more likely. Consider the example of the microprocessor-based controller module. Occasionally, the controller module stops working. It'll freeze up. After a short period, the independent watchdog timer circuit within the module resets the microprocessor. The module then restarts normal operations—the failure is transient. Obviously, no physical failure has occurred. After extensive troubleshooting, the autopsy report shows that a logic gate occasionally responds to the noise pulse and clocks the microprocessor too rapidly. The microprocessor interprets this as an instruction and stops operating. Although environmental noise, a random electrical stressor, triggers the failure, a design error has caused this functional failure. The designer did not understand the environment and the intended usage of the logic circuit. The design was not strong enough. Unless the design is changed or improved, the susceptibility remains constant. It is hard for designers to anticipate all possible conditions. The primary defense against design fault is a careful review by qualified experts.

Manufacturing Faults

Manufacturing faults occur when some step in the process of manufacturing a component or module or system is done incorrectly. An example of this kind of fault is when a resistor in a circuit has a corroded wire that no longer conducts properly. Now, this resistor was coated to protect against corrosion, but closer examination shows that the coating was not applied correctly when the resistor was made. Small voids in the coating occur because the coating machine was not cleaned on schedule.

The number of failures due to manufacturing faults typically decreases with time. That is because the high-susceptibility units will fail first, early in the expected unit life. As these units fail, they are removed from service, leaving only the stronger units. Thus, the average susceptibility of a population decreases. And when susceptibility decreases, failure rate decreases. Many of these faults can be detected by the vendor during accelerated testing, as when vendors cycle their sub-assemblies several times between the hot and cold extremes of their temperature specifications over a 2- to 3-hour ramp-up, a soak of several hours, and a ramp-down, to force out any "infant ailures The vendor will usually operate the equipment while in an environmental chamber, using this accelerated testing, called burn-in, on all newly manufactured product. The technique will often cause the manufactured faults to quickly become failures. This process will weed out many of the manufacturing defects, rapidly decreasing the failure rate because of manufacturing faults.

Module Over-Temperature

The control system should integrate sensors that measure the internal temperature of control modules. Over-temperatures should be alarmed when they exceed the manufacturer's rating. Even if the module is operating, if it is involved in some critical process it may be wise to replace it before an unexpected failure occurs as a result of its previous stresses.

Environmental Faults

External environmental failures frequently are related to temperature. This is not just because direct temperature causes failures, but also because temperatures help speed along many of the chemical processes that cause failure, including corrosion, diffusion, oxidation, and evaporation. Many other industrial failure sources exist, such as large electrical currents being switched thereby generating wideband electrical noise. And mechanical processes such as mixing, loading, and stamping can cause shock and vibration. This could cause a memory chip to vibrate out of its socket, increasing its susceptibility to coming into electrical contact with other components.

Modules and circuits are susceptible to electrical stresses because they are typically connected with field cables to sensors and other modules. These cables pass through areas of high electrical stress. Studies indicate that 65 percent of failures are caused by external electrical overstress, such as transients, lightning, electrostatic discharge (ESD), and radio frequency interference (RFI). As a result, voltage spikes can easily exceed the ratings of the input amplifiers. Unless these failure stress sources are thwarted, they will cause failures. A stronger design can utilize special protective components to absorb energy, thereby limiting the voltages and currents.

Mechanical Environment

Mechanical vibration, such as that caused by resident frequencies, can fracture metal components. Stronger designs use bracing to withstand these failure sources. Now, it could be argued that all the environmental failures are really system-level design errors since the designer did not use a product with enough strength. This distinction can be arbitrary, however. Normally, if the design strength is greater than the anticipated environmental stress, the failure is an environmental failure and not a design failure.

Excessive shock and vibration can also cause electronic failures that can be severe and difficult to diagnose. Examples of such failures are intermittent open circuits caused by vibrating connectors and "cracked" PC board traces, such as those that occur when improperly secured modules are dropped from racks, then quietly returned, after which they seem to function until some time later. One approach to overcome these failures is to use pin- and socket-type connectors, rather than card edge connectors. Pin and socket connectors have been proven to be much more reliable than card edge connectors, especially in high-vibration situations. With pin and socket connectors, the pin is completely enshrouded by the socket. Card edge connectors should have spring-loaded fingers that touch a mating contact.

All cable connections into and out of the system should be secured either with screw clamps or rugged spring clamps. Modules ought to have a screw that holds it in the card rack. Lastly, the PC boards ought to mount on a steel plate that is slid into the card guides. This keeps the PC board rigid, even in areas of high vibration. Other systems, in which the PC board is slid into card guides, allow the PC board to flex under vibration. This flexing can cause intermittent open circuits by cracking PC board traces.

Moisture and Corrosion

Humidity and corrosive chemicals in the atmosphere can cause serious and difficult-to-diagnose failures in electronics. One approach to protecting modules from humidity and corrosion is to apply multiple layers of protection. The first, and by far the most effective, layer of protection is the use of conformal coating on all PC boards. Conformal coating, which is essentially spraying an assembled PC board with a polyurethane-like coating, virtually eliminates the effect of corrosion and humidity on PC boards. Some vendors dislike this approach because the coating can retain the heat. If the coating material is selected properly, it can be a conductor of heat, helping it to dissipate. Components that cannot be coated, such as connectors, use gold-plated contacts that are lubricated with a special antifretting compound.

Furthermore, a module packaging can completely enclose the electronic assembly, diverting corrosive airflow away from the electronics. Field enclosures ought to be rated NEMA 12 or NEMA 4, minimizing the amount of corrosive air entering the enclosure.

Stress Candidates for Short-Circuit Mode Failures

Solid-state switching components typically have two modes of failure—short circuit or on and open circuit or off. The most common is the short circuit. Stresses that contribute to this include the following:

- High temperature. The failure rates of solid-state components typically double for every 18°F rise in temperature.

- Electric noise. Nearby switchgear, welding equipment, and equipment that emits radio frequency energy can cause solid-state devices to change state.
- Incorrect polarity. In some situations, incorrect polarity can cause damage to controlled equipment or the unintended actuation of outputs.
- Rate of rise. Solid-state controls can be affected by rapid changes in voltage or current (dV/dt or dI/dt) if the rate of rise exceeds the maximum permissible value specified by the manufacturer. Voltage applied at a rate exceeding the dV/dt rating can switch the device on without an input signal being applied. Common causes of high dV/dt are the switching off of inductive loads and the presence of high-frequency electrical noise.
- Surge current. Brief high current (inrush) as much as ten to twenty times the steady-state current is common when energizing certain loads. These currents can be damaging to unprotected circuits and will fatigue protective fuses.
- Transient overvoltage. Solid-state devices are especially sensitive to excessive voltage. Permanent damage may occur if peak voltage ratings are exceeded, even for a fraction of a second. Damage to the device typically causes it all to fail short-circuited on and be incapable of being turned off!

Maintenance Faults

Examples of internal maintenance faults could include incorrect repair procedures, which could cause failures. For example, a controller module on a dual-fault tolerance system fails; the system continues to operate because its redundant backup module is now controlling. While installing your replacement controller module, the repairperson plugs the output switch cable into a communications socket and shorts the system. Since maintenance activities are human reliability problems, they are affected by many variables. Complexity, system repairability, or foolproofing, condition of the repair person, training, familiarity with the system, and time pressure all contribute. Like operational failure rates, maintenance failure rates are hard to estimate. Failure rates should be estimated on a site basis by reviewing historical plant maintenance logs. All these factors just described should be taken into account and used as adjustment factors based on the specific experiences of your plant.

Some features that can reduce maintenance errors include making it possible for modules to be inserted and removed from the card cage without removing power; making it possible for each module to be keyed so that modules can only be inserted into the correct slot; and using cable connectors that can be keyed only one way to be inserted.

Common-Cause Failures

Common-cause failures are defined as the failure of more than one component, module, or system from the same cause. A common-cause failure could be disastrous to a fault-tolerant system. Such systems provide two or more modules to prevent system failure when a module failure occurs. If two or more modules fail from a single cause, a fault-tolerant system will fail. This is not a theoretical problem. Actual studies of some field installations have shown control system availability to be much worse than reliability models have predicted.

Environmental failure sources are the most obvious. When the magnitude of the environmental stress is high enough, that is, above the design rating of the device, *more* than one component fails. Examples of high environmental stress include high heat or fire; high electrical stress, like lightning; high vibrations, such as an earthquake; high humidity such as in a flood; or high mechanical shock as in a vehicle crash.

Design errors are a major source of common-cause failure. Consider the design process. During the development of a product, testing is extensive, but, even so the complexity of control systems precludes complete testing. If a system component does not operate as needed, the system does not operate properly, so by definition it is considered a failure. And if redundant elements are identical, they suffer from the same design errors and may fail in exactly the same way, given the same inputs. Although hardware design errors do occur, the vast majority of design errors are software.

Operational faults or maintenance faults can also be responsible for common-cause failures. In the operation of a system, certain functions can affect the multiple resources of a redundant system. These actions include system configuration errors, incorrect shutdown commands, or forced-contact types of commands. Maintenance actions including incorrect upgrade in the installation, repair procedure errors, bad calibration, and failure to replace renewable resources like batteries and disks can affect multiple components. Often the same procedures are used on all portions of redundant systems, thus these common-cause failures can occur.

Most environmental stress factors vary as a function of physical distance. Many abusive environmental failure sources can be segregated by putting redundant control modules in separate cabinets. Control systems whose redundant resources are physically separated will be less susceptible to environmental common-cause failures simply because the common environment has been reduced.

In dealing with operation and maintenance-type failures, other creative patterns have to be used. Foolproofing techniques can be used for both operations and maintenance. Repairable assemblies should be keyed so that the modules and connectors cannot be installed improperly. Automatic diagnostics should be added to detect wiring errors, field sensor failures, and other faults that could be caused by incorrect maintenance. Preventative maintenance can be helpful. For systems that require filtered airflow. a clogged filter will prevent cooling. If redundant resources are in one cabinet, they are all evicted by the resulting heat stress. Sensors measuring the differential pressure across filters will detect when a filter becomes clogged. This signal could be brought directly into the control system, and an alarm could alert the operator that maintenance is required. Similar devices can be put around other parts of the system.

An early architecture conceived to tolerate both safe and dangerous failures is the two-out-of-three (2oo3) concept—that is, two out of three units are required for the system to operate. This configuration requires three controllers—two outputs from each controller are required for each output channel. The two outputs from the three controllers are wired in a voting circuit that determines the actual output. The output will equal the majority. When two outputs conduct, the load is energized. When two outputs are off, the load is de-energized. This means that if there's a failure in one controller, the odds of a failure in the other two controllers are low and therefore the system continues to function. However, a common-cause failure, in which two or more of the controllers fail, will cause this system to fail also. This is because the actual output agrees with the majority and the majority will have failed; therefore, common-cause failure in which controller outputs deenergize will transition the model directly to a failed state.

Finding Fault 36

In the previous chapter, we talked of the problem of locating faults that are "internal" to the system, and especially identifying them for quick resolution. In most process systems, it is economically essential to find these faults on-line and keep the process in operation in spite of them. Whether the system uses the diagnostics to trigger some transparent back-up technique, or merely to be able to quickly isolate and replace an offending component, the key is to find the problem in the first place. In this chapter we discuss some of those "finding techniques."

Diagnostics

Microprocessor-based equipment can easily have diagnostics inherent in many of its functions, which can notify the operator and sometimes-even trigger automatic corrective action. Digital equipment has an advantage over analog equipment in that the information is stored and registered and can easily be read. This means that the status of different parts of the circuitry can be checked continuously and faults quickly detected and located. Things happen so quickly in digital computation that it is easy to have the circuits check themselves by making test runs, comparing the results and stopping if serious faults exist. The results of such diagnostic checks are usually displayed on video screens so they can be used to identify the trouble.

By providing continuous online monitoring of system performance, self-diagnostics minimizes the component mean time to repair (MTTR) through the prompt and timely reporting of component failures. Conversely, failures undetected by self-diagnostics will contribute substantially to statistical system unavailability, since such failures could only be detected through the routine maintenance inspections. Thus, it's important to strive for at least 99.8 percent or better system coverage of failures in order to minimize the system mean time to repair. With today's electronic technology, self-diagnostics is a very practical and cost-effective implementation.

Earlier we discussed the importance of redundancy. For the use of any redundancy to be effective, however, comprehensive online failure detection is required to support prompt repair of the failed component. Unmonitored redundancy can be useless since failed components remain unknown until both components fail.

Various types of testing and redundancy can be used to detect and cope with faults caused by both component failure and transient disruptions (Figure 36-1). In our discussion here, we will not go into the details of input/output detection problems because many of them can be handled through the use of the control strategies themselves, which is another topic.

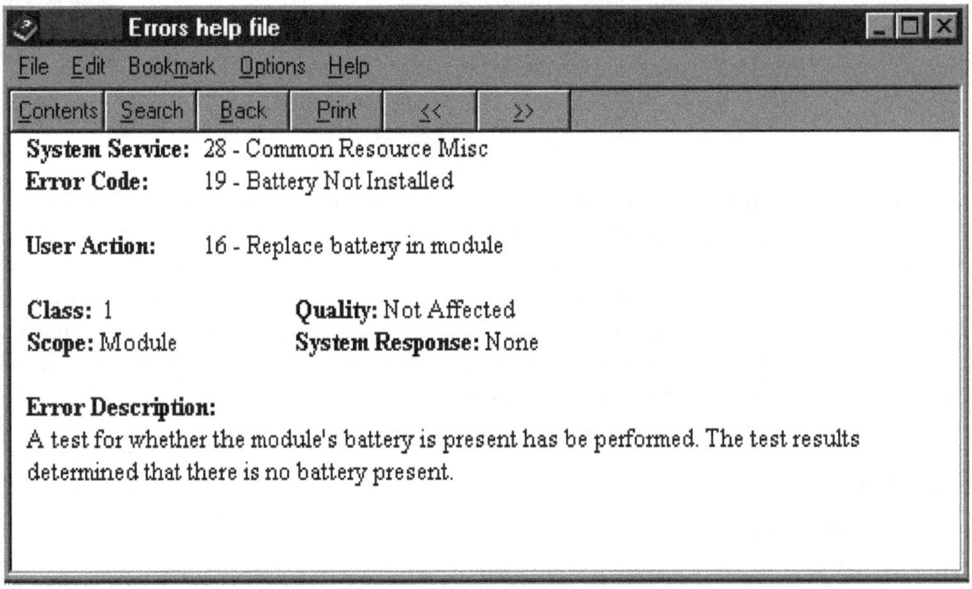

Figure 36-1. User Clicks on System Error Annunciation for Window Pop-up Containing Detail of Problem with Indication of Severity

There certainly are onboard diagnostic techniques to detect open or shorted inputs or outputs to sensors and final elements. This includes continuous control outputs of 4 to 20 mA to detect whether the signal is in fact being provided within the proper range. It also includes pulsed control outputs for position adjusting type (PAT) signals, which are typically used for motor control and drive motors and use a position feedback signal to monitor the actual physical result from the output to the process.

Some failures are not so direct as to have a simple notification such as that shown in _Figure 36-1. In those situations, it is sometime possible to present views, which _combine several different parameters from which the user can begin to deduce the nature of the problem.

There are techniques for using discrete output cards to measure the integrity of the _output, frozen relay outputs, or the various control limitations. Analog inputs, such as high-level analog inputs typically of 1 to 5 high volts dc can be monitored and checked with automatic digital zeroing of an analog-to-digital-converter. Low-level analog input cards with high-gain amplifiers, which require a greater stability and have their own measurements, should be monitored particularly for open or shorted thermocouples and resistance temperature devices. Reference junction (R/J) compensation resistors should be monitored. Discrete input cards should have optical or transformer isolation for each input to conform to IEEE 472 surge protection standards. Light-emitting diode indicators for each discrete input are essential to display on/off status. Critical discrete inputs can be made redundant with logical congruence checks to report any detection of "noncongruence."

All of these measurements are straightforward, and can direct users to a specific _problem area. The issue which drives users mad are combinations of problems that statistically shouldn't happen, but that seem to be the most frequent occurrences. Quite often, the vendor cannot anticipate everything that can go wrong, but in some cases may be able to provide tools to help the user to analyze the situation.

Processor Cards

Processor cards in the communication path depend on a wide range of diagnostics to detect hardware failures. Any of the following diagnostics that detect an error should initiate the transfer to backup equipment:

- **Register Check**—performed by writing a known value to a register and reading it back.
- **Code Processor Test**—an argument is sent to the code processor, and the result is compared to the proper result.
- **PROM Check Sum Test**—the contents of a PROM is banked into RAM, and the check sum is computed. The result can be compared with the value check sum result, which can be burned into PROM.
- **Dead Man (Watchdog) Timers (DMTs)**—timers that must be reset at specified intervals to determine that the programs are still executing. Some dead man timers will alarm if the reset is too often, indicating a program loop around the reset command.
- **Semaphore Lockup Test**—semaphores used to limit access to a memory record can be tested to ensure that one user is not holding up the record too long.
- **Stack or Buffer Overflow or Underflow**—when general memory is used for stacks or buffers, tests must be in place for areas outside the stack or buffer area to detect use.

In addition to these diagnostics, each processor is dependent on its associated input/output. It is important to be able to declare whether the loss of a particular module is fatal or nonfatal to controller operation. The plant engineer should be able to designate which state is appropriate for each control station. In a nonfatal declaration, controllers should alarm; in a fatal declaration, there should be an alarm and a shutdown sequence.

All processors in the system (not just in the controller module) should be monitored by at least one watchdog (dead man) timer to detect if that processor has stalled or is hung in an endless loop. This should automatically disable all input/output circuits involved with that function if there is no redundancy.

Dead Man (Watchdog) Timer Failure

Microprocessor circuits should use dual watchdog timers—one digital, the other analog. They should be crosschecked to determine if either has failed.

Memory Cards

If there is a large database common to many processor cards, then in many systems it is often stored on a single memory card. The random access memory (RAM) of this card should be either nonvolatile or battery backed up. If battery backup is used, the capacity (the ability of the battery to sustain current over time) of the battery should be known to the system, and low capacity should be alarmed. This can be accomplished by periodically loading the battery, checking its voltage to determine how much life is remaining, or by monitoring the total usage of the battery current over time. The result can be stored within the controller or processor and alarmed when the battery life is consumed to a given level.

Memory Corruption, Losses

All control system memory (RAM, ROM, EEPROM, etc.) should be fully tested upon power up, as well as continuously tested on line with background diagnostics. Volatile (RAM) memory should be battery backed up, and a "low battery" diagnostic should indicate to the operator when a battery needs to be replaced.

Large important databases warrant some form of error detection and correction. Soft errors can be caused by the ionizing radiation of alpha particles changing the memory cell charge in semiconductors with high impedance nodes. These errors are generally known as alpha hits. Error correction codes (ECC) for checking and correcting memory errors can be used along with a "memory scrub" regimen to clean out errors from seldom-used memory locations. Such codes are useful as both diagnostic tools as well as a technique for maintenance without interrupting the process. Error correcting codes can be made such that all data put in the memory is encoded in such a way that any single-bit failure can be detected when the data is recalled. Further, that bad data bit can be located and corrected by using idle processor time to read and then write back all memory locations periodically. The memory is "scrubbed clean" of one-bit errors.

For additional effort, any two-bit failure can also be detected and trapped. The hardware cost of this added reliability is the addition of memory bits and hardware to detect and correct any one-bit error. To detect any two-bit error requires five extra bits of memory for an eight-bit word, and six extra bits for a sixteen-bit word. Now this may seem like a high cost, but the resultant increase in reliability is often worth it. The enhancement factor (ratio of mean time between failure [MTBF] with error correction code to mean time between failure without error correction code) for a sixteen bit-word is twenty-four. Since a one-bit error is corrected; it is not necessary to transfer control to backup hardware upon detection. The error should be alarmed so memory diagnostics can be run in the event that a hard fault exists. Since it cannot be corrected, a two-bit error should result in transfer to backup.

Communication Faults

Communication between devices is a likely source of short disruptions. As the distances between communicating devices increase, the likelihood of disruptions caused by the environment may increase. Extra precautions must be taken to make such communications secure and to provide a fault-tolerant system.

Communication Between Cards on a Backplane

Backplane communications most often take the form of reading and writing to and from memory on a database card. An effective technique for detecting a bad write to memory is to read back each piece of data immediately after it is written. Since backplane noise might be responsible for an error in data, a second attempt can be made when a fault is detected. If successive attempts fail, transfer to backup is called for. The number of attempts allowed before the transfer to backup depends upon the amount of time available to complete the communication and the likely duration of transient noise.

In the case just described, it is necessary to have a strategy to protect the system from a fault-tolerant technique. That is, in the preceding technique a second try was made to handle the case where the noise-corrupted data was being written. What if the noise resulted in a bad address? The result would be writing data to the wrong place. To guard against this, key areas of the database are check-sum protected; that is, such areas are transferred to local RAM and a check sum is computed. If the check sum is incorrect, transfer to backup occurs before any of the corrupted data is used.

Addressing Errors

All intermodule communications should include a source address and a message address in the message header to ensure the correct delivery of the message.

Communication Between Cards on a Long Bus

Communications between controllers and I/O cards can be accomplished by using a parallel bus for speed and cabling for distance. In this case, the environmental hazards are greater than in the case of cards on a backplane. For this reason, several steps must be taken to protect the integrity of information transferred on the bus.

It is necessary to perform a check-before-execute sequence on the output transfers. This should include parity checks and the automatic read back of data. Since noise can result in transient interruptions, retries should be attempted before transferring control to the backup system. Implementation of the I/O bus interface on a single LSI (large-scale integration, multifunction microprocessor) chip assures highly reliable performance.

Communications Corruption, Losses

Intermodule communications should be confirmed with diagnostics that can detect corrupted messages or the loss of communications. CRC (Cyclic Redundancy Check) is a reliable technique for confirming the correct transmission and receipt of data. Watchdog (dead man) timers should also be deployed at every module on a bus to detect a loss of bus activity. The control system should also automatically set its outputs to a safe state when an I/O module has lost communications with its controller module.

Cyclic Redundancy Check (CRC)

Basic error-checking mechanism for link-level data transmissions, typically bit-oriented protocols. The integrity of the frame is checked using a polynomial algorithm that is based on the content of the frame and matched with the same calculation made and sent by the originating station.

Communications Between Stations on a Network

Communications between stations on a network over long distances require additional precautions than do the backplane or long bus communications discussed earlier. There are two primary criteria to consider when judging a long distance communication network: network security and system response.

Network communication load should not effect system response. System response defined in terms of video screen update time should not vary—not even when a plant is in an upset condition. A typical screen update rate is maybe seventy-five points per second. A network that becomes overloaded during upset conditions cannot guarantee the secure and timely transmission of information. The key to providing proper system response is to use the proper communications strategy.

Nondeterministic Communications

There are two commonly used communication strategies today for network communications between stations: broadcast method and token passing. With the broadcast method, all the stations on the network try to send their data at any one time. If there is a collision (more than one broadcaster), each station must retry sending its message with different time delays until data is sent with no collision.

This method of transmission is labeled "nondeterministic" because the maximum time to send a message cannot be determined. A busy network can have many stations colliding and retrying until all the messages have been sent. High transmission speeds, 2 to 10 MHz, can improve performance but not guarantee response, particularly under plant upset conditions. This can be overcome by maintaining all potential activity to below 25 percent of bandwidth by limiting the number of stations or message requests. Otherwise, this type of communication is best suited for office work, such as memos and reports, where speed of response is not critical.

The likelihood of noise in an industrial communications network is much greater than is encountered in an office. With faster data rates, such as those used in nondeterministic networks, the steady state of a logical "one" or "zero" exists for much shorter periods than with lower data rates. It is also not possible the for driving gate to change instantaneously from a logical one to zero, or vice versa, and the change of status is limited by the maximum slew rate (output of data bits). With a shorter steady-state period, there is an increased chance of a data bit being missed because of noise or the driving gate's. Thus, data sent at a faster data rate is much more likely to be corrupted by noise in an industrial environment. New emerging technology will overcome much of this problem. The problem of anemic performance from overloaded non-deterministic communication systems is being overcome by some of the techniques mentioned in Chapter 24

One solution is to use frequency-shift keying (FSK) to encode the digital data rather than using simple voltage levels to represent logical one and zero levels. In this technique, a sine wave of a different frequency is transmitted to represent a logical one, a logical zero, and the carrier wave. Rather than detect absolute voltage levels, the receiving circuit needs only to detect the number of zeros crossing in a given time to determine the state of the transmitted bit. This technique is less susceptible to corruption by noise, but the slew rate of the transmitting gate still needs to be considered.

It is possible to use gates with very fast slew rates, but these devices tend to be more expensive than the slower equivalents. The ideal answer had been to use the slowest volt rate possible that will still achieve the desired data throughput. This can be done more readily if techniques other than the broadcast method are used. Again, new technology and increased volume are bringing the costs down, allowing these approaches to become more viable.

Deterministic Communications

The popular method of network communications for process control in the middle 1990s is the token-passing method. Instead of having to resolve network conflicts and collision, this approach avoids contention by giving each station periodic access to the network. This method of transmission is labeled "deterministic" because the maximum time it will take to send a message can be determined. The token-passing approach is preferable to the use of a message director, which can result in a single point of failure.

The attributes of a well-designed token-passing scheme include the fact that the system should be "masterless," with all the stations getting a chance at the network mastership within the system's scan cycle. Typical token-passing rates on a "masterless" network should be two to three hundred times per second for data-gathering operations. The minimum rate should be guaranteed at least a number of times to support a system scan cycle of the controller actions. For example, if a control station has a quarter-second scan of all of its inputs and outputs and control functions, then it has no need to get any communication to or from the network faster than a quarter second.

During each scan cycle, when a station receives a token, it can request data or present alarms. All stations on the network can reply to the station with the token. Making transmissions on a need-to-know basis can minimize traffic on the network. This approach, which is a combination of IEEE 802.4 and IEEE 802.5, reduces network traffic, maintains a constant system response even during plant upsets, and permits the addition of stations up to a preassigned limit without the worry of overloading the network.

Fault tolerance can be designed into the scheme by allowing each station a minimum of three tries to respond to a token message. If, after three tries, the station fails to respond, the strategy can be arranged to skip that station and provide a communication alarm to the operator.

It is significant to note that fast network response is not necessarily related to fast transmission rates, as we discussed before. It is actually determined by network traffic, turnaround time for the completed task, and message format. Response from any queried station should be received within one second. Clustered or multiple data transmissions should be supported. Since mastership is relinquished, a considerable number of other tasks can continue to be performed by each individual station during the interval between those times that particular device has had the token.

Network Security Using Redundancy

Full network redundancy is essential to long distance communications security. To be fault tolerant, full network redundancy should have the following characteristics:

- Each network of the redundant pair should be hardware independent, including the driving and receiving gates at each station modem.
- Each network should operate continuously thus eliminating the need for a multiple switchover mechanism, which can fail or delay the signal.
- All data should be transmitted over both networks (the redundant pair). If one should fail, the full flow of data should be able to proceed over the remaining network.
- Diagnostics should announce the location and nature of the failed portion.

Thus, with full redundancy and proper network design, continuous network operation can be supported in the event of major faults or disruptions.

Network Security Using Transaction Types

Networks can provide two types of transactions: open and closed. An open transaction is a broadcast of information with no response from any of the receivers, as in a public speech on radio or television. A closed transaction is when the receiver responds to the receipt of the message, as in most one-on-one conversations in person, over a telephone, or over similar communication links. All control actions should be closed using an explicit query from a master or operator station to a secondary or a control station or to another operator station, with that secondary then responding to the desired information. This is the most secure form of network transactions.

Open transactions, which are commonly broadcast, are useful when no explicit response is required. An example of an open transaction is a diagnostic or process alarm generated by a station that, when that station is in control of the network, is broadcast to any of the operator stations and/or other appropriate user interface stations without that station asking for the information. In some systems, when the control station does broadcast an alarm, it also makes that known during the handshaking routine when it passes the token around. Each operator station looks for both signals. If only one is heard, then it will directly ask that controller to either repeat the alarm or acknowledge a failure. In this way, every broadcast can be securely confirmed.

Network Security with Error Detection

Keep in mind that when an incorrect transmission is received; retrying the transmission may not correct the problem. The response must be analyzed before communication can continue. Full strategies are available for network error detection and system security. Typically, they are as follows:

- Check-before execute (CBE). Data transmission through a check-before-execute scheme reduces the probability of undetected error to essentially zero. The echo is a transmission of the message image formed in the receiving station's buffer. The response to the transmission is not made until the sending station indicates that a correct message was actually received.

The CBE sequence of messages is as follows:

1. Station A sends message to B with CBE bit set in the control field;
2. Station B echoes the same message back to A with the response bit set in the control field and the source and destination address reversed;
3. Station A sends B an execute command, if the echo checks with the original message. Otherwise, the original message is repeated;
4. Station B sends A the "acknowledge response" to the original message.

- Command/response time-out or loss of carrier. To detect a low response or lost response each station that initiates a transmission includes a time-out function. Upon expiration of the time-out function, or the detection of the loss of carrier, one or more frames are retransmitted, starting with the last unacknowledged sender's transmission. Prior to retransmission, the sender station will verify the lack of a carrier from the receiver to ensure that a momentary loss of character has not occurred.
- Cyclic redundancy check (CRC). This is formulated to detect frame-length changes as a result of the erroneous addition or deletion of zero bits at the end of the frame as well as to detect errors introduced within the frame. The message polynomial used in the numerator of the basic equation includes the contents of the address, control, and information fields. Any frame received with the CRC error is discarded.
- Exception conditions and error-recovery action. The error-recovery procedure is under the control of the sender station because of a transmission error, station malfunction, or operational situation. There are only three responses from the receiver station:

  1. the requested action,
  2. no response, and
  3. incorrect transmission

When the sender station receives an invalid response from the receiver, it will retry the last transmission and wait for a valid response. If still unsuccessful, the procedure should be repeated a third time. If still unsuccessful, the transmission is marked as unacceptable, and the sender station proceeds to the next transition. When an incorrect transmission is received, retrying the transmission may not correct the problem. The response must be analyzed before communication can continue.

A continuous log is kept of any faults that occur, which individually logs the different types of fault. Different types of fault are caused by different problems (noise causes different faults than the faults caused by an intermittent receiving circuit.) Logging the faults helps to diagnose the cause and thus reduce the mean time to repair (MTTR) and increase system availability.

Network Security Using Fiber Optics

Fiber-optic technology is particularly attractive for long distance communications, such as distances over two hundred feet. The fault-tolerant attributes of fiber optics include the following:

- Complete immunity to noise from power lines and equipment
- Total protection from lightning
- Insensitivity to radio frequency interference (RFI), such as from communications equipment
- No control signal ground loop problems
- Resistance to moisture and corrosion
- Meets the requirements of intrinsic safety in hazardous atmospheres

The installation of optical cable is no more complicated than that of conventional electrical cable. It can be buried, strung on poles, or put in ducts. It can be hand pulled, even with lengths longer than is possible for copper cables. Splicing and termination today is no more complex than for coaxial cables. As with coaxial cables, installation is usually done with predefined, factory-tested lengths.

The fiber-optic network can then be connected to individual clusters of stations through redundant sets of optical/electrical interfaces (Figure 36-2). Those stations can be mounted in control cabinet groups or in the video electronics cabinet of operator stations. Problems with these interference's usually occur outside the cabinetry. None of the stations within a cabinet have a need for the advantages of fiber optics. Therefore, the optical/electrical interface can be mounted within the cabinet, and all of those stations within that cabinet can be connected to the electrical portion of that network.

System-Level Considerations

If a control system's inputs fail on or fail off, there should be some method to detect these conditions. One approach is to have internally redundant input circuits that provide constant comparison between present and expected operation, check analog-to-digital conversion on discrete inputs, and pulse testing.

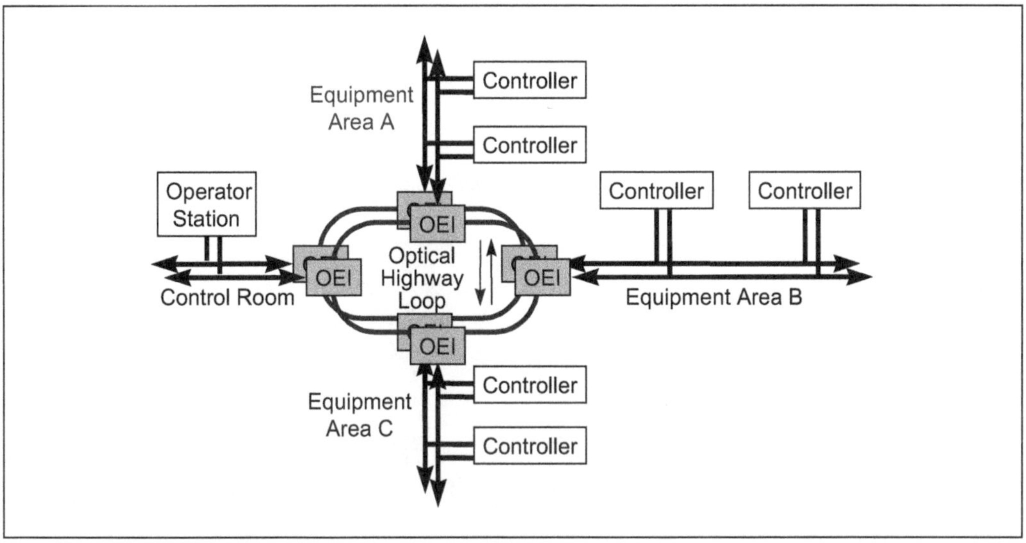

Figure 36-2. Fiber-Optic Links Between Equipment Cabinets Eliminate Ground Loops

If outputs fail on or fail off, the use of read-back circuits incorporated into these output circuits can detect both conditions. A failed on condition can be automatically corrected through a built-in diagnostic cutoff relay.

Because control system diagnostics are generally limited to the self-testing of field wiring, the control system engineer must add more system-level diagnostics to account for field device failures. One commonly implemented method is known as "proofing." This uses field-mounted sensors, such as limit switches, to measure the actual position of output hardware. Proofing is generally applied to indicate valve position or valve-stem "end of travel." Motor drive units often have a built-in feedback slidewire to confirm position. Other system-level diagnostics include comparing analog transmitter values to the state of interlock switches and voting dual- or triple-redundant sensors to detect field device failure.

37 Operational Security

Any system that allows a human operator to command a system operation can fail because of an incorrect command. For example, an operator intending to enable the remote set point of a control loop selects the wrong point on his or her video screen in the operator station. This incorrect control loop is instead switched from automatic to manual. These errors do happen and are listed in the accident reports of many industries. Yet some say there's no such thing as an operator error, but rather that complex and coupled systems are the real cause of the problem. Certainly operator faults are affected by such factors as system complexity, the design of the human-machine interface (HMI), or fool proofing, the operator's familiarity with the system, operator condition such as fatigue or boredom, and the reliability of the instrumentation. Operator faults can even be induced by production pressures, which some call-management induced operator errors. But sometimes the operator just does the wrong thing. The many factors involved in operator errors make it hard to accurately estimate the operator failure rates. Again, some estimates can be made by reviewing historical plant failure logs. The failure rate is calculated by dividing the number of failures by the operator hours. And relative system complexity can be estimated and used as an adjustment factor.

Operational Consistency

To alleviate operator errors, review the screen view information and expected responses. Are the views unambiguous? Do they display real understanding to the operator? Is the operator led to the appropriate responses, perhaps through screen prompts? Is it appropriate to lock out certain displays during some stages of the process, perhaps not even show some views at that time?

> If is appropriate to lock out actions or views from some access levels or during certain stages of the progress of the process, always show a screen prompt stating that fact! If this is a transient lockout, indicate when that locked period will be over. Otherwise, the user will presume there was equipment failure and may cause an unnecessary disruption of the process.

Chapters 8 through 21 addressed the many considerations behind good screen design and management. It is imperative that screen design and hierarchy structure be developed and reviewed regularly. Good design will ensure consistent actions from all operators, regardless of the time, shift, or degree of plant upset urgency. Many corporations have been including their control room operators in this effort. Within reason, it is practical to have sets of views unique to each operator that are triggered by the entry of an access code, such as a name and employee number.

Operation Access Security

The restriction of access to some operations can be implemented in most systems today. In some situations, there may be several areas of responsibility for different locations in the process. Yet it may be necessary for each operator to view controllers from other areas of the plant so as to make good decisions without having the access to make changes to those controllers. Provisions may have to be included to allow exceptions, for example, if the operator station in that other location becomes inoperative or if certain emergencies occur.

Other reasons for restricting access can include the different skill levels of employees while they are becoming acquainted with the process. This could also reflect their skill levels to operate certain stages of the process or to operate during various conditions. There could also be craft union restrictions that must be incorporated. For any of a number of reasons, access to the same controller may be limited to different "depths," such as access to acknowledge alarms but not to change the alarm limits access to or change the set point but not the tuning parameters. It may be appropriate to make distinctions between online adjustments and those done off line, say, during maintenance shutdown.

When a particular user comes on shift, he or she would enter his or her user name and password. This will "open" all that is appropriate to that user (Figure 37-1). It could also provide that user's personal set of screens (that is, personal in layout and appearance—the screens would *functionally* be the same as everybody else's for that "category"). If the user does not show any activity for some preselected length of time, automatic logoff could occur to protect against inadvertent access.

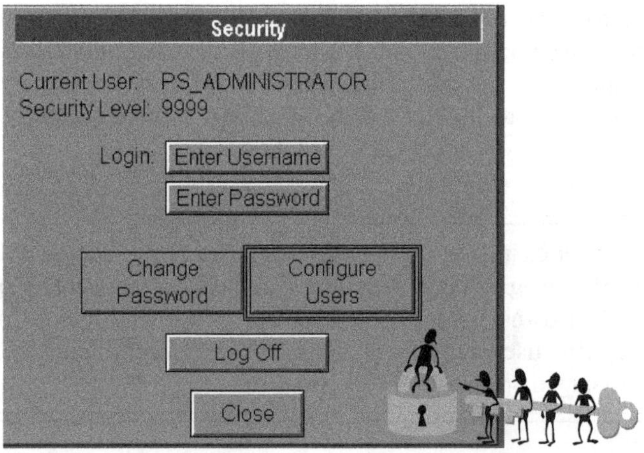

Figure 37-1. Typical Pop-up Window: Security Access is the Lock, the Password is the Key

With many of the control systems in use today, very sophisticated access code matrices can be implemented in a very easy and direct way (Table 37-1). Shown in the following table is a rather simple matrix of security levels that might be appropriate in a plant. The arrangement here has over ten thousand different access code combinations that could allow the easy entry of very customized use without the need for custom programming. It is limited only by the user's imagination.

Table 37.1 Example of Process Control System Security Levels by Job Function

Users→ Use↓	Guest	Maint.	Operator	Supervisor	Plant Manager	Engineer	Business Manager	System Admin-istrator
Manage Users								X
Configure Controllers				X		X		X
Exit/Switch Applications				X	X	X	X	X
Tune/Alarm Limits				X		X		X
Acknowledge Alarms			X	X	X	X		X
Change SP/Out/ Mode			X	X	X	X		X
Make Business Reports			X	X	X	X	X	X
Make Process Reports		X	X	X	X	X	X	X
View Diag./ Maint. Windows		X	X	X	X	X	X	X
View Process Windows	X	X	X	X	X	X	X	X

Systems For Process Safety 38

Plant and process safety used to be the province of insurance companies. Traditionally the safety system did into improve productivity, but rather hindered it due to unavoidable false-alarm shut-downs. Today, changing technology is fueling an awareness among plant owners that well-placed safety systems can not only save the cost of insurance, and the costs of catastrophes, but can sometimes even improve productivity. Some of the benefits will come from standards... again.

Vic Majoli, formerly of DuPont, helped bring about the first American process safety standard (S84) and is helping to shape what is likely to become the world safety standard (IEC 61508), which is in a similar structural form. Both specifications took more than a decade to launch, and both had to accommodate strong partisan opinions. More than twenty countries are involved in the international IEC standard. The intent is for each industry group to work from IEC 61508 in forming their own industry-specific standard, appropriate to their own unique needs. One example of the impact of this is NFPA 8502, a standard of the National Fire Protection Association that is followed world-wide, and that addresses boiler control and the prevention of explosions of boilers. "Prevention of..." is the purpose of safety systems, the concern in this arena is not fault *tolerance*, but rather fault *avoidance*.

Failure Effects

At first glance it might seem that the effect of a failure is always the same—a system that does not work. A closer look reveals one of the many subtle aspects of reliability evaluation. Failures can have drastically different effects on a control system. For example, consider a safety protection system in which a fail-safe concept is used. The process operates only when certain valves are open. Energy is required to keep the valves open. Abnormal or unsafe conditions are alleviated merely by deenergizing the valves. For example, assume the process requires heat. The heat is provided by a hot water line with a normally closed solenoid valve. Energy in the form of electrical current is required to keep the hot water valve open. When energy is removed by stopping the flow of current, the steam valve shuts with a spring action, and the heat source is removed from the process. This configuration is known as "deenergized to trip."

In most fail-safe operations in a plant, the rule of thumb is to remove the heat from the process to prevent serious consequences (Figure 38-1). Sometimes you remove the heat to stop up the flow of heat going into the process or to begin the flow of cold going into the process, so you may wish to fail open rather than fail closed. This is part of the overall design of the plant, not just of the control system. The control strategy is a significant part of the safe operation of a plant, and it can be designed around a "what-if" scenario involving the failure of various components in the system. The "what-if" scenario will then be used to determine the safe setting of the process itself as a result of any single or multiple failure.

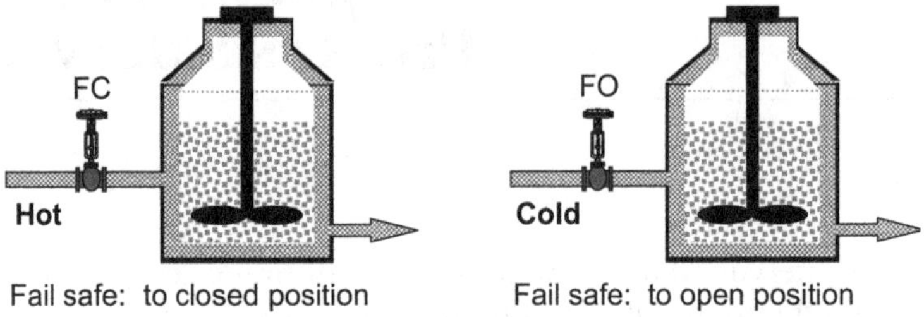

Figure 38-1. The Fail-safe Condition in Most Processes Is to Remove Energy

Fault Avoidance

Fault avoidance is, as the name implies, the ability of a system to avoid faults. This is achieved by a high-strength design and by the use of extensive diagnostics. A safety system must be designed, built, and tested so as to be very rugged—high strength is the foundation of this formula. What this means is that the safety system should be able to operate successfully in harsh environments that would cause failures in a less hardened system. Diagnostics detect and inform operators of abnormalities that could lead to failures if left unattended.

For many years, safety systems were constructed from non programmable, hardwired electromechanical relays that were designed to fail in the open-circuit, de energized mode. Modern safety systems are controlled primarily by standard programmable logic controllers (PLCs) for many reasons, including lower cost, ease of installation, lower false-trip rate, more sophisticated logic-solving capability, mathematical capability, fewer required spare parts, and so on. PLCs were designed to replace relay logic systems, but they do not match the safety of relay systems. A significant problem when using these microprocessor-based systems is the potential for the solid-state switching circuits to fail in an energized (dangerous) condition. Do not confuse the reliability of PLCs with that of the relays! The mechanical relays are certainly more susceptible to wear and are therefore more vulnerable. The question is, when they fail, can there be a guarantee that they fail safe?

The possibility of a dangerous failure is the reason why many insurance companies and corporate standards do not allow conventional PLCs to be used in safety applications.

Does this mean that PLCs should not be selected for the control of safety systems? Not at all. It is important, however, to understand the operating characteristics, environmental limitations, and failure modes of industrial equipment that incorporates solid-state technology. Much of this has already been covered in Chapters 33 to 36. We will build on that discussion here because there is a need for good design to provide appropriate protection to reduce failures and to contain those that do happen so they occur in a predictable manner.

Safety Systems

The functionality of safety systems is assuming a higher-profile role in many process plants and is increasingly a factor in the selection of large, integrated control systems. Safety standards such as ISA S84.01 in the United States and IEC 61508 internationally are creating a more stringent safety environment for plants around the world. In many parts of the world, customers have traditionally purchased safety systems and process control systems separately from different suppliers. These customers felt that systems from different suppliers provided them with the highest level of conformance. This view is now changing in favor of integrated control and safety systems.

An appropriate safety solution depends on the "Safety Integrity Level" (SIL) designation, which should go beyond the safety of the equipment to the safety of the process and the personnel as well. This solution can vary from the lowest level, implemented with a conventional process controller or PLC, through the higher levels, implemented with double and triple modular redundant (DMR and TMR) controllers. The essential criteria for SIL are exposure to personal injury, property loss, and opportunity loss. At the levels requiring DMR or TMR, the nature and level of integration between control systems and safety systems is strictly defined and rigidly enforced.

Safety system operation must be totally independent of the control system. Data transfer from the safety system to the control system is acceptable, but commands and diagnostics transferred from the control system to the safety system are not. Even with these restrictions, data integration provides a single view of the plant state for decision support and of the plant state history for fault analysis. This single view is the value to users of integrating control and safety systems. Achieving this integration has presented a challenge to control system suppliers. The blending of data from dissimilar systems is difficult, and for large systems where the value is greatest traditional interfaces are not up to the task. Resolving these issues usually requires the control system supplier to make a significant investment so as to establish the safety system as an integral component of the control system architecture. The level of investment, the desire to preserve that investment, system security, and system management are all compelling arguments for control system suppliers to acquire safety system companies.

There is also a middle ground between safety systems and control systems. This is a specialty area called "critical control" where safety and extraordinary availability are paramount. Turbo machinery control and nuclear power applications are examples. Safety systems have been successfully applied in these applications and can be treated as logical extensions of the control system without the limitations discussed earlier.

Living with Safety Systems

There are many advantages to using a proper safety system to control your critical applications. Some very important considerations often elude the process engineer who has not encountered the nightmare of unnecessary plant shutdowns or the absence of a shutdown when conditions require it. The full understanding of the role of safety systems is an emerging technology, and not all systems sold for this purpose include all of the various features we are going to discuss here.

The need for safety systems exists in certain critical operations:

- High-availability process control
- Burner management systems
- Safety instrumented systems
- Fire and gas protection systems
- Turbine control systems

In addition to moral reasons and public relations issues, there are strong economic reasons to assure that a process operates safely. These include possible equipment losses, personnel injury and loss, and production downtime as a result of an accident. When quantitative risk analysis is combined with techniques for developing life cycle costs, many companies realize that the financial impact of safety risk is much higher than they imagined. Recognizing this significant impact on business losses, technical societies, insurance companies, and government regulatory agencies are creating standards and approval requirements for industrial process safety. OSHA, EPA, NFPA (National Fire Protection Association), and internal corporate standards all seem to be getting tougher. OSHA is pushing for more "Hazard and Operability Studies" (HAZOPS). NFPA has brought out newer, tougher requirements. ISA has issued the S84 standard. Process design is not becoming any easier. This need to meet regulations and properly implement safety protection equipment adds just another dimension to the trade-offs that must be made by a process engineer. Questions need to be asked. How much safety is actually required? How is it best achieved? Must hardwired equipment be used, or can programmable electronics be used?

EPA (Environmental Protection Agency). Primary agency responsible for enforcing U.S. federal environmental laws.

NFPA (National Fire Protection Association). Developer of fire safety standards including those for burner management systems

OSHA (Occupational Safety and Health Act). U.S. federal law passed in 1970 specifying the requirements an employer must follow to guard against employee illness and injury. Also, the Occupational Safety and Health Agency responsible for enforcing that act.

Specific problems with conventional PLCs include input circuits that get stuck, output circuits that jam in the on condition, I/O addressing errors caused by shorts or opens in the parallel backplane, covert watchdog timer failures, memory corruption or loss, processor instruction failures, and many others. Several of these potential failures have been specifically identified in insurance industry documents. In spite of these problems, with extra resources it is possible to increase the safety of an ordinary PLC.

Fail-safe Practices for New Class of "Safety PLCs"

- Protected outputs—1oo1D (one-out-of-one-with-diagnostics)
- Hardware diagnostics
- Redundant diverse watchdog timers
- Safety-critical boards, no dangerous undetected failures
- Full CPU/RAM/Comm. testing
- I/O fail-on, fail-off software diagnostics
- Bounds checking
- Memory integrity verification
- Program flow control testing

Safety Programmable Logic Controllers

A specially designed class of PLCs, called safety-PLCs, provide high reliability and high safety through the use of special electronic design, special software, and preengineered redundancy. The safety-PLC has I/O circuits that are designed to be fail-safe with built-in diagnostics. The processor of a safety-PLC has built-in diagnostics for memory, processor operation, watchdog timer, and all communications systems. I/O module addressing is done through serial communications messages that have full automatic error checking. One-out-of-one-with-diagnostics (1oo1D) architecture uses specific diagnostic circuits to convert dangerous failures into safe failures by deenergizing the output.

Traditionally, the need for safety systems, with all of the typical false shutdowns of the process (how many times has your smoke alarm gone off without a fire?), plays havoc with any effort to gain productivity! In most companies, the expense of adding safety systems is only undertaken to satisfy the insurance company, certainly not as a contribution to productivity!

Many of the components used in conventional PLC circuits, as shown in the upper part of Figure 38-2, can fail in such a way so as to *energize* the output switch! In this state, the controller cannot deenergize the output and perform its protection function. This type of failure could lead to a condition that is threatening to both equipment and personnel.

In the one-out-of-one-with-diagnostics safety-PLC architecture, shown in the lower part of Figure 38-2, output energy flows through "dual switches" to the load. A solid-state switch provides the normal controller output. A relay, controlled by the built-in

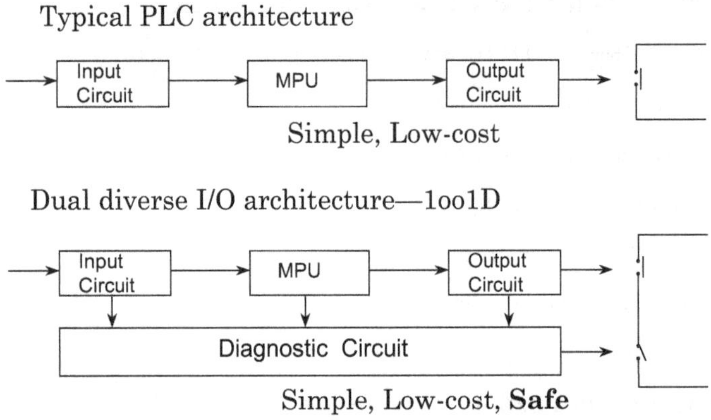

Figure 38-2. Simple Safety System Technique for Safety-Protected Outputs

diagnostics, supplies the second switch through a set of normally open contacts. If a dangerous failure is detected within the output channel, the relay contacts are opened. This action deenergizes the output, ensuring that the output fails in a safe manner.

When high system availability is an important addition to safety, a redundant architecture can be used. Two primary traditional PLC architectures can be used: one-out-of-two-with-diagnostics and the two-out-of three method. The equivalent "safety-PLC" method would use one-out-of-one with diagnostics, and one out-of-two with diagnostics, respectively. The former provides safety through diagnostic circuits and an extra series of output switches (Figure 38-3). High availability is obtained by the parallel connection of two sets of electronics (Figure 38-4). If one fails, the other takes over and maintains the load. Depending upon the mix of analog and digital I/O, the cost of a safety-PLC is typically not much higher than that of conventional versions. Sometimes it can be less. One significant advantage of one-out-of-two-with-diagnostics is the elimination of any special engineering, external circuitry, and application-level programming that would typically be needed during the installation of conventional PLCs. The *installed* cost of a safety-PLC can be significantly lower.

Many agencies, particularly those concerned with safety, require that online diagnostics detect all dangerous failures even in the presence of other component failures.

While the first priority of a critical control system is safety, the system must also maintain high system availability to avoid unnecessary shutdowns. Safety systems should achieve high availability through extensive redundancy options that range from internal standard redundancy features, to redundancy of a single control module.

A safety-PLC system also offers the option of physically separating redundant systems into separate cabinets. This minimizes the system's susceptibility to common causes, such as cabinet temperature or cabinet damage.

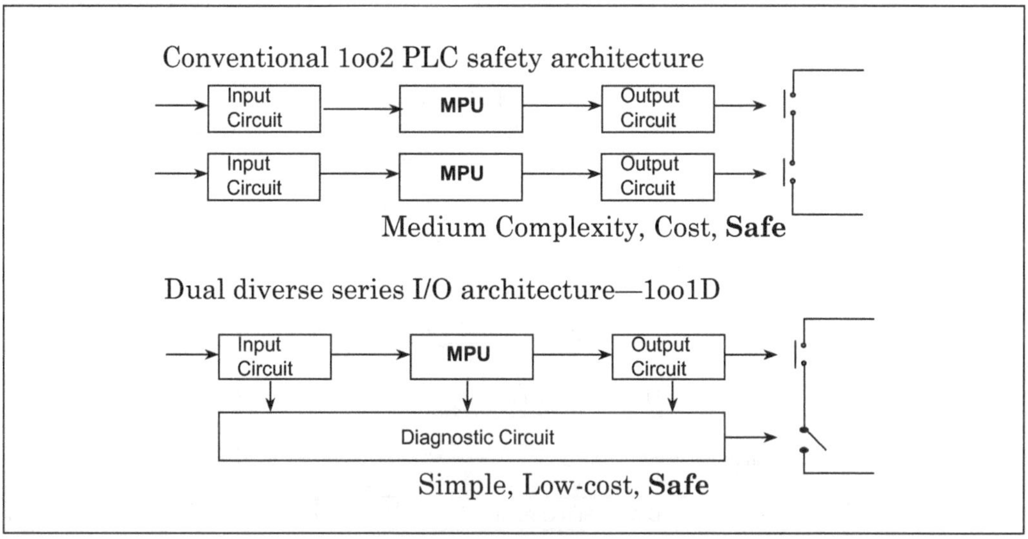

Figure 38-3. Two Safety System Architectures: One-out-of-Two of the Conventional PLC and One-out-of-One-with-Diagnostics of the Safety-PLC

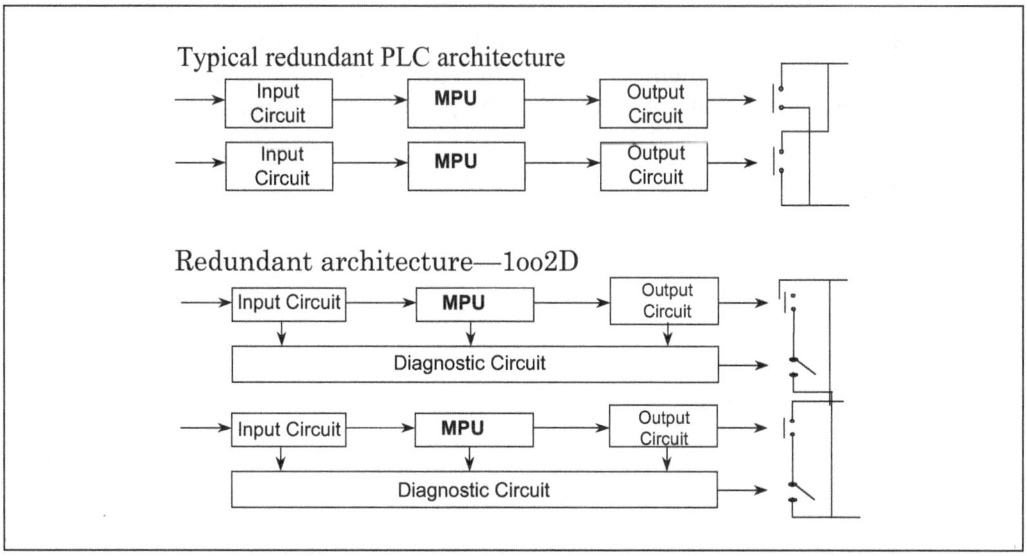

Figure 38-4. Redundant Safety Systems to Assure Availability

Figure 38-5 shows a comparison between *triple* redundancy of a conventional PLC using a voting circuit with a "safety PLC" using complete diagnostic circuits across each of a redundant *pair* of PLCs. Although it appears safe, the triple redundancy version does not account for common-cause effects (such as all in the same cabinet or using same power supply) nor the vulnerability of the voting circuit itself. What if two are inaccurate? This circuit will switch to one of the "wrong" circuits, avoiding the correct one!

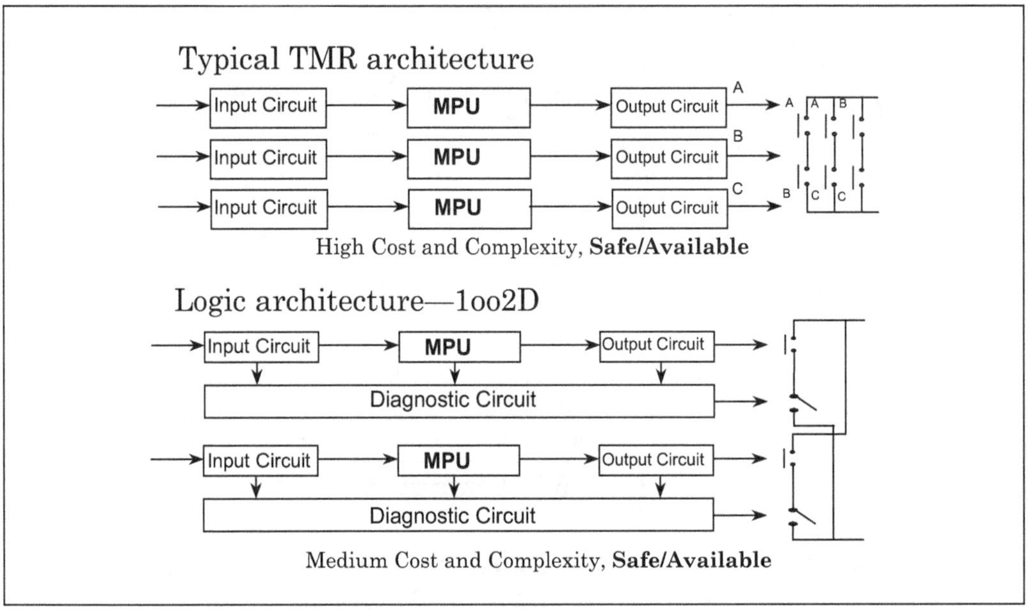

Figure 38-5. Triple Modular Redundancy Is Not the Only Way to Availability

A safety-PLC architecture, shown under the TMR architecture in Figure 38-5, uses independent diagnostic circuits, which assure differentiation between the failed controller and the good one. Each of the two can easily be placed under separate power.

Part I

Typical Vendor Architectures

Older Examples 39

This chapter shows the architectures of some popular distributed control systems available during the middle 1990s. These companies by no means represent all versions of such systems in the world, nor has any effort been made here to favor one system over another. These may not even be the most current versions of these systems when you read this. *The systems shown, however, do represent the vast majority of the well over one hundred systems currently in operation!*

The systems shown in this chapter are examples of how architectures are put together for process control and the variations used by different vendors. Many of the combinations of architectures come as a package with that vendor's system. The user does not generally get to pick and choose parts of them as if assembling a construction set. Understanding the vendors methods will help here, but any one vendor will use some combination of those things we have discussed in this book. Each vendor selected that blend of technologies and architectures that provides the best advantages of

- the electronic systems he has picked to perform the functions within his stations and
- the optimal method of moving information over the network between the stations.

There are some disadvantages with every architectural approach, whether it be a communication protocol or a topology. Usually, however, by using diagnostics, limiting the number of stations, and so on, they can combine these approaches to get the optimum traffic on their network. The use of proprietary systems is not for competitive advantage between the vendors but represents a valiant effort to obtain the real-time movement of information over these networks. Vendors have created these designs to overcome the absence of standards that operate fast enough for process control. Most standards that have evolved so far have been suitable for business traffic over networks, but very few can handle real-time. Therefore, each of these vendors has combined aspects of existing standards that have been modified to fit their functional requirements for real-time operations.

Vendor Architectures—Never Stagnant!

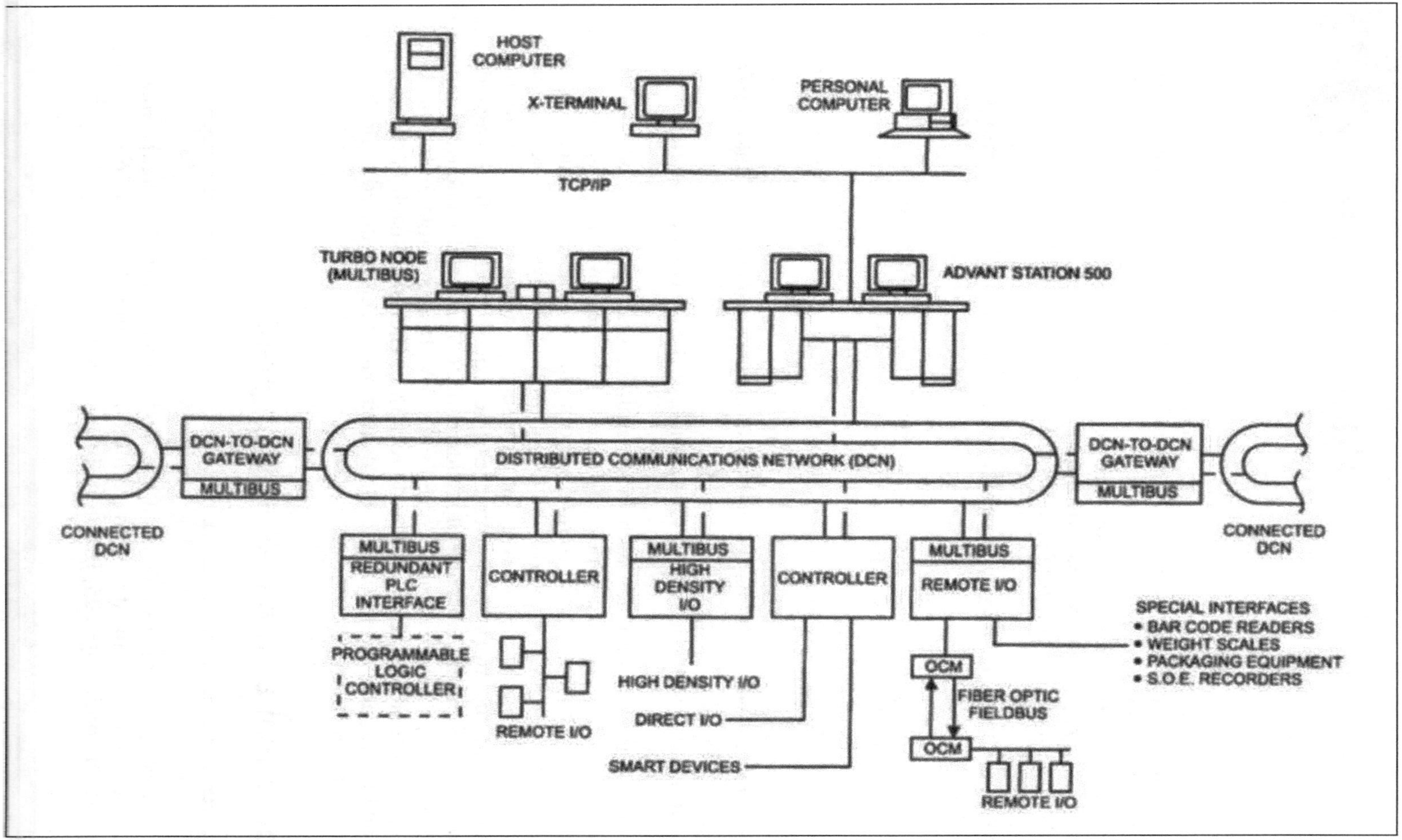

Figure 39-1. Typical MOD 300 System

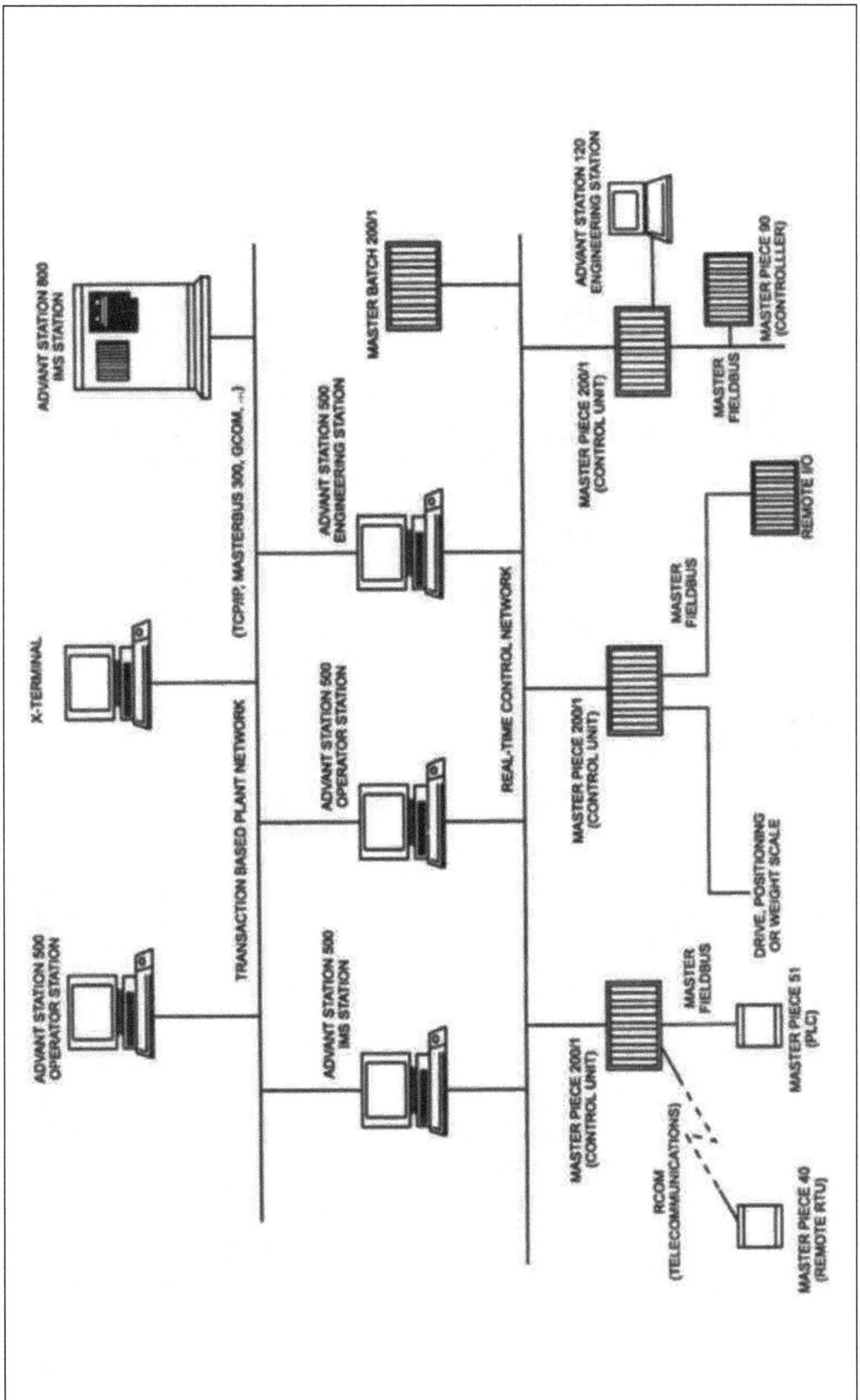

Figure 39-2. ABB Master System

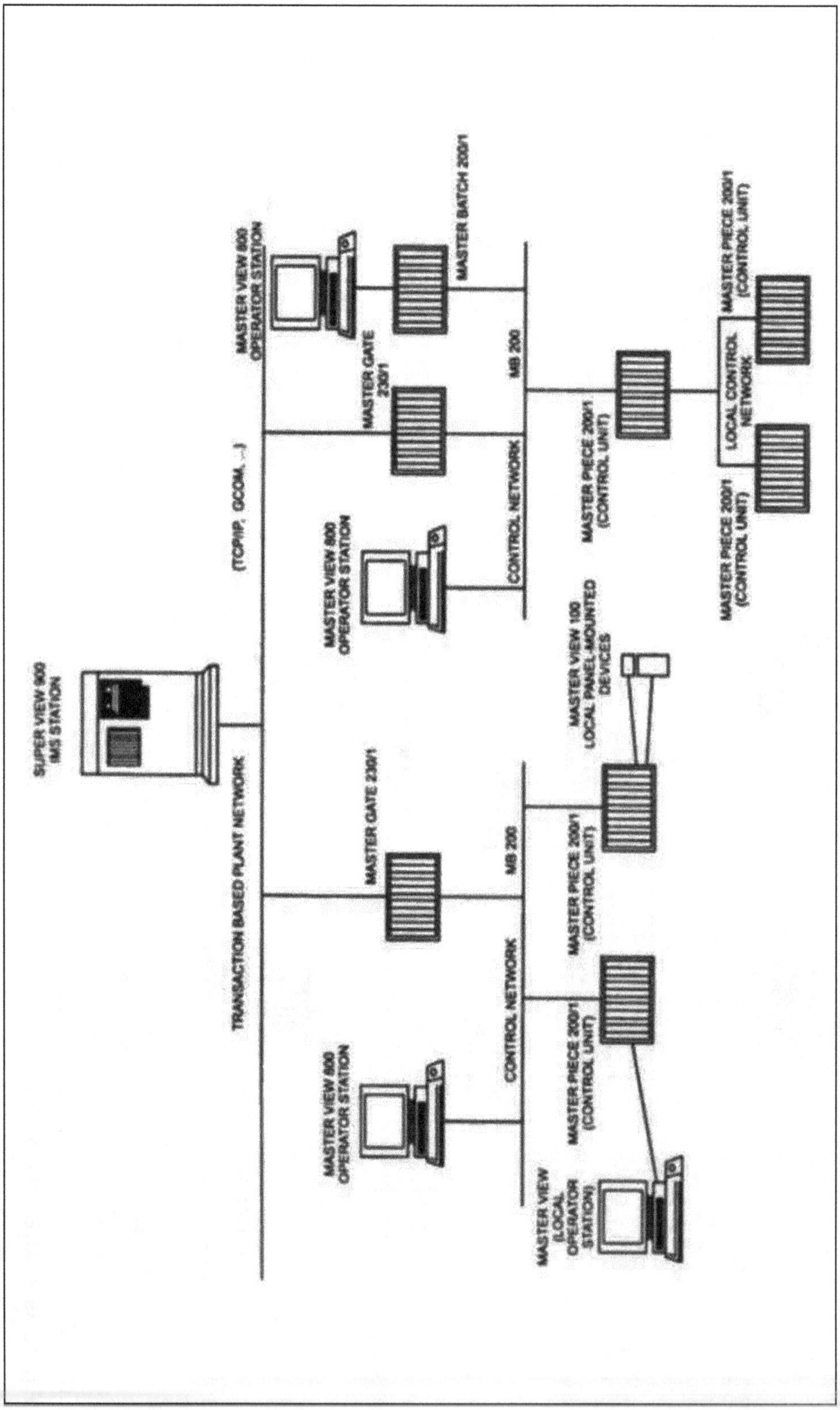

Figure 39-3. Alternate ABB Master Architecture

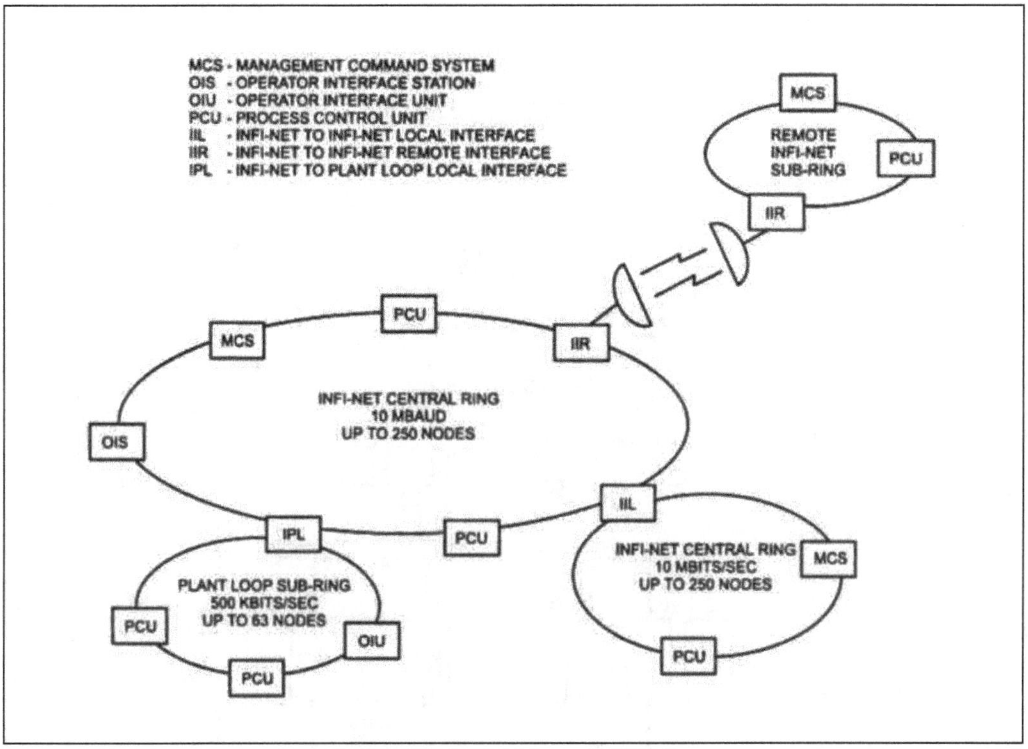

Figure 39-4. Bailey INFI-NET Communications

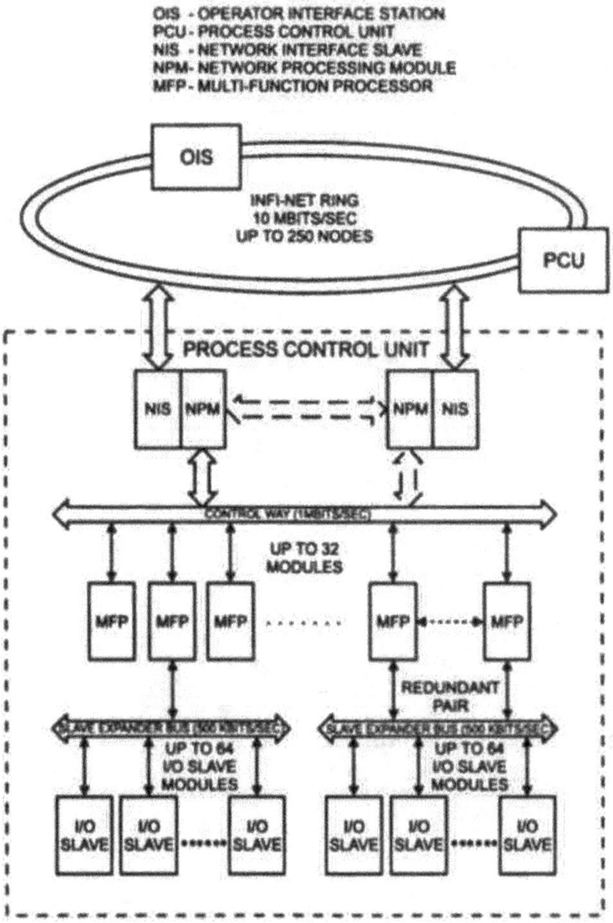

Figure 39-5. Bailey INFI-NET Controller Architecture

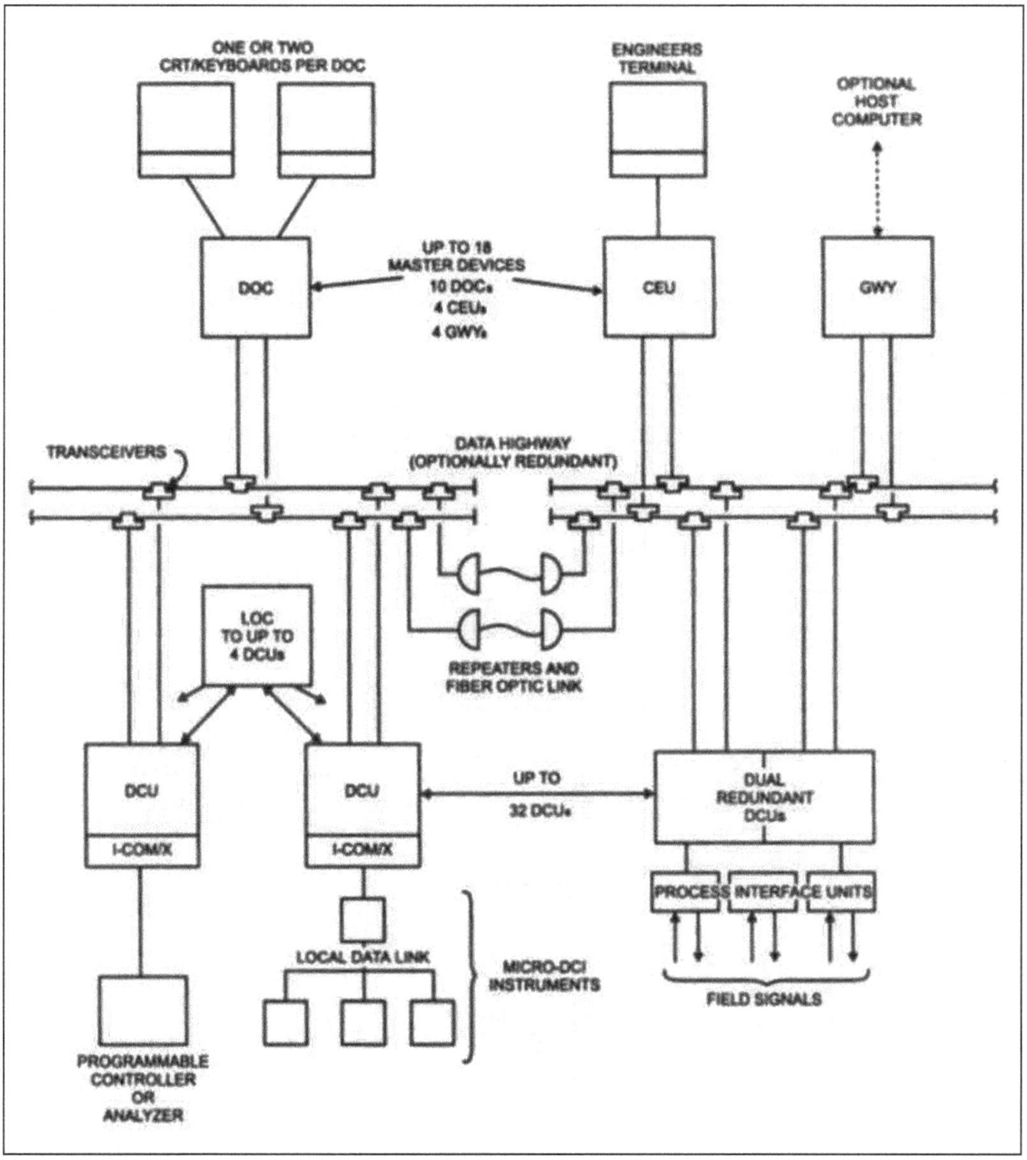

Figure 39-6. Fischer & Porter DCI System

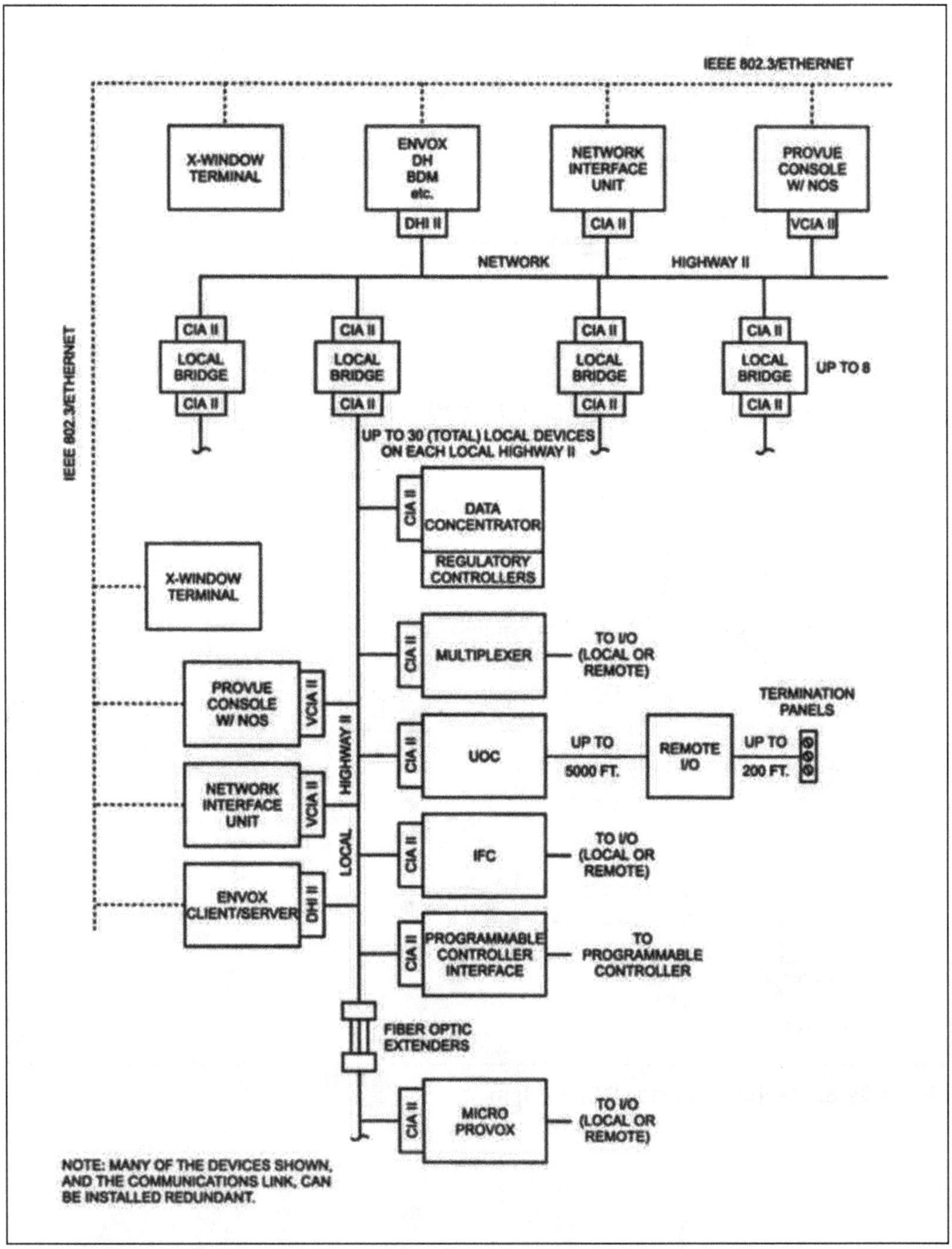

Figure 39-7a. Fisher-Rosemount PRoVOX System

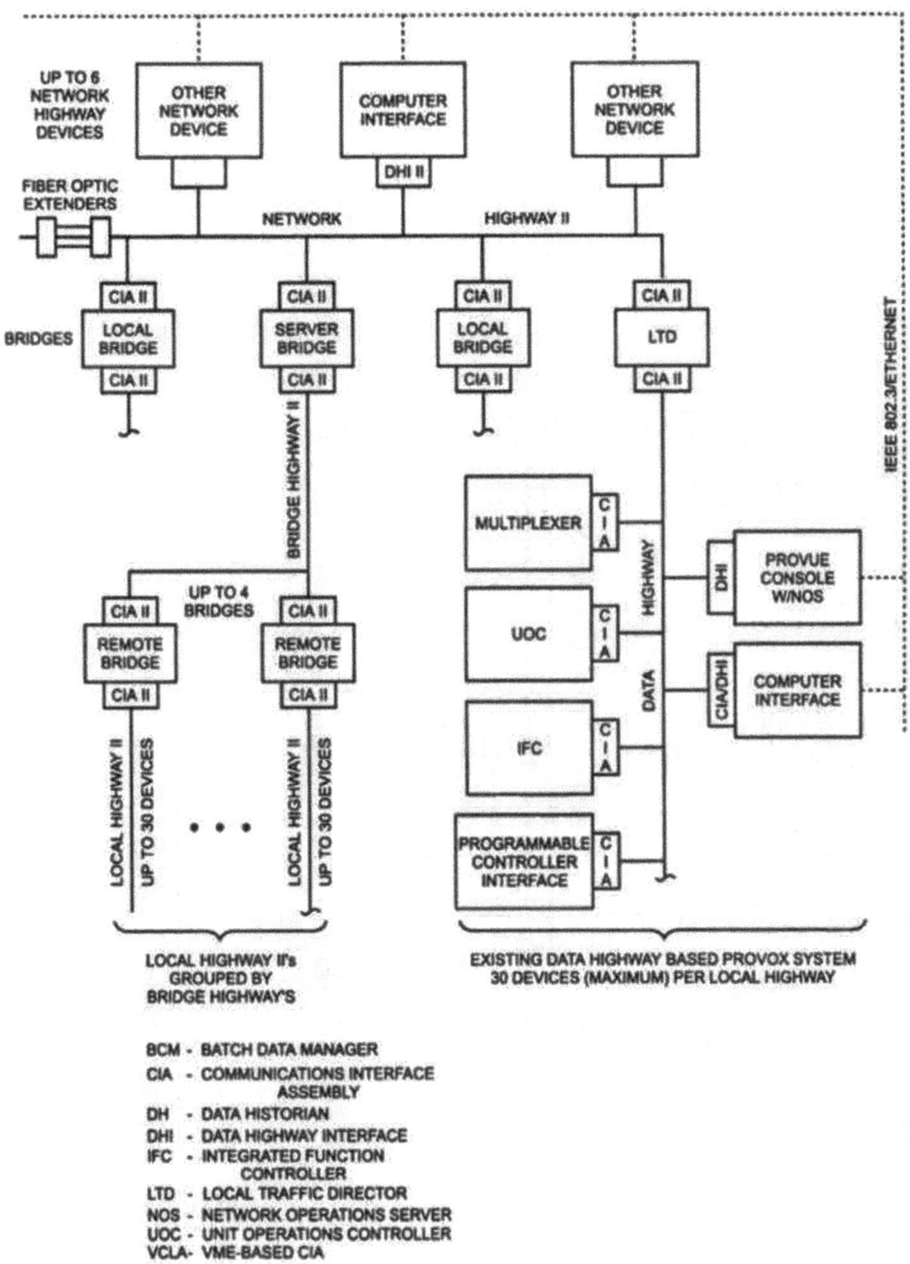

Figure 39-7b. Fisher-Rosemount PRoVOX System

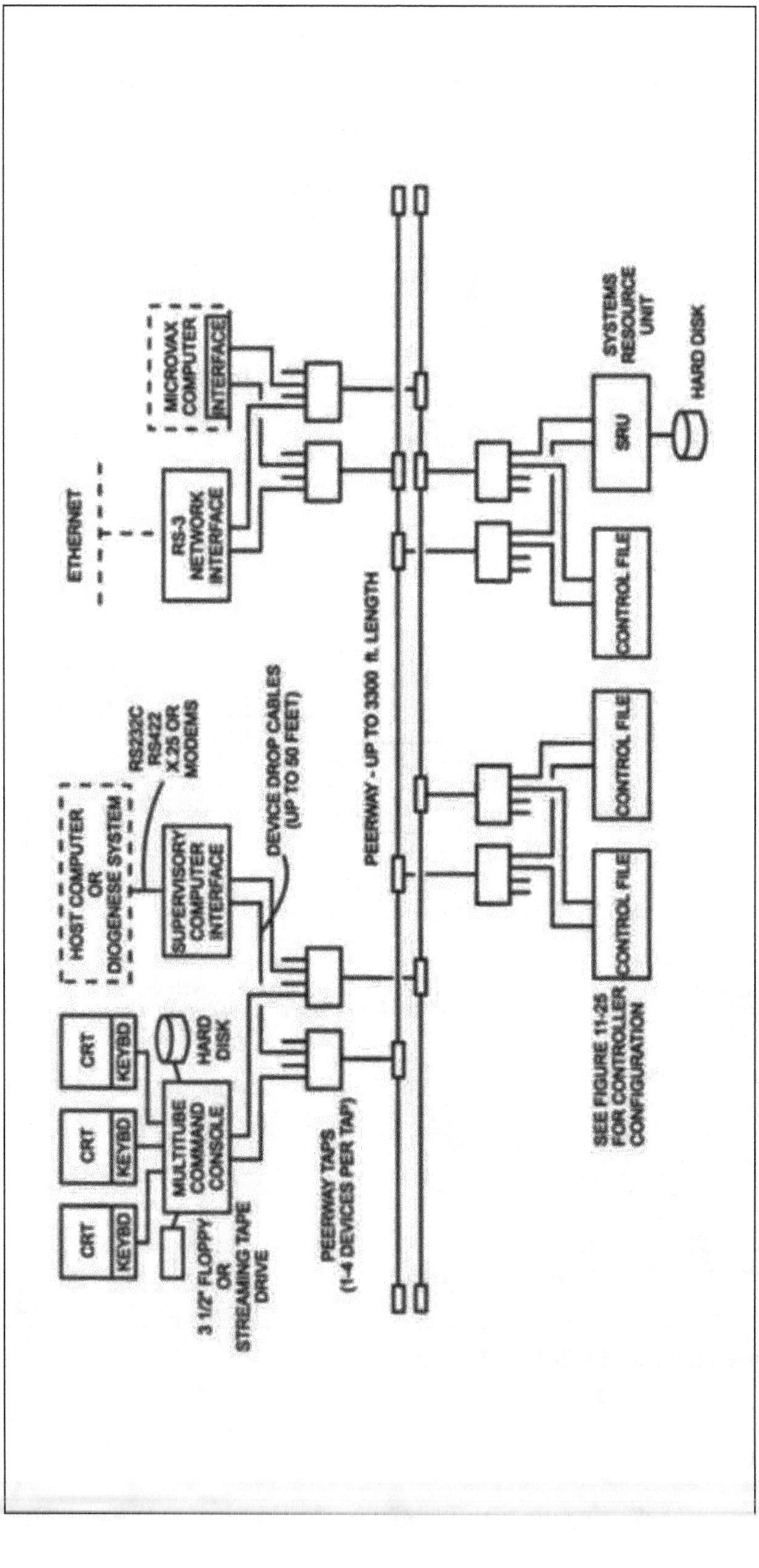

Figure 39-8. Fisher-Rosemount RS-3 System

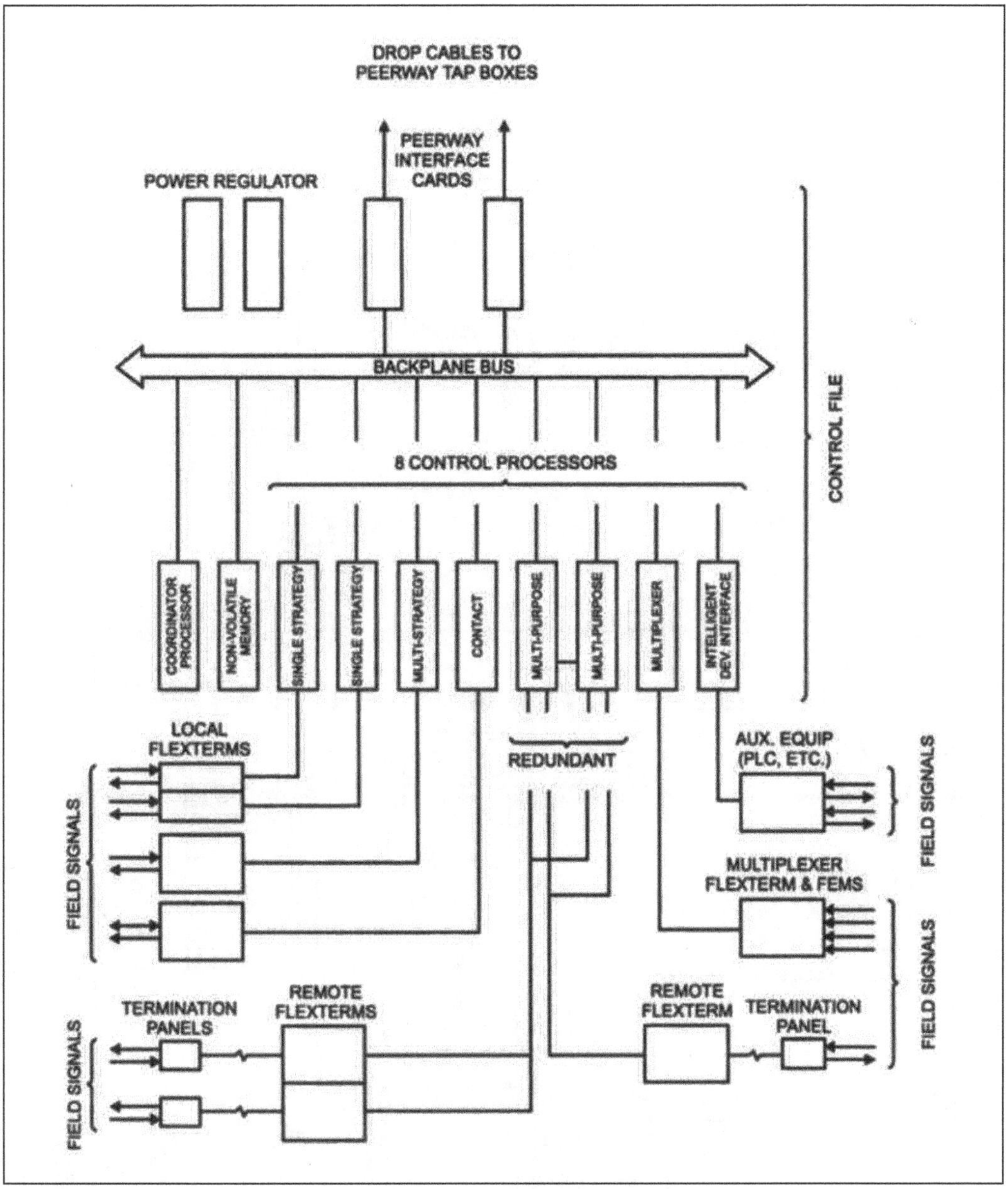

Figure 39-9. Fisher-Rosemount RS-3 Controller Architecture

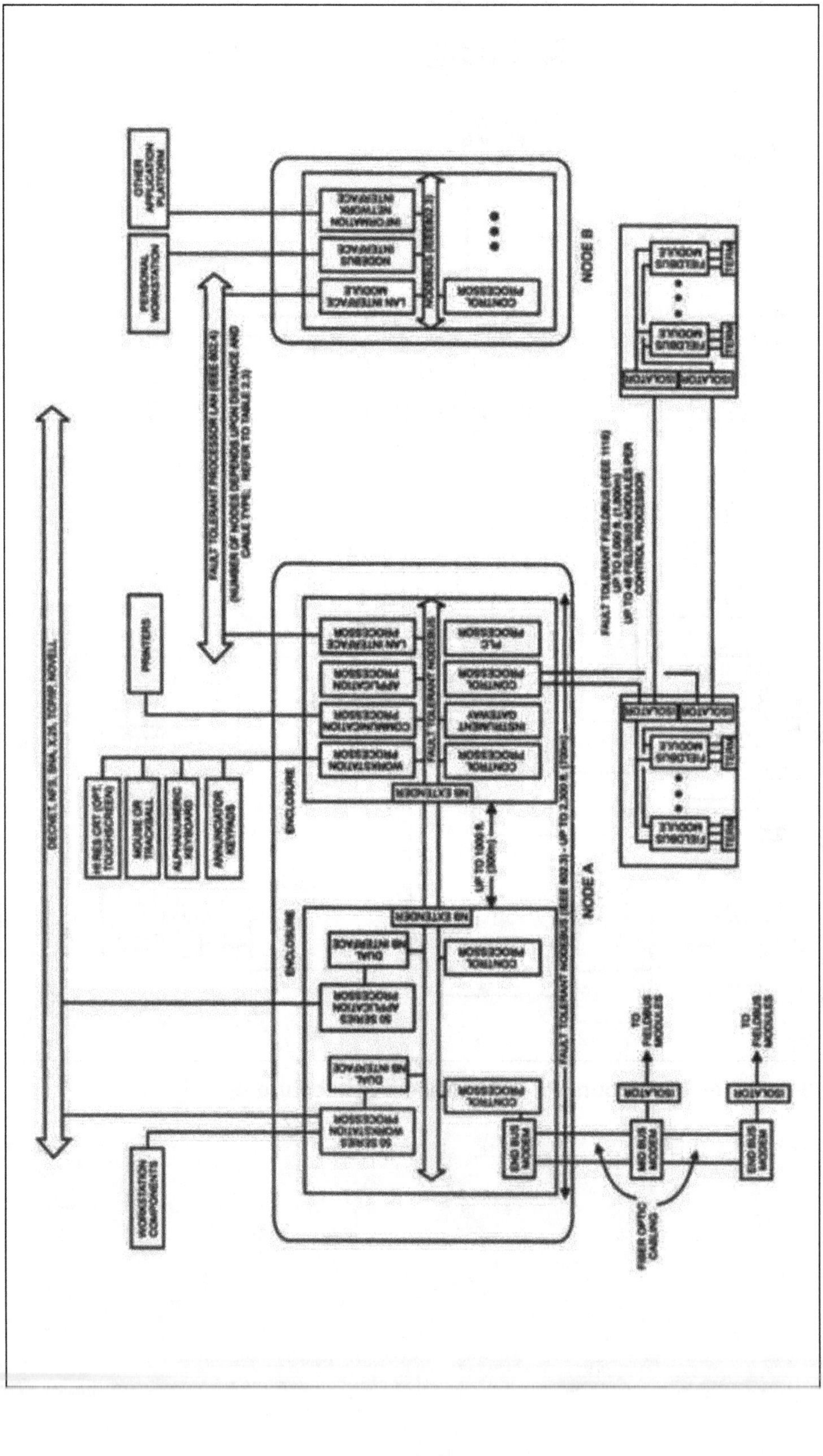

Figure 39-10. Foxboro I/A System

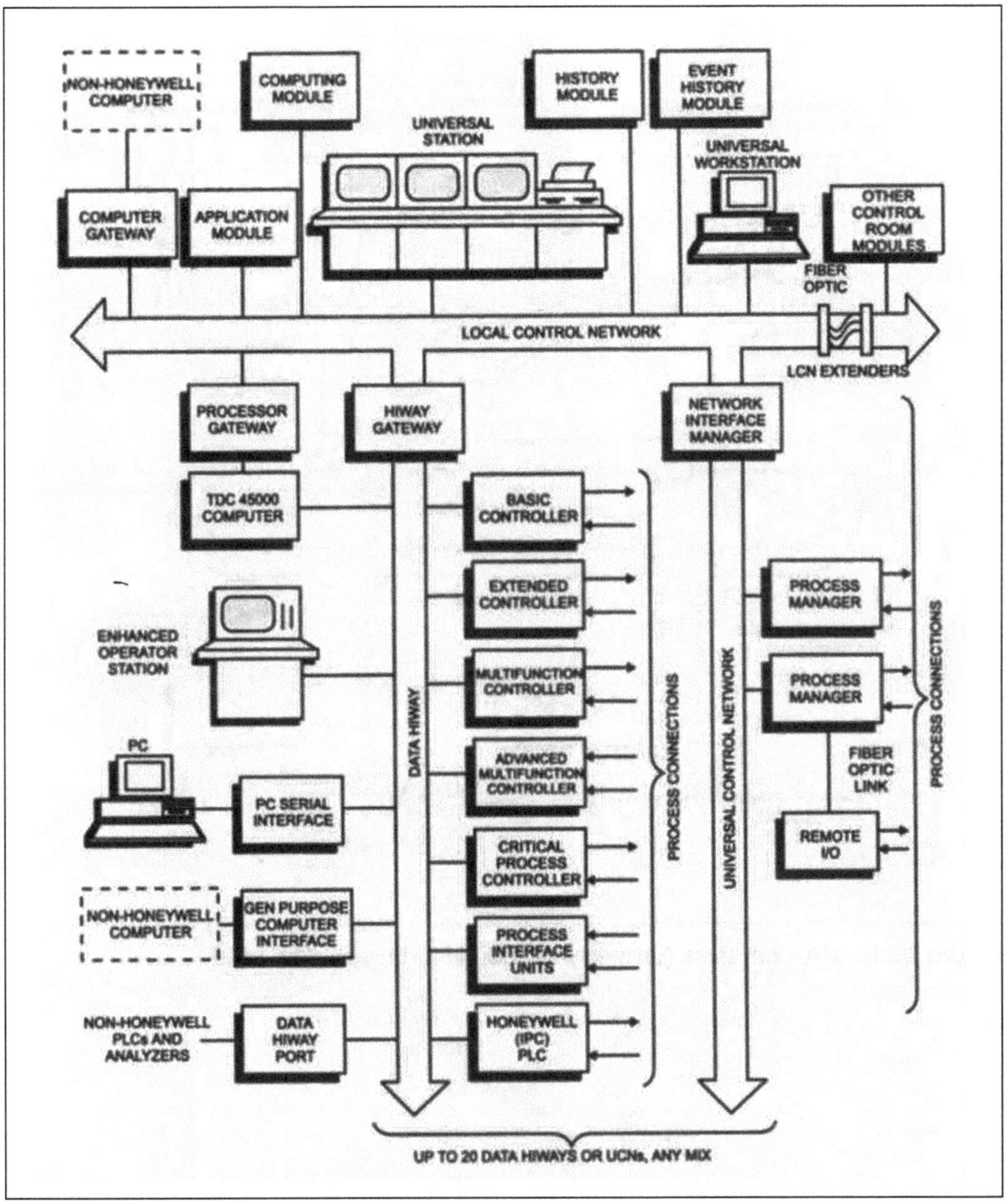

Figure 39-11. Honeywell TDC 3000 System

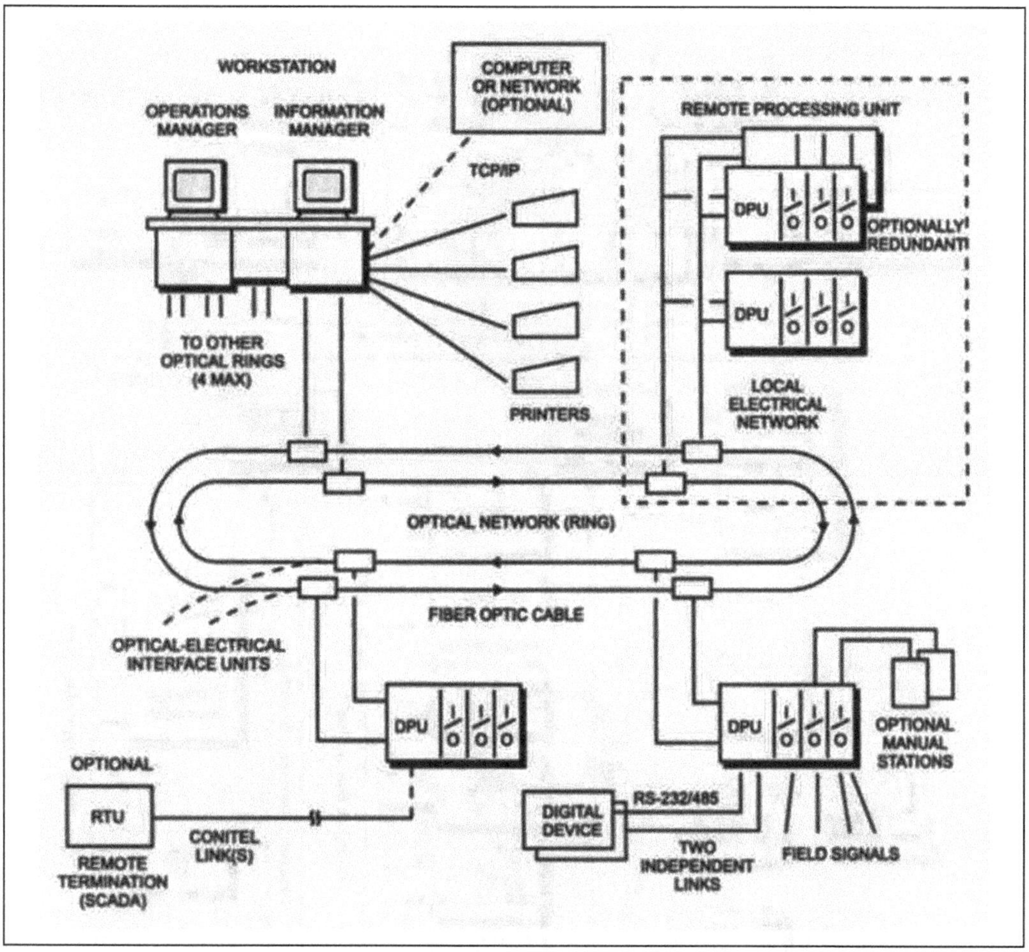

Figure 39-12. MAX controls (formerly Leeds & Northrup) MAX 1000

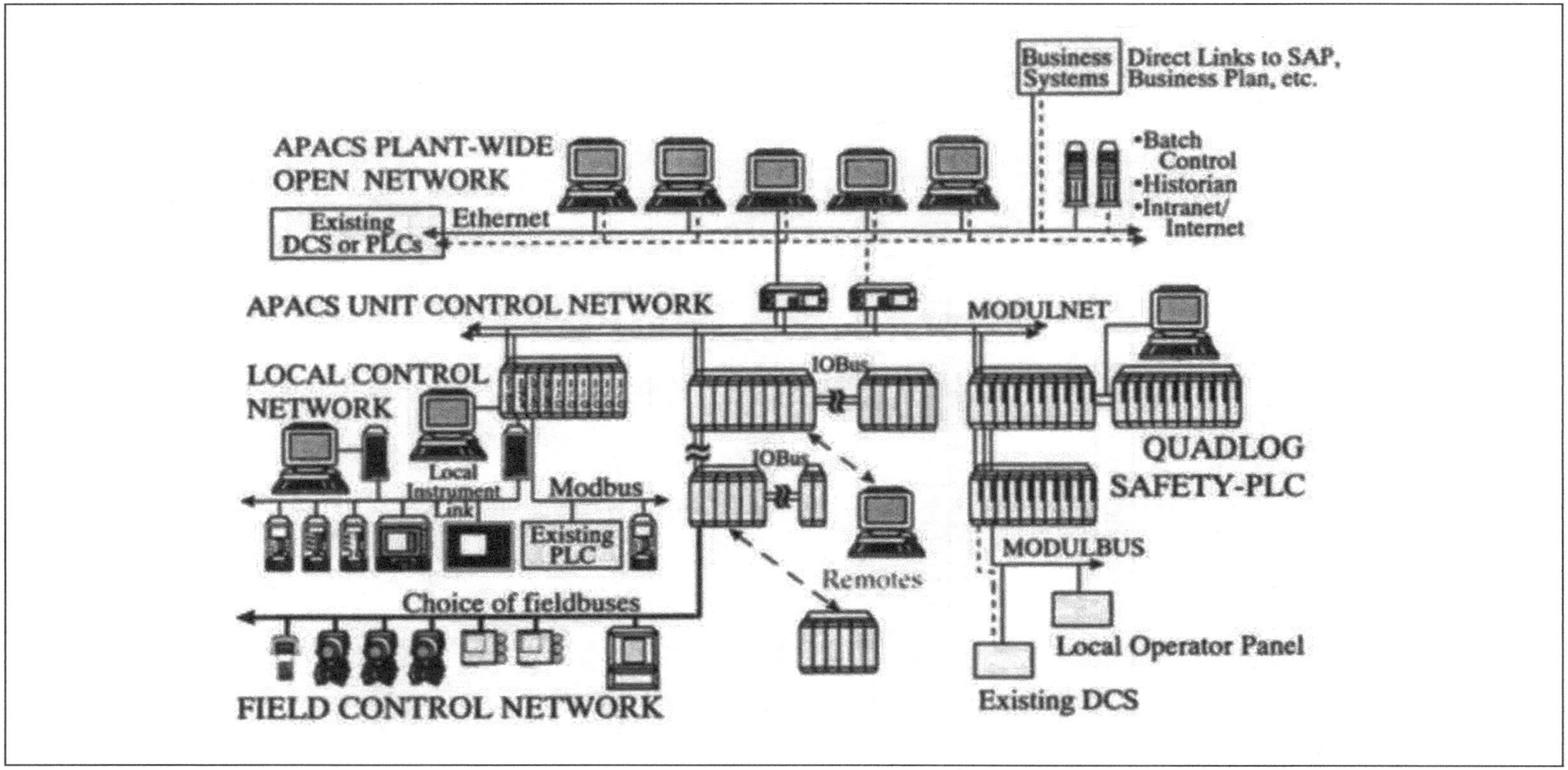

Figure 39-13. Moore Products APACS System

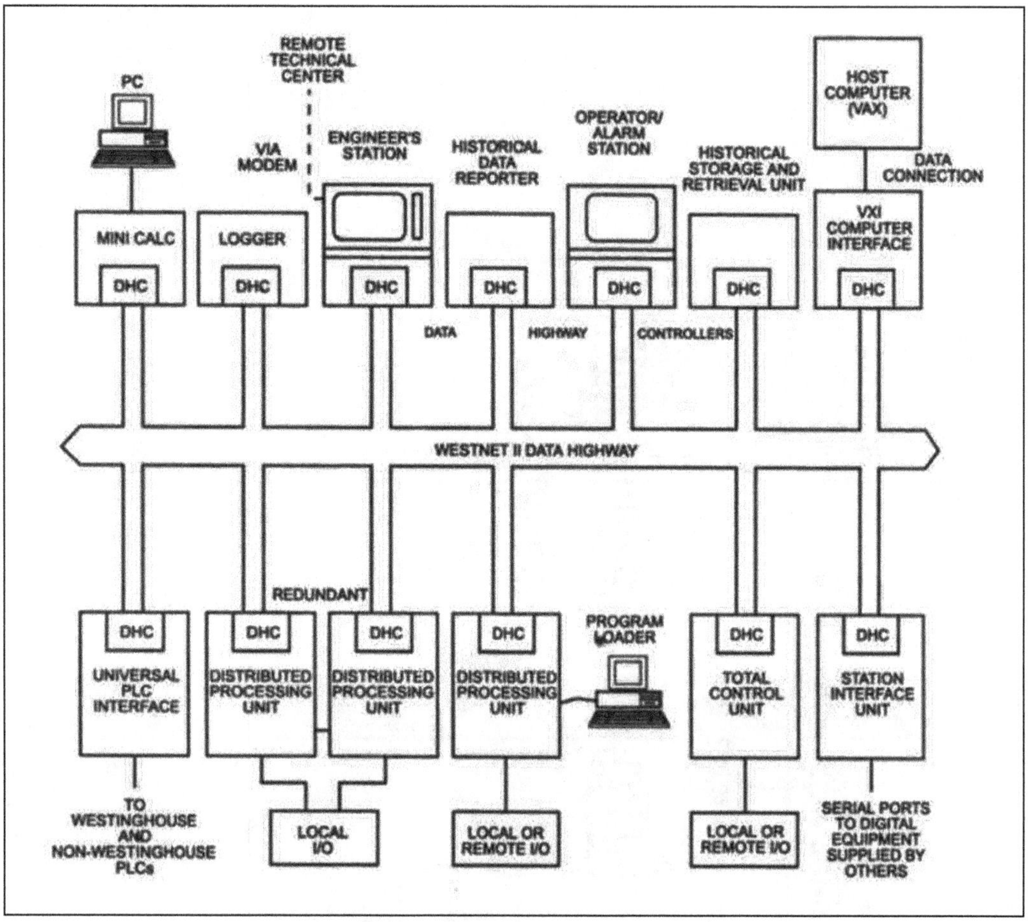

Figure 39-14. Westinghouse WDPF-11 System

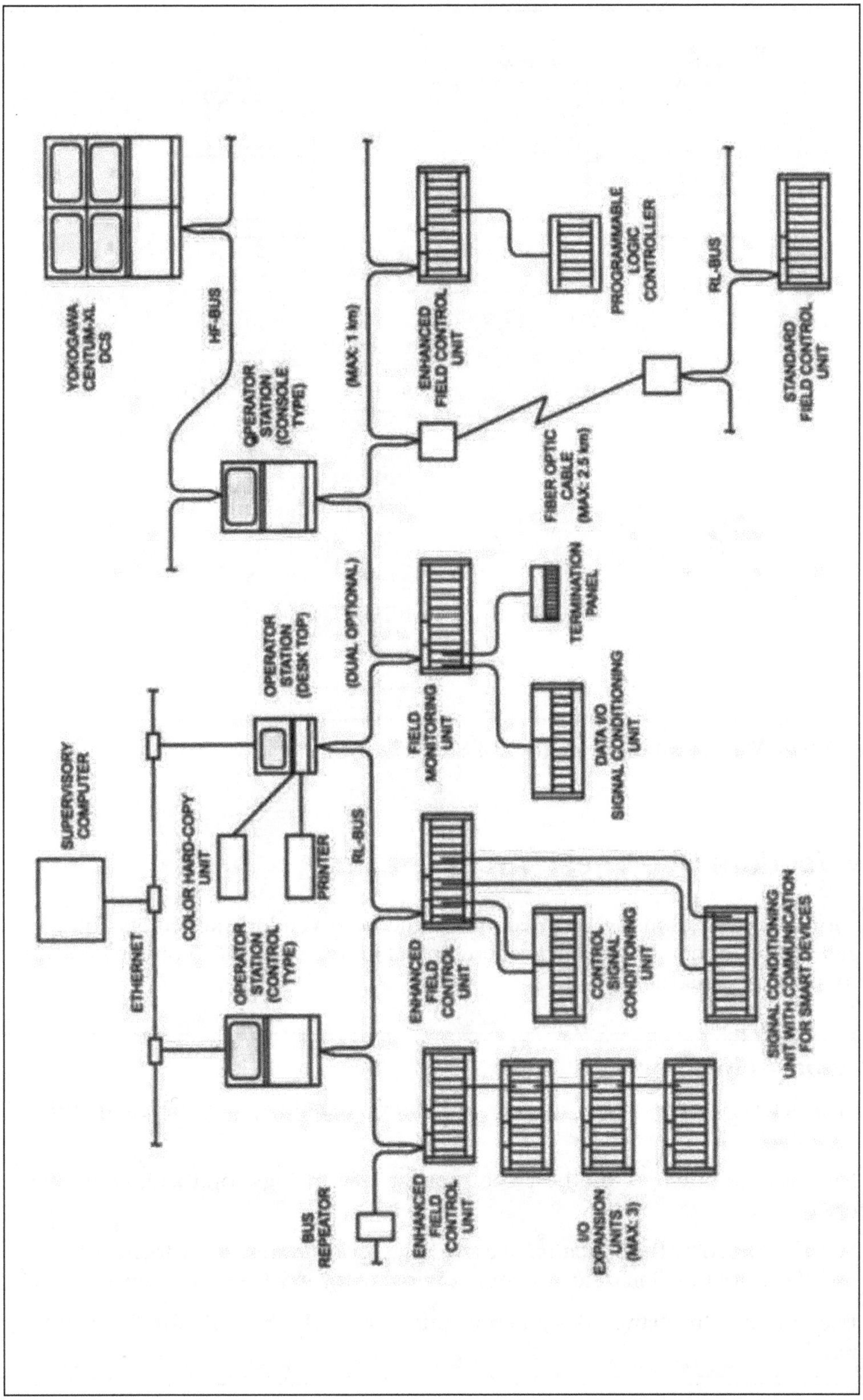

Figure 39-15. Yokogawa microXL (m XL) Large System

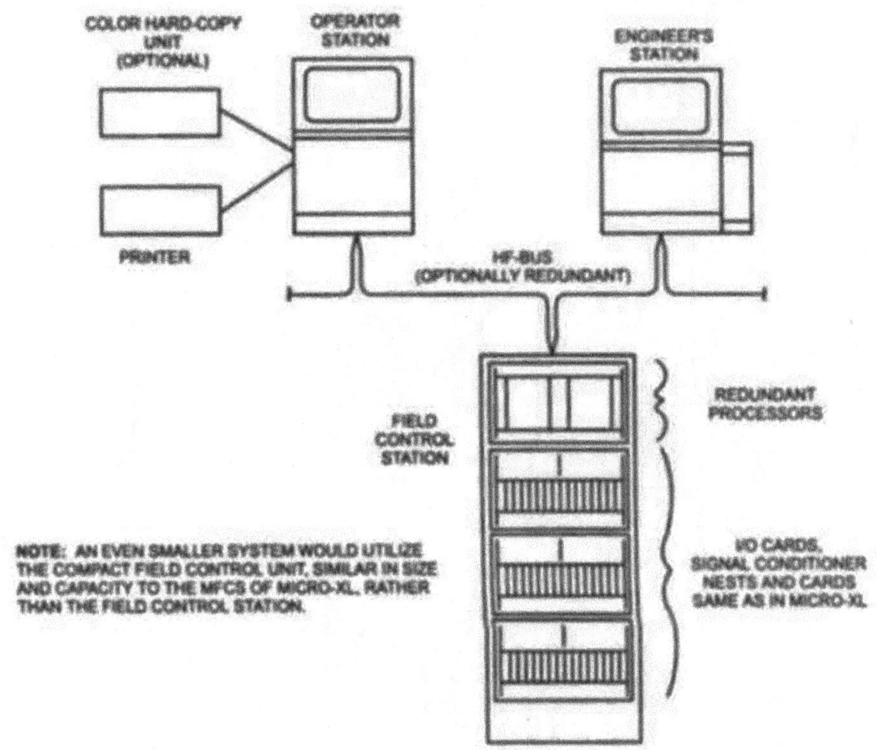

Figure 39-16. Yokogawa microXL (m XL) Small System

How Vendors Use These Architectures

Many of the combinations of architectures come with vendor's system as a package. User generally does not get to pick & choose parts of different design philosophies as if assembling a toy construction set.

Vendor Architectures

- Proprietary systems were chosen to achieve real-time, not for competitive advantage
- Each vendor attempts the best compromise of topology, protocol, controller design, etc.
- Vendors overcome the limitation of each design by restricting network nodes, I/O, use of control functions, etc., to assure optimum, *affordable* performance
- User rarely can change design mix, but selects the best fit for the plant's needs

---

Each vendor selects the blend that provides the best advantages of controller and I/O functions within stations along with the optimal method for moving data over the network.

Advantages and disadvantages will come with every system because of this built-in compromise. Vendors try to blend combinations of topologies, protocols, the limited number of nodes, diagnostics, and so on to get optimum performance for the best cost.

The use of proprietary systems is not for competitive advantage but a valiant effort to obtain the real-time movement of information through devices and over networks. Vendors have created these designs to overcome the absence of standards that operate fast enough for process control.

Most standards that have emerged so far have been suitable for business traffic through devices and over networks, but very few can handle real-time. Therefore, each of these vendors has combined aspects of existing standards and modified them to fit the functional requirements of process in general and often for specific types of processes (and the industries that use them).

Remember: It is not the technology that a company uses that is important, it is how that company *uses* the technology!

As the 1990s draw to a close, nearly all of these vendors claim to have, or are moving toward, open systems. Nevertheless, as we asked in Chapter 25, "what is open?"

Selecting an Open System

Now that you circled every "bingo card" you could find in all the trade magazines, how can you sort out which ones you can use? Your boss said you should integrate open PCs into the process somehow because that's the new technology! How does all of this fit? All of those nice salespeople are beginning to call about the literature you received and lining up to give you demonstrations You have enough to do with your "real job" without all this added aggravation. What are the considerations involved in comparing systems? How well will they really fit into your plant? Are you being set up for certain failure? How can you turn this around to actually improve plant productivity and performance?

Be ready to compare systems using the evaluation methods suggested in Chapter 43. When looking for vendors of distributed control systems that claim to be open, heed the following advice:

- Keep in mind that there is no "pure open" in a world searching for real-time. For most users and vendors, the best we can do is "real-enough-time." How fast "real-time" is depends upon the requirements of the process! Don't get caught up in the "specsmanship game" that some vendors seem to promote. "Know thy process" and what it really needs!
- Openness is a matter of standards and drivers

1. Do they support generally accepted standards (such as DDE, ActiveX, ODBC, and the like) for software components as well as physical connectivity through protocols like TCP/IP?
2. Do they (and/or others) have a large library of cost-effective drivers for connections to other devices (without a lot of obscure and expensive "specials")?
3. Are new drivers easy to create and therefore, cost-effective)?

- Can the vendor connect its controllers easily (cost-effectively) to multiple platforms, such as PC, VMS, or more than one variety of UNIX?
- Does the vendor provide tag-based access to the controller rather than register locations, bits, and word codes?
- Does the vendor support more than one language for accessing the system, such as FORTRAN, Pascal, Basic, C, hybrids of C, Visual Basic, Java?
- Like it or not, toward the end of the 1990s, there is a distinct migration towards the Microsoft model. This means that because of the volume, it will be relatively inexpensive to continue to grow with the technology in manageable increments and connect with a wider variety of capabilities from other suppliers.
- Vendor attitude is very important here. There are those who claim that attitude is 50 percent of the requirement, and the drivers/standards are only the other 50 percent. Some vendors provide a little window into their system and claim openness, but they will offer no real support in helping you interconnect to other systems. For true, cost-effective connectivity, the vendor must be willing to share the secrets of its system to any other, including another vendor. The vendor must be forthright about what the system can do and what it cannot! They can't just say "Don't play in my sandbox" when you ask about connectivity; they must be willing to allow others in to play with their toys. The vendor must be willing to be vulnerable (just like people) to make real solutions possible.

Open tools allow a vendor to bundle "best-in-class" solutions from various suppliers while offering tight integration and maintaining reasonable costs.

Part J

Control System Implementation

Justification 40

As we learned earlier, there are many kinds of architectures that can be used in a control system—some for very simple unit process control and some for very complex operations. The complex may require hybrid networks with both programmable logic controllers (PLCs) and traditional controller racks and use several computers connected to plantwide systems. Needless to say, the size and scope of these projects would have everything to do with how you have to implement them (Figure 40-1).

- Justification
- Preparation and definition
- Specification
- Selection process
- After purchase

Figure 40-1. Theory Is Fine, but How Do I Get One of These Systems into My Plant?

System Considerations

The selection of a system can be based on buying an off-the-shelf system and installing it as it is, buying a number of parts from a number of vendors and interfacing them all yourself, or buying a turnkey job from a systems house. Remember that, in all cases, someone is going to have to do the systems engineering. It may be you, it may be the instrument supplier, it may be an architect engineering firm, but somebody is going to have to do it.

Justification

- System considerations
- Purpose of this system
- Production
- Consistency
- Efficiency
- Safety
- Cost

Distributed network systems cannot be thought of as a product that can be taken out of a packing case, installed, and expected to work. It is part of a system that includes field-mounted equipment and other equipment interfaced to it. As you approach the selection of a system with this conception in mind, you may find that your estimates for start-up time will have to be extended.

What Is the Purpose of This Specific Control System?

This seemingly obvious question is often overlooked when planning a new control system. Perhaps everybody knows that the system must be upgraded. The question is, "*Why* should it be upgraded?" What will it do differently than it did before?

In the beginning of this book, we talked of plant (process) control goals. (See "There Must Be Goals for Improving a Plant Control System," Chapter 1.) In the very beginning of the project it is imperative to define on paper an agreed upon statement covering exactly the improvements expected from the system as well as some sort of cost analysis of the value those improvements will give you for required investment. Another help may be the "presentation" in Part K of this book, "Why Distribute My Control? "

Production

The following production goals should justify the system:

- Optimize the production schedule and equipment assignments for best throughput.
- Track time and the type of equipment used, and alert operations people to the exact time and requirements needed for cleaning/maintenance.
- Alert the operator and/or automatically act when deviation from normal limits begins.

Consistency

The system should be justified by improved consistency in several areas:

- Repetitive batches are always the same no matter how long ago the last run occurred.
- Ensure quick response to equipment degradation (equipment wear, valves sticking, etc.).
- Use screen prompts to operators so every person and shift reacts the same way, all the time.

Efficiency

The new system should be justified by the following improvements in efficiency:

- Current technologies permit more tuned loops.
- Capabilities exist for affordable multivariable control.

- Many types of new sensors are available today to measure process variables that in the past were not easily defined or measured very well.

Safety of Personnel, Plant, and Product

The system should offer real safety improvements in several ways:

- This involves recognizing process upsets and alarms and giving the operator direction.
- Perform multiple checks on related measurements and their correlation.
- Ensure the reasonableness of operator entries compared to defined norms.

Cost

- A microprocessor system may cost less than earlier technology.
- Many useful new functions may come as standard features, reducing the cost of additional devices.

Mission Statement

Regardless of size, the project must have a mission statement of goals and objectives in order to succeed. This statement is created by the individual in charge on small projects or by a team's effort on mid to large projects. The statement should be followed by a clear, brief summary that defines:

1. Your needs that the project will satisfy.
2. Your alternatives without the project effort.
3. How you intend to go forward and in which areas.

   —Project scope
   —Expected initial cost
   —Expected return-on-investment (ROI)
   —Expected start/end dates, with major milestones

It is imperative that this proposal always has a place for management to sign off, with a list of their specific items of support and a definition of the beginning and end points of the project and/or project phases. It would be wise to connect these defined "milestones" to the execution of the appropriate management items of support and management's signed approval rather than to calendar dates.

Develop a Plan

Following a clear justification exercise, you are now equipped to develop a plan (Figure 40-2). Do not rush this stage. Consider it an ongoing function throughout the entire project, even after the system is successfully installed. The plan may be very simple for a small installation, and very complex for a large one, but at this stage you should always consider every step carefully regardless of the size. You will no doubt not need every consideration listed here for every plan, nevertheless, *think about each one*.

Always make a list of the reasons why skipping steps in the plan is appropriate. This will make later reassessments far easier if conditions change!

Then in a summary document that "rides" with the project, list the exact reasons why those steps are not needed (or are minimized) for each item. This list will help you keep focused farther into the project, and will help new people (especially managers) understand the thought process that led to the project direction. Otherwise, there will be much revisiting of the decisions, wasting valuable time. Remember, however, that projects have a habit of changing as they progress. This list will help to quickly assess what else may have to change or be added when those new directions happen.

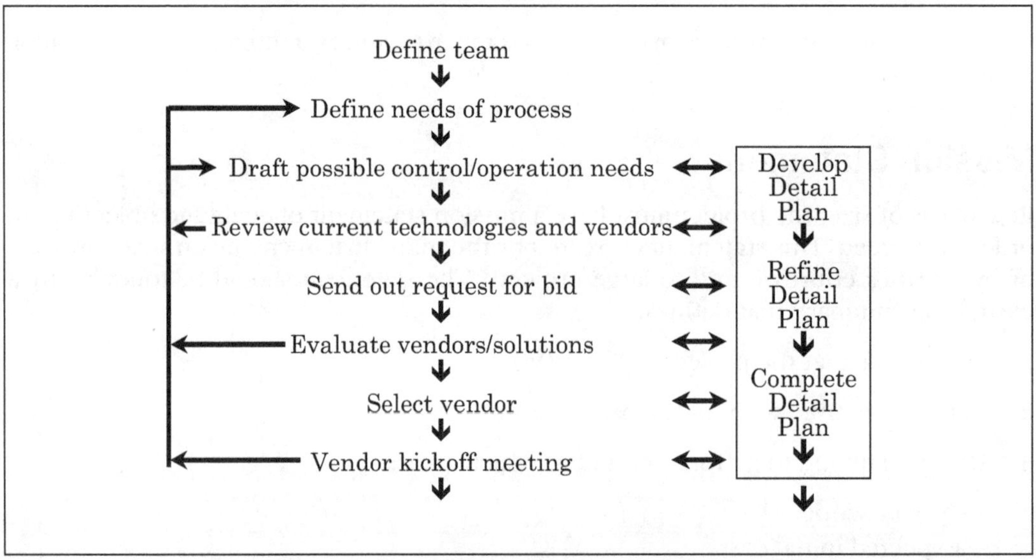

Figure 40-2. Implementation Requires a Complete Plan

41 Preparation and Definition

Once the plan is started (keep in mind that it will constantly be revised), your attention must be directed to the team members. Your plan at this stage will be little more than an outline, and you should expect that the team members will be adding to that plan as they come on board. The purpose of the team at this point will be to prepare a specification based upon the justification findings. That justification will lead to the definition of the specification. Define the items in Figure 41-1 carefully, or you will have a disaster, no matter the size of the system!

- Team members
- Defining the project
- Defining the process interface
- Nature of *your* control system
- Operator interfaces
- Environments
- Equipment room
- Distributed equipment
- System power
- Grounding
  - Earth grounding
  - Signal common
  - Signal isolation
- Physical considerations
- Training and assistance

Figure 41-1. Define These Items Carefully or Expect Disaster, No Matter the Size of the System

The Team Members

One of the most important considerations in preparing a justification for a new control system and especially for the specification for that control system is involving the correct people.

It must be certain that every group whose work will be affected by this system is given a chance to comment on the specification as well as the justification. They must be prepared to give any required support. The people you would normally expect to be included in this team are:

- The process engineer—has thorough knowledge of the processes involved and of all the critical parameters and control problems of this process. This person must ensure that the selected system can control the process and help define the required control schemes.

- The equipment engineer—is totally familiar with the plant equipment and instrumentation and with its maintenance. This person should be empowered to make equipment changes as required for the new control system.
- The operations supervisor—has responsibility for hiring and training Plant operations personnel and for the actual operation of the plant. This person's people will be operating the system.
- The applications engineer—responsible for implementing both continuous and sequential control schemes using the selected system and for creating users' guides and for any application documentation. This person is also responsible for creating any special lines and reports required by the plant, and should have both a good process control as well as a microprocessor computer background. If your plant does not employ someone of this background, the system vendor may be able to provide somebody, or if not, you may wish to hire a consultant.

What you need here is the knowledge and experience of the process itself as well as all the other skills that we listed. As with any project, it is very important to have a good leader. A good approach is to assign a senior project engineer to supervise and coordinate all the team activities. Team members should represent all aspects of the process/plant influenced by the project; bringing their concerns and experiences. The main reason for having such a diverse collection of talents is to insure that the resulting specification covers all the areas, which concern the plant and the capabilities of the system being purchased. The other reason for using all these people is to insure that the departments they represent all get a chance to provide inputs into the system design.

Defining the Project

The first thing that must be done by the team is to define exactly what is going to be required of the project. What is the scope of the changes being made or the process being built? It makes sense to know as much as you can about what is available in the new technologies of your industry, especially in the development of the type of process you are working. You should look very carefully at any changes in the way the process is being performed in the industry and what is practical and appropriate for the way your plant does it. You should also consider any new innovations that your team members may have on how to make improvements in the process. This is in light of their own experience as well what they have heard and read about, or maybe they have seen in other plants.

A starting point would be to picture the fundamental job of this process, and to visualize what you would expect an operator to do to cause this process to happen. You should look at all of the things that could change in that process on its way to becoming the final product. You should decide all of the actions the operator should take in order to keep the product on track with the best quality. You should then look at what information the operator needs in order to perform those functions. Only then should you decide perhaps what automatic controls could be done to assist the operator in performing the art of making your product.

Keep in mind that the role of the operator will probably change. Because of automatic control, the operator will become more of a business manager than a valve turner. In these discussions, you should look for surprisingly new ways to view the process that may have been "done that way for centuries." You will then have to philosophically define the roll of the operator—what is automatic and what requires operator intervention. This job is not to replace the operator but rather to redefine his role. You may discover that it will be a far more powerful improvement in the productivity of the plant by going through this exercise.

It is absolutely backwards to start with an input/output count. Rather you should look to any new or upgraded control system from the view of the ultimate operator. It will probably be far more revealing to what is the nature of your process.

Furthermore, the team should be investigating various kind of control systems from different vendors. The team must be very open minded about this. They should visit and talk with a variety of types of vendors, perhaps not just the traditional vendors they're used to working with. This is so all of the team members can become familiar with what control techniques are currently on the market as well as all of the various features of operator interfaces as well as record-keeping and report-writing techniques. Keep in mind when it comes to developing reports you may not wish to generate paper but rather a database from which management can tap for their business spreadsheets. With today's technology, this does not have to require exotic or custom-built software or hardware.

Remember that when you make this list of control system needs, do not add into it the best features of everybody's system, because, you will create a very expensive custom system.

After visiting and viewing many vendors' approaches to working with your specific control requirements, the team should then analyze what is truly required by your plant. Begin with the functions you really need and then decide who can best address those functions. This will go into the development of your specification. The process is reiterative—that means you will be continually updating your new knowledge as you discover other new features in each vendors' system, as well as new approaches on how you can perform you process. The team should regularly review from the beginning all of its basic assumptions, on the role of the control system as well as the functions required to achieve that role.

Who Implements

All major process control system vendors (and some PLC-based vendors) have the capacity to provide system implementation. Some have departments which are capable of performing both large and small-scale integration. They each may also have some degree of experience with your specific industry or application, which will differ from one to the other.

Many times, especially on large and/or complex projects, or on certain applications, the vendor may have an alliance with a particular independent system integrator. You may also have your own preference for a list of system integrators because of:

- Their application knowledge.
- Their understanding of special requirements, such as validations and best practices.
- Their proximity (and therefore responsiveness) to the installation site.
- Your previous experiences and rapport working with them.
- Their ability to provide application-specific "value-add" software or implementation products.

Progressive system integrators are increasing their efficiency by using standard, modular products and designing solutions from prior project experience. Because of one or more of these reasons, you may want to approach system integrators with your request for bid, rather than system vendors.

Now you have opened the possibilities of:

- Doing the project yourself, purchasing the control system directly from the system vendor, and doing the system integration yourself.
- Doing the project exclusively through a system vendor, using that same vendor as the system integrator as a "turn-key" job.
- Doing the project exclusively through a system integrator, allowing that integrator to purchase the required components from a controls vendor.
- Doing some combination of the above, such as "cutting a purchase order" to a control systems vendor separate from one to a system integrator.

Only you or your team must decide which arrangement is best for your circumstances and budget.

What Goes Where?

Your company may have a corporate business information system or may be in the process of developing one (Figure 41-2). We talked of the issues involved within Chapters 28 & 29. What is the type and quantity of information the business system will need? What should it provide to your proposed control system? The information exchange between your business system and your control system can range from simple production schedules to more elaborate quality, inventory, and process management instructions. The amount and type of information that your business system will need from your control system can also vary widely. They may only be passing averaged process values, or it could include information on alarm, quality, operator action, production record, and materials movement. The amount of information exchange will determine the level of integration required between your automation system and business system.

Figure 41-2. Some Very Serious Thinking Must be Given to the Way the Control System is Integrated to the Plant Business, Especially in Batch Operations.

There are a number of production management functions such as quality, documentation, maintenance, production scheduling, and quality management. You need to decide whether these functions are to be performed by your business system or by your control system, or partially by both. Where you keep the main database for your process information is also important. Quite often, the information within that database is shared by both systems and you will need to clearly define their interfaces.

Defining Process Interface

As we said before, the whole system can revolve about proper definition of the process needs, that is done best by developing a functional flow chart of the process itself, and by deciding how the process should really be done. Only then can you decide what the functions should be in the system used to controlling it. What are the redundancies needed? Where is manual intervention required? Where do you need visibility of what's going on in the process? What record keeping do you need?

Only from these kinds of questions, will you have some idea of how many sensors and final elements you will need, and can you develop an input-output definition. This I/O definition must *follow* the definition of the functions needed in the plant, and after the nature of the types of sensors and final elements are determined. This I/O definition is a detailed list by equipment area of all the process signals and interfaces. All unusual signal types should be detailed. Special smart devices should be described, and spare capacities should be enumerated and defined.

There are often many questions about spare capacity and the actual spare I/O points. If you want empty slots or racks, say so. If you want I/O hardware actually provided, say so. Transmitter powering and signal fusing can also be expensive items to overlook. Keep in mind that the I/O definition may very well be a subset of what kind of control you're trying to achieve in the plant. Sometimes, with the improvement of sensors in both price and capability, you may want quite a few more sensors than used to be traditional. This has to be accounted for in the cabinet space required to connect them into the system as well as the potential for expansion in the future as technology advances.

There also may be significant differences if you have many low-level inputs, say thermocouple inputs, or lots of discrete action inputs and outputs in the operation. These often use different termination configuration than traditional analog signals. With the advent of more and more direct digital signals between the controller and the sensor and the final element itself, there should be some serious consideration on the nature of the fieldbus. As of this writing, a formal fieldbus specification has not been completed, and there are several versions vying for attention. This situation will probably continue for another decade.

Nevertheless, you should very carefully analyze the requirements of your plant, and if there is an acceptable solution already available. If there is a fieldbus consideration appropriate in your system, you should then consider at which remote location the actual inputs and outputs can meet the process, rather than trying to bring the signals from a long distance through marshaling cabinets. A properly phrased specification could open an invitation to a supplier to make recommendations in this area. Don't make it so open, however, that it confuses your selection of vendor, because you will certainly get peaches and apples to compare.

Clearly if the system you're defining is of any size, you may decide to have several sessions with various potential vendors to discuss the considerations and listen for their ideas. Those with the most creative ideas may very well be those who could best do your system.

The Nature of Your Control System

In order to help define what type of equipment you will need, you'll have to analyze the nature of what your process requires. How many analog loops of control will there be? Is there a large amount of digital logic? A lot of discrete I/O and switching action? Perhaps programmable logic controllers should be considered.

Is the requirement primarily that of data acquisition? If it is, then some sort of dedicated information gathering equipment should be the thing to use. How flexible must it be? Is this important? If you expect to change control strategy during or after the initial installation has been completed, you'll want to look at system that's easily configured and re-configured. Be careful with this! Many people presume they already how to control a system. Once the plant's running, many people discover changes they would like to have.

To produce a long life cycle on this system, you want to have the ability to alter this control strategy as time goes on (Figure 41-3). This is to meet not only the technology changes of the equipment, but also the requirements of the marketplace in which your plant sells product. As that market changes, new production techniques may be required of your plant, and new control techniques will be needed. Most of the time, you want a system flexible enough to grow with the needs of your industry.

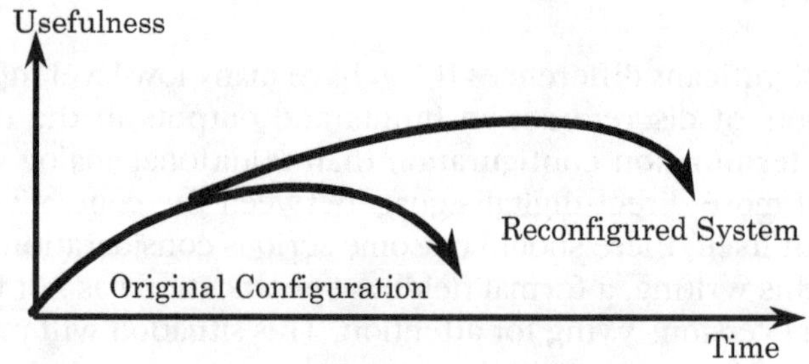

- Ability of reconfiguration to meet new requirements increases value of initial investment

Figure 41-3. Investment Value of the System.

This will extend the life of your system and make it much more cost effective over the years, rather than become obsolete in a short time. You should also consider how sophisticated is the control strategy. For something like small heaters, tank level control, and simple combustion control, you probably don't need more than some simple control loops. Processes with a lot of interaction, load changes, formulation of inferred values, however, it is much more effective to have a system with very powerful algorithms and control capabilities.

A very important consideration is the ability the plant personnel accept the new concept. Will they have to be trained or have to be "sold" on the idea? It is important, I believe, to keep plant operating personnel involved in some of the decisions. Then they can buy into the changes and become part of the solution, rather than part of the problem.

Change is Constant

How do you live with the dilemma of continually changing technology? To purchase a control system while technology is changing so fast that the design becomes obsolete while the ink is drying on the contract is quite a challenge indeed. Still emerging from proprietary systems, many control system vendors struggle with the same problem, but from the other side of the issue.

Many engineers (in any field) tend to write extremely hardware-specific software. This is not to be obstinate, but to be more efficient in their programming, and to take the best advantage o the capabilities of their hardware. Of course, there will also be a chance to be more clever. It presents a problem, however, when that software must be migrated to new and different platforms, or even when the chipset changes or becomes obsolete. The control system vendor has no control of the chipset supplier, and changes in chipset technology is the rule, not the exception!

What can the control system vendor do? More specifically, what can you as the buyer look for in a vendor's response to these regular changes? The solution is to use higher level programming languages or systems wherever possible. The system needs to have common, inexpensive platforms, and/or cross platforms. You as a buyer should look for systems with these characteristics. Typically you could ask, for example, if the user has a choice of operator interfaces to use with the controller, or must the user require only that provided by the control system vendor. In other words, actually how open *is* the system?

It will also be helpful to try to understand basic elements of emerging technology. This will reduce the chance of being seduced by vendor hype, as compared to significant change. You might also try to keep up with your vendor's development activities and directions.

I have to say again: It is not the technology that a company uses that is important, it is how that company USES the technology!!

Operator Interfaces

Remember about defining your process? We said earlier you should consider how the process is to be operated by the *people involved*, keeping in mind that the operation of all process is an art, and sometimes that art is very hard to define Many companies use control operators as part of the design team for valuable, practical, and cost-saving ideas. Only after you have defined how you should best run your process, can you define the role each of the operators must play. Should operators be distributed around the plant? Should they be concentrated in one area? Are they in constant attention to managing the controls or are they also responsible for other activities and merely adjust the controls from time to time?

Operators may not need a chair in front of the video screen, but they may very well need a video screen. If all that is needed is a periodic visit for an adjustment, and a view for making a decision on where in the process to check, then it might make a big difference on how the control room is configured. In fact, there may not be a central control room! The plant or process may have several control points.

There may very well be, as time goes on, the capability of floating locations of system control using portable interface devices so the operator(s) can handle and control the system with a hand-held device.

This concept is already being done in factory automation systems and we can very well expect this to happen soon in process plants. Much consideration should be given to how operator screen views impact the ability of the operator to respond. This is the subject of Chapter 18. Nevertheless, the topic is very important and will make a difference on the nature of the equipment needed for the operator to work with the process for the best production efficiency.

Since the system will work only if the operations people accept and use it, the operator interface needs should be well defined. All the labs, reports and custom displays should be specified in great detail. If possible, it is highly recommended that the operators get hands on experience with all of the vendors systems that you're are considering. This will help operators to develop an importance factor for the available display types, and help you specify the displays you consider essential. It will also help the operators to "buy into" the system, and also help them to begin to recognize the features of various systems that will be an advantage for them to perform their job. Many companies use control operators as part of the design team. Quite often the initial decisions of the type of equipment available and the functions and features needed within the operator station and also for the training of other operators.

Reiterate:

At this point, in order to truly define the system, you ought to go back and re-read everything from "Defining the Project," but make notes.

Environments

If, in fact, there is a control room where several operators will either be functioning regularly or functioning occasionally, the equipment must generally be suited to the same conditions that humans are. This is a relatively benign environment designed for the comfort of the operators as well as the protection of the hardware, so you would expect typical environments such as temperature of 50 to 80°F, with a thermal shock of about 1°F per minute change and relative humidity of between 20 to 80% non condensing.

Usually there are very few requirements for vibration, shock, dust or corrosive atmospheres, but if the control room happens to be exposed to that, it certainly should be included. In those parts of the country subject to violent storms, or earth tremors, it would be important to take that into consideration as well. With larger control systems and use of video screens, keep in mind that part of the environment includes radio frequency interference with the screens, as well as electrical interference with the screens. If that is a necessary consideration in your plant, you should take it into account, and make a note of that in your specifications.

If you follow the National Electric Manufacturers' Association (NEMA) classification closures, a NEMA 1 enclosure (general purpose indoors) is quite adequate for the protection of electronic equipment in a control room environment. Standard mass memory media, such as floppy disks and hard disks and display hardware, such as video screens, can be used without concern about dust or vibration. Any panel board instrumentation indicators, switches, and trend recorders generally require no special consideration for the packaging design.

Because of this benign environment, the cost of the hardware used in control rooms can probably be minimized at the expense of maintaining the controlled environment, normal heating and air conditioning costs for the entire package. Generally there is only one central control room in the plant and its size is limited so this expense usually isn't all that excessive.

Equipment Room

If a control system is large enough, it often requires an equipment room to provide a central location for the bulk of the control and data acquisition equipment used in any industrial process automation system. Typically, you would find rows of standard sized cabinets, floor-mounted arranged to allow either front access or sometimes front and rear access to the internal electronic hardware, power supplies, and field termination panels. The wiring is usually routed to the termination panels through either the top or bottom of the cabinets. If this is a retrofit plant, this might have been called the relay room from the days of the pneumatic or electric control.

Even if expected to operate in lower ambient temperatures, modules and components will last longer if they are designed to tolerate wider temperature ranges.

Generally the environment is not controlled as closely as the control room itself, but it's usually situated indoors and not far from the control room (box). This location gives some protection from outdoor environment and the typical requirements might have temperatures of 32° to 110°F with a thermal shock of 5°F per minute change, and relative humidity of about 10 to 90% non condensing. It will probably have mild non-explosive, non-conducting dust and negligible requirements for relative vibration, shock or corrosive atmosphere. Now, while these specifications cover a wider range of operating conditions, they're not so harsh as to place an extremely severe demand on the packaging designer. Commercial electronic hardware can usually be used in this environment as long as it's protected by industrial grade enclosures. Usually NEMA 2 (drip-proof indoor), or NEMA 12 (industrial use), dust tight, drip tight, indoor enclosures are quite adequate to protect the electronics from the mild dust conditions and occasional liquid splashes that are typical of these environments.

Most of the cabinetry should have enough space for not only the mounting of equipment, but room to run wiring and make connections. Sometimes the controller designs are clever in placing equipment and wires, but no room for a hand to get in there and make changes. Newer designs allow pullout drawers and swing-away portions to make this job easier. Dependence on active cooling such as fans should be minimal. Low maintenance dust filters should be provided if ambient air is to be introduced into the cabinet itself for cooling purposes. If the system requires active cooling, there should be redundant cooling fans in each cabinet plus remote alarming for cooling fan failure.

NEMA—(National Electrical Manufactures Association); trade association of electrical equipment manufactures which develops many manufacturing specifications, included are cabinet ratings such as:

NEMA 1—Dust resistant general purpose,

NEMA 2—Drip tight,

NEMA 3—Splash proof (weather resistant),

NEMA 4—High-pressure hose proof,

NEMA 5—Dust tight,

NEMA 6—Submersible,

NEMA 7—Hazardous indoor (NEC Class I Groups A,B,C,D),

NEMA 8—Hazardous indoor/outdoor (NEC Class I Groups A,B,C,D),

NEMA 9—Hazardous indoor/outdoor (NEC Class II Groups E,F,G),

NEMA 10—Mine Safety and Health Administration (MSHA) 30 CFR part 18,

NEMA 11—General purpose drip and corrosion resistant from liquids and gases,

NEMA 12—General purpose indoor use drip/dust/rust resistant,

NEMA 13—General purpose resistant to dust/rust and spraying of water/oil/ non-corrosive liquids.

Distributed Equipment

In today's technology, microprocessors are appearing within sensors and final elements, and full-blown control strategies can be done at the location of the process itself. As a result of these various "smart" transmitters and end elements, the need for environmental protection of control equipment now extends throughout the plant. It is necessary to consider very carefully the specs needed for these remote devices.

Sometimes the remote device is a single but complete controller rack with all of its inputs and outputs, and a connection to the control system through the communication network. It is now practical to place operator interfaces throughout the plant as well as in some central control room. Environmental protection for each of these situations must be carefully reviewed.

The trend is away from proprietary hardware made by specific vendors. As a result, you will see more generic PC-based hardware with enough power and performance to do the control jobs needed in most processes and plants. This equipment is becoming more plant hardened, and available off-the-shelf. It is also possible to put these into various cabinetry, commercially supplied in small or large boxes, to protect PC-based equipment from extreme environments.

As technological changes continually make it more commercially practical to distribute additional functions among remote hardware, we are beginning to see the marketplace provide appropriate equipment. There are many commercial cabinets for NEMA 3, for outdoor dust tight, rain tight, sleet resistant, or NEMA 4 for indoor watertight and dust tight cabinetry, depending on its location. Typical specifications on these remote environments where the temperature of 0 to 130°F, with a thermal shock of 5°F per minute change, relative humidity of 5 to 95%, non condensing. These enclosures protect equipment from heavy dust environment that's non-explosive, but may contain flammable or conductive particles, corrosive atmosphere, such as hydrogen sulfide, sulfur dioxide, chlorine, and so on. They also provide for other conditions specific to the environment like seismic shock, water or salt spray, blowing sand, fungus, or bacterial contaminants.

All of these are important parameters to include in specifications, if required. Several of these may also include hazardous locations, as defined by the national electrical code, such as those containing flammable or explosive gases or vapors or dust or fibers. These specialized environments call for specific features in the design of electronics, the cabling, packaging, and sub-assemblies beyond the level we are discussing here. These severe environmental specifications can place restraints on the design of the equipment location which are well beyond the normal commercial and industrial practice.

Some circumstances might require military specifications of the design of components as well as the protection of them within cabinetry. Rather than very expensive design on the electronic equipment itself, it generally is more practical to put that equipment into properly hardened cabinets for the purpose. It may be necessary, however, in hazardous atmospheres, to be sure that these cabinets are connected through, say, fiber optic highways or data communications systems rather than mere metallic cabling.

System Power

Microprocessor equipment requires clean and regulated power. If your plant can't provide it, and you expect the vendor to provide it, you should make this clear. Any grounding problems should be spelled out. In any electronic or industrial control system, the power system must convert the available line power to the voltage and current levels required by the electronic modules, most of which use digital components. This also includes the cooling hardware and many of the sensors and transmitters in the field.

Various power levels, voltages, and current capacities differ in divergent parts of the world, so you must consider what is the available power and how constant is that power. The equipment itself should accommodate the available line power and frequency, typically 115 to 230 volts, 50 to 60 Hertz nominal, with a typical variation of ±10% in voltage, and ±2 Hertz in frequency. You should consider harmonic distortion in your supply. That is the variation from a pure sine wave, which can be up to maybe 3% RMS (root mean square) or more. This deliverable power should be available in all the components required.

Consider transmitter needs of 1 to 5 volts, or 4 to 20 milliAmps, and electronic needs which are usually 24 volts DC with solid state switching requiring typically 48 volts DC at 125 volts DC and so on, some of it at line voltage and frequency. Now, of course, equipment for each user may have some specific needs to adjust to custom bases. The power system must include sufficient fuses and current limiting resistors to protect the power supplies from likely component failures and human errors, such as, shorting the outputs to ground. And all the electronic modules should be isolated from power lines transients, electromagnetic interference (EMI) and radio frequency interference (RFI).

Power systems for all or a significant part of the control system must not be subject to a single point of failure as an active element. That is, the system should not have to be shut down if a single element like an individual power supply fails. If such a failure occurs, it must be possible to remove and replace the failed element with a good one without shutting the power system down. All power sources and voltages should be monitored and alarms sent automatically to the operator if a failure does occur. This means that the power system must be included in the total system diagnostic hierarchy. The power system should be designed to permit operation despite the loss of primary line power source for a specific period of time, usually 15 minutes to 1 hour. This capability can be an option that the user selects at the time of purchase to allow sufficient time to shut the plant down in an orderly and safe manner after the line power is lost. These kinds of systems are usually referred to as uninterruptable power supplies.

Grounding

The power system must have a provision for a safety ground connector to be joined at the power entry point. Generally the cabinet structure is connected at this grounding point through the power system within each cabinet. If the power system in one cabinet is also providing power to components in the other cabinets, there must be a mechanism for connecting the structures of the latter cabinet to a safety ground point in the first cabinet, so that there's only a single point of ground.

Within each cabinet, a separate grounding system, called system common must be provided while the common terminal to *other* DC power supplies is shielded. This assures the process I/O signal wiring and the signal commons (that is, the signal grounding points) are tied together at a single point or ground bus. It must be possible to connect this bus to a site ground through a connector that is separate from the safety ground connection.

In the case of multiple cabinets powered by a single electrical supply, there must be a means to allow interconnection of the system on buses in each of the cabinets. Keep in mind that there should be a total separation between the communications network from the power network. In no way should they be electrically connected to each other throughout the plant system: local electrical codes should always be considered, as they are usually directed to personal safety Electrical isolation is usually accomplished through the use of transformer coupling in the communication wires, or the use of fiber optics in the communication system between cabinets. This is to avoid the nemesis of all control systems, ground loops.

Physical Considerations

Wherever control system is used, in the control room, in an equipment room (rack room), or in remote locations, space must not be overlooked.

- Do cabinets need both front and rear access?
- What are the overall clearances of height, depth, width?
- What is the space needed with doors opened?
- Is there room for maintenance?
- Is there room to remove hardware?
- What is footprint (actual portion of equipment or cabinet touching floor)?
- What is floor-loading requirements?
- What are heat dissipation requirements?

Training and Assistance

In defining plant needs, consider what kind of training is necessary. How many people will be trained and in what roles and functions. Think of engineering, plant operators, maintenance people, service and repair people. Consider the extent of assistance needed at all levels when considering new technologies. If you're not sure how many people are needed for the kind of equipment that you are considering, talk to the vendors and ask them for their recommendations. Some equipment may be less complicated in its use—more "user-friendly" in today's popular language—than others, particularly if the control system does not need special programming, but has more intuitive configuring capabilities.

A little later on, we'll talk more in detail about testing, but consider what kind of testing is being provided by the various vendors: factory acceptance testing, and site testing after delivery. Most vendors have a standard test procedure that will meet most of your requirements, but ask to review it. Take a look at it before writing your definition of needs, and it might give you ideas of what's necessary in the specification.

Another consideration is how much applications assistance you will need. If you need training for your own applications people, and possibly some other application assistance on how to use the vendor equipment, create a detailed description of how much effort is involved. It is a good idea to assign any of your own applications engineers to the vendor facilities during the project, so that these engineers become very familiar with the system and with the vendor. in quoting application assistance, keep in mind it's very difficult unless detailed information can be provided. This should include the process and instrument diagrams, ladder diagrams, flow charts, recipe information, and so on. The more you can provide, the more accurate will be the quote from vendors.

Field assistance during the project from the vendor should include meetings at your facility, supervision of system installation, start up, warranty support, and acceptance test, and so on. All of these activities should be called out and defined so that the vendor can include these services in the quote.

Specification 42

It is absolutely necessary to understand the application for which the equipment is to be used. This has already been said, but it's so important it needs repeating. Without knowledge of the system requirements and intended functions, it is impossible to make any meaningful distinctions between vendors. A good way to organize this information for yourself and to create a basis for comparing quotations is to write out the specification.

Writing the Specification

System Specification

- Writing the specification
  - Clearly define process
  - Clearly explain functions
  - dentify services required
- The wish list
  - Musts versus wants
- Prescreening vendors
- Trivia quizzes
- Terminology

Specifications should be written in the context of the requirements. They should be as general as possible so all bidders have equal opportunity to reply, but it must match the needs of the specific application. The following subjects should be considered when writing the specification. The user must carefully decide which of these apply to the real needs of the application.

1. Vendor/system integrator qualifications

   - What are their corporate capabilities?
   - What are their personnel capabilities?
   - What are their international capabilities if this applies in your case?
   - What is their corporate viability?
     - Longevity
     - Liquidity
     - Profitability
     - Growth rate
     - Domestic & foreign distribution channels

—What is their market share?
—Can they be bought, sold, or taken over?
—During periods of economic change, what strengths & assets will carry them through?
—Will they survive against their competitors?

Vendor finances should be checked carefully. One of the worst experiences for a user is to wind up with an "orphan" system, bereft of support. The most likely cause for this is either the vendor failing financially or being bought out by another vendor.

- What is their strategic direction for new business?
  —New products planned?
  —Industries targeted?
  —Are they leading, keeping up, or trying to catch up?
  —Will this help you meet your own needs?
- What are their core competencies?
  —How can you use those?
  —Will they carry both you and themselves where you each need to be?
- What commitments have they made in your industry?
  —Do they participate in standardization efforts?
- What alliances do they have?
  —What relationships do they maintain with other suppliers that complement their offerings?
  —What do *those* suppliers say?
  —What commitments are there to keep those relationships?
- What is their experience in handling projects of this size?
  —What is their systems engineering department's experience?
  —What kind of installation and start-up support can they supply?
  —What is their track record?
  —How many installations have been sold?
  —How many have been installed and started up?
  —And how long have these been operating?
- What is their application experience? Is it appropriate to your needs?
- What is their service and support experience?
  —What is the extent of their continuing technical support? Does it match your needs?
  —Is it responsive to your degree of expected urgency?
  —Is it available over the expected lifetime of the system?
  —Can you get service from independent firms?
  —What are the locations where spare parts are stocked? Are they nearby the plant, or do they have an easy way to deliver them?
  —Can you easily make configuration changes yourself, or must you bring in the vendor or a system integrator (SI)?

—What kind of documentation is available, that is, instruction books, service manuals, engineering drawings, configuration forms?
—How easy is it to do business with them?

2. What kind of constraints of environment, distance, or clearances and spare capacity are required in your system?
3. What are the functional requirements, including diagnostics and data acquisition and the contents of the algorithm library for the variety of functions needed?
4. What are the requirements in specifying the communications architecture, redundancy and any multiplexing needs?
5. What is the cost for providing detailed descriptions beyond normal product documentation for the equipment that is going to be used in this particular project?
6. How much programming or configuring is required? Depending on your own capability, you may want to do it yourself or you may want the vendor to do it. Or it may be possible for the vendor to work with you to program or configure it the first time, so that when he leaves, you still know how to do it.
7. Of course, the number of inputs and outputs, digital and analog.
8. If possible, you should provide the piping and instrumentation diagrams (P&ID) relay ladder diagrams, or Boolean logic diagrams as part of the specification.
9. Do not ask for a system guarantee that the *process* will operate, as you require it to operate. The vendor has no control of the process, only over his own equipment.
10. Define the requirements for the following activities needed in the controlling of the process.
    - Operator displays and capabilities.
    - Creation and management of graphics.
    - Alarm management and plant upset provisions.
    - Trending capacity and display capabilities.
    - Historical and archiving capabilities.
    - Printing, logging, report management.
    - Data management capabilities.
    - Engineering displays.
    - Algorithm l.
    - Memory capacity, such as disk drives.
    - Internal memory does not require drives.
    - Modularity, or reconfiguring and rearranging the controller after it is installed or adding to it at a later time.
    - Excess capacity needed for expansion.
    - Output voltages, transmitter power, etc.
11. List the services to be performed by the *purchaser*, including receiving equipment, storing it, installing it and wiring it.

12. List the services to be provided by the *vendor or system integrator* (SI). These may include the following:
    - Database generation.
    - Building mimic displays.
    - Interfacing with computers and other equipment.
    - Application programming.
    - Special algorithm functions.
    - Training.
    - Staging of equipment. This may be done before the equipment is shipped and should be attended by the purchaser's representatives, and the staging requirement should be specified.
    - Documentation. If drawings are required for approval, this is the place to define which ones are required.
    - Burn in time to diminish "infant mortality."
    - Acceptance testing.
    - Schedule. If the approval of drawings is required, shipping schedules should be based on time after approval, not time after the placement of order.
    - Packing requirements.
    - Shipping responsibility (FOB, Source, or Destination).
    - Guarantees and warranties, which should begin after start up rather than after purchase.
    - Storage time after shipment. What are the considerations here?
    - Start-up assistance. Have the bidder define its payment requirement for service time.
    - Time for acceptance after operation,
    - Legal considerations, such as who is at fault if the equipment is not on time or do not work at the specified time? If a delay in the plant occurs, to what extent, etc.

The Wish List

Once the range of available system products has been examined either from visits to the vendor's plant or by reading the vendors' technical literature you are ready to write the specification. The specification is your way of telling the system vendor what you are going to expect the system to do for you. As such, the specification should contain as much factual information about your process, control problems, and operating goals as you can provide without violating company secrecy prohibitions.

Vendors can often suggest alternatives that you haven't considered if you give them sufficient data from which to work. Be realistic in your expectations (Figure 42-1). Be prepared to accept the fact that a "wish list specification" usually results in a glut of complicated vendor responses, because no one can reasonably respond to all of your requirements except with a high price tag and long deliveries. As noted previously, a better approach is to prescreen the vendors by creating a list of important and/or essential features that you require and having these vendors demonstrate that they can provide these features or their equivalents. Using this method, you can eliminate a lot of vendors from the final quotation stages and eliminate a lot of wasted time on your part.

It must be said again: What are important are the FUNCTIONS of operating your process. Each vendor will have many clever FEATURES to perform those functions. You will have to decide which collection of features best perform the most important of the functions you need!

The essential features list should be included in the specification. This will take lot of soul searching. What are the true "must haves" and what are the "wants"? By visiting several vendors, you can in fact get ideas from the technology available. But keep in mind, your should stick to the *functions* you need to run the plant, not choose one each of every vendor's different features. Some of the features are mutually exclusive, just like in any other engineering design. Having a beautiful feature of one type may preclude the ability to have other kinds of features.

In evaluating the vendor bids, there will be three types of responses that you should expect in response to the requirements listed in your specification:

- To comply—vendor states that his product exactly meets the stated requirement.
- To clarify—vendor can offer something similar to your requirement that it feels meets the intent of your specification.
- To take exception—vendor cannot provide this feature or anything close to it for a reasonable price.

You must decide the importance of each feature and its worth so you can determine which vendor can give you the most for your money. By this time you will have already screened out all the vendors who (at least in your mind) could not provide the required features and services. Later in this chapter we will provide a table that was used by someone who tried to compare different vendors, rather successfully, by making a list of all the conditions and features that were important. What you must do is get the project team to agree on the weighing values for each feature, and that may not be easy. After these evaluations are complete, they must be biased with the cost per value of each of the features.

Prescreening Vendors

When you review the available products, you'll probably discover a great number of common features among the vendor's systems. You will also see some major differences among the vendors' systems, especially in the areas of redundancy, centralized screen displays, and so on. In order to prescreen the vendors, you must make a list of features, and assign importance to each feature, and figure out which vendors qualify to bid for your business. It is essential that you be careful in the way you disqualify vendors, as it is often possible to misread literature and misunderstand sales personnel. If at all possible, vendors' engineering staff should be allowed to respond to your prescreening evaluations so that a potentially acceptable vendor isn't accidentally kept off your bidders list. But in the final evaluation, you must decide who is acceptable and who isn't.

Sometimes the vendor or the vendor's representatives are, let us say, rather optimistic about the success of their previous projects. Be sure to check references! Do not forget to check into the viability of the company itself. It is not a question of whether the company is small or large, but rather the likelihood that the company will continue to be in a position to support you during the expected life of the system. In the volatile 1990s, we saw large companies bought out by others; reliable, venerable century old companies go out of business; large companies put up for sale following a merger-expansion phase; and, yes, small companies enjoy continued growth and success. There are never any easy answers.

Trivia Quizzes

Upon reading all the literature and making all those visits, the temptation is to create a questionnaire—what is known in the industry as a "Trivia Quiz." Now, it is important that during the prescreening of the vendors you list any questions about equipment capabilities as well as clarifications of corporate responsibilities. Be sure, however, that your trivia quiz centers around the functions you need, not some nitpicking detail in the vendor quotes.

The temptation is to overwhelm the vendors with your cleverness and expertise to intimidate them into thinking that you're a formidable person and that they should not try to pull one over on you. Don't try it. You may have the *vendor* disqualify *you*. It has happened too many times that of the trivia quiz wrote it quiz author to impress his boss rather than the vendor. This will show up immediately in the form of copious detail from the vendor that seems unnecessary. Always give the reason for the question, for it will often clarify your concern and help get you an appropriate answer.

If, when reading the vendor's literature, you do not see a capability that you need, put this lack in the trivia quiz. Pose the question in terms of the function you're trying to achieve, however, not in terms of the performance of a small-unrelated portion of the equipment. Quite often the wrong questions are asked. For example, I have seen users ask for bits per second to determine the "speed" on a network when what they really wanted to ask for was information flow. Because there are several parameters that determine information flow, several systems with higher bits per second actually have a lower information flow than one with lower apparent "speed." The real question may be about response to alarms.

If, however, the *function* you are trying to achieve requires a certain speed, memory performance, capability, or calculation performance it is important to ask for it. Know what you need; however, do not fall for the biggest "techie" answer.

Terminology

In working with a specification or any technical inquiry, be sure everyone understands the terminology. It is imperative that both parties agree on the meaning of any terms that could be confused with other terms. For example, if the system has a component that is *compatible* to a specification, it may not be *compliant.* Compatible means that the device can coexist with the rules of a recognized standard, but may not be compliant with it. For example, the specification-compatible device will operate on a standard communications system, will communicate with other devices on that system that are made by the same vendor, and will not interfere with devices made by other vendors operating on that same system. It does *not* mean, however, that it will be able to communicate with the devices of other vendors.

Compliant means the device conforms exactly to the rules of the recognized standard. For example, a specification-compliant device will operate on a standard communications system and will communicate with all other devices on that system made by any other vendor who is similarly compliant.

Two other terms that have emerged with the advent of fieldbus are "***interchangeability***" and "***interoperability.***" In reference to fieldbus interchangeability is the ability of a vendor's product to be fully replaceable with a similar product by another vendor. The functions must be identical, although they may not always include extensions beyond the standard specifications for that function. For example, some features may differ, such as the self-tuning technique of a PID function block, while the PID function itself remains identical.

In reference to fieldbus interoperability is the ability of products from different vendors to coexist on the same network; send, receive, and interpret messages; respond correctly to their instructions; and even allow cascaded control functions to occur between the devices. They share the same applications software.

There may be other terms that will be ambiguous depending on how the user or the vendor understands them. It is not that the user or the vendor is trying to trick the other, but rather that their differing professional backgrounds may give rise to some discrepancies in the way they understand these terms. These discrepancies should be clarified with questions on the specifications or in your response to a bid.

By now you know that it is not the role of a questionnaire to ask how many bits or bytes of memory or bits per second of "speed" on the highway a vendor can offer when the real question is about response to alarms. Better, more specific questions about *system capabilities* may be as follows:

1. How quickly will the control system respond (automatically) to a process upset?
2. How quickly will an operator be notified of an alarm?
3. How quickly will an operator know how to respond to an alarm?
    - How many keystrokes to an appropriate view to analyze a situation?
    - Is the operator clearly and unambiguously guided through those keystrokes?
    - Is the discovered corrective action(s) intuitive . . . or directed?
4. How quickly will an operator know that a failure of a component or of a communication path will prevent an alarm from being seen?

(Of course, you must decide what performance is really needed for your own application. Not all applications need the same response times. Asking for more than is needed (of anything) could result in a higher price.)

Most vendors will try to give you the things you require at the best price they can offer. It is really never in their best interest to cheat and mislead you. However, in mind as you talk to vendor's various salespeople and engineers that their interpretation of terminology might be different than yours, so there could be misunderstandings. If you are open and clear about what *functions* you want, the vendors will attempt to meet your requirements. The best way to get your money's worth is to evaluate and select a vendor and then build this into an open and mutual working relationship with them. That works to both your benefits. Remember, the vendor wants to put your project together quickly and easily just as much you do. He wants a good reference; you want a productive plant. Communication is the key here.

Specification Outline

This will vary with the needs and scope of the actual project. Because it is always easier to edit a list rather than try to start with a blank sheet of paper, we provide you the following outline:

1. General requirements
   - Project objectives.
   - Instructions to bidders.
   - Information required with proposal.
   - Scope of work by each party involved.
   - System performance criteria.
   - Codes and standards required for this project.
   - Project schedule and delivery.
2. System layout
   - System functional overview.
   - Environmental requirements.
   - System block diagram.
   - Expected expansion needs (scalability).
   - Utility requirements (electrical, A/C, etc.).
   - I/O list and groupings.
3. Control functions
   - Control actions.
     —Continuous loops
     —Sequential functions
     —Logic control
     —Interlocks, permissive, overrides
     —Performance requirements for these control actions
   - Process/plant management of information.
     —Simulation/optimization
     —Batch management
     —Recipe management
     —Quality management

—Maintenance management
—Documentation management
—Interface parameters/functions to business system

4. System hardware components & performances

- Sensing needs/transmitters/intelligence.
- Final element needs/device types/intelligence.
- Field-to-controller communications.
- Controller requirements/groupings/locations.
- Controller network needs (peer-to-peer? etc.).
- Operator workstations.
- Engineering workstation.
- Plant manager interface.
- Connectivity.
  —Computers
  —Other control systems
  —Unique field devices
  —Foreign device interfaces
  —Business system network
  —Any other network
- Cabinet requirements/locations.
- Cable protection/distances.
- Redundancies (extent/performance/alternatives).
  —I/O
  —Control strategies
  —Communications (which networks/what situations)
  —Equipment interfaces
  —Personnel interfaces
- Diagnostics.
  —System communications
  —System components
  —Connected devices
  —Non-system equipment
- Packing and shipping protection/destinations.
- Spare parts issues.

5. System integration services

- Project management.
- Systems engineering.
- Configuration.

- Process displays.
- Applications programming.
- Factory acceptance testing.
- Installation, site testing, and start-up services.
- Test equipment required for user.
- Maintenance, servicing, field support.
- Training.

6. Documentation
   - Cabinet arrangement and power distribution drawings.
   - Outline dimensions, footprints, weights, etc.
   - Module configuration/location drawings.
   - System implementation manuals.
   - Product manuals/bulletins/update services.
   - User manuals/maintenance manuals/update services.
   - System configuration and programming manuals.
7. Terms and conditions
   - Commercial requirements.
   - Division of responsibilities among multiple system suppliers.
   - System warranty.
   - Pricing system.
     —Initial/spares/services
     —Progressive payments/phasing/timing (extended project)
     —Subsequent equipment and services
   - Project requirements (progress reviews, etc.)

Selection Process 43

Comparing vendors will be very much like comparing peaches and apples. All they have in common is that they are both fruit. All through this book we have been discussng how each vendor has traditionally taken different design approaches on just about every part of a system. On top of that, you have all of that marketing hyperbole, which certainly muddies the waters. The answer is to stick to the functions you need! Compare the respective abilities to perform the jobs you really need.

Comparing Vendors

There are three general ways to compare vendor systems:

1. On the system hardware only cost basis, which is typically the way people purchased programmable logic controller projects in the past.
2. On a total project cost basis, which includes the hardware cost, project planning, and the implementation cost, which is the way distributed control systems were purchased in the past.
3. System life cycle cost basis, which over the lifetime of the system includes:
    - Initial hardware & software
    - Initial project cost
    - System expansions
    - Personnel training
    - On-going maintenance
    - On-going use of spare parts
    - Investments in advanced control

Selection Process

- Comparing vendors
- Evaluating quotations
  —Basis of input/output
  —Basis of configuration
  —Basis of operator interface
  —Basis of network capabilities
  —Basis of reliability
  —Basis of installation & maintenance
- Method to organize vendor comparison
- Vendor evaluation meetings

We strongly recommend that you compare vendors on a system life cycle cost basis, but you have to be careful to get a correct assessment. Life cycle costing is important because a realistic overall cost of the control system may be many times the initial purchase price, so you want it to last as many years as possible. The longer the system will last, the less cost per year you are amortizing over the life cycle of the system. As much as 70 to 80% of lifetime costs can be fixed by the decisions made at the time of the selection of this control system. Remember to calculate the cost of making no change in an existing system, including the loss of improved production.

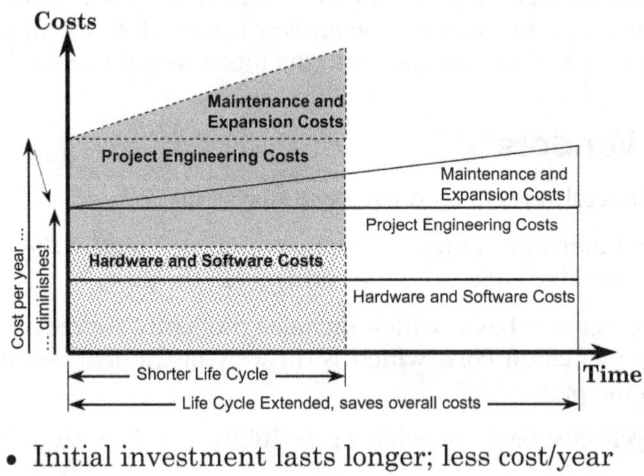

Figure 43-1. Importance of Life Cycle Costs

Most automation investments are vastly underutilized. When companies look at an automation investment, they're just targeting the replacement cost instead of looking at the advance functions that can be continually adding down the road. This is particularly true as the process matures, or the plant encounters changes in market strategy. Therefore, users should really base the system selection criteria on more than immediate requirements; they should also be looking at the vendor's full extent of capabilities and develop quality suppliers.

Life Cycle Value = Life Cycle Benefits - Life Cycle Costs

Where the Life Cycle Benefits is the sum of all the annual cost savings plus + the annual production increases + the annual yield increases over the expected life of the system; and

Where the Life Cycle Costs, as stated differently above, is the initial system price, engineering, and installation costs added to the sum of all the annual costs for engineering, operations, and maintenance.

Companies should also attempt to standardize on a uniform basis across the whole plant. This of course is very difficult in an economy where many of the suppliers are merging, combining, or literally going out of business ... even after as much as 100 years of operation. Nevertheless, you must systematically try to develop as many facts as you can about the project and make your decision based on the known facts and not on any assumption of what has happened in the past.

Types of considerations for comparing vendors are:

- Technical features of each of the vendors offering.
- System pricing, including subsequent purchase price of spares, not just the immediate sale price of those shipped with the job.
- System support from each vendor and their capabilities.

Must Reiterate: It is not the technology that a company uses that is important, it is how that company USES the technology!

I have to strongly recommend, in light of the changing conditions of many system suppliers, that when you purchase a system, learn to use it, and become as thoroughly independent of the vendor as you can possibly be. The easier this system is to use, to configure, to *re*configure the better it is. You should be able to expand with as much non-proprietary hardware as possible. All of this will pay off in the long run should changes occur with the vendors' company or corporate policy. This has happened with the largest and most stable of vendor's worldwide, so there are no absolute guarantees in this area.

Evaluating Quotations

The time to ask questions is before the purchase order is placed, not afterwards. Before you have made a final selection and placed an order, it is in the best interest of vendors to give you any information you need in order to make your selection. This is the time to be thoroughly objectionable if it is the only way you can get answers.

Sales people should be cooperative in arranging for you to talk to members of their engineering department if you need to know why a particular design was chosen, or to project handling personnel so that you can evaluate the experiences of the supplier to apply his product to your application. When planning time to do evaluations of quotes, be sure to allow for sufficient "turn-around time" to ask a reasonable number of questions of each vendor, which may in turn require time for complete and thoughtful answers. Often talking to these people will reveal aspects of the equipment that sales are either not familiar with or do not care to discuss.

When you are evaluating quotations prepared in response to your specification, design considerations influence the rating of the supplier. You may want to consider the following subjects after narrowing down the choice to one or two suppliers. Many of these may not be important to your specific situation, but reading them through may suggest other areas that you should investigate. They are presented more to provoke thought than to cover all the possibilities.

In the previous chapter, under Writing the Specification, we already discussed what you should consider when evaluating the supplier, both vendor/manufacturer and system integrator. From this point on, we will review considerations about the system itself.

Evaluating Input/Output Capabilities:

Be sure to consider all the signal requirements for your interface to the process. Especially be alert to any changing regulations occurring in your industry that may impact your installation shortly after you install it and start up.

1. Consider the advantages of termination cabinets. How long are the communication links from field equipment to remote controllers? Can the vendor's design reach?
2. Is there physical room for the wires and cables?
3. Will separate low level single condition units have to be provided? Or are they part of the available design?
4. What kind of signal conditioning is available? Can high level, low level, RTD, thermocouple, and pulse inputs be directly accommodated? Must you use only transmitter inputs (requiring purchase of transmitters)?
5. Can one module handle both analog and discrete values (saving space & cost)?
6. Where will the wiring connections to the remote equipment be made? If connections are made directly to printed circuit cards, how hard will it be to replace those cards?
7. Is dc power for transmitters available from the distributed control equipment? Is it fuscd?
8. Are analog computing modules supplied externally? If so, they will have to be mounted and wired.
9. What is the current capacity of output drivers, digital or analog? Must interposing relays be provided to handle digital outputs?
10. Are inputs and outputs optically isolated?
11. Can you readback output signals to assure they were correct when they left the system?
12. Can signals be quality coded?
13. What happens to signals on power failure?
14. What happens to signals when the power comes back on? What happens to the mode of functions when the power comes back on?
15. Is there audible annunciation of alarms?
16. Is there a requirement for intrinsic safety? Is it offered? Is it inferred?
17. Is there a requirement for emergency safety shutdown? Is it offered?

Evaluating Control Configuration Capabilities:

Remember always that everything changes. Even as you progress in the project, changes will be required. Some will come from wrong estimating on your part, some will come from discoveries during the completion of the design, and many will likely come from discoveries during start-up. The easier it is to reconfigure both software and hardware, the less expensive the system will really be.

1. Is the system easily scaleable? Expandable in the future with no penalty in the initial costs or procurement provisions? Are you buying a lot more loop capacity than you really need? What is the practical number of loops in a controller, compared to the number promised in the literature? On the other hand, will you have an adequate spare capacity?
2. Do you have to be aware of modular memory utilization in order to not exceed the time constraints?
3. Can cascading be handled by soft wiring? Do control functions that are cascaded have to be located next to each other in the controllers?
4. Are flag bits from value thresholds or status changes within the function blocks available for soft wiring?
5. Can process, motor control, logic, sequential, or batch functions be configured within the same controller? Can they all be configured using the same overall techniques (languages)?
6. If an emergency safety shutdown capability is also provided, can it also be configured in the same way (use the same techniques) as the basic control system?
7. Is the configuration technique appropriate to the applications (i.e. batch-related, etc.)?
8. Does it use higher languages? Does the configuration language follow a standard, such as IEC 61131-3?
9. If using multiple standard languages such as described in IEC 61131-3, can they be blended seamlessly to perform functions within the same configuration/controller?
10. Can it be configured easily, even graphically?
11. Can it be configured on-line? If so, can those changes be "uploaded" into or in some way retained within the configuration database and documented?
12. When running, can the engineer see values and quality coding in the graphically configured view?
13. Must configuration be done only through a special workstation?
14. Can configuration be started beforehand, without the controller hardware in place? Can separate units be easily configured as part of an overall package?
15. How easy is it to change configuration? Must only the vendor or system integrator do it?
16. Are there on-line debugging tools? Are the help screens for use on-line?

17. What kind of forms are available for documenting the configuration? How involved are they? Is the system self-documenting?
18. Does the configuration work on a common, inexpensive platform and cross platforms?

Evaluating Operator Interface Capabilities:

In this area, you must listen to your experienced operators. Even if they are fearful of new technology, listen carefully to their concerns, which are very important. Look for features of the system that address those concerns. Real or imagined, resolving these concerns is critical for the success of the project. Resolution may be through redesign, or through re-education. If the latter, do not take the issues lightly and merely supply "a pile of words!"

1. How many consoles will the system support/ How many seats at each console? How easy is it to expand sometime after installation? What performance trade-offs, if any?
2. Can the consoles be used in a dual configuration for redundancy?
3. Is there a choice of HMI vendors, or must only the vendor's version is used?
4. Is there a choice of HMI platforms, or must only the vendor's version is used?
5. How many keyboards are required? Are keyboards required? Can touch screen be used effectively? Mouse? Trackball? Other?
6. Is a printer available? Readily added?
7. Do you need mass memory storage? Are disk drives satisfactory for your requirements? How much storage is needed? Do you need back-up storage?
8. Does each operator station have the capacity to manage the amount of process tags which must be controlled, displayed, alarmed, etc.?
9. What is the video screen call-up time? Refresh time? How long does it take to respond to an operator request?
10. Can the same view span several screens? Is there Windowing? Panning? Zooming?
11. Does this system come with some structure of pre-configured view hierarchy and templates for an easier start in developing the human interface? Is this easy to modify to fit specific application needs? Is it intuitive to work with?
12. Are screen graphics easily created? Is their creation intuitive?
13. How many characters are available for tagging *service* descriptions, digital output values?
14. How many process variables can be trended simultaneously? What are their time *bases*? How many points are indicated in one trend display? How many trends can be displayed at one time?
15. Are there operator actions? Can these be blended into other events and alarm within the plant?

16. Are there operator prompts built in? user definable?
17. Are there easily used, context-specific "help screens?"
18. In a windowing system, are critical screens ever covered up?
19. Is screen navigation intuitive for the application (little or no learning curve)?
20. Do views represent the tasks involved, need only five minutes to learn (separate from learning the task itself)?
21. Do views provide direct access to next needed views? Logical structure to follow?
22. Can you do the functions needed? Alarms, controls, data trending, access history and archiving, look at control databases, do statistical process control, quality control, etc.
23. Is there a workable alarm response routine? How many keystrokes are required to acknowledge an alarm? Does it display change as a result of these keystrokes?
24. Can you define priorities for alarms?
25. Can alarms be defeated? Automatically? Manually? Can groups of alarms be defeated? Is there a reminder that these are defeated, so that, at a later time, they can be restored?
26. Are alarms lost as the alarm list extends, or are they always retained in memory?
27. Are the diagnostics easy to decipher? Will a code have to be learned?
28. Can you view operations live in the configuration diagram?
29. Is it possible to tune and configure from the remote locations?
30. Can editing be locked out? How many levels of security do you need?

Evaluating Network Capabilities:

Keep in mind that the network must be evaluated in the context of the whole system. Design of each of the devices using the network is an integral part of the picture. (Remember the "on-ramps" and "dirt roads" connected to highways.) For example, turn-around-time processing of a device can affect its performance as much as it's raw bits-per-second capacity.

1. How much input/output information can the system handle? Does this limit your operation? What performance trade-off, if any?
2. How much control loop information can the system handle (not bits per second)? What performance trade-off, if any?
3. How many users (controllers, operator stations, etc.) can connect to the control network? What performance trade-off, if any?
4. Is peer to peer communication possible between the users of the network? What performance trade-off, if any?
5. Can it support time synchronization between devices on network?

6. Can it support transmission of quality coding of input signals? Of time stamping of high-speed sequence of events reporting?
7. Can the network do error detection and correction, and other maintenance diagnostics?
8. How thoroughly is the integrity of the *information* checked?
9. What is the maximum allowable control network length? I/O network length? What performance trade-off, if any?
10. How many branches or spurs can there be to the control network? How many networks will one system support? What performance trade-off, if any?
11. Is the I/O network redundant? Is the control network redundant? Is redundancy supported in the upper layers of the system?
12. Does the network connect to other products made by the vendor and currently within your plant? Does it allow inter-operation with any of the vendor's earlier control systems there?
13. Does the network allow connectivity to other non-control vendor systems, such as MES, ERP type business systems?
14. Does the network allow connectivity to other control vendor systems? Do they already have a library of "APIs"? What is their performance?
15. Will the network support hardware be made by any vendors other than the principal supplier? Specifically, can it support chromatography, programmable controllers, data loggers, and computers without significant custom programming?
16. Does the network support any standards for connectivity to other devices? Does it allow wizards, drivers, other non-programming methods?
17. Is the network truly open? That is, if you should decide to use an HMI from another supplier, can it be done, or must you use only the vendor's version workstation?

Evaluating System Security:

The object of the game here is everything that allows you to keep operating. It is really all that goes into system availability ...it's there when you need it!

1. Check standard redundancy in the design of the equipment you are considering. Does supplying additional redundancy reduce the signal handling capacity? Does it reduce performance? Is there a common point of failure in the redundancy design (where both are shut down by the same fault)? Can the redundant controller be powered independently? Is there some switchover time? Must a database be loaded from another location? Is the redundant controller monitored to assure it is fully functional should switchover be needed?
2. What are the results of equipment failure? This affects the cost of backup. Will it be necessary to provide an uninterruptable power supply? A battery back up? Or what is called graceful degradation? Will single loop integrity, possibly with analog backup, be maintained?

3. What kind of backup is offered by the system?

   - Manual control stations—will manual control operate when there's a power failure?
   - Graceful degradation—that is, if the microprocessor fails and the back-up station then fails, is there also a layer of manual control following that?
   - For controller integrity—in redundant systems, will everything operating in a controller be backed up by the redundant controller in exactly the same way and within perhaps one operating second from the current data status of the primary controller?
   - Loop to loop integrity—whether or not the controller shares loops, will any one loop still function seamlessly during a backup switchover
   - Separate Analog Back-up. Look at the design for weak points, especially if tracking and bumpless transfer is required.

Consider the comparison between the cost of spare parts and the cost of down time of your process—what is required to get an orderly shut down in case of emergencies? How many backup units will be required? What is your power stability? Consider battery backup versus voltage regulation versus an uninterrupted power supply.

Consider the length of time the data base battery backup will last in the context of expected storage time.

Does the controller module design permit plug-in replaceability of electronic components? This is an important consideration in reducing mean time to repair.

1. Can modules/cards be replaced under power, avoiding shutdown of system (and process)?
2. Are the modules ruggedly constructed and will they tolerate the expected abuse/environment?
3. Is there anything that the operator would do that could cause the system to lock up? Overload? Slow down performance (screen views, communication, control actions)?
4. Are there the needed security codes (passwords) appropriate to your type of operations?

Evaluating Installation & Maintenance Capabilities:

Concomitant to the concept of reliability is the necessary area of good checkout capabilities (how do you turn it on?) as well as maintenance (how to keep it running), and of course service (what to do when it stops). Think of all of the unthinkables here.

1. Do you need a turnkey job? This is a consideration when there is a requirement for interconnecting programmable logic controllers, computers, data acquisition equipment and distributed control equipment.

2. Can the vendor and system integrator work together (if the project takes this direction)? Are there references of this from previous experiences?
3. What training will be required? Who should be trained? At what project stage must they be trained? Does the vendors training availability fit these?
4. Can you run a check on configuration without activating discrete and analog outputs?
5. Is signature analysis available for troubleshooting printed circuit cards?
6. Can a process simulator be provided if required for check out?
7. How many spare parts should you have? And where are they stocked? From where does the service come?
8. Is the system scaleable and flexible to modify to different application over time, if need be?
9. Is the system scaleable and flexible to modify to different sizes (number of nodes, tag counts, I/O points, database values, calculations, trending, alarms, event logs, etc.)?
10. Will your plant personnel be able to continue understanding and use your system even if the well-intended vendor is later bought by another company, or the system that he offers is discontinued?
11. Is there upward compatibility to other products and other developments coming from that supplier? What has been their policy? Anything new expected to cause that policy to change (if the company changes hands, for example)?
12. Is there compatibility to previous products from the same vendor (if they already exist in the plant and if this would help)?
13. Is there interchangeability or interoperability with other devices made by other vendors?
14. Who will be responsible for on-going support (vendor, company representatives, system integrator, other third party)? What has been their past support history? References? Will support be available for the expected life of the project?
15. What is the maintenance policy of the supporting group? For hardware & spares? For software and upgrades? What is their proximity to the system location? Do they have a "hot line" for fast service? Emergency plan?

A Method to Organize Vendor Comparison

The hardest part about comparing the many features of different systems is finding a method to put them all on an even scale. There are so many different features and variations of the product and the services offered that's it's very difficult to compare them equally. One approach that you should try is to make some sort of spread sheet to compare similar categories of capabilities. That way you have some way of organizing your thinking. This is especially true when looking at all the capacity, compatibility, capability of the system, and establishing a weighing factor on how that applies to the needs of your particular system.

Compare the incomparable:

Functions/Issues	Weight	Vendor 1	Vendor 2	Vendor 3
Overall System Expansion Needs Standards Control Needs Configuration etc.				

- One method, perhaps to inspire better methods...
- List all functions & issues by categories
- Create a team to develop weighing factors for importance of these
- Develop different evaluation teams to grade each of the vendors
- Calculate totals

Figure 43-2. Comparing Vendors

Every plant and every process is unique. There is no way to buy a system based on how well it worked at some other company, particularly if they are in a different industry. My friend, Larry Goettsch, now of Process Automatic Systems in Murry, Utah *(740 East Pontiac Drive, Murry, UT 84107),* once worked for a large company with such a problem. Within that company were three different camps, each camp has their preferred vendor. Poor Larry was assigned the job as instrument engineer to pick one control system that everyone would agree on. It was clearly an impossible task.

Larry built four teams:

- Team 1 was made up of those who favored Vendor 1;
- Team 2 was made up of those who favored Vendor 2;
- Team 3 was made up of those who favored Vendor 3;
- Team 4 was process people who understood the needs of the plant, had no biases to either team. This last team was made up of selections of people different from the other teams, for balance and fairness.

This fourth team developed an analysis of the process and plant functions. They put a weighing system in for each aspect of the specification which determined what was needed in the plant and how important that need was. The weighing factors were not shared with the other three teams; each team worked independently. All the teams had the same specification. The first three each evaluated their respective (favorite) vendor. Of course you may not have an adversarial situation, but human nature being what it is, this plan will help avoid any subtle misgivings on the selection.

I obtained Larry's permission many years ago to provide you with the chart that he used as a result of this specification, which I have since somewhat updated. The items on the original list matched the items described in the specification he developed, and in the same order. It was coded with matching paragraph numbers. This list provides a lot of features that were important to them which may not be important to you. [I modified some]. **For this reason the list looks quite cryptic in places.** Nevertheless, it may inspire you as to what are the appropriate issues for your own situation.

Larry multiplied the weighing factors by each vendor's capability. Then he added the scores for each vendor, the vendor with the highest score wins, or at least that's the theory. You will notice that some of the issues in that list seem to repeat themselves, but are under different headings. For example, in your own list, there will be operator display needs mentioned under the engineering department requirements, as well as under the operations requirements. This allows for specific functional necessities in each of those respective areas.

Of course, there is a continual changing of technology and some of the statements listed in here may not be as appropriate today as they were when the original, or even this modification, was made this up. Nevertheless, I'm sure you can make your own list based on the suggestions in here, and figure what are your own needs. Larry was kind enough to let me use this chart back in 1984 when he first created it, and I have been using it ever since within my ISA Course, *Understanding Distributed Control.* It has been very popular with many hundreds attendees of that course, and it has been shared with countless other people. This is now evolving a bit beyond that original table, **but still cryptic without seeing the spec itself!**

Instructions for Evaluation of Control Systems

→ →Items in list relate to descriptive paragraphs in full specification.

Weighting factor for plant/process need:

8, 9, or 10	In the functional specification, and is a MUST
5, 6, or 7	In the functional specification, and is a SHOULD
2, 3, or 4	Not in the functional specification, but WOULD HELP
0 or 1	Not in the functional specification, and is LITTLE USE

Vendor grading on ability or quality:

8, 9, or 10	Meets the functional specification, and is CLEARLY STATED
5, 6, or 7	Meets the functional specification
2, 3, or 4	Does *not* meet functional specification, but CAN BE APPLIED/CREATED
0 or 1	Does *not* meet the functional specification, and IS NEEDED

Vendor Value = Vendor Grade x Weight Factor

Guidelines for evaluation teams:

1) Generally the higher the number, the better we like it.
2) Negative numbers may be used if itemized functions degrade overall system!
3) Think Functional!—Think Generic!—Think Requirements!—Think Costs!

Vendor/Manufacturer	Weight	Vendor 1		Vendor 2		Vendor 3	
		Grade	Value	Grade	Value	Grade	Value
Name:							
Location:							
Years in business							
Years providing control systems							
Company reputation/history							
Company owned by other(s)							
Company can be bought/sold							
Competitive position							
Strategic direction fit							
Core competencies fit							
Commitments to industry							
Application experience fit							
Comparable Systems (type, size)							
User list/references							
Sales support							
Engineering support							
Service support							
Parts support							
Attitude/flexibility							
Other considerations							
Totals							

Distributor/Representative/System Integrator (can be manufacturer)	Weight	Vendor 1		Vendor 2		Vendor 3	
		Grade	Value	Grade	Value	Grade	Value
Name:							
Location:							
Years in business							
Years providing control systems							

Distributor/Representative/System Integrator (can be manufacturer)	**Weight**	**Vendor 1**		**Vendor 2**		**Vendor 3**	
		Grade	**Value**	**Grade**	**Value**	**Grade**	**Value**
Number of like systems installed							
Application experience fit							
User list/references							
Company owned by other(s)							
Company reputation/history							
Company philosophy							
Company financial condition							
Works well with manufacturer							
Attitude/flexibility							
Sales support							
Engineering support							
Service support							
Parts support							
Project management							
Factory acceptance							
Training							
Per diem rates							
Totals							

Overall System	**Weight**	**Vendor 1**		**Vendor 2**		**Vendor 3**	
		Grade	**Value**	**Grade**	**Value**	**Grade**	**Value**
Goal							
Type							
Overall system size (as bid):							
—Analog inputs							
—Analog outputs							
—Discrete inputs							

Overall System	Weight	Vendor 1		Vendor 2		Vendor 3	
		Grade	Value	Grade	Value	Grade	Value
—Discrete outputs							
—Pulsed inputs							
—Pulsed outputs							
—Field bus type(s)							
—Serial ports P							
—Parallel ports							
—I/O network length(s)							
—Other I/O needs							
—Number of process tags							
—Character lengths for tag names							
—Video pages needed							
—Nodes on control network							
—Control network length							
General specifications:							
—Power requirements							
—Dimensions							
—Environmental requirements							
—Noise immunity							
—Grounding							
—Performance data							
—Signal path MTTF							
—Signal path MTTR							
—System Availability							
—Intrinsic safety							
—Standards required							
Diagnostics							
Configuration languages							
Control Accuracy							

Overall System	Weight	Vendor 1 Grade	Vendor 1 Value	Vendor 2 Grade	Vendor 2 Value	Vendor 3 Grade	Vendor 3 Value
Redundancy							
Analog back-up							
Expansion ease							
Control execution performance							
Storage devices							
Printer/plotters							
Algorithm capability							
Security							
Degree of openness							
Interfaces with:							
—Central computer							
—Programmable logic controllers							
—Analog field devices							
—Digital field devices							
—Field bus							
—Serial devices							
—Parallel devices							
—Safety Systems							
—Other vendor HMIs							
—Other vendor devices							
—Other vendor control systems							
—Plant-wide business system							
—Corporate-wide ERP system							
Communications:							
—Network type							
—Network speed of information							
—Network concept							
—Peer-to-peer							

Overall System	Weight	Vendor 1		Vendor 2		Vendor 3	
		Grade	Value	Grade	Value	Grade	Value
—Serial							
—Parallel							
Graphics							
Trending							
Alarming							
Consoles							
Video screens per console							
Interlocks							
Totals							

Expansion Requirements	Weight	Vendor 1		Vendor 2		Vendor 3	
		Grade	Value	Grade	Value	Grade	Value
Maximum size:							
—Process tags							
—Control network drops							
—I/O network size							
—Analog inputs							
—Analog outputs							
—Discrete inputs							
—Discrete outputs							
—Field bus							
—Serial ports							
—Parallel ports							
—Time slots							
—Nests							
—Displays:							
—Overviews							

Expansion Requirements	Weight	Vendor 1		Vendor 2		Vendor 3	
		Grade	Value	Grade	Value	Grade	Value
—Group							
—Unit							
—Detail							
—Control Loop							
—Input pages							
—Trends							
—Mimic pages							
—Faceplates							
Network:							
—Maximum length							
—Maximum number of drops							
—Information speed							
—Traffic directors							
Totals							

Standards	Weight	Vendor 1		Vendor 2		Vendor 3	
		Grade	Value	Grade	Value	Grade	Value
Company standards (list each)							
ISA standards (list each needed)							
IEEE standards (list each needed)							
IEC standards (list each needed)							
DIN standards (list each needed)							
Factory Mutual							
Underwriters Laboratory							

Standards	Weight	Vendor 1		Vendor 2		Vendor 3	
		Grade	Value	Grade	Value	Grade	Value
Canadian Standards Association							
CE Mark							
Other(s) appropriate to project							
Totals							

Data Acquisition	Weight	Vendor 1		Vendor 2		Vendor 3	
		Grade	Value	Grade	Value	Grade	Value
Analog inputs:							
—1-5 Vdc							
—4-20 mA							
—Thermocouple							
—RTD							
—Pulse							
Analog outputs							
Discrete inputs							
Digital outputs							
Motor drive outputs							
Field bus type							
Serial							
Parallel							
Calculated variables							
Filtering							
Addressing							
Peer-to-peer							
Quality coding							
Isolation							
Totals							

Storage Requirements	Weight	Vendor 1		Vendor 2		Vendor 3	
		Grade	Value	Grade	Value	Grade	Value
Floppy disk storage							
Hard disk storage							
Tape storage							
Resident memory storage							
Historical trending							
Recovering old data							
Totals							

Data Analysis Requirements	Weight	Vendor 1		Vendor 2		Vendor 3	
		Grade	Value	Grade	Value	Grade	Value
Analytical programs							
Auxiliary functions							
Communications							
Reports							
Display generation							
Control							
Level of expertise required:							
—Operate using faceplates							
—Operate using mimics							
—Acknowledging alarms							
—Operator prompts							
—Help screens							
—Configuration							
—Mimic generation							
—Report writing program							
—Logic/sequence program							
—Basic, FORTRAN, etc.							

Data Analysis Requirements	Weight	Vendor 1		Vendor 2		Vendor 3	
		Grade	Value	Grade	Value	Grade	Value
—Changing algorithms							
—Changing PID parameters							
—Changing CRT grouping							
—Changing faceplate layout							
—Changing operator lockouts							
—System security							
Data transmission types:							
—Within remote controller							
—From controller to HMI							
—From I/O to controller							
—Fieldbus types							
—From network to computer							
Data transmission speed:							
—Within remote controller							
—From controller to HMI							
—From I/O to controller							
—Fieldbus link(s)							
—From network to computer							
Video screen call-up time							
Video screen refresh time							
Controller update speed							
Error checking							
Diagnostics							
Data security							
Single point of failure							
Totals							

Alarm Requirements	Weight	Vendor 1 Grade	Vendor 1 Value	Vendor 2 Grade	Vendor 2 Value	Vendor 3 Grade	Vendor 3 Value
Number of alarms per unit							
Total number of alarms							
Speed of alarm acceptance							
Types of alarms:							
—Process variable absolute							
—Deviation							
—Calculated							
—Discrete input							
—Electrical signal limit							
—Self diagnostic							
—Communication (network)							
Alarm priority							
Keystrokes to acknowledge							
Hard copy required							
Printer information							
Totals							

Logging Requirements	Weight	Vendor 1 Grade	Vendor 1 Value	Vendor 2 Grade	Vendor 2 Value	Vendor 3 Grade	Vendor 3 Value
Hourly, shift, and daily logs							
Insert missing data							
Custom reports							
Alarm logging							
On demand screen printout							
Totals							

Data Displays	Weight	Vendor 1		Vendor 2		Vendor 3	
		Grade	Value	Grade	Value	Grade	Value
Overview display:							
—Standard faceplates							
—Mimic							
Group or unit display:							
—Standard faceplates							
—Mimic							
—Trending							
Detail or control display:							
—Short term trending							
—Process variable information							
—Setpoint parameters							
—Alarm parameters							
—Output parameters							
—Tuning parameters							
—Input address							
—Output address							
—Algorithm parameters							
—Time slot/nest location							
—Standard faceplate							
Alarm list							
Input page							
Directory page							
Network status							
Mode menus							
Mimics:							
—Resolution							
—Displays							
—Colors							

Data Displays	Weight	Vendor 1		Vendor 2		Vendor 3	
		Grade	Value	Grade	Value	Grade	Value
—icon and shapes libraries							
—Directory							
—Custom							
—Other							
Trending:							
—Total number of points							
—Points per trend view							
—Sample rates							
—Pan and zoom							
—X-Y and XbarR charts							
—Resolution							
—Colors							
—on-line scaling							
Totals							

Process Control	Weight	Vendor 1		Vendor 2		Vendor 3	
		Grade	Value	Grade	Value	Grade	Value
Continuous process control:							
—Configured							
—Algorithms							
—Process language							
—Sequence control							
—Regulatory control							
—Software							
Batch process control:							
—Configured							
—Algorithms							
—Process language							

Process Control	Weight	Vendor 1		Vendor 2		Vendor 3	
		Grade	Value	Grade	Value	Grade	Value
—Sequence control							
—Regulatory control							
—Software							
Distribution:							
—I/O rack location							
—Remote processor unit location							
—Central processor unit location							
—Operator station location							
—Network interface location							
—Communication location							
—Other equipment location							
Totals							

Software Requirements	Weight	Vendor 1		Vendor 2		Vendor 3	
		Grade	Value	Grade	Value	Grade	Value
Standard configuration language							
Function Blocks							
Ladder Logic							
Structured text							
Sequential function charts							
Programming language							
Graphic configuration							
Custom function blocks							
Linking to other devices							
Multitasking							
Totals							

Operator's Interface	Weight	Vendor 1		Vendor 2		Vendor 3	
		Grade	Value	Grade	Value	Grade	Value
Video console:							
—Number required							
—Function							
—Displays							
—Screen size							
—Call-up rate							
—Refresh rate							
—Screen Resolution							
—Screen colors							
—Dedicated Keys							
—Soft keys							
—Alpha and numeric keys							
—QWERTY							
—Mouse/trackball							
—Touchscreens							
—Prompting and guidance							
—Keystrokes required							
—Wrong keystroke prompts							
—Help screens							
—Windowing							
—Home screen							
—Covering windows							
Printers:							
—Number and location							
—Line or character							
—Function							
—Alarm logs							
—Reports							

Operator's Interface	Weight	Vendor 1		Vendor 2		Vendor 3	
		Grade	Value	Grade	Value	Grade	Value
—Manufacture							
—Model							
—Speed							
—Type							
—Font size							
—Color capability							
Plotters:							
—Number and location							
—Function							
—Type of plots							
—Manufacture							
—Model							
Video copier:							
—Number and location							
—Function							
—Manufacture							
—Model							
Engineer's terminal:							
—Number and location							
—Function							
Annunciator panel:							
—Number and location							
—Function							
—Other							
Manual station:							
—Number and location							
—Function							
—Security							

Operator's Interface	Weight	Vendor 1		Vendor 2		Vendor 3	
		Grade	Value	Grade	Value	Grade	Value
—Other							
Emergency shutdown:							
—Location							
—Keystrokes							
—Programming							
—Security							
Totals							

Peripherals	Weight	Vendor 1		Vendor 2		Vendor 3	
		Grade	Value	Grade	Value	Grade	Value
Bulk memory storage:							
—Hard disk							
—Floppy disk							
—Tape							
—Core							
—Other							
Memory storage locations:							
—Control parameters							
—Algorithms							
—Control strategy configuration							
—Diagnostic routines							
—Faceplates							
—Mimics							
—Trending							
—Operating system							
—Selection of control strategies							
—Calculations							

Peripherals	Weight	Vendor 1		Vendor 2		Vendor 3	
		Grade	Value	Grade	Value	Grade	Value
—Reports							
—Other							
Serial Ports:							
—RS232C							
—RS422							
—4-20mA							
Parallel Ports:							
—IEEE488							
Totals							

System Environmental	Weight	Vendor 1		Vendor 2		Vendor 3	
		Grade	Value	Grade	Value	Grade	Value
Electrical Power:							
—Voltage							
—Phase							
—Amperes							
—Noise							
—Grounding							
—Isolation							
—UPS requirements							
—Redundancy							
Air Conditioning:							
—Temperature limits							
—Humidity limits							
—Heat rejection							
—Corrosion							
—Coated circuit boards							
Grounding:							

System Environmental	Weight	Vendor 1		Vendor 2		Vendor 3	
		Grade	Value	Grade	Value	Grade	Value
—Specification							
—Ground loop avoidance							
—Other							
Power failure:							
—Fail-safe mode							
—Power up							
—Power supply failure							
—Restore memory							
—Restore clock							
—Restore configuration							
—Restore mimics							
—Restore trending							
—Restore interlock logic							
Uninterruptable power supplies							
Totals							

Redundancy	Weight	Vendor 1		Vendor 2		Vendor 3	
		Grade	Value	Grade	Value	Grade	Value
Controller power supplies							
Network							
Controllers							
Operator stations							
I/O racks							
Interfaces							
Backplane failure							
Totals							

Diagnostics	Weight	Vendor 1		Vendor 2		Vendor 3	
		Grade	Value	Grade	Value	Grade	Value
On-line:							
—Hardware failures							
—Software failures							
—Other							
Off-line:							
—Hardware failures							
—Software failures							
—Other							
Totals							

Network	Weight	Vendor 1		Vendor 2		Vendor 3	
		Grade	Value	Grade	Value	Grade	Value
Type							
Information speed							
Concept:							
—Token passing							
—Director							
—Mastership							
—Protocol							
—Handshake							
Interfaces:							
—Operation							
—Remote controllers							
—Control computer							
—Devices external to system							
—Input devices							

Network	Weight	Vendor 1		Vendor 2		Vendor 3	
		Grade	Value	Grade	Value	Grade	Value
—Output devices							
—Modems							
—Fieldbus types							
Totals							

Documentation	Weight	Vendor 1		Vendor 2		Vendor 3	
		Grade	Value	Grade	Value	Grade	Value
Operation							
Programming							
Installation							
Dimensions							
Description							
Software							
Totals							

Maintenance	Weight	Vendor 1		Vendor 2		Vendor 3	
		Grade	Value	Grade	Value	Grade	Value
Special tools							
special training							
Parts availability							
Number of spare parts needed							
Card replacement procedures							
Documentation							
Service contracts							

Maintenance	Weight	Vendor 1		Vendor 2		Vendor 3	
		Grade	Value	Grade	Value	Grade	Value
—Per diem cost							
—Expenses							
—Response time							
Totals							

Training	Weight	Vendor 1		Vendor 2		Vendor 3	
		Grade	Value	Grade	Value	Grade	Value
Locations							
Courses							
Schedules							
Cost							
Totals							

Delivery	Weight	Vendor 1		Vendor 2		Vendor 3	
		Grade	Value	Grade	Value	Grade	Value
Totals							

Existing System in Plant	Weight	Vendor 1		Vendor 2		Vendor 3	
		Grade	Value	Grade	Value	Grade	Value
Preferred vendor							
Preferred manufacturer							
Experience with performance							
Service record							
Maintenance personnel trained							
Engineers trained							

Existing System in Plant	Weight	Vendor 1		Vendor 2		Vendor 3	
		Grade	Value	Grade	Value	Grade	Value
Operators trained							
Spare parts in plant							
Compatibility with other systems							
Totals							

Cost	Weight	Vendor 1		Vendor 2		Vendor 3	
		Grade	Value	Grade	Value	Grade	Value
Hardware							
Software							
Spare Parts							
Engineering							
Start-up							
check-out							
Service							
Training							
—Maintenance							
—Operators							
—Engineers							
Programming							
Totals							

Accumulated Totals	Weight	Vendor 1		Vendor 2		Vendor 3	
		Grade	Value	Grade	Value	Grade	Value
Vendor/Representative							
Distributor/Manufacturer							
Overall System							
Expansion Requirements							

Accumulated Totals	Weight	Vendor 1		Vendor 2		Vendor 3	
		Grade	Value	Grade	Value	Grade	Value
Standards							
Data Acquisition							
Memory Storage Requirements							
Data Analysis Requirements							
Alarm Requirements							
Logging Requirements							
Data Displays							
Process Control							
Software Requirements							
Operator Interface							
Peripherals							
Environmental Requirements							
Redundancy							
Diagnostics							
Network							
Documentation							
Maintenance							
Training							
Delivery							
Existing System in Plant							
Cost							
Totals							

Notes and Remarks:
Selection:
Reasons:

Vendor Evaluation Meetings

These meetings occur prior to vendor selection, and allow you to present your needs and problems to each vendor. The vendors may use this time to demonstrate the capabilities and limitations of his product, system and services. You will probably find the need to meet with the vendor after you begin to develop the vendor comparison chart. Whether you do it with separate teams, or a common team, should be a consideration that your project team makes.

You should be prepared to ask detailed questions concerning your control problems, and operational goals. Make the vendor aware that you expect good engineering responses to these questions. It is also important to use these meetings to develop a rapport with the vendor. If you do not feel comfortable working with him at this stage, you may have serious problems working with him at the detailed project level. You may not have very many chances, perhaps only one, to meet with a given vendor prior to the selection. Make these meetings as useful as possible.

Prepare a list of topics you wish to address, as well as the equipment and demonstrations you would like to see. Most vendors have a standard "dog and pony show" to use if the customer has not asked for anything in particular. Never be shy about asking to discuss any topic you consider important. If you prepare an agenda and send it to the vendor well in advance of your list, the vendor can arrange for the appropriate resources and demonstrations.

44 The System has been Bought!

Finally you have bought the system, or at least you've decided to buy the system from a specific vendor. The contract has been signed, but there still could be many unresolved questions resulting from possible misunderstandings. As a result, it maybe necessary to have a series of meetings that will be never ending in your mind until your plant is up and running. It is very important that your teams get together and develop a relationship. There should also be a single point of contact between your team leader and the vendor's team leader and always a traceable record of any interaction between the two groups. A very orderly, organized record of all of the transactions between the groups is very essential, especially if the project is large (Figure 44-1). By using one, the pain and confusion of misunderstandings will be kept to a minimum. Remember, you're dealing with human nature here and all that implies.

- Running the project
- Project kickoff meetings
- Meeting-tracking system
- System master inventory
- Project status meetings
- Technical review meetings
- Internal meetings
- Factory testing
- Shipment of the system
- Installation
- Project is over
- Continual improvement

Figure 44-1. After the Sale Planning is Essential

Project Kickoff Meetings

The best way to get a project to stay on schedule and be successful is to get the project rolling as quickly as possible. Your team and the vendor team should plan to spend, depending on the size of the project, about a full workweek together. At these meetings, your specification and the vendor's bid are reviewed to make sure everyone is in agreement about what the system should look like and how it should perform. Never assume that the vendor totally understands your expectations. After all, he or she had only a few weeks to read your specification, while you may have spent many months or even years learning your plant needs and preparing the specification.

You should have an agreement as to what is to be done; describing the process as it is running now and improvements to be incorporated into the new system. This is the hard part. If you have been building this process description early on in the project to develop your specification, it is a chance to review and be sure that everyone in your team agrees and understands how the new system will work.

The group should do the following:

- Break the process into units.
- Count the discrete and analog input/output plus control loops by unit.
- Determine the regulatory control, the interlocks and the sequencing complexity by unit. Describe and decide on the human interface and reporting requirements.
- Determine scan speeds (if necessary), database and network communication requirements, and the total information system needs.
- Regulatory controls, interlock sequencing, and throughput requirements will determine if total distributed or a total programmable logic system could be used overall. Otherwise, determine exactly how a hybrid PLC or DCS will work. Today, many control companies provide a controller that covers the capabilities of both a distributed control function block system and programmable logic control. Be careful that the capabilities of these boxes include all of your requirements and do not have to be "kludged together" to make it work.
- On the basis of human interface, reporting, supervisory requirements, and communication needs, determine what the function of any additional computers is.

At the kick-off meetings, you must establish the lines of communication and the rules for document review, approval, and transfer. Again, there should be an implementation plan (Figure 44-2), which is really a continuation and expansion of what was already started. You should flesh out a preliminary schedule containing the major project milestones. Agree upon a format for written communications and meeting notes. The project teams will exchange ideas, make commitments, and agree upon milestones and many other things, which must be tracked in some form of meeting notes. Create a meeting tracking system.

Meeting Tracking System

It is imperative that all teams fully understand what is going on, and good record keeping will make this happen. Create several documents, that will act as the basis for all this communication for all the subsequent meetings during the life of the project. These would include; meeting notes, an action item list, an unresolved questions list, a project schedule, and a system master inventory.

Meeting notes. The result of every meeting, both those will the vendor and those with the customer should be written down and distributed to members of both teams for review and comment. The notes should include a list of whom attended and who made which statements. The date and place of the meeting should be recorded. If the meeting was called for a special purpose, a few sentences detailing the meeting's purpose and the results should be included.

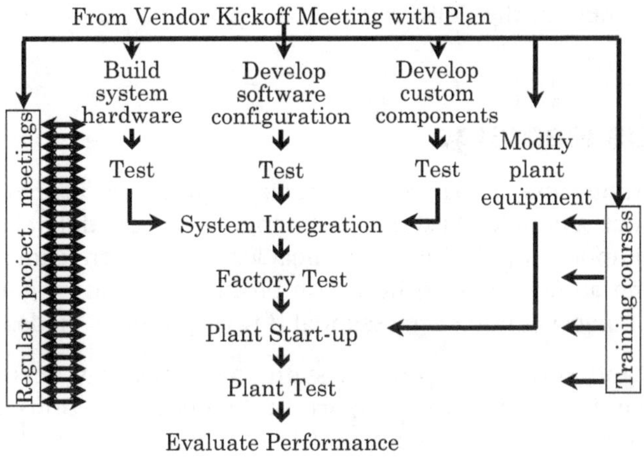

Figure 44-2. More Planning, Regardless of Size

Action item list. There are tasks to be performed and dates to be met by both the vendor and the customer. Each specific task should be noted and assigned a unique number, a responsible party should be designated, and a target completion date should be established, if at all possible. It is often better to break this into separate customer lists and vendor lists. Again, all the team members should receive these lists.

Unresolved questions lists. There will be questions that arise for which no specific action can be formulated but that will eventually requires an answer. These questions should be tracked and reviewed. When things become clearer these items can be converted into action items to be implemented.

Project schedule. Obviously, a jointly approved and maintained schedule should be created. The schedule should list all the major milestones and give some idea of the order in which things will be done. Some people prefer PERT (program evaluation and review technique) charts, others a timeline approach. The important point is to create a schedule that both you and the vendor can use and understand. It is very important when laying out this schedule that you be realistic in the time estimates. You cannot begin by allocating one month to do a two-month project and attempt to make all the tasks to fit. This will not only fool you, but also create considerable problems with management. If there is a serious time problem, make the vendor aware of the problem at the outset so *he or she* can take action to ensure timely delivery and project completion. Keep in mind that a team of nine women has never been able to give birth to a single baby in one month, even though management may often to refuse to believe it can't be done.

System Master Inventory

Vendors should maintain a copy of the system configuration, including a detailed parts breakdown. In this way, changes in the scope of the project can be tracked and reflected in changes in an agreed upon equipment list. In this way, you will be able to verify the completeness of the delivered system by comparing the actual items against this parts list.

Project Status Meetings

At the status meetings, you and the vendor review and revise your action items, question list, and project schedule. Also, scope changes and schedule changes can be discussed and agreed upon. Appointing a technical leader for each team and breaking into separate submitting allows more to be accomplished. Obviously, good records and a consolidated set of meeting notes are essential if this split-up is made.

At the beginning and end of the project, status meetings may need to be held on a monthly basis, from three to five weeks apart. In the middle portions of projects, status meetings may be required less often. Regardless of when these meetings are scheduled, if a problem arises, or you *think* a problem has arisen, call a meeting so you can quickly settle the issue that aroused your concern.

Technical Review Meetings

Once progress has been made in the system's construction whether in a special configuration in the programming, or in the applications design it is advisable to review the progress with the vendor. If a mistake is being made, a review meeting will keep the mistake from becoming too large. Major points of progress that may call for technical review include the following:

- Completion of the system software design implementation document
- Completion of an application design specification
- Completion of any major hardware assembly design
- Completion of the testing of any software application or hardware assembly
- Completion of continuous control implementation
- Completion of input/output database definition
- Completion of operator interface packages

By reviewing technical progress as it is being made, the level of problems that arise may be kept to the cosmetic level instead of rising to the major redesign level. Technical review also keeps you abreast of the actual status of the system construction schedule.

Internal Meetings

In addition to the vendor and customer meetings, it's very helpful for your team to have weekly internal meetings on the status of the project. Perhaps a complete half-day should be set aside each week. Accurate notes of these meetings are just as vital as they are with vendor meetings. These internal meetings often generate action items and questions; thus copies of meeting notes should go to the vendor, just as the vendor should be sending you copies of his or her weekly notes.

Somewhere in the life of the project you will have to deal with scope changes. They may be the result of features you want to add or ones you want to remove. On occasion, a scope change may be the result of a misunderstanding between you and the vendor. You may feel that you have something coming and the vendor feels it is an extra cost item. The first type of scope change is easily handled. Tell the vendor what you want; he or she will give you a price estimate, plus or minus the original cost, and a schedule impact that represents a plus or minus on the timetable. To make clear what is affected by the scope change, the vendor should supply you with a detailed written estimate of all the work to be done or not done and the charges for labor and materials used or not used. You should review the estimate as quickly as possible and discuss it at the next possible meeting. If there is anything you don't understand, make a point of asking for clarification.

Most changes become more costly, both in time and money, the further into the project you go. For this reason, it is essential to get the vendor to provide you with a list of major dates. These dates correspond to events that affect the cost of any scope change. Scope changes that arise from disagreement with the vendor are usually not as easy to resolve. Obviously, you do not want to pay for anything you feel you have coming to you already. If there is a clear case of mutual mystification and both of you can admit that the other party may have a valid argument, the best route may be to pay a fair share of the scope change price. Often this will be the actual cost of the change plus a mutually agreed upon percentage. If the document is beyond the level where agreement will be reached quickly, it is in your best and mutual interest to agree not to hold up on going project work while you hammer out this particular issue.

Factory Testing

The factory test is the last chance you and your vendor will have to find and fix problems with the system. Since it cost you both a great deal to fix problems in the field, it's important to work together to perform a very thorough testing operation. This is a major milestone on your project schedule, and as with all the other meetings you should come prepared if you want to get the most out of the testing.

It is a good idea to develop a written test plan well in advance of this stage. The plan must be worked out between you and the vendor. A good starting point is the vendor's standard test procedures. He may be able to customize those procedures to meet your needs without having to start from scratch. If you require especially complex or unusually elaborate tests, be sure to mention this in your specification. Otherwise, the vendor will offer only his or her standard procedures.

Expect to run into some problems during the acceptance test. If you have worked well with the vendor and you both did your homework at the project start, you should encounter no major problems. If you find small problems, as long as they're logged, repaired, and the corrections demonstrated prior to the end of the testing you should be OK.

By this time, your testing personnel should have taken all the recommended training courses, so they are familiar with the system's operation. The order in which testing is performed is important because you can tell how far to backtrack if a problem arises. For example, if you run a full hardware diagnostic prior to testing the configuration, it's fairly certain that the programming problems are not hardware related. So the sequence should be as follows:

- Hardware functional testing that includes the complete performance of all diagnostics on all the hardware modules and assemblies, all the inputs and outputs, and all of the redundancy systems and back up.
- Software functional testing that runs all of the configurations in their normal operating mode and performs all the potential operations through the operator interfaces. As many of the configurable operations as possible should be demonstrated in their normal operating conditions.
- Applications correctness testing, which would that at least to the correctness of the configurations as far as the control system goes. This does not mean that the application devised by the user is in fact the proper one for the process. It merely confirms that the equipment can perform the functions defined by the user.
- Failure mode testing which allows you to know the system's reaction to every major component failure so you can be prepared to cope with these failures. By simulating failures, you can verify the proper functioning of back-up systems.

Acceptance Test

1. Orientation meeting

   — Review the testing schedule, the personnel, and the procedures
   — Identify testing teams and leaders
   — Provide system overview and description
   — Provide documentation review and approval

2. System inspection

   — All major components inspection of and familiarization with
   — Component and module interconnection
   — System start-up and shut-down procedures

3. Hardware diagnostics

   — Memory diagnostics
   — Processor diagnostics
   — Input/output diagnostics
   — Communications diagnostics
   — Any special diagnostics

4. System start-up

   — Power up and system reload
   — Power failure and recovery testing, both for momentary and long-term
   — Brownout testing
   — Power line spike and transient testing
   — Module-by-module power loss test

5. Failure mode operations

   — Redundant module tests

- — Selective component and assembly failure effects
- — Backup communications operations
- — Communications disruptions

6. Process interface testing

- — Thermocouple calibration
- — RTD calibration
- — Voltage and current calibration
- — Point-by-point analog and discrete input and output tests; any interface tests for special sensors or smart transmitters; any signal drift correction test.

7. Control functions

- — Control loop actions
- — Interlocks and logic functions
- — Sequential operations
- — Down-load, up-load of online configuration changes
- — Start-up and shut-down routines
- — Plant upset routines

8. Operator interface

- — Standard video displays
- — Alarm displays
- — Any recipe displays in batch operations
- — Trending displays
- — Creation of logging and reports

9. Engineering functions

- — Optimizing routines
- — Statistical packages
- — Communications diagnostic packages
- — Application-specific packages

10. Environmental testing

- — Temperature cycling
- — Vibration
- — Humidity
- — Pressure seal tests
- — Any other testing appropriate to conditions expected

Shipment of the System

Quite often, G-force and temperature sensors can be attached to packing crates and cabinets so you can be determine if the system was exposed to excessive physical abuse during shipment. If any indicator shows that the conditions have been exceeded, the vendor should be asked to make a comprehensive examination of the equipment regardless of whether or not there are any obvious signs of damage. In most cases, you will want to have the vendor's representative present to observe and oversee the unloading and placement of the system in your facility.

Installation

Provision should be made at the plant, particularly if labor unions are involved, to physically place the control system where it is to operate. This will include removing the shipping straps and braces and the connection of power to the system, aligning any cabinetry, and checking to make sure that all doors fit and swing clear. If necessary, also check that any sealing from the environment is properly done. Again, it is wise to have the vendor have some representative there for this function.

Before the control system arrives all of the sensors and final control elements on site should be independently tested to be sure they are properly hooked up and have the proper voltage or current levels, or digital signals, as the case may be. This will uncover any unexpected errors that will be far more difficult to find after the system is connected. Once the control system is in place but before these inputs and outputs are connected, the system should be turned on so it can scan all the inputs and outputs and record the failed connection, or the absence of connection. All of these inputs and outputs should show up in a failed state. As each is connected, the scanning can detect that connection and indicate that it's been recovered or returned to some non-failed value. A log of these events should be kept for later reference during the start-up.

Making a voltage check on each input or output before wiring them into the control system could save you a lot of money. If some low-level signal is actually at line voltage, this check will prevent a considerable amount of damage in the control system itself. It is also wise to have a stock of spare components for input/output boards on hand during these checks. After connection, it would be wise to go over every analog and discrete input and output and exercise full zero to 100 percent on all analog ramps in each discrete to the on and off state. An operator can also manually command the control system to manipulate selected outputs while the instrument mechanics check the operation of the equipment.

During this time, the vendor should also send a start-up team that includes equipment technicians and system engineers. Plant application engineers should be part of this team. It would also be a good idea for the vendor's local field service people to be included in the plant start-up because they will eventually take over the support responsibility. This may be their first and only chance to work with the home office personnel who bought your system.

In every system, the chances of failure are high when it's first put into operation. The failure rate of individual modules and components is high during the earlier range of their lives. The longer a component operates, the better the chances the component won't fail after all, at least because of manufacturing and material defects. Of course, eventually everything breaks, and the longer you go without a failure in the later portion of a component's life, the higher the probability of failure becomes. The average life expectancy of properly treated electronic components can be as much as 10 to 20 years.

The main point is that you can expect some kind of failure problems when you first place your system in operation. The vendor will have burned in your system long enough to get through these "infant mortality" stages. Even so, there will be some failures, if for no other reason than your own wiring errors that place high-voltage AC where low-voltage DC ought to be. Prepare to have a complete stock of available spares and components on hand. Your vendor can usually recommend the appropriate complement of spares that you should carry through the system's commissioning and through a normal operating time span.

Once your control system is installed, checked out, and made operational, begin to implement your control functions and perhaps make some trial runs. The testing of appropriate configurations is usually done a layer at a time, starting with pure continuous control and adding sequencing logic and finally whatever else is complex about it.

During the testing phases, it's better to have all the persons validating and correcting the application documents coordinate all the changes made to the control configurations. If no documentation and coordination are done, you'll find yourself correcting problems, only to have them reappear when uncorrected copies are accidentally used in place of the corrected version. This is a very common problem when strict procedures aren't enforced. You and your vendor should agree on a procedure for documenting and formally implementing all changes and corrections to the system configuration and hardware during the start-up phase.

The Project Is Over

Now that your control system has been installed and has been running for a couple of weeks, you will expect that your plant performance has been improved as you had expected, everybody is happy, and management is singing. Of course, you are already aware that the trick is to keep the system running, and that requires steady and regular maintenance. These maintenance recommendations came with the system and were part of the contract. To implement them properly, you may need some assistance from the vendor.

Most vendors offer a variety of maintenance contracts depending on the specifics that you need for your system. These contracts would include a normal response time for coming out to a plant maybe within one or two days, for repair that goes beyond the routine diagnostic check and word swapping. There will be another contract, perhaps, that would call for a more urgent response, usually within the half-day or quarter day. Under this contract, the maintenance personnel can come out, probably draw from your own spare parts, determine the nature of your problem, and resolve it.

If your new system is equipped with a modem, then it's quite possible that the vendor can diagnose your system from his plant. The advantage there is that there will be other people at the plant that he can consult if he sees something beyond normal. If the problem is caused by some kind of programming dilemma, that fix could even be downloaded over the phone if your system has a phone modem with a direct diagnostic link. In very large plants with an instrument team that supports the entire final elements and sensors, they could also be trained to do most of the repairs on your control system. This might be your own team of maintenance people, it could be the contract team of a third party, or it could be one provided by the vendor themselves.

If your system is redundant you'll probably keep operating so your process continues to make product. That will give you time to locate the nature of the problem and get the spare part or failed device back in operation.

Continual Improvement

What is really significant is that with today's microprocessor-based devices the continual improvement of plant performance can come about by changing your control strategy. The need for these changes can be caused by changes in government requirements, by emissions, by contamination of effluent. New technology in the equipment you use for your process changes in your customer requirements, new ways to save energy, and market changes all impact your production methods. How you configure your plant and the order in which you do your process to accommodate these configurations will determine the life of your plant. All of these configurable changes are on going, and your control system should be flexible enough to absorb them.

This will continue as long as you have your supplier available to buy more parts and spares if you need to because your equipment expands. Ideally, most of these changes will not require further purchases but merely the rearranging of the function blocks of the system you already have. If the system has been made from commercially available parts and not proprietary hardware, then you can feel secure in the fact that the system will probably continue on for maybe as long as twenty years.

The vendor did not supply you with generic control software because that is probably where the value in his system lies. The control system software will probably continue on once you get past that first or second year and have overcome all of the different system bugs. After that, more than likely your software can be continued on and loaded in similar equipment purchased later. As time goes on, the capability to not have to rely on the vendor who sold you the system will become more and more feasible, particularly with the advent of fieldbus-like structures and architectures.

Part K

Why Distribute My Control?

Selling Change 45

This section is included to provide some presentation material to those who must "sell" change to their corporations. Though this topic may be basic to those involved with these systems, the issues here are not all that obvious to those involved with the process operations side of the business.

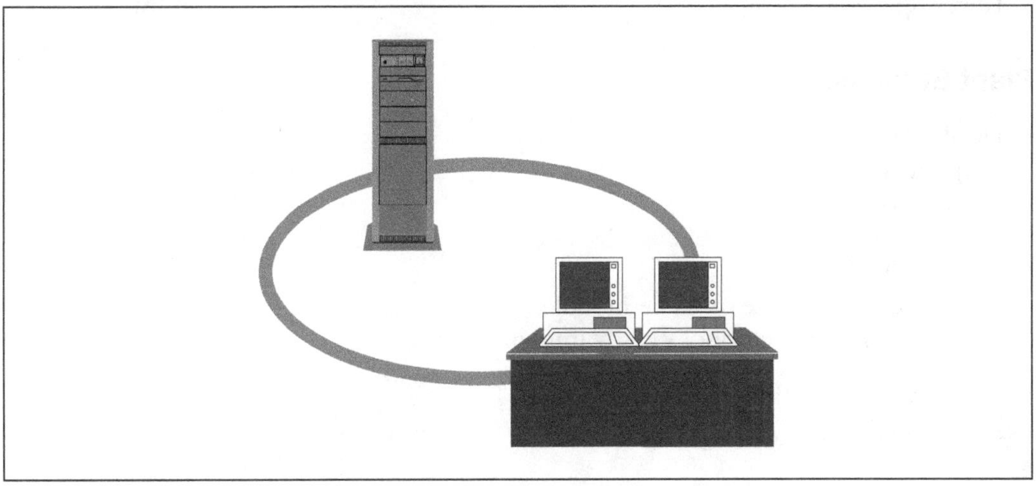

Figure 45-1. Value in Distributing Control Functions

An Outline of Arguments for Distributed Control

This is a management summary (in outline) that can be adapted in a form appropriate for the presentation needed:

Ease of Implementation

- Hardware
  - — Many modules alike
  - — Cable-connected versus hardwiring
  - — Fewer mistakes
- Software
  - — No programming but library of configuration modules; "cut and paste"
  - — Fewer mistakes

- Understanding
  - Fewer hardware types to, buy, learn, and repair
  - Fewer mistakes

Operator Productivity

- Easy to see change
- More information to make good decisions
- Improved ability to respond to any upset
- Consistent actions by all operators
- Fewer upsets

Plant Efficiency

- Flexibility
  - Hardware modules
  - Software modules
- Sophisticated control
  - Analog and discrete on same module
  - Comprehensive interlocks easily implemented
- Extensive information
  - Available to suggest improvements
- Optimization
  - Local
  - Plant wide

Maintenance of Records

- Process history:
  - Plant operations
  - System changes and growth
  - Various configurations
- Suggest improvements
  - Trends of process
  - Analysis (X-Y, XbarR, etc.)
  - Relational database manager (RDBM)

Reliability

- Distributed risk
- Redundant paths

- Graceful degradation
- Fast detection of any system failure
- Easier to replace parts
- Longer life cycle

Improved Maintenance

- Improved visibility of many types of system problems
- Diagnostics for rapid discovery and location
- Performance statistics provide advanced warning before catastrophic failures

Long Life Cycle

Easy Expansion & Change

- Capability and capacity
- No reprogramming
  — Existing system will accept new additions
- Modules all alike
  — Add only what is needed
  — Nothing to buy ahead of time
- No need to know the future
  — Nature of changes
  — Amount of changes
  — Timing of changes ... or even if they will occur

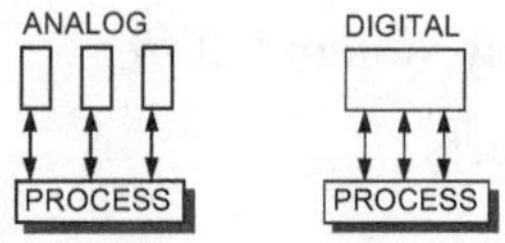

	(Dedicated)	(Centralized)
• System Organization	**Familiar**	Unfamiliar
• Operator Interface	Rigid	**Flexible**
• Risk of Failure	**Distributed**	Central
• Diagnostics	Limited	**Extensive**
• Sophisticated Control	Complicated	Program
• Record Keeping	Awkward	**Built-in**
• Plant Computer Interface	Difficult	**Inherent**
• Ability to Change	Complex	Reprogram

Figure 45-2. Analog versus "Mainframe" (Any "Single Box")

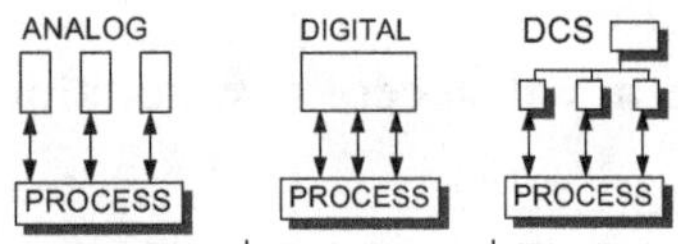

	(Dedicated)	(Centralized)	(Distributed)
• System Organization	**Familiar**	--------	<— same
• Operator Interface	---------	**Flexible**	<— same
• Risk of Failure	**Distributed**	--------	<— same
• Diagnostics	--------	**Extensive**	<— same
• Sophisticated Control	--------	--------	**Objects Config**
• Record Keeping	--------	**Built-in**	<— same
• Plant Computer Interface	--------	**Inherent**	<— same
• Ability to Change	--------	--------	**Modular**

Figure 45-3. Distributed is Best of Both Worlds, and Then Some

Part L

Future Trends

46 Distributed Ain't Dead!!

As we explained in the Preface, the name "Distributed Control" came into disfavor after a marketing war between two major vendors. The campaign was that "Distributed Control is Dead." Many people jumped onto the bandwagon in agreement. Yet the systems are even more distributed than ever! It's all in the semantics. At this point, as I read the various trade journals, I see many people describing distributed control systems in ways that differ from the original meaning of the words, just as they are doing with SCADA systems. As a marketing person, all I can do is sigh. *Sigh.* (Sorry about that, Judy.)

Distributed Processor Systems for Control

The original distributed control systems (DCSs) came about because computing could be done with the then new concept of using many microprocessors rather than a central mainframe computer. To improve, it required several technologies, yet to improve, such as communication between the processors and the appropriate packaging. The original DCS was the FUNCTIONAL distribution of the central mainframe computer; it provided a distributed risk of system failure similar to that of stand-alone controllers.

As time went on, various vendors developed communication methods to reliably allow *some* separation of the process-controlling functions. We began to see PHYSICAL distribution among several processes. More had to be done in the areas of redundancy and backup to assure reliability. There was now also the capability to easily combine discrete action along with the modulating control actions. With that capability emerged the practical possibility of using control strategies, not just a collection of loops. Many ideas that were decades old could now be reasonably implemented.

Microprocessors began to assume a more aggressive role in both consumer and commercial markets, and the increase in volume brought prices down. Industrial markets were then able to apply "big computer" capability too much smaller process solutions. Along with this came changes in the way data could be presented to the operators and engineers of the plants.

Concurrent with these developments were advances in memory capacity and processing performance. Therefore techniques were required to manage an increasing flood of data and to present it as useful information. Large single central computing systems became distributed, but the information became centralized!

Maturing of Technology Allows Maturing of Application

All this capability allowed many industries to mature and thereby required the development of more unique capabilities. We are now seeing the need to redistribute centralized information to specific areas. It means rearranging data to provide business information in a form that help's management make meaningful decisions. Operating data must be transformed into meaningful information for those immediately managing the process itself. Performance data must be arranged to be useful to plant engineers, to continually improve the product, and to reduce plant operating costs. The list goes on.

Through all of this, the architectures of distributed control systems have been continually changing. When those in the programmable logic controller world recognized their own architectures were changing, they too claimed to have distributed control. People in the process world dismissed the concept because "that was different." Well, there may be some very significant differences between the manufacturing and packaging, batch processing, business planning, and "traditional" process control worlds, but it is still all distributed processing over networks! For these reasons, I believe we should be talking about Distributed *PROCESSOR* Systems—DPS!

Control Loops Stretched Out Over the Network

Architectural transformation is occurring (Figure 46-1) for the following reasons:

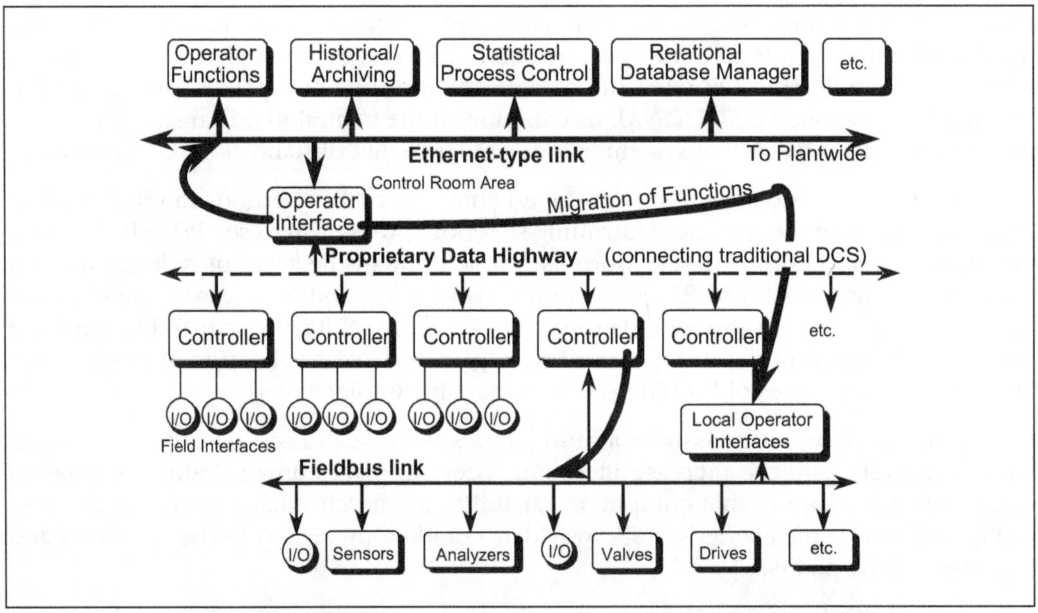

Figure 46-1. In the Future of Distributed Evolution, Functions are Migrating!

- Advances in memory media, such as PCMCIAs, CD-ROMs, etc.
- Significant improvements in microprocessor speeds and costs
- Fieldbus-type (two-way) communication is now possible

We already see migration of control software to sensors, valves, and drives. What this means is that the elements of the control loop itself are becoming distributed! There is considerable need to review loop security and determine on what occasions to allow distribution. Certainly we must consider the impact of distributed multiloop strategies even within just a portion of a process.

Advanced control techniques such as fuzzy logic, neural networks, genetic algorithms, and the like have already challenged traditional thinking about how to control processes. Portions of these techniques are frequently distributed as well, insofar as they all imply multivariable and even multistrategy control.

Premise

Fieldbus, memory media advances, improving μP speeds and costs, government regulations, client needs for functions that distributed process control systems can provide (such as advanced control techniques like process model control, neural networks, fuzzy logic, genetic algorithms) these factors will change who will use "stand alone" control (single loop. multiloop, and batch), who will use a networked system (even on a small-unit process), and why they will!

DCS is not dead but will be transformed so that DCS functions will appear in DPS (distributed processor systems). Those systems distribute the computer processing of functions over some network, regardless of size.

Transformation of Architecture:

- Traditional operator interface migrating down to local levels, where more processing power and capacity exists, and up to "plantwide" for better business information.
- Fewer interface links to "plantwide"; more functional capabilities to control room.
- Controller functions migrating to plant "floor" within smart field devices.
- Proprietary data highways will no longer be necessary for speed and capacity.

Information Distribution—How Much and How Fast?

The need for higher quality, environmental responsibility, operational accountability and government compliance all requires tighter control, closer management, and extensive record keeping. Where this data is used and how it is converted to usable form will impact the kind of communications system that will assure appropriate delivery.

Proprietary data highways had been necessary to achieve the performance and capacity of real-time data. Even if standards from other industries were used (such as Ethernet from the business world), significant modifications and limitations were needed. (Try, for example, to operate at the same time any collection of controllers and operator stations from any combination of those vendors who have "Ethernet highways," or "MAP-compatible" systems.)

In each industry, some very critical decisions must be made about what is needed, when it is really needed, and at what price. More capability is possible, so more will be expected. This will require flexibility, which always seems to be at odds with the need for standardization. Nevertheless, standardization will come. Ethernet will emerge to move *informational data*, and a fieldbus will eventually happen to move *real-time control signals*. This will significantly influence architectures.

Observation, Decision Making, and Intervention

In some plants, processes are increasingly linked together, and more sophisticated automatic control is becoming practical. There is a great deal of philosophy that must be explored. Who should operate the plant? To what detail? From what vantagepoint? With what information?

The advent of fieldbus-type communication seems to invite more local operator interfaces to serve immediate needs at different positions around the plant or process. The capability is there to provide more interchange of information between these locations, reducing the need for traditional central control rooms. These remote locations may be manned only periodically or during unique times in the process.

A central location may become more of a dispatcher of information and/or an operator of business efficiency. This may be especially true in plants with traditionally separate processes that are not necessarily running as a contiguous operation. An example of this trend would be a company that performs heat treating for many other companies who have divested themselves of their old furnace and outsources the operation when needed. The heat-treat shop could easily service simultaneously many small projects from these various other companies, much as office services are done for clusters of small (and even larger) businesses.

Market Domains 47

"What is new is not because it has never been there before, but because it has changed in quality..."

Robert Oppenheimer, Physicist

"When innovation takes place, there is an intimate linkage or fusion of two or more elements that have not been previously joined in just this fashion, so that the result is a qualitatively distinct whole... If we may use a biological analogy, an innovation is like a genetic cross or hybrid; it is totally different from either of its parents, but it resembles both of them in some respects."

H.G.Barnett, from *Innovation: The Basis of Cultural Change*

Changes in Capability Spawns Changes in Function—and Traditional Domains

When looking at the world of distributed processing, we should remember that the technology is now beginning to reach very small users who in the past could never have expected to be able to make the capital investment for computer-based systems. The "big architecture" should not be viewed as a monolith. Various subsets of it can be cut from it as stand-alone operations.

For example, a small user may now economically bring a handful of formerly stand-alone loops together with a simple local operator station and some "off-the-shelf" data management software. The investment could be little more than the personal computer already on the manager's desk. In some cases, the same machine could even be shared! Viewing these loops together, new control techniques will become apparent. Advanced control capabilities "on a chip" make control strategy change practical and efficient. The same analysis could result in fundamental changes in the way the process itself is achieved. This becomes a new market for the instrument vendor.

Batch operations fall into two areas: those incorporated as part of larger process operations and those that by nature stand-alone. The latter could grow into multiples of the same separate operations. Here again, there are two playing fields for the smaller, separate operations. One is where the operations themselves become more sophisticated than before. The other is where the business itself becomes more automated, interconnecting these operations for reasons other than the process control strategy. Actually, both may easily happen in a given plant.

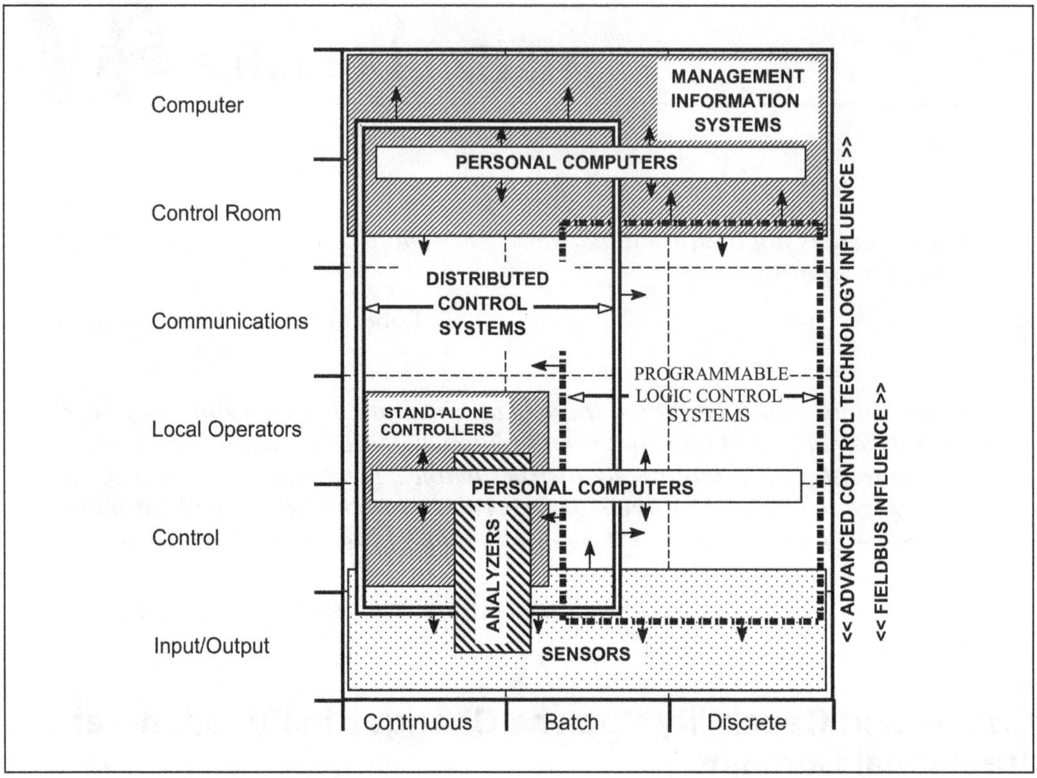

Figure 47-1. Transformation of Domain!

Transformation of Domain (Figure 47-1):

- The illustration in Figure 47-1 shows approximate areas of influence in markets, but not market shares!
- Most of the technologies typically found in one market area are growing into Adjacent markets, shown by the arrows in Figure 47-1.
- So-called open software has more of an influence on the MIS and control room Than do the so- called open system networks. "Openness" is on the computer end.
- For now, the influence of fields impacts process interfaces and local control.
- Advanced control technologies impact all areas, though in varying degrees.
- Stand-alone controllers (single and multiloop types) will undergo a more dramatic transformation fieldbus and increased internal capabilities at low cost.

Changes in Domain Make Traditional Market Identifications Very Difficult

Traditionally, the term *DCS* was applied to larger continuous processes as found in refineries, power plants, and the like. Now, the same power can be applied to a grouping of single loops connected to a personal computer. The term *DCS* also applies to control functions along a fieldbus of various devices, which can also be operated through a personal computer.

On the other side of the controller, traditional control room operator interface functions are being performed in very powerful workstations. These are also capable of performing more than was done in separate computers, such as history, archiving, application-specific functions, statistical process control, and so on. Further connections to the business are achieved through "open" links to the "plant business computers." Several tiers of the hierarchical layers of the computers of a few years ago are being compressed into fewer and smaller machines.

Because process controllers and programmable logic controllers (Places) are both so much more powerful today, they frequently have the capability to do several functions that were traditionally separated into "discrete" or "process" strategies. This is especially true in the overlapping area of batch processing. The decision of which of the two is used often has more to do with the vendor's application experience than the actual hardware used.

Expanding Role of "Personal Computers" (PCs)

Once looked down upon (as were PLCs and DCSs before), PCs also have had the advantage of increasing microprocessor speeds and memory capacity. Hardened for the industrial environment, "off-the-shelf" PC hardware is readily available from many suppliers. This "hardware openness" allow users to regularly update microprocessor performance and memory capacity as the technology grows. Not only will users reduce their chances of being "frozen in time," they no longer need to be "held hostage" by vendors.

In fairness to the many control vendors, remember that in the past there were no alternatives for providing real-time equipment for process control. These requirements demanded unique designs beyond the standard designs available for hardware and software. The technology is rapidly changing, paving the way for different architectures. Yet the processors will continue to be both functionally and physically distributed.

With the low cost of PLCs and with the processing variety of DCSs, industrial grade PCs now function as control stations. Their robustness is dramatically improving. These stations can have complete function blocks for blending process, logic, sequential, and motor control. PCs used as consoles can be used to graphically configure control strategies as well as operator views and can also be used as operator stations. What is exciting and much more fun to speculate about is the future of control room use of PC technologies. Already there is a company in Massachusetts that makes a device using force-feedback technology that enables you to feel you are actually touching and manipulating objects on the computer screen! You move through virtual space on x, y, and z axes by inserting your finger into a thimble, which controls the on-screen motion. The software allows the computer to interpret your finger's position in three-dimensional space and apply an appropriate and variable resisting force. This process is performed about one thousand times a second, allowing smooth and textured surfaces, curves and sharp corners, and friction to all be represented. Both hands can be involved. What's that about "touring the plant?"

Digital links into the PCs used as control stations receive I/O signals from existing I/O modules made from a variety of other vendors specializing in that technology. This link also has the potential to readily become a port for any of the fieldbus protocols and to be modified to the emerging standard. Such a system can truly start small and grow plant wide in very economical steps. With such incremental steps, it could even be possible to replace an older system with no plant shutdown!

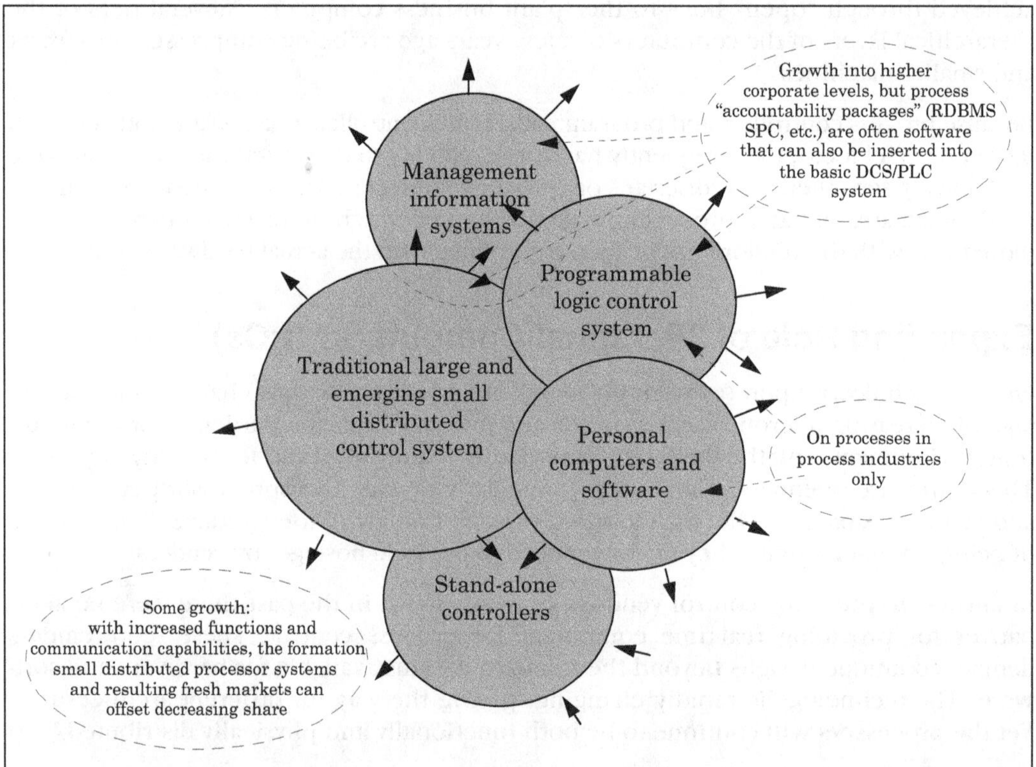

Figure 47-2. Business Pressures are Continually Altering the Marketplace Dynamics of Control Systems

---

Business Pressures (Figure 47.2):

- The illustration in Figure 47-2 relates specifically to process industries and is subject to interpretation.
- **The programmable logic control** market here attempts to show process functions within the process and process batch segments not within the much

larger PLC discrete market of automotive, manufacturing, packaging, and non-process functions within the process markets.

- **Management information systems**, as implemented in separate "guest" computersand separate computing modules on a network, are now migrating into workstations.
- **The distributed control systems** market is growing into new segments as size and cost decreases and power and function increases. Both PLCs and PCs are taking some of this market, while smaller DCSs are taking some the stand-alone control market.
- **The stand-alone control** (single, multiloop, and batch) market is losing some market share with the diminishing use of single loop controllers in part because of the evolution of "smart" field devices and fieldbus. Growth, however, is possible through small multiloop versions and fieldbus-type communication links. Some growth continues through the developing new markets resulting from the increased functions now possible.
- World market sizes are based on a blend of Frost & Sullivan and Idea Network evaluations.
- World market growth and the segments, impact upon each other are inferred from indirect sources.

What's in a Name?

We have been stuck with the differences in discrete and process controllers as well as the architectures associated with different industry needs and vendor solutions. Today, it appears that as time goes on processors will become even more distributed throughout these systems. It seems natural to me that a less confusing term for these architectures both large and small should be called Distributed Processor Systems, or merely DPS.

Bibliography

Adams, James, 1992. "An Object-Oriented Operator's Interface for Real-Time Process Control Expert Systems," *ISA Transactions* 31, No. 3: 65-74.

Dalrymple, Phillip W., III, 1998. "Protecting against Attacks on Open Systems." *I&CS* 71, No. 2: 51-55.

Feeley, Joe, 1998. "A Network Computer—Your Next Operator Interface," *Control 1*1, No. 3: 40-45.

Ghosh, Asish, Hills, Dick, Benoit, Paul, Perkins, Susan, and Catha, Andy, 1996. *Automation Strategies: System Selection and Implementation* (Automation Research Corporation).

Gingrich, Chester G., Kuespert, Daniel R., and McAvoy, Thomas J., 1992. "Modeling Human Operators Using Neural Networks," *ISA Transactions* 31, No. 3: 81-89.

Goble, William M., 1992. *Evaluating Control Systems Reliability: Techniques and Applications* (Research Triangle Park, NC: ISA).

Gordeuk, Nicholas A. 1989. "Designing Central Computer Control Rooms." *Control* 2, No. 1: 44-52.

Herbert, Daniel A., 1998. "Voice Control: Walking the Talk, *Control* 11, No. 3: 46-51.

Hirsh, Dan, 1997. "Are They 'Objects' of Affection or Anxiety?" *I&CS* 70, No. 6: 57-60.

Hodson, W. R., 1997. "Fieldbus to Change DCS Role, but Death Reports 'Greatly Exaggerated.'" *InTech* 44, No. 11: 36-39.

ISA-TR77.60.04-1996, "Fossil Fuel Power Plant Human Machine Interface—CRT Displays" (Research Triangle Park, NC: ISA).

Jensen, Holland, Tomasello, Heidrich, and Etterich, 1992. "The Process of Selecting a Man-Machine Interface Package for Use in a Process Control System," *ISA Transactions* 31, No. 3: 101-110.

Klein, Mike, 1997. "PCs in Control," *Industrial Computing* 16, No. 6: 22-26.

Laduzinsky, Alan J., 1986. "Would SCADA by Any Other Name Still Be the Same?" *Control Engineering* 33, No. 2: 72-75.

Land, David R., 1991. "Select the Right Distributed Control System," *Chemical Engineering Progress* 87, No. 5: 76-78.

Levy, Markus, 1997. "Windows CE at the Center of a Juggling Act," *EDN* 42, No. 15: 38-48.

Lukas, Michael P., 1986. *Distributed Control Systems*, (New York: Van Nostrand Reinhold).

Merritt, Richard, 1998. "Five Standards that Will Change Process Control," *Control* October Supplement.

Moore, J. A., and Herb, S. M. 1983. *Understanding Distributed Process Control* (Research Triangle Park, N C: ISA).

Moore, Robert L., 1997. "Distributed Embedded Intelligence Blazing Processing Trails," *InTech* 44, No. 3: 50-53.

Morris, Henry M., 1994. "Signal Conditioning Is Becoming I/O Processing," *Control Engineering* 41, No. 9: 52-53.

Nelson, Paul R. and Shull, Richard S., 1997. "How to Organize for S88 Batch Control," *InTech* 44, No. 7: 44-47.

Shaw, John, 1992. "Consider the Operator Interface in Control System Upgrades," *ISA Transactions* 31, No. 3: 75-79.

Shaw, William T., 1984. *From Specification to Plant Installation* (Cockeysville, MD: EMC Controls).

Sperber, Bob, 1998. "Hard Realities in Harsh Environments," *Software Strategies,* special topic: PC-Based Control, pp. 4-9.

Stoffel, Jane, 1994. "Integrating Information with PC-based DAC Software." *Control Engineering* 41, No. 3: 99-102.

Stokes, David, and Hubby, Robert N., 1989. "Technologies of Computerized Control Systems and Network Communications," paper presented to the International Conference on Industrial Control for the '90s, Tel Aviv, Israel.

Studebaker, Paul, 1996. "Are Your Safety Systems up to Standards?" *Control* 9, No. 4: 28-35.

Studebaker, Paul, 1998. "Be Careful What You Ask For," *Control* 11, No. 1: 50-56.

Thompson, Lawrence M., 1985. *Analog and Digital Signal Transmission* (Research Triangle Park, NC: ISA).

Toffer, Derek E., 1995. "Designing an Operator Interface? Consider User's 'Psychology.'" *InTech* 42, No. 11: 52-56.

Velázquez, Dennis, and Gilbert, Michael, 1998. "Customize Off-the-shelf Automation Software with Visual Basic," *I&CS* 71, No. 3: 39-43.

Wade, Dr. Harold L., 1994. *Distributed Control Systems Manual* (Houston, TX: Applied Digital Research).

Wehrer, Wayne, 1995. "Touch Screen Technologies Cover Variety of Application Bases," *I&CS* 68, No. 5: 67-73.

Worthington, Shari L. S., 1992, "The Personalization of Manufacturing: Redefining the Human Interface," *ISA Transactions* 31, No. 3: 91-99.

Ziegler, J. G., Nichols, N. B., 1942. "Optimum Settings for Automatic Controllers," *ASME Transactions* 64, No. 8: 759-768.

Glossary, Acronyms, and Abbreviations: Beyond Distributed Process Control

The field of distributed process control systems transcends the fields of process control, factory automation, computing, communications (including the phone, video, and Internet industries), desktop publishing (screen displays, reports, information systems), fiber optics, software, hardware, and even psychology (human/machine interface, artificial intelligence). Because of the increasing attempts to link the plant floor to automatic business planning operations, we now have even more terminology to address. Professional societies, various industrial standards and practices, and many different government agencies are also providing additional domestic and international input. Because of this, a huge collection of cryptic acronyms, abbreviations, and terminology show up in literature on the subject and the definitions sometimes conflict. Included here are hundreds of multiple meanings across several disciplines. With all of this profound content, I just had to introduce a slight bit of humor as well.

I created this continually changing list, which stems from my attempt to understand many magazine articles. I am also personally publishing this growing list as a direct response to the countless questions from the many students I have encountered while teaching many instrumentation courses worldwide, especially those involving distributed processor systems. Because it has been accumulated over such a long period, it would be impossible to properly source every definition. Some selections are modified for their significance to distributed process control from *Webster's New World Dictionary of Computer Terms* (Simon & Schuster), *The New Penguin Dictionary of Electronics* by E. C. Young (Viking Penguin), and the ISA Standard on Process Instrumentation Terminology. Some other modified inspirations also came from various issues of Black Box's catalogs (Pittsburgh) and Omega Engineering's catalogs (Stamford, CT) as well as from John Zagame of Moore Process Automation Solutions, Bill Hodson of Honeywell (formerly of Leeds & Northrup) and Gene Murphy of Honeywell. This list will always be incomplete and enigmatic.

—Sam Herb

A

A—Means "analysis" when used in the first alpha character position of the ISA instrument function tag; it means "Alarm" if in the succeeding position [see ANSI/ISA S5.1-1984 (R1992)]. *Also*, the availability of a system or device, that is, the proportion of time that it will properly function and not fail [A = MTBF/ (MTBF + MTTR)].

α—(alpha) average percentage change in resistance per degree of pure metal resistance of device between 0°C and 100°C, usually designated by the Greek letter alpha, with units of Ω/Ω/°C.

Å—Angstrom; ten to the minus tenth meters (10^{-10}) or one millimicron; unit used to define the wavelength of light.

ABI—Applied Binary Interface; to run without porting.

A/B roll—In video development, a process that uses two sources whose content is mixed during editing to create dissolve, wipe, or effect; see *B roll.*

ABS—Aerylonitrile butadiene styrene; frequently used for enclosures; good high-temperature resistance with high impact strength and cold-temperature impact, good overall chemical resistance; can be adversely affected by ultraviolet. *Also*, American Bureau of Shipping, which creates standards that equipment must comply with to be placed on ships of American registry.

absolute pressure—Gauge pressure plus atmospheric pressure; total force per unit area exerted by fluid.

absorption—In fiber-optic cable, the loss of power from the conversion of optical energy into heat; usually caused by impurities such as transition metals and hydroxyl ions.

AC (or AC)—alternating current; electric current that reverses its direction at regularly recurring intervals, such as 60 times/second (60 Hz).

accelerators—Used by some computer applications to create keyboard alternatives to the use of screen menus for selecting choices; the keystroke has special meaning within that particular application, saving more involved, but usually more "user-friendly," procedures to make request or entry.

acceptance angle—In fiber-optic cable, half angle of cone within which incident light is totally reflected internally by the fiber core.

acceptance test—Series of tests used to demonstrate capabilities and workability of a new system; usually conducted by the manufacturer to show the customer that the system is in working order.

access—Used as verb in computing; usually the act of locating and obtaining or placing data.

access code—Group of alphanumeric characters that identifies the user to the system so information can be placed or retrieved by other devices in the system.

access line—Portion of leased communication line, such as with a telephone system, that permanently connects the user with the serving central office or wire center.

access time—The time the computer system takes to locate and transfer data to or from storage.

accessible—In process operation, a term applied to a device or function that can be used or seen by the operator for the purpose of performing control actions in process, such as set point changes, automanual transfer, or On-Off actions from the front of the control panel or its equivalent on the video screen.

accessory—A peripheral device supporting a main system function, such as a floppy disk drive or printer.

accuracy—The degree of conformity of the indicated value to a recognized, accepted standard value, or ideal value.

accuracy rating—A number or quantity that defines the limit that errors will not exceed when the device or system is used under specified operating conditions.

ACE—Advanced Computing Environment initiative; alliance of more than twenty firms who support software standards for MIP architecture based on common ABI and API. *Also*, Asynchronous Communications Elements.

ACF—Actual cubic feet.

ACK—Short for acknowledge; control code of received transmission. *Also*, sequence of operator action(s) that recognizes new alarm.

acoustic coupler—Device that converts electrical signals into audio signals, enabling data to be transmitted over the public telephone network through a conventional handset.

ACPDP—See *alternating current plasma display panel*.

ACR—Automatic cartridge recorder. *Also*, Attenuation-to-Crosstalk Ratio (of signal cable).

Acronymcompoop—Person who overuses acronyms. ☺

ACSE—Association Control Service Element; for ISO layer 7, for MAP 3.0.

ACT—Acoustic charge transport; technology that processes signals in their natural analog domain, taking advantage of the 10,000-to-1 simplification that results when using analog rather than digital circuits. Converts analog input signal into discrete-time signal, sampled in time, not quantitized in amplitude.

ACTFEL—Alternating-current thin-film electroluminescent; type of liquid crystal display (LCD) flat-panel display device; see *electroluminescent displays*.

active application—Computer application that currently has the keyboard focus, in a Windows environment; usually the "top" window that is "open."

active device—Any component, device, or circuit that introduces gain or has functional direction; usually considered to be any device except pure capacitance, inductance, resistance, or combinations of these. In current loop applications, a device capable of supplying current for the loop.

Active-matrix liquid crystal displays (AMLCDs)—Liquid crystal display (LCD) technique where the pixels on the screen are controlled by voltage signals applied in rows and columns, and an array of thin film transistors (TFTs), with one per pixel, keeps the pixels energized at all times with no need to reenergize on each scan. Thus, they respond faster and are brighter than PMLCDs; compare with *passive-matrix displays*.

ActiveX—Active component eXtension; Binary reusable software object (COM component) that plugs into object linking and embedding (OLE) software, which allows different software packages to communicate and interact with one another in a networked environment, making possible plant floor integration through the Internet and intranets; since the advent of Internet, Microsoft has preferred this term over "OLE" because of its expanded scope (and flashier marketing).

Activity-based costing—Information system that maintains and reports data on the activities, products, and processes of plant or company.

actuator—Generally an energy converter for providing physical action. In the disk drive, it is mechanism that moves the read/write head to the desired position over the disk drive. In process control valves it is a device that converts the controller output signal to valve stem position.

ACU—Automatic calling unit; Dialing device that permits a business machine to automatically dial calls over a communications network (auto answer/dial modem).

A/D—Analog-to-digital conversion of signal.

Ada—Computer language named after Ada Augusta, Countess of Lovelace, assistant to Charles Babbage. Based on Pascal, it was created under a contract to the United States Department of Defense for weapons system tracking, but has since been used throughout the federal government for applications way beyond this initial purpose.

adapter—Device that makes possible compatibility between different equipment.

adaptive control, adaptive tuning—Continuously adjusting the gain (proportioning action) of the control loop from a signal external to that loop. Sometimes other parameters are (also) modified, particularly integral (reset action). *Also*, when referring to advanced control techniques, the term has come to have a broader definition for a system of advanced process control that is capable of automatically adjusting (adapting) itself to meet a desired output despite shifting control objectives and process conditions or unmodeled uncertainties in the process dynamics and often performed through neural networks and/or fuzzy logic coupled with traditional PID-type algorithms.

adaptive dithering—Form of graphic dithering in which a program looks to the overall image to determine the best set of colors or shapes when displaying that graphic on a system with different-sized palette than that on which it was created.

adaptive system—A system displaying the ability to learn, change state, or otherwise react to stimulus; capable of adapting itself to changes in its own environment.

ADC—Analog-to-digital Converter. *Also,* Automated Data Collection.

ADCCP—Advanced Data Communications Control Procedures; bit-oriented communications protocol standard defined by ANSI.

additive primaries—In color reproduction, red, green and blue; when lights of these colors are added together, they produce the sensation of white light.

add-on—Component or device added to a system to increase storage capacity, modify architecture, or upgrade performance; this capability is one of the powerful benefits of a good distributed control system.

Additive Primaries—In color reproduction, red, green and blue; when lights of these colors are added together, they produce sensation of white light.

address—Identification of a location in memory; number, label, or name that represents the hardware or memory location within the system, for convenience in obtaining access to the data residing there so it can be used in other parts of that system.

administratium—Heaviest element known to science; it is chemically inert because it has no protons or electrons and thus has an atomic number of zero. Nevertheless, it does have 1 neutron, 75 vice neutrons, and 111 assistant vice neutrons, all held together by mesonlike forces called morons. ☺

ADO—Ampex Digital Optical: in video development, a traditional video editing system component that allows video frames to appear to be in motion.

ADPCM—Adaptive differential pulse code modulation; encoding format for compressing and storing audio information in digital format.

ADS—Address data strobe.

ADSL—Asymmetric digital subscriber line; a technique that compresses the amount of data needed to send computer, voice, and video data over normal phone lines (a compared to coaxial cable) so those three services can function independently and simultaneously. The asymmetrical component means that the upload speeds are slower than the download speeds, but most delays occur during downloading.

advanced design—Beyond comprehension of the sales force. ☺

advanced process control (APC)—process control strategies beyond straightforward PID loop control, which is usually defined as "classical" advanced control. They involve a combination of PID loops, dead time compensators, lead/lag feedforward function blocks and single-variable constraint controllers.

AE—Application entity; active element within an ISO layer. *Also,* Architectural Engineer; *Also,* Application Enabler.

A&E—Architecture and Engineering; company that designs and builds the process plant; now called EPC. See *EPC.*

AEB—Australian Electrotechnical Board; standards association of Australia, a member of IEC.

AECMA—Association Européenne des Constructeurs de Matériel Aérospatial. European standards group for aerospace industry.

AENOR—Asociación Española de Normalización y Certificación; standards group in Spain.

AFAN—Advanced factory automation network.

AFM—Audio frequency modulated.

AFNOR—Association Française de Normalisation; standards group in France.

AGA—Advanced Graphics Architecture; chip set for driving high-resolution multimedia tools. *Also,* American Gas Association, a national trade association founded in 1918 in the United States, composed of about three hundred gas distribution and transmission companies to act as clearinghouse on gas energy information, and act as a catalyst in technical and energy policy matters, and as a voice for gas industry.

agent—Computing program performing some information-gathering or processing task in the background, usually some very small, well-defined task. Some feel that the human mind consists of thousands or millions of agents working in parallel, so "true" artificial intelligence (AI) machines should also contain many agents with some system for arbitrating among competing the results of this activity.

agile manufacturing—Phrase coined by the Iacocca Institute at Lehigh University to describe a manufacturing enterprise in which "information flows seamlessly among inventory, sales, and research departments as well as between organization and its suppliers and customers." Work within an agile organization occurs concurrently rather than sequentially.

AGP—Accelerated graphics port; provides the capability for three-dimensional and full-motion video graphics in workstations.

AGVS—Automated guided vehicle system; controls vehicles that proceed along predetermined routes or guide-paths, performing scheduled material-handling tasks without operators.

AHP—Analytical hierarchy process; approach to using multiple criteria in decisions that aids in the meaningful organization of information, provides the ability to easily change weights and ratings for "what-if" analysis, and verifies that the approach to evaluation is logical and consistent.

AI—See *artificial intelligence*.

AI/O—Analog input/output.

AIA—Application integration architecture; method of Digital Equipment Corporation for allowing programs to be portable between VMS and ULTRIX.

AIFF—Audio Interchange File Format; method for saving digital audio in electronic memory, used for exchanging data between computers. Developed by Apple and used in Macintosh computers with a compression standard called Macintosh Audio Compression/Expansion (MACE).

AIM—Avalanche-induced migration.

alarm—Warning signal presented whenever a critical deviation state from normal conditions occurs in a process. Technically, alarm is a condition (not an event); an event is when the alarm condition begins; another event is when that condition ends.

ALARP—As low as reasonably practical; acceptable control system failure designation based upon IEC 1508 specification.

ALE—Application link enabling; allows a message exchange between different applications within or between computer systems.

ALGOL—Algorithmic Language; computer language designed by committee of the Association for Computing Machinery and European computer industry representatives. Useful for mathematical problem-solving; first block oriented computer language.

algorithm—In computers, a prescribed set of well-defined, unambiguous rules or processes for solving problem in some finite number of steps.

aliasing—In digital signal processing (see *DSP*), distortion due to sampling continuous signal at too low a rate. See *Nyquist Rate*. *Also,* in digital bitmapped graphics, a jagged boundary along the edges of shapes and different-colored shapes within an image.

all new—Parts not interchangeable with existing models.☺

alphanumeric—The sequencing or ordering of a list using both initial letters and numbers.

alpha test—Trying out a new product at vendor's own company before subjecting it to a beta test; software undergoes alpha testing as a first step in getting user feedback. *Alpha* must be Latin for "doesn't work." ☺

Alternating current plasma display panel (ACPDP)—A type of liquid crystal display (LCD) that relies upon the emission of photons from gas that has been ionized by electric charge; electrodes that are covered by insulation layers to protect them from working gas and therefore assuring longer life. Compare with *direct current plasma display panel*.

Alternating-current thin-film electroluminescent (ACTFEL)—A type of Liquid crystal display (LCD) flat panel display device; see *electroluminescent displays*.

ALU—Arithmetic logic unit, which is the portion of the central processing unit (CPU) that performs arithmetic and logic functions (rather than memory organization and data transfer functions).

Alumel—Aluminum nickel alloy used in the negative leg of a type K thermocouple; trade name of Hoskins Manufacturing Company.

A/M—Auto/manual switch. *Also,* Auto/manual station to provide process control signals.

AM—Amplitude modulation; transmission technique in which amplitude of carrier is varied in accordance with signal. See *PM* and *FSK*. *Also,* in electronic publishing and screen displays, halftone screening, as opposed to FM screening, has dots of variable size with equal spacing between dot centers. See *halftone*. Compare with *FM* and *stochastic screening*.

AM/FM—Automated mapping/facility management; electronic mapping, a branch of the Geographic Information System (GIS). See *GIS*.

AM/PSK—Amplitude modulation/phase shift keying. *See phase shift.*

ambient compensation—The design of equipment or a measuring instrument such that changes in ambient conditions do not affect the performance of that equipment or the readings of that instrument.

ambient conditions—The environment surrounding equipment or a system, such as humidity, temperature, pressure, vibration, shock, magnetic fields, etc.

AMLCD—*See active matrix liquid crystal displays*.

Ampere—Amp. Unit of measure used to define the rate of flow of electricity (current) in a circuit; one coulomb (6.25×10^8 electrons) per second.

ampersand (&)—In the typographical composition of screen displays and printing, the symbol for the Latin word *et*, meaning "and."

amplifier—A device that produces output that is a function directly corresponding to input, but that increases its magnitude by drawing from an external source.

amplitude—The height of an alternating or oscillating signal.

amplitude of deviation—Total variation from the desired set point of system; sometimes called "closeness in control," expressed as "closeness of control is ±2°C" or a system bandwidth of 4°C.

AMR—Automated meter reading.

analog–A continuously varying (modulating) signal; in communications, a transmission using variable and continuous waveforms to represent information values, where the interpretation by the receiver is an approximation (quantification) of the encoded value; compare digital.

analog backup—Alternative method of process control by using conventional analog instrumentation in the event of a failure in the computer system.

analog control—Automatic process control loops using pneumatic, electromechanical, electrical, or electronic equipment; compare *digital control*.

ANDF—Architecture-Neutral Distribution Format; an OSF/1 term.

anemometer—An instrument for measuring and/or indicating the velocity of airflow.

Angstrom–Ten to the minus tenth meters (10^{-10}) or one millimicron; a unit defining the wavelength of light, designated by the symbol Å.

angular misalignment—In fiber-optic cables, the loss of optical power caused by deviation from the optimum alignment of the fiber to the fiber at the coupling.

animation—Process of making an object move across a video screen by rapidly displaying a series of pictures of it (icons), each in a slightly different position.

ANN—Artificial neural network.

annotation—Comment, note, or descriptive remark added to printout, screen view, or even in memory itself.

annunciator—Visual or audible signaling device that indicates the conditions of monitored points, loops, circuits, equipment, etc.

ANSI—American National Standards Institute; nonprofit, independent organization supported by trade organizations, industry, and professional societies for standards development and coordination in the United States. They represent the United States to the *ISO*; they defined *ASCII*.

ANSP—Advanced Networking Security Protocol.

antialiasing—In digital graphics, a technique for reducing the jagged appearance of aliased bitmapped images, usually by inserting pixels that blend boundaries, especially color boundaries.

anticipatory control—In process control, sensing a change in the input of the process so as to cause a change in the control signal to one of the other inputs to that same process; does not have self-correcting action as with closed loop (feedback) control; also called feedforward control or open loop control.

antihunt circuit—Circuit designed to prevent oscillation in a feedback process control loop, thereby stabilizing it.

antireset windup—A feature that can appear in a three-mode (PID) process controller that prevents the integral function (*see automatic reset*) from performing when the process variable is outside the proportional band.

AOE—Application Operating Environment; design for UNIX by AT&T.

AOI—And/or invert.

AOX—Adsorbable Organic Halides, a consideration in EPA (United States) regulations.

AP—Application platform; part of software systems management services that provide the environment for management application development, debugging, and execution.

APC—Advanced process control; process control strategies beyond straightforward PID loop control, which are usually defined as "classical" advanced control; APC involves a combination of PID loops, dead time compensators, lead/lag feedforward function blocks, and single-variable constraint controllers.

APD—Avalanche photodiode; diode that exhibits internal amplification of photocurrent through avalanche multiplication of carriers in the junction region.

API—*See Application programming interface.*; a set of formalized software calls and routines that can be referenced by some application program so as to access underlying network services. Programs that use API-compliant calls can communicate with any others that use that same API; the interface between applications software and the application platform.

APL—A Programming Language; a computer language developed by Kenneth Iverson and used mainly in scientific applications; known for its scope compactness, and facility with arrays, it has a highly specialized character set that can be mapped to keyboard.

APP—Application Portability Profile; developed by NIST, includes X Windows, POSIX, SQL, Information Resource Dictionary System (*see IRDS*) for database systems, Open Systems Interconnections (*see OSI*), NFS (*see NFS*), COBOL, C, and Ada.

APPC—Advanced Peer-to-Peer Communications; network architecture definition by IBM that is specified as featuring high-level program interaction capabilities on a peer-to-peer basis.

APPLE—Arrogance Produces Profit-Losing Entity. ☺

applets—Small software application packages for functions that are subsets of larger ones, such as spell-checking function within a word processor application.

application—Computer program, or group of programs, used for a specific task, such as word processing.

application enabler—Software product that allows the rapid development of a software application through the use of productivity tools, standard components, and the reuse of previously developed software.

application layer—Logical entity of the OSI digital communication model; the topmost of seven layers and the one that interfaces with the network user. Performs network services like file transfer and e-mail.

application-oriented language—Problem-oriented programming technique that employs statements that resemble the terminology of the user, rather than of the programmer.

application program—Program developed to perform a particular industry-specific activity, especially one with an interface to the user that requires little or no special training.

application program interface (API)—A set of formalized software calls and routines that can be referenced by an application program to access underlying network services. Programs that use API-compliant calls can communicate with any others that use that same API; the interface between applications software and the application platform.

application software—Programs that process or manipulate data such as database managers, word processors, text editors, and spreadsheets, which are run by the operating system of a computer.

Application-specific software—Computer program that is adapted or tailored to specific user requirements for the purpose of data collection, data manipulation, data archiving, or process control.

APT—Automatically Programmed Tools; computer-aided part programming system for numerically controlled machine tools developed for multiaxis milling machines and for point-to-point and turning work.

Arc—Electric current through the air or across the surface of an insulator and associated with high voltage; can damage components.

Archie–Internet software tool for finding files stored on anonymous FTP sites. User needs to know the exact file name or substring for it; there are over twelve hundred Archie servers on the Internet that allow someone to search through indexes of over two million files through text strings, keywords, and file names, and that allow the use of search limiters and Boolean operators.

architecture—The logical and physical structure (internal operations) of a system.

archival (archive)—Long-term storage of data, usually onto some auxiliary storage medium, such as a separate disk or tape.

ARCnet—Attached Resource Computer network; a token-passing network developed by Datapoint in 1977 using an active hub star at 2.5 Mbs; specifies only the bottom few layers of the ISO model; combines token-passing scheme with star, bus, or tree topologies rather than ring topology (such as token ring).

armature—Part of an electromagnetic device that moves in response to magnetic forces; the rotor of a motor and the moving portion of contacts are examples.

ARP—Address Resolution Protocol; TCP/IP process that maps Internet Protocol (IP) addresses to Ethernet addresses; required by TCP/IP for use with Ethernet.

ARPA—Advanced Research Projects Agency; operates within United States Department of Defense, which developed the first major packet-switched digital computer network.

ARPANet—Advanced Research Projects Administration Network. A precursor to the Internet, developed in the late '60s & early '70s by the United States Department of Defense as an experiment in wide area networking that could survive a nuclear war.

ARQ—Automatic request for retransmission; in digital communications, where a receiver asks a transmitter to resend a block or frame, generally because of errors detected by the receiver.

artifact—In video development, the area within an image or characteristic of image that is the result of system limitations, such as weird shimmering, jaggies, or other undesirable distortion. *Also,* in digital graphics, image imperfections caused by data compression.

artificial intelligence (AI)—That branch of computing that involves capabilities that resemble human thought processes, such as reasoning, learning, vision, aural recognition, and even self-improvement; a term coined in 1956 by John McCarthy at MIT.

artificial language—Programming language based on a prescribed set of rules established ahead of time, such as BASIC, COBOL, Pascal, etc.

AS—Air supply.

ASA—American Standards Association.

ascender—In typography, that part of a lowercase letter rising above the main body, as in the characters "b" and "d."

ASCII—[*pronounced* asky] American Standard Code for Information Interchange; binary character code, each representing a single computer character, to define 128 upper- and lowercase characters, numerals, punctuation marks, and special communication control characters. A standard method for encoding characters into seven or eight binary bits, typically seven-bit-plus-parity code, representing alphanumeric data for processing and communication compatibility among various devices. Defined in ANSI X3.4-1986 and normally used for asynchronous transmission.

ASE—Application Service Element within an ISO layer.

ASHRAE—American Society of Heating, Refrigerating, and Air Conditioning Engineers.

ASI—Actuator sensor interface; European "fieldbus" for binary sensors and actuators.

ASIC—Application-Specific Integrated Circuit.

ASN.1—Abstract Syntax Notation One; ISO IS 8824 and IS 8825 encoding and decoding structures.

ASPC—Algorithmic statistical process control; closed loop version of normally open loop SPC.

ASQC—American Society of Quality Control.

ASRS, AS/RS—Automated storage and retrieval system.

Assembler—Program that translates symbolic source code (written in assembly language) instructions into machine language instructions.

assembly language–Machine-oriented computer programming language in which mnemonics instead of numeric instructions are used to represent each machine language instruction; low-level symbolic programming language closely resembling machine code. Each CPU has its own specific assembly language.

assignable—In instrumentation, a term applied to a feature that permits the channeling (or directing) of a signal from one device to another without the need for switching, patching, or changes in wiring.

assignment statement—Computer programming language statement that gives value to some variable, such as in x = x + 5, y = 8

association—In communications, a program-to-program logical relationship; may be dynamically established and torn down; may be assumed, may not be required. See *connection*.

associative memory—Neural network architecture used in pattern recognition applications, in which the network is used to associate data patterns with specific classes or categories it has already learned.

AST—Aboveground storage tank.

asterisk–Symbol often used in calculations to represent multiplication. Also, used as general request in some computer search tools to mean all references in some particular category, such as "*"file = all files.

ASTM—American Society for Testing and Materials; scientific and technical organization that develops material standards and testing methods.

ASU—Activated sludge unit.

asymmetrical compression—Data compression system that requires more processing capability to compress an image than to decompress an image. Typically used for mass distribution of programs on media such as CD-ROM.

asynchronous—Computer logic or communications in which all operations are triggered by a free-running signal not related to specific frequency or timing; successive stages are triggered by the completion of the preceding stage. *Also,* in the Open Applications Group specification, a method of communicating via separate responses instead of typing the client session to some singular job.

ATC—Air to close (pneumatic valve actuator that will fail open)

ATE—Automatic test equipment.

ATG—Automatic tank gauge(ing).

ATM–Asynchronous transfer mode; type of packet switching that transmits fixed-length units of data, and being asynchronous the recurrence of cells does not depend on the bit rate of the transmission system, only on the source requirements (packets include address of their destinations). Provides a very fast and efficient transfer mode for multimedia applications (up to ten thousand text pages per second), allowing, for example, real-time video transfer and groupware slide projection. *Also*, abbreviation for atmospheres, a unit of pressure measurement.

atmospheric pressure—The force exerted on unit area by the weight of the atmosphere.

ATO—Air to open (pneumatic valve actuator that will fail closed).

ATPG—Automatic test pattern generator; used in video raster alignment.

ATRAC—Adaptive transform acoustic coding; coding method to create minidisks using a varying number of bits per sample depending upon "critical" frequencies encountered.

ATS—Automatic test system.

attenuation—Decrease in the strength of a signal, measured in decibels, as it passes through control system or transmission line; opposite of "gain."

attribute—Characteristic quality of a data type, data structure, element of data model, or system. In object-oriented programming, it is some piece of information that describes the characteristic of the object.

audio frequencies—Frequencies that can be heard by the human ear, usually between 15 and 20,000 cps (cycles per second).

AUI—Attachment unit interface; twisted-pair telephone wire IEEE standard for Ethernet.

authoring system—Software that helps developers design interactive courseware easily, without the painstaking detail required in computer programming.

authoring tools—Software capabilities that allow the creation of applications without the tedious details of programming.

auto answer—Modem that can automatically answer incoming telephone calls from computers and provide data to that system.

auto dial—Modem capable of connecting to a telephone system and dialing a number; modem and communications software to perform proper procedures so computers may exchange data.

Auto/manual station—In instrumentation, a synonym for *control station*.

automatic—You cannot repair it yourself. ☺

automatic error correction—Technique for detecting and correcting errors that occur in data transmission or data handling.

automatic reset—Feature of on/off limit controller that automatically resets that controller when controlled signal returns to within set limits of the bandwidth. *Also,* integral (I) function on two-mode (PI), or three-mode (PID) controller that adjusts the proportional bandwidth with respect to the set point in response to a change in the process variable (due to a change in the load).

automation—Using current technology (tools) to improve the performance, quality, and cost of formerly manual operations.

auto restart—Capability to perform automatic initialization functions to resume operations following an equipment or power failure.

auto tuning—Technique within controller that analyzes a change in the set point of a closed loop or in the control output of an open loop and adjusts or recommends tuning parameters based upon that analysis. Change is necessary to allow the tuner to learn the magnitude and period of process response, which is used to calculate new parameters. See *self-adaptive tuning.*

availability—Ratio of time that a system is operating correctly to the total hours of scheduled operation. Prior to 1962 was calculated as the value of MTBF ÷ (MTBF + MTTR), after 1962 defined by military specifications. as MTTF ÷ (MTTF + MTTR), which is a *calculation* of those times, not a tested value. Very much dependent on environmental conditions, MTBF will drop by about half for every 10°C increase; all other ambient factors will have a similar impact.

avalanche photodiode—Diode that exhibits internal amplification of photocurrent through the avalanche multiplication of carriers (electron hole pairs) in junction region.

AVD—Audio/video driver.

AVI—Audio video interleaved; digital file format by Microsoft developed for dynamic graphics.

AVK—Audio/video kernel.

AVL—Audio/video library.

AVSS—Audio/video subsystem.

AWG—American Wire Gauge; United States standard system used for designating the size of electrical conductors; gauge numbers are inverse to size.

B

b—Baud rate if referring to communication speeds, representing the number of signal elements (typically bits) transmitted per second. *Also,* B (upper case) = byte if referring to storage. *Also,* b (lower case) = bit if referring to storage. *Also,* B (upper case) is a symbol of ANSI thermocouple type for Platinum 30 percent Rhodium vs. Platinum 6 percent Rhodium. *Also,* means "Burner, Combustion" when used in first alpha character position of an ISA instrument function tag, as defined in ANSI/ISA S5.1-1984 (R1992).

ß—(beta) beta ratio: ratio of the diameter of a pipeline constriction to unconstricted pipe diameter.

B roll—In video development, video footage that is edited over voice to illustrate issues being discussed; see *A/B roll.*

backbone network—Traditionally, transmission facility designed to interconnect low-speed distribution channels or clusters of dispersed user devices. Currently defined as a high-speed line or series of connections that form the major pathway within a given network.

background—In computer multiprogramming, environment in which low-priority programs are executed. *Also,* in screen displays, that part not occupied with characters or graphics (which are "foreground").

backplane—Wiring board, usually constructed as a printed circuit, used to provide required connections between logic, memory, and input/output modules. Usually located in the back of a rack, which has sockets into which specific boards fit for interconnection.

backscattering—In fiber-optic cable, the return of portion of scattered light to the input end of the fiber; the scattering of light in a direction opposite to its original propagation.

backup—System, device, file, or facility that can be used as an alternative in the case of malfunction or loss of data.

backward compatible—Designs that provide compatibility with earlier versions; usually called *reverse compatible.*

BACnet—Building Automation and Control network; object-oriented model of standard automation system network supported by ASHRAE for a high-speed, low-cost network for commercial building services, but not designed for industrial process control.

bad break—In typographical composition of screen displays and printing, starting a page or ending a paragraph with single word, or "widow."

balloon—In instrumentation, a synonym for *bubble*, a circular symbol used to denote and identify the purpose of an instrument or function; it may contain tag number.

ballot box—In typographical composition of screen displays and printing, an open square bullet, usually intended to receive a check mark. See also *check box.*

BALUN—Balanced/unbalanced; in the IBM cabling system, refers to an impedance-matching device used to connect balanced twisted-pair cabling with unbalanced coaxial cables.

band pass filter—In digital signal processing *(DSP)*, a filter that passes signals in a certain range of frequencies and attenuates signals above and below that range.

band splitter—In communication, a multiplexer designed to split available bandwidth into independent narrower band subchannels, each suitable for transmitting data at a fraction of the total channel's data rate.

bandwidth—In communication, the range of frequencies available for signals; the range of frequencies occupied by transmitted modulated signal and lying to each side of the carrier wave frequency; the difference, expressed in Hertz (Hz), between the highest and lowest frequencies of transmission channel (generally, the greater the bandwidth, the more information can be sent through at a given time). *Also,* in electronics, the range of frequencies that can pass over a given circuit. *Also,* in process control, a symmetrical region around the set point in which proportional control occurs. *Also,* amount of space occupied by a group of musicians. ☺

baseband—A technique in which a signal is transmitted in its original form and is therefore not changed by modulation; Ethernet, token ring, and ARCnet are examples that use the entire bandwidth of media without modulating the digital signal; signal frequency below point where signal is modulated as analog carrier frequency. *Also,* in modulation, the frequency band occupied by aggregate of transmitted signals when first used to modulate the carrier (IBM). *Also,* a group of musicians playing low-frequency instruments. ☺

BASEEFA—British certification and testing laboratory responsible for testing the equipment of different vendors to some common standard.

baseline—In typographical composition of screen displays and printing, the imaginary line on which the bases of characters sit.

BASIC—Beginner's All-purpose Symbolic Instruction Code; computer language developed at Dartmouth to teach students programming; it features array and string manipulation, is widely used for educational and business applications as it is easily understood and appropriate for solving small problems. Also, Bill's Attempt to Seize Industry Control. ☺

BAT—Best available technology economically achievable for complying with EPA (United States) pollution prevention requirements.

batch manufacturing—Technique for manufacturing parts or finished goods in groups, lots, or batches in which each part or finished product in the batch is identical.

batch processing—In data processing, a technique in which data is accumulated and processed in batches, as compared with interactive processing. *Also,* in industry, a production operation that does not operate continuously but must be stopped for loading and unloading after processing a quantity of material or a limited number of items.

baud—Bits at unit density; unit of digital signal speed; number of discrete conditions per second such as changes in frequencies, amplitudes, etc. When each event represents only one bit condition, only then does baud rate equal bits per second (bps).

Baudot—Data transmission code in which five bits represent one character; use of letters/figures shift enables sixty-four alphanumeric characters to be represented; named for Emile Baudot, pioneer in printing telegraphy.

BBD—Bucket brigade device.

BBS—Bulletin board service; general access provided for users of computers connected to a phone line and provided by a group for the general exchange of messages, illustrations, software, etc. A BBS can be commercial (paid subscribers), volunteer, or perhaps provided by product vendors for use by their customers.

BCC—Block check character; the result of the transmission of a verification algorithm accumulated over a transmission block, normally added to the end, such as CRC, LRC.

BCD—Binary-coded decimal method to express individual decimal digits in four-bit binary notation. (1 = 0001; 2 = 0010; 23 = 0010 0011).

BCH—Bose-Chandhuri-Hocquendhem; error-checking technique.

BCS—Batch control system.

BDAT—Best demonstrated available technology economically achievable in complying to EPA (United States) pollution prevention requirements.

BDS—Committee for Standardization and Metrology (in Bulgaria).

BEDO—Burst extended data out; technology for high-speed (66 MHz) bus access to computer memory.

behind the panel—In instrumentation, a term applied to a location that is within the area that contains the instrument panel, its associated rack-mounted hardware, or an enclosure within the panel. "Behind-the-panel" devices are not accessible for the operator's normal use, and are not designated as "local" or front-of-"panel-mounted." Generally, this term is equivalent to saying "not normally accessible to operator."

BEL—In communication, control character used when a need exists for a call to attention; may also control alarm or attention devices.

Bell—AT&T standards for devices that transmit over telephone lines, such as modems.

benchmark—Fixed point of reference; standard for comparison; outstanding example, appropriate for use as a model.

bend loss—Form of increased attenuation in optical fiber that results from bending the fiber around restrictive curvature (microbend) or from minute distortions in that fiber (microbends).

bend radius—Smallest arc in cable that can be made without causing damage.

BER—Bit error rate.

BERT/BLERT—Bit error rate testing/ Block error rate testing; error-checking technique that compares received data pattern with known transmitted data pattern to determine the transmission line quality.

beta test—Pretesting of product with selected "typical" users to discover bugs before releasing to general sale. Software undergoes beta testing shortly before it is released. Beta must be Latin for "still doesn't work"; see alpha test. ☺

Bézier curve—Description of character, symbol, or graphic by its outline; used by computer drawing programs to define shapes.

BFSL—Best fit straight line; line midway between two parallel straight lines, enclosing all charted values of measurement. Also known as independent linearity, which allows zero and full-scale values, used to establish the position of a reference line, to be moved to points that minimize the nonlinearity specification of an instrument, often when zero is generally not zero and full scale will seldom equal the actual or desired full scale of the instrument, such as with pressure devices.

bias—Signal applied to electronic device to ensure that it operates on particular portion of its characteristic curve.

BILBO—Built in logic block observer.

bill of material—Listing of all subassemblies, parts, and raw materials that go into parent assembly.

bimetal thermometer—Temperature-sensing instrument in which two dissimilar metals are bonded together so that the differential expansion of the dissimilar metals actuates the pointer, indicating temperature.

bin—In video development, place for storing a piece of video footage.

binary—In instrumentation, a term applied to a signal or device that has only two discrete states; when used in its simplest form, as in "binary signal" as opposed to "analog signal," the term denotes an on/off or high/low state, that is, one that does not represent continuously varying quantities; base 2 counting system.

binary notation—Method of numerical representation with two as the base and thus having only two digits, "0" and "1"; easily represented in computing and transmission by two states in frequency, phase, amplitude, voltage, current, etc.

biometric—To measure through biological techniques, typically for security, but also for an interface to process control with voice, face, fingerprint, iris, retina, etc.

BIOS—Basic input/output system; commands used to tell a CPU how it will communicate with the balance of the computer; the information typically needed upon start-up; in some operating systems, that part of program that customizes it to its specific computer.

BIPS—Billion instructions per second (rough measure of processing power).

BIS—Business information system. *Also,* Bureau of Indian Standards, member of IEC.

B-ISDN—Broadband Integrated Services Digital Network.

BIST—Built-in self-test.

BISYNC—Binary synchronous transmission; byte- or character-oriented communications protocol created by IBM that has become industry standard; uses a defined set of control characters for synchronous transmission between binary coded data stations; also called BSC.

bit—Abbreviation of "binary digit"; digit (1 or 0) representing number in binary notation; smallest unit of information recognized by computers.

bitbus—Process control and data acquisition communication by Intel using the seven-layer OSI model, EIA-485 comms, plus SDLC protocol, plus 8044 chip; twisted-pair, multipoint, up to twenty-eight stations per segment, up to five hundred round-trip messages per second.

bit depth—In digital graphics, the number of bits used to represent the color of each pixel in image: bit depth of 2 = black and white pixels, 4 = 16 colors or grays, 8 = 256 colors or grays, 16 = 65,536 colors, 24 ≅ 16.7 million colors, etc.

bit duration—Time it takes for one encoded bit to pass a point on transmission medium; relative unit of time measurement used for the comparison of delay times, such as propagation delay or access latency, where data rate of (typically high-speed) transmission channel may vary.

bit error rate/block error rate testing—BERT/BLERT; error-checking technique that compares received data pattern with known transmitted data pattern to determine transmission line quality.

bit map—In computer imaging, the electronic representation of a page or a chosen area of a page or illustration, indicating the position of every possible spot (zero or one); pixel-based (typically higher resolution on video screen) rather than object-oriented (typically higher resolution on printer).

blackbody—In temperature-measuring devices, a theoretical object that radiates the maximum amount of energy incident upon it; not necessarily black in color, the name was chosen because the color black is defined as the total absorption of light energy.

black box testing—See *functional testing*.

BLOB—Binary large object; in object-oriented programming, a BLOB can contain all kinds of data, such as images, sounds, graphics, programming codes, animations, etc.

Block—Group of digits transmitted as a unit, over which a coding procedure is usually applied for synchronization or error control purposes; also called *frame*.

block diagram—Illustration in which the parts of the process are represented by blocks or similar symbols.

BMP—Bit-mapped format method for saving graphics in electronic memory, used for exchanging data between computers. *Also,* best management practices, an EPA (United States) term for a practice that is not standard per se but must be adhered to no matter what or result in permit loss, even if effluent limits are met.

BMS—Burner Management System; terminology originating in power generation industry.

BNC—Bayonet-Neill-Concelman; bayonet-locking connector used on Ethernet 10Base2 thinnet coaxial cabling.

board—In instrumentation, synonym for panel or panel board; see *panel*.

BOB—Break-out box; testing device that permits the user to cross and tie leads using jumper wires.

BOD—Biochemical oxygen demand of pollutants, calculated for EPA (United States) regulations. *Also,* business object document.

Bode diagram—Diagram in which gain or shift in feedback control system is plotted against frequency; named from *Bode's Theorem*, which shows the interdependence of phase angle and rate of change of gain of desired frequency.

boldface—In typographical composition of screen displays and printing, the heavier typeface version of a type family.

BOM—Bill of materials.

Boolean algebra—A process of reasoning or a deductive system of theorems using symbolic logic and dealing with classes, propositions, or on/off circuit elements such as AND, OR, NOT, EXCEPT, IF THEN, and others to permit mathematical calculations.

booster—Repeater station that amplifies and retransmits received signal.

boot—To start or restart a computer system by causing instructions to be read from a storage device (disk, etc.) into computer's memory; involves loading part of operating system into computer's main memory. If computer is already operating it is called a "warm boot"; otherwise, it is called "cold boot."

BORAM—Block-oriented random access memory.

BOSFET—Bipolar metal oxide semiconductor field effect transistor; an optically isolated FET.

Bourdon Tube—Tubular, elastic pressure-sensing element that may be single-turn, multiple-turn, helical, or spiral in nature; as pressure increases, the element tends to straighten.

boustrophedon—Writing lines "as the ox plows," that is, lines are written (or printed) alternately back and forth, right to left on one, left to right on the next, etc.

BPCS—Basic process control system.

Bps, B/s—Bytes per second; unit of data transmission rate.

bps, b/s—Bits per second; unit of data transmission rate.

BPT—Best practicable control technology currently available in complying with EPA (United States) pollution prevention requirements.

break—In digital communications, a signal to another station, usually to interrupt the process of transmission.

breakdown voltage rating—The DC or AC voltage that can be applied across insulation portions of a circuit or device without causing arcing or conduction above a specific electrical current value.

breakthrough—Vendor finally figured out how to sell it. ☺

bridge—In communications, a device that connects local area networks (LANs) at the data link layer (physical connection), using the same communications method, medium, and addressing (using the same protocol). *Also,* in measurement, a four-sided circuit of common elements (resistors, capacitors, etc.), in which one element of equal value is located in each of the four arms so that one element will vary with an unknown change (to be measured), and one other element is adjusted to match the change (determined by nulling the current or voltage drop across circuit), thereby measuring amount of change.

brightness—*Also, luminance*; in video displays, the greatest light that a monitor can emit without losing focus; measured in units called footlamberts.

Brix scale—Hydrometer scale for sugar indicating the percentage by weight of sugar in solution at a specified temperature.

broadband—Multichannel communications technique that has greater bandwidth than a voice-grade line and is potentially capable of greater transmission rates. Transmits on one frequency, receives on another; multilevel duobinary AM/phase shift keying. Sometimes called *wideband*.

broadcast—In digital communications, a method of simultaneously transmitting messages to all stations on a network whether they have made request or not; protocol mechanism whereby group and universal addressing is supported.

brouter—Device that determines whether data uses a protocol that it can route and bridges data that it cannot route. Performs many of the tasks of bridges and routers without the protocol restrictions of a router; expensive, complex, and difficult to install.

browser—Software program designed to facilitate navigation along the World Wide Web to find information, download files, and print copies.

BSC—See *BISYNC*.

BSI—British Standards Institution; British certification laboratory for testing the equipment of different vendors to some common standard. Member of IEC.

BSL—Best straight line; see *BFSL*.

BSR—See business service request.

BTEX—Benzene, toluene, ethyl benzene, and xylene; a consideration in EPA (United States) regulations.

BTF—Bend to fit; this comment is the unstated last step of all do-it-yourself instructions. ☺

BTG—Boiler turbine generator combination; terminology originated in power generation industry.

BTL—Bridge tied load; power amplifier technique.

BTU—British thermal unit; roughly the quantity of thermal energy required to raise one pound of water (at its maximum density) 1 °F.

bubble, balloon—In instrumentation, circular symbol used to denote and identify the purpose of an instrument or function; it may contain tag number.

buffer circuit—Isolating circuit interposed between two circuits to minimize the reaction from output to input; usually has high input impedance and low output impedance.

buffer coating—In fiber-optic cable, a protective layer such as acrylic polymer applied over fiber cladding for protective purposes.

buffer memory—Temporary storage device used to compensate for the difference in data rate and data flow between two devices (typically between a computer and printer). *Also,* called spooler.

buffer solution, buffered solution—In pH terms, a solution that maintains a set pH value regardless of added acids or bases; often used for calibration.

buffer tube—In fiber-optic cable, hard plastic tube to hold one or more fibers.

bug—Error or fault in software or hardware, so named by Capt. Grace Hopper, USN, after a moth shorted a relay in the first electric computer (ENIAC, c. 1940). She dutifully logged in her required report, "reason for problem, bug in system." *Also,* defined by some wags as "an annoying feature." ☺

bulb—In liquid-filled thermometer, the area at tip (sensing portion) of a filled system containing the liquid reservoir, hence, the largest proportion of the expanding fluid (minimizing inaccuracies).

bullet—In typographical composition of screen displays and printing, a solid dot used as an ornamental character, usually to highlight an important item in the text.

bulletin board (service)—General access provided for users of computers connected to a phone line, by group for the general exchange of messages, illustrations, software, etc. A BBS can be commercial (paid subscribers), volunteer, or perhaps provided by the product vendor for use by its customers.

burst pressure—Maximum pressure applied to a device such as a transducer, sensor, or case without causing leakage.

burst proportioning—Fast cycling output form on-time-proportioning controller used in conjunction with solid-state relay, typically used in the control of electric furnaces to prolong the life of heaters by minimizing thermal stress.

bus arbiter, bus scheduler—Device dedicated to the task of regulating the fair allocation of bus bandwidth.

bus—Transmission path or channel; an electrical connection with one or more connectors through which all attached devices receive all transmissions at the same time. Linear LAN topology such as Ethernet or token bus, where all network nodes "listen" to all transmissions, but each responds only to those addressed to it.

BVS—*Berggewerkschaftliche Versuchsstrecke*; German certification and testing laboratory for testing the equipment of different vendors to some common standard.

byte—Binary element string functioning as a unit, usually shorter than a computer "word"; bytes made up of six to eight bits are the most common. Also called a "character"; allows representation of up to 256 different pieces of information (00000000 to 11111111).

C

C—In thermometry, degrees centigrade (scientific notation, degrees Celsius). *Also,* Thermocouple type for tungsten 5 percent Rhenium versus tungsten 26 percent Rhenium. *Also,* formerly meant "Conductivity" (electrical) when used in first alpha character position of ISA instrument function tag, still means "Control" if in the succeeding position [see ANSI/ISA S5.1-1984 (R1992)]. *Also,* full name of programming language designed for UNIX operating system (and successor of language named B); known for compactness, memory conservation, and power, allows bit mapping and strong typing. *Also,* symbol for patchboard or matrix board connection. *Also,* c (lowercase) in math is abbreviation "centi-" for 10^{-2} (=0.01).

C+, C++—AT&T extensions to C program language to provide object-oriented features (objects, services, data abstraction, inheritance, sets). Introduced by Bjarne Stroustruo of Bell Labs in the early 1980s.

CAA—Clean Air Act; United States federal law calling for air pollutant emissions standards for motor vehicles and stationary sources; first passed in 1970, reauthorized in 1977 and 1990.

CAAA—Clean Air Act Amendments of 1990 in United States which expand EPA enforcement powers and place restrictions on air toxins, ozone-depleting chemicals, stationary and mobile emissions sources, and substances implicated in global warming and acid rain formation.

cable—Assembly of conductors that has some degree of flexibility; conductors are insulated from each other and enclosed in common sheath. Cables most commonly used for data highway systems are coaxial and twinaxial (shielded twisted-pair), but fiber-optic and multiconductor are also available.

cache memory—High-speed, buffer-type memory filled at medium speed from main memory and temporarily stored locally so that information can be retrieved quickly by some application(s).

CACSD—Computer-aided control system design. Package that couples tremendous numerical capabilities with the graphical analysis techniques of desktop computers to produce complete, easy-to-use computer software for designing and simulating control systems.

CAD—Computer-aided design; the use of high-resolution graphics in wide range of design activities, allowing quick evaluation and modification. *Also,* computer-aided drafting.

CADD—Computer-aided drafting and design.

CADET—Can't Add Doesn't Even Try; name given to first (nonarithmetic) PLCs in 1969 by Richard E. Morley and coworkers at Modicon. ☺

CAE—Computer-aided engineering; the analysis of design for basic error checking or to optimize manufacturability. *Also,* Common Applications Environment.

CAI—Computer-assisted instruction.

CAID—Computer-aided industrial design.

CAL—Computer-augmented learning. *Also,* CAN Application Layer; Controller Area Network that is used as a base for various (initially proprietary) control digital communications systems.

calibration—Test during which known process values are applied to a device or system and corresponding output readings are recorded under specified conditions.

calibration cycle—Calibration of device with increasing signal and decreasing signal (both upscale and downscale directions).

calorie—Quantity of thermal energy required to raise one gram of water 1°C at 15°C.

CAL—CAN application layer; see *CAN*.

CALS—Computer-aided acquisition and logistic support standard.

CAM—Computer-aided manufacturing; the use of computer technology to generate data to control part or all of manufacturing process. *Also,* content addressable memory. *Also,* common access method.

CAMAC—Computer-automated measurement and control; instrumentation interface standard, developed in 1970s by users of the European nuclear physics community, that was promoted for industrial process control.

camera tube—Device contained in television camera that acts as an optical-electrical transducer to convert the optical image of the scene to be transmitted as electrical video signals. The two basic types are image orthicon and vidicon tubes, from which many others have been developed.

campaign—Limited run of product through process; can last from days to months; typically used in chemical industry; control strategy and physical process changes may accompany campaign.

CAN—Controller Area Network; developed by Intel and Robert Bosch Gmbh for real-time automotive industry needs. Primarily European, it provides data link for J1939 used with off-road construction, agricultural, and other vehicles; often used on top of EIA 485, more recently on ISO DIS 11898. Allen-Bradley, with twenty other companies in 1994 promoted DeviceNet on top of CAN; Honeywell promoted MICROSWITCH using SDS on top. *Also,* short for *cancel*, character in digital communications indicating that data preceding it is in error and should be ignored.

canned configurable software—Computer software designed for a specific function, based on general principles, and applied to many applications to achieve desired capability of computer system, that is, process control systems, spreadsheets, historical data collection systems, statistical process control systems, etc.

capacitor—Component that consists of the arrangement of two or more conductive surfaces separated by dielectric (insulator); designed to hold voltage for a limited time; has been used as a memory device to hold values in multiplexing (hence, "hold stations").

capacitor start/capacitor run motor—An AC motor used for hard-starting loads; features a high capacitor for starting the motor and a low capacitor for running the motor; start-up and running windings are always energized; centrifugal switch changes the connection between high and low capacitors.

capacitor start/induction run motor—An AC motor capable of generating larger starting torques; it has a capacitor dedicated to creating a larger magnetic field for heavier start-up requirements. This capacitor is cut out as the motor reaches operating speed.

capacity—In computers, storage capability for a quantity of information, usually given in bytes (KB, MB, GB).

CAPE—Concurrent Art-to-Product Environment; computer-aided design tools used for (drawing) "concept-to-finished-product" efforts.

cap height—In typographical composition of screen displays and printing, the height of capital letter measured from baseline to top.

CAPISCE—Computer Architecture for Production Information Systems in a Competitive Environment; project funded by ESPRIT to unite three layers of manufacturing architecture (planning, execution, and control); first effort by major CIM vendors toward seamlessly integrating information from control systems into business planning systems.

CAPP—Computer-aided process planning; data management framework designed to assist functions of process planning.

caps—In typographical composition of screen displays and printing, capital letters of the type font.

carpal tunnel syndrome—Irritation of tendon sheath and lining involving the median nerve at the human wrist; can affect typists, computer operators, and anyone who uses hand tools.

carrier—Continuous frequency capable of being modulated or impressed with a communication signal.

carrierband—Single-channel communication technique that transmits and receives on the same frequency. *Also,* phase coherent FSK. *Also,* group of musicians stationed on a naval vessel that accommodates the landing and take-off of aircraft. ☺

carrier insertion—In digital communications, media access protocol method (ISO data link layer 2) whereby a station in the network monitors message stream of all messages passing through it until it detects a lull in traffic, whereupon it inserts its own message while buffering and later retransmitting any additional incoming messages. Also known as "ring expansion" because the method "expands" the ring of data by one message until the original message or acknowledgment by the receiving station returns to the sender.

Carrier Sense Multiple Access with Collision Detection—CSMA/CD; in digital communications, a media access method (ISO data link layer 2) for local area networks. IEEE 802.3-like standard by Intel, Xerox, and DEC in which contention between two or more stations is resolved by detecting the simultaneous transmission and causing each to retry after waiting a predetermined time, which is different for each station on the network and is usually several microseconds.

CAS number—Number assigned to specific chemicals by the Chemical Abstracts Service. In most cases, these numbers are unique numerical identifiers; in others, this item may show a "mixture" of chemicals within some product.

CASA—Computer and Automated Systems Association (of SME).

cascade—Method for connecting a series of devices (hardware, software, or firmware) so that the output of one becomes the input of another.

cascade control—Automatic control scheme where the output of one process controller is the set point input of another; sometimes used when the output signal of the controller provides other input parameters (ratio, bias, gain, etc.) of another.

cascading—In communications, the connection of twisted-pair hubs by running twisted-pair cable from one hub to another.

CASE—Common Applications Session Element; part of layer 7 for MAP 2.1. *Also,* Computer-aided software engineering; the use of object-oriented programming and other techniques to streamline the generation of programming code as well as to access information from a relational data base. *Also,* Conformity Assessment Systems Evaluation; voluntary program for NIST to check the competency of manufacturers, testing groups, standards groups, trade associations, or other organizations involved in quality assurance.

CAT—Computer-assisted training. *Also,* Current Adjusting Type process control output (4-20 mA).

CATT—Controlled Avalanche Transit Time.

CATV—Community antenna television; often referred to in relation to a type of coaxial cable used for data transmission.

cavitation—Explosive effervescence caused in fluid when pressure is suddenly reduced, such as in the downstream side of valves and some flowmeter designs and eventually causing damage; the same process, however, results in cleaning action in ultrasonic cleaners.

CB—certification board; certificate issued by National Certification Board (NCB) to provide assurance to the end user that claims of product performance have been verified by an independent party, attesting to the quality and safety of that product. Differs from European CE Mark in which testing is done by the manufacturer who makes that product. See also *NCB*.

CBDS—Connectionless broadband data service; definition of which is emerging from the European Telecommunications Standards Institute; expected to be equivalent to and compatible with SMDS. See *SMDS.*

CBEMA—Computer and Business Equipment Manufacturers Association.

CBL—Computer-based learning.

CBT—Computer-based training.

CCD—Charge-coupled device; charge transfer device that consists of an array of MOS capacitors designed so charges can be moved through the semiconductor substrate in a controlled manner. Essentially a shift register, it can be used to form analog or digital serial memories, can function as a dynamic filter, and can be used for imaging as in solid-state cameras, etc. See *MOS.*

CCITT—Consultative Committee for International Telephony and Telegraphy [Comité Consultatif Internationale de Télégraphie et Téléphonie]; international association that sets worldwide communications standards, such as V.21, V.22, X.25, etc. Replaced by ITU-TSS (International Telegraphic Union—Telecommunications Standards Sector).

CCL–Connection control language; in computers linked through phone networks, a file that contains a list of commands the modem needs to work over a network to other "foreign" modems.

CCR—Concurrency, commitment, and recovery.

CCT—CNMA conformance testing. See *CNMA.*

CD—Compact disk; for digital memory, using light to detect information: popular use includes digitized music because it combines robustness with the ability to be mass produced rather cheaply with very sophisticated control and detection system. Size was specifically formatted by Sony and Philips to store Beethoven's Ninth Symphony as conducted by Herbert von Karajan with the Berlin Philharmonic, resulting in standard of seventy-two minutes of capacity per disk, which stores roughly 2 KB per sector and spins at 75 sectors per second, yielding throughput of 150 KB (2K x 75) per second. *Also,* Compatible digital in video data handling.

CDA—Compound Document Architecture; multimedia format by Digital Equipment Corp.

CDDI—Copper distribution data interface; unshielded twisted-pair, shielded twisted-pair, dual-grade twisted-pair options; see *FDDI.*

CDE—Common desktop environment.

CD-E—Compact disk-erasable; reusable CD-R. See *CD-R.*

CDF—Compressed data format; method of saving data to electronic memory expressly for the purpose of exchanging data between computers.

CD-I—Compact disk-interactive (with video); powerful marriage of audio, limited motion video, digital data, and still graphics (publishing) by Philips; provides up to seventy-two minutes of motion video and will support both digital audio and CD-ROM data storage formats.

CDMA—Code Division Multiple Access; in digital communications, a media access protocol (data link layer).

CDPD—Cellular digital packet data; one of the emerging wireless digital communications technologies useful for true SCADA systems, CDPD sends packets of data using existing cellular communications technology for a given region. While cost is still a constraining factor with CDPD, this technology has proved effective for regions without direct telephone or leased lines. See also *SCADA*.

CDR—Critical design review; used to identify issues in final design release; compare *PDR*.

CD-R—Compact disk-replicator (recordable); made by using glass substrate to create disk from which plastic replicas are made through injection-molding process for volume copies.

CD-ROM—Compact disk-read-only memory; used to expand computer memory; 4.75-inch laser-encoded optical memory storage medium with the same constant linear velocity spiral format as compact audio disks and some video disks; some can store up to 663 MB of data. *Also,* Consumer device, rendered obsolete in months. ☺

CD-ROM/XA—Compact disk-read-only memory/extended architecture; extension of the CD-ROM standard, but hybrid of CD-ROM with CD-I and promoted by Sony and Microsoft. Adds ADPCM audio to permit the interleaving of sound and video to animation, with sound synchronization.

CD-RTOS—Compact disk-real-time operating system.

CDTV—Commodore Dynamic Total Vision; consumer multimedia from Commodore, which includes CD-ROM/CD audio player, Motorola 68000 processor, 1 MB RAM and ten-key infrared remote control.

CE—Conformité Européene; CE Mark must be applied to products placed on the EU market. Is a mark of conformity indicating the declaration by a manufacturer or its representative in EU that the product or system complies with European law (directives) regulating the necessary level of protection with respect to safety, health, environment, and consumer protection (such as electronic emission and electrical safety requirements) but not any guarantee of quality. It does not replace agency listings such as FM, UL, CSA, or TÜV certification board. CE means tested by manufacturer of product; compare with role of *NCB*.

CEA—Certified environmental auditor (United States); certified category listed by National Registry of Environmental Professionals (NREP).

CEB, CEBus—Consumer Electronics Bus; EIA draft (9/93) to integrate utilities, sensors, controls, and communications in the home. *Also,* Comité Electrotechnique Belge; Belgian member of IEC.

CEF—Comité Electrotechnique Français; French member of IEC.

CEI—Comitato Elettrotecnico Italiano; Italian member of IEC.

cell—In measurement, device that produces electricity by chemical means (electrolytic, voltaic, etc.). *Also,* in manufacturing, a cluster of operations to perform a single function in the assembly line (such as, "drill then tap set of holes, bolt on mounting bracket, attach device").

cell constant—In conductivity measurement, ratio of conductance electrodes to area of electrode surface.

cell controller—Typically a programmable logic controller or an interconnected cluster of them for performing operations in a "cell" on the manufacturing line. The term is sometimes broadened to include portions of process, but with varying interpretations.

CEM(S)—Continuous emission monitoring (system).

CEN—Comité Européen de Normalisation. Its objective is to harmonize national standards of member countries for a common standard throughout European community; European equivalent to ISO.

CEN/CS—Comité Européen de Normalisation/Central Secretariat.

CENELEC, CLC—Comité Européen de Normalisation Electrotechnique; its goals are similar to those of CEN, but focused on electrical and electronic products; European counterpart of IEC.

CEN/TC—Comité Européen de Normalisation/Technical Committee.

central processing unit (CPU)—Part of a computer that contains circuits that control and perform the execution of computer instructions; in personal computers (PCs), the CPU controls the operation of the computer system and executes the arithmetic and logic functions of particular programs.

centripetal force—Force exerted on an object moving in a circular path, which is exerted inward toward the center of the rotation (opposite the centrifugal force).

CEPEL—Centro de Pesquisas de Energia Elétrica; Brazilian certification and testing laboratory for testing the equipment of different vendors to some common standard.

CERCLA—Comprehensive Environmental Response, Compensation and Liability Act (also known as Superfund). United States federal law authorizing the identification and remediation of unsupervised hazardous waste sites.

Cerenkov radiation—Light caused by the radioactive decay of elements.

CESI—Italian certification and testing laboratory for testing the equipment of different vendors to some common standard.

CF—CompactFlash; high-capacity, removable digital memory storage/transfer media that is usually rigid (non-rotational).

CFA—(CompactFlash Association); independent corporation of ten companies working to help create CompactFlash standard: Apple, Canon, Eastman Kodak, Hewlett-Packard, Matsushita, Polaroid, NEC, SanDiak, Seagate, and Seiko Epson.

CFC—Chlorofluorocarbon; a consideration in EPA (United States) regulations; any compound containing carbon and one or more halogens, usually fluorine, chlorine, or bromine. Used as a refrigerant and solvent and as a propellant in aerosol sprays. Those CFCs containing bromine are used in fire extinguishers; CFCs have been identified as a cause of depletion of the Earth's protective ozone layer.

CFH—Cubic feet per hour; standard.

CFI—CAD Framework Initiative standard.

CG—Computer graphics.

CGA—Color/Graphics Adapter (Array); video standard (for IBM PC in 1981), offering 320 x 200 pixels with four colors, or 640 x 200 pixels with two colors. In text mode, up to sixteen possible colors. See *EGA, PGA, SVGA, UXGA, VGA, XGA*. *Also,* continuous gas analyzer.

CGI—Computer Graphics Interface. *Also,* Common Gateway Interface; Internet web standard for methods used by servers, external programs, and scripts for intercommunication.

CGM(IF)—Computer Graphics Metafile (Interchange Format); standard for archiving and transferring graphics data.

CGMP—Current good manufacturing practice; regulations by FDA for finished pharmaceuticals.

CGRM—Computer Graphics Reference Model; ISO/IEC JTC1/SC24 tools for computer graphics to ensure that application programs and pictures are portable.

CGS—Centimeter-gram-second; system of fundamental units for mass, length, and time; now obsolete, replaced by MKS system from which SI units are developed. See *MKS.*

CG/VDI—Computer Graphics/Virtual Device Interface.

chain fall—Method for manually operating remote valves by mechanically using chains and sprockets.

change control—In process validations, formal system by which qualified representatives of appropriate disciplines review proposed or actual changes that might affect validated status; the intent is to determine the need for action that would ensure and document that the system is maintained in validated state.

channel—In communications, specified frequency band or particular path used in the reception or transmission of electrical signals. *Also,* in data processing, the route along which information may travel or be stored within a computer.

character—Standard eight-bit unit representing symbol, letter, number, or punctuation mark—generally, but not always, means the same thing as byte; letter, digit, or other symbol that is used as the representation of data.

character generation—Production of typographic images using font master data generated to screens or output devices.

characteristic impedance—Impedance termination of an (approximately) uniform transmission line that minimizes reflections from the end of that line.

character-oriented—Describing a communications protocol or transmission procedure that carries control information encoded in fields of one or more bytes. *Also,* someone attracted to unusual people. ☺

character string—Connected sequence of characters.

chatter—Rapid cycling on and off of a device, such as a relay in control process, due to insufficient bandwidth in the controller.

check box—Small square box which appears on video screen display, usually within a dialog box, which is used for selecting choice of options within some application. See also *ballot box.*

checksum—The summation of digits or bits according to an arbitrary set of rules and used primarily for checking the integrity of data; can detect single-bit errors and some multiple-bit errors.

chemical vapor deposition—Semiconductor fabrication process in which material is deposited on a substrate by means of reactive chemicals in the vapor phase, on occasion at low pressure (well below atmospheric pressure) or plasma-enhanced (in presence of plasma discharge).

CHI—Computer human interface; see also *HMI, MMI.*

chip—Small piece of single crystal of a semiconductor material containing either a single component or device or an integrated circuit.

choke—Inductor used to present relatively high impedance to alternating current.

choked flow—Fluid flow condition through valve that, with constant upstream state, cannot be further increased by lowering downstream pressure.

chopper—Device that creates alternating current by periodically interrupting or reversing a continuous source of direct current.

chromel—Chromium nickel alloy used in the positive leg of type K and type E thermocouples; registered trademark of Hoskins Manufacturing Company.

CI—Computer integration.

CIAC—Computer Incident Advisory Capability; established in 1989, this United States Department of Energy group provides computer security services (such as computer virus alerts) to its employees and contractors.

CIE—Commission Internationale de l'Eclairage; international standards group for color and illumination, the first to specify color in terms of human perception rather than just listing the ingredients needed to make a particular device produce a given color. *Also,* computer-integrated enterprise.

CIEE—Computer-integrated extended enterprise.

CIM—See computer-integrated manufacturing.

CIM-AF—Computer-integrated manufacturing application framework; a framework ("protocol" is too restrictive) based upon distributed object-oriented technology to allow control computers to communicate with equipment in plant, and ideally to implement manufacturing execution systems (MES).

CIME—Computer-integrated manufacture and engineering.

CIP—Clean-in-place, typically done in food/pharmaceutical processing vessels where parts are not removable.

CIR—Committed information rate; in network communications, a traffic measurement that is the average bandwidth that is provided over a given time sample; often mistaken as the amount of bandwidth that carrier is guaranteeing.

circuit—Completed communications path through two or more points that finishes where it started; circuits frequently pass through a combination of several electrical devices and conductors that, when connected together, can perform a specific function; these devices may be discrete components or combined in a single integrated circuit (IC).

circuit switching—A method of communications in which an electrical connection between calling and called stations is established on the demand for exclusive use of the circuit until the connection is released. See also *message switching* and *packet switching*.

CISC—Complex instruction set computing; developed by Intel to provide the greatest number of independently functioning units by using them to perform tasks in parallel so the processor makes the most out of each tick of the clock; compare with *RISC*.

C/J—Cold junction; the reference junction of a thermocouple.

cladding—In fiber optics, outer layer that surrounds the fiber core and has a lower index of refraction.

cladding mode—In fiber optics, the mode confined to cladding; a light ray that propagates in cladding.

clamping voltage—Predefined "sustained" voltage held by the clamp circuit at some desired level.

clamp time—in power lines, how fast the surge protector responds to block power surge.

class—In object-oriented programming (OOP), the definition of objects according to their common characteristics. See *OOP*.

classic IBM—A term that usually refers to the original PC-XT or AT bus architecture.

CLB—Configuration-logic block.

client—One of usually several devices on a computer network being supplied by another processor acting as server of data, memory, or function(s); client software requests and receives these functions from server software. See *server*.

client/server architecture—Approach to computer processing where the functions of an application are shared between multiple computers on the same network; it distributes the computing load among several computers on the network.

clip—(As noun) in video development, a piece of video footage.

clipboard—Storage area for holding data (text, bit map, graphic object, etc.) of video-based computer system where some content from a screen window (application) is copied so as to be "pasted" into another application.

CLNP—Connectionless network protocol.

CLNS—Connectionless network service.

clock—In computer intercommunications, shorthand term for source(s) of the timing signals used in synchronous transmission; more generally, the source(s) of timing signals sequencing electronic events.

closed loop control—In process control, any system in which part of the output is fed back to the input to effect regulatory action and in which the controlled quantity is measured and compared with a standard representing the desired value or performance. Any deviation from this standard is fed back into the control system in such a way as to reduce deviation; usually called feedback control. See *feedback*.

closeness in control—Total variation from the desired set point of system; expressed as "closeness of control is ±2°C" or "system bandwidth of 4°C." Also referred to as "amplitude of deviation."

CLS—Connectionless server.

cluster—Collection of terminals or other devices at one location.

CLUT—Color lookup table; used by video display station to define its color palette to use an 8-bit or lower digital image file.

clutter—Unwanted signals caused by noise (EMI, RFI). *Also,* unwanted images on video screen, such as shapes and messages that become unrecognizable because of zooming.

CLV—Constant linear velocity of rotation, as found with compact disks; a formatted LV-ROM.

CMAC—Cerebellar Model Articulation Control; technique used in neural networks.

CMEX—Continuous media extensions to X Windows.

CMIP—Common Management Information Protocol (ISO network management standard).

CMIS—Common Management Information Services (ISO network management standard).

CML—Current mode logic.

CMM—Color matching method; scheme for determining the best color approximations in a color management system.

CMMS—See *computer maintenance management system.*

CMOS—Complementary metal-oxide semiconductor; uses very low power; less heat to be dissipated.

CMR(R)—Common mode rejection (ratio); (measure of) ability of a device to cast off power line interference.

CMS—Cable management system.

CMYK—Cyan, magenta, yellow, black; model or color space used to convey color information; combining differing amounts of these *subtractive* secondary colors produces all the colors in color space. Used by most printers, CMYK works by starting with all light waves (white paper) and then *subtracting* quantities of cyan, magenta, yellow, and black wavelengths with pigments (theoretically, a maximum of CMY produces black, but inks are not pure so the usual result is a muddy brown, hence the addition of black); compare with *RGB.*

CNC—Computer numerical control; allows the control of motion in an accurate and programmable manner through the use of a dedicated computer within the numerical control unit, with the capability for local data input such that machine tools are freed from the need for hardwired controllers.

CNEC—Comité Nacional Español de la CEI; member of IEC.

CNMA—Communications Network for Manufacturing Applications; "sibling" of MAP in Europe that includes IEEE 802.3 and X.25 in the set of reference standards.

coax—Coaxial cable; popular transmission medium that is formed from two or more coaxial cylindrical conductors insulated from each other. The outermost conductor is usually grounded and encased in either wire mesh or extruded metal sheathing. Frequently used for television and radio signals as well as digital signals because its design is less likely to cause or be affected by external fields. Many varieties are available depending upon the shielding needed and the voltages/frequencies to be accommodated.

COBOL—Common Business-Oriented Language; computer language developed by the Department of Defense and fine-tuned by Captain Grace Hopper, USN. One of the most widely implemented, it is primarily known for business applications; highly structured but wordy, it is Englishlike and intrinsically self-documenting.

COD—Chemical oxygen demand; consideration in EPA (United States) regulations.

codec—Compression/decompression algorithm; any of several unique methods for emulating data from digital video (compression) and then redisplaying it with data substituted or assumed from the original (decompression). The term originated during the 1950s for digitizing voice signals for transmission over analog telephone lines and trunks using PCM; disk drive industry uses similar term *ENDEC.* See *PCM, ENDEC.*

coefficient—Constant that is to be multiplied by a variable; in digital signal processing *(DSP),* the values of the coefficients in the filter determine the bandpass band and stop band characteristics.

COFF—Common Object File Format; file format within UNIX.

COIN—COS OSI Information Network; allows the coexistence of the OSI and TCP/IP protocols.

cold junction—Reference junction of a thermocouple, which is held at a stable, known temperature.

collision—In digital communications, the term used when electrical signals from two network devices in CSMA/CD media access system run into each other, triggering retransmission by each but at different times so a second collision is unlikely.

collision domain—In digital communications, a single CSMA/CD network that may consist of two or more Medium-Access Control (MAC) sublayers; MAC sublayers separated by repeater are within the same collision domain. MAC sublayers separated by bridge are within different collision domains; splitting hub or repeater into separate or multiple collision domains is often incorrectly referred to as "segmentation."

color depth—In video development, refers to the number of bits of data used to define the pixels' color (8 bits = 256 colors, 16 bits = 65,535 colors, 24 bits = 16.7 million colors).

colorimeter—Instrument for measuring color in the way the eye sees color.

color mapping—In digital graphics display, assigning colors to the presented image by referencing color palette.

COM—Communication, usually means serial communications port. *Also,* Component Object Model, in computing, a connection mechanism and protocol used to link different applications in the object linking and embedding (OLE) environment. Allows the development of independent, interoperable software objects. De facto object standard by Microsoft competing with CORBA. *Also,* common signal, usually instrument signal electrical ground separate from equipment ground (Earth).

common carrier—Private data communications utility company that furnishes communications services to the general public; originated in the transportation industry, but expanding from the movement of goods and passengers to include signals.

common mode rejection ratio—Ability of an instrument to reject interference from common voltage at its input terminals with relation to ground (versus Normal Mode); usually expressed in decibels (dB). See *normal mode rejection ratio.*

common object request broker architecture (CORBA)—An approach to creating open, object-oriented system architectures; specifies the interoperability of Object Request Brokers (ORBs). This emerging object-oriented programming standard is being presented by Object Management Group (OMG). Planned by eleven companies, including IBM, Hewlett-Packard, and Sunsoft; competes with the de facto object standard COM, by Microsoft.

COM(M)S—Customer-Oriented Manufacturing (Management) System. Software package that promotes closer communication among various departments of a manufacturer, customers, and suppliers. Envisioned by Advanced Manufacturing Research (AMR) as being linked through a manufacturing execution system (MES) to plant controls; counterpart to ERP by Gartner Group. See *ERP, MES.*

communication—In microprocessing, the transmission and reception of data between processing equipment and related peripherals.

communications server—Device on a LAN, usually a dedicated computer, that provides network users with communications programs and links telephone lines and multiplexing facilities with which to transmit data into and out of the network.

communication stack—Layers of protocol that provide communication between the physical layer and user layer.

compaction—See *compression.*

CompactPCI—Connection standard for industrial-grade personal computer interfaces that readily allows modular architectures, yet is rugged enough to greatly reduce ground bounce, improve noise immunity, and reduce noise emissions.

comparator—Circuit that compares two inputs and produces output that is a function of the result of that comparison, such as a differential amplifier.

compatible—Meaning, "can coexist with rules of recognized standard, but may not be compliant" (see *compliant*). For example, a specification-*compatible* device will operate on a standard communications system and communicate with other devices on that system made by same vendor and will not interfere with devices made by other vendors on that same system, but it will not necessarily be able to communicate with those other devices. Merriam-Webster's definition: "existing together in harmony."

compensated range—Range of values within which all tolerances specified for zero, sensitivity, etc. are applicable.

compensating loop—In thermal measurements using a resistance temperature detector (RTD), the lead wire resistance compensation for this type of element where an extra length of wire is run from the instrument to the RTD and back to instrument, with no connection through the RTD. See *resistance temperature detector.*

compensation—The addition of specific materials, devices, or values to counteract some known error.

compiler—Computer program that translates high-level language statements into some form (typically machine code, or some other lower level language) that can directly activate the computer hardware.

compliant—Conforms exactly with the rules of a recognized standard (versus *compatible*); for example, specification-*compliant* device will operate on standard communication system and communicate with all other devices on that system made by any other vendor who is similarly compliant; [Webster definition: submissive].

component RGB video—In video development, red, green, blue, and luminance signals are processed as separate signals (or components), thus achieving higher quality; generally found in professional-grade equipment. See *composite video*.

composite link—Line or circuit connecting a pair of multiplexers or concentrators. *Also,* a circuit carrying multiplexed data.

composite video—In video development, a video signal that combines chrominance (colors red-green-blue) and luminance (brightness of black, white, and gray) information into one signal relayed on single a waveform or over a single wire. Used by most consumer-grade products.

compound—In object-oriented programming (OOP), means "consisting of a combination of elementary objects."

compression—Any of several techniques used to reduce the number of bits required to represent information in the storage or transmission of digital data (saving memory or bandwidth), in which the original form of the information can be reconstructed. *Also,* called compaction; see *asymmetrical compression, JPEG, MPEG, symmetrical compression.*

computer—Device capable of solving problems or manipulating data by accepting data, performing prescribed operations (mathematical or logical) on the data, and supplying the results of these operations.

computer graphics—General term identifying pictures or diagrams, as different from letters and numbers, presented on a computer video screen or hard copy device.

computer-integrated manufacturing (CIM)—The application of computer and communications technology to automate and integrate manufacturing processes. Usually encompasses complete material value-adding chain from order entry to delivery of product. BHP model functions are involved in a set of six layers, colloquially termed the "CIM model." This model is based on the ISO/TR 10314-1, "Industrial Automation—Shop Floor Production—Reference," model for the standardization and methodology to identify requirements.

computing device—In instrumentation, a device or function that performs one or more calculations or logic operations, or both, and transmits one or more resultant output signals; sometimes called "computing relay." See *relay*.

computerized composition—All-inclusive term for the use of computers to automatically perform the functions of hyphenation, justification, and page formatting.

computer maintenance management system (CMMS)—General classification of computer programs designed to assist in managing the maintenance of process plants and other facilities; provides the history and future work scheduling of assets, including tracking preventative maintenance schedules for these assets. Sophisticated CMMS systems keep an inventory of spare parts online with work orders, inventory control, automatic purchasing, receiving, and physical counting as well as providing personnel with information for making appropriate decisions based on costs and operating efficiencies. See *preventative maintenance*, *predictive maintenance*, and *total productive maintenance*.

computer telephony—Broad term for the many combinations of (PC) computers and telephones for new and unique applications.

concatenate—To link together in a chain, such as macros in a software program, message frames in digital communications, or terms in a mathematical equation, etc.

concentrator—Any communication device that allows shared transmission medium to accommodate more data sources than there are channels available within that transmission medium. In twisted-pair Ethernet networks, a multiport repeater with diagnostic and administrative capabilities (often referred to as "hub" or "repeater").

concurrent engineering—Structuring the design process so that all concerned parties, including manufacturing, sales, and customers, are involved from the beginning so as to bring about a more meaningful result faster.

concurrent processing—The simultaneous processing of more than one program.

condensed type—In typographical composition of screen displays and printing, a slender or narrow type face.

conditioning—Modification of a signal in one form or media to match that of another, such as preparing digital output for voice-grade channel transmission, or transforming a 4-20mA nonlinear transmitter signal into a linear digital signal within the controller.

conductance—In conductivity measurement, a measure of the ability of a solution (fluid) to conduct electricity; thus, it is reciprocal of resistance.

conduction—The conveying of energy (usually electrical or heat) through or by means of conductive material.

configurable—In instrumentation, the term for a device or system whose functional characteristics can be selected or rearranged by selecting from libraries of algorithms, images, and "soft-wiring" techniques (generally, methods other than programming languages); the concept generally excludes physical (hard) rewiring as a means of altering the configuration.

configuration—Selection of hardware devices, firmware, or software programs to fit the application technology to its particular use.

conformance testing—Running a standard set of tests to determine whether some product meets a set of standards and/or specifications. Testing does not guarantee that products can interoperate, only that they conform to specification.

conformity—In process signal conditioning, resolution of an analog-to-digital or digital-to-analog conversion; how close the digital represents the analog curve. *Also,* the ability of a product to meet a set of standards and/or specifications. See *compatible*, *compliant.*

conforms—Agrees fully with the rules of a recognized standard, is compliant. See *compliant, compatible*.

connection—In communications, connection implies a transport link-level control circuit. See *association*.

connection head—Enclosure attached to the end of a thermocouple within which electrical connections are made.

CONS—Connection-oriented network service; from MAP.

console—The part of a computer used for communicating among the operator and/or engineer and the control equipment as well as the computer itself. That part of a terminal providing user input and output capability.

constantan—Alloy of copper (50% to 60%) and nickel that has a very low temperature coefficient of resistance with comparatively high resistance, making it very suitable for precision wire-wound resistors and for forming thermocouples with iron, copper, silver, etc. Used as a negative lead in types E, J, and T thermocouples.

constant voltage power supply—Power supply capable of maintaining fixed voltage across variable load resistance and over defined input voltage and frequency change. Output current is automatically controlled to keep the product of output current times load resistance constant.

contacts—Elements used to mechanically make or break an electrical circuit. *Also,* people you know who can do the same in business.. ☺

contention—Facility provided by the communications network that allows multiple terminals to compete on a first-come, first-served basis for a smaller number of computer ports.

context switching multitasking—Multiple applications can be loaded into the computer, but only the one in the foreground is giving process time. This simplest level of multitasking is how early versions of Microsoft Windows worked; that is, once an application is in the foreground, all other applications stop. Compare *cooperative multitasking* and *time-slice multitasking.*

continuous duty—A device able to operate continuously with no off or rest period.

continuous flow production—Method of ongoing production typical of the process industries, as compared with *batch manufacturing*.

control algorithm—In process control, a mathematical representation of the control action to be performed.

control character—Character whose occurrence in a particular context starts, modifies, or stops an operation that affects the recording, processing, transmission, or interpretation of data.

control circuit—A circuit in equipment or an electrical circuit that carries the signal that determines the control action, as distinct from the power used to energize the various components.

control L—In video development, a device control standard used in many consumer and prosumer devices; allows rewind, play, and record commands to be triggered externally.

controlled variable (CV)—In process control, generally that portion of the process changed as a result of control action (usually because of output signal from controller).

controller—Device or program that operates to regulate the controlled variable; it may be a self-contained analog or digital instrument, or it may be the equivalent of these in a shared control system, as in DCS. An automatic controller varies its output automatically in response to the direct or indirect input of a measured process variable. A manual controller is a manual loading station, and its output is not dependent on the measured process variable but can be varied only by manual adjustment. The controller may be integral with other functional elements of the control loop.

controller file—Circuit card cage in which the control functions of several process loops were shared by the full set of cards within it; a term more common with those distributed control systems (DCSs) of the late 1970s through 1980s that used this style.

control mode—Output form or type of control action used by process controller to drive end elements (valves, SCRs, etc.) such as on/off, time proportioning, PID, etc. See *SCR.*

control point—Process control value that the control system is to maintain during operation.

control station—In instrumentation, a manual loading station that also provides switching between the manual and automatic control modes of the control loop; sometimes called an auto-manual station. The operator interface of a distributed control system may be regarded as a control station. *Also,* in communications, a station on network that supervises that network's control procedures such as polling, selecting, and recovery. It is also responsible for establishing order on the line in the event of contention or any other abnormal situation arising between any stations on that network.

control subsystem—Portion of DCS that directs the sequence of operations, interprets coded instructions, and initiates appropriate commands to computer functions prior to executing process actions.

control system—System in which the deliberate guidance or manipulation of various elements is used to achieve a prescribed value of variable(s) so as to cause the desired result within process.

control unit—In computers, those parts that effect retrieval of instructions in proper sequence, the interpretation of each instruction, and the application of appropriate signals to the arithmetic unit and other portions based on that interpretation.

control valve—A valve with known performance characteristics over the full-open to full-closed range, permitting accurate flow adjustment; usually not a hand-actuated on-off valve or self-actuated check valve.

convection—Circulatory action that occurs in fluid at nonuniform temperature due to the variation of its density and action of gravity. The transfer of energy (heat) by this automatic circulation of medium (gas or liquid fluid).

convergence—In a multibeam electron tube, such as a color picture tube, it is the intersection of the beams at a specified point, causing the appropriate colors.

converter—Depending on the field of use, a device that converts AC to DC or vice versa, changes the frequency of the signal (frequency changer), has different electrical properties at its input and output and may be used to couple dissimilar circuits (impedance converter), changes an information code (compiler); or converts one type of energy to another (optical-to-electrical transducer, sound-to-electrical, etc.). In process control, an instrument that changes the sensor's output to a standard signal is properly designated a transmitter, not a converter; a converter is also referred to as a transducer, but that term is completely general, and its use specifically for signal conversion is not recommended.

convolution—In digital signal processing *(DSP)*, a mathematical process that describes the operation of filters. In discrete convolution, the values of corresponding samples are multiplied and added together to form a new function.

cooperative multitasking—Common to the Macintosh platform, this is a step above context switching. Background applications are given processor time but only when the foreground task is idle and allows it, such as while waiting for a keystroke; compare *context switching multitasking* and *time-slice multitasking*.

coprocessing—Microprocessor dedicated only to the task of processing numeric functions very fast and accurately; works in conjunction with "normal" microprocessor, offloading it to dramatically improve the performance of all tasks required of the system. Especially useful when using math-intensive programs such as spreadsheets and CAD functions.

copy—Any furnished material (typewritten manuscript, pictures, artwork, etc.) to be used in the creation of screen displays or in the production of printing.

copyfitting—In typographical composition of screen displays and printing, the calculation of how much space the provided copy will use in a given screen or page, the selection of type fonts and size, art and the performance of scaling and placement, etc.

copy preparation—Providing the directions for and checking illustration details, placing the text and graphic elements in the design of the screen displays and page layouts.

CORBA—See *common object request broker architecture*.

core—In fiber optics, the central region of the optical wave guide through which light is transmitted. Typically 8 to 12 microns in diameter for single-mode fiber, 50 to 100 microns for multimode. It has an index of refraction higher than that of the surrounding cladding.

Coriolis force—Result of centripetal force on mass, moving with velocity radially outward in rotating plane; phenomenon used in flow measurement.

corrective maintenance—To continue to operate process or system until failure occurs, then make necessary repairs. Compare *preventative maintenance*, *predictive maintenance*.

COS—Corporation for Open Systems.

COSE—Common Open Software Environment; effort by the UNIX community to unify the various versions of UNIX.

COTS—Commercial off-the-shelf; in reference to hardware, firmware, and/or software that is not proprietary to one specific vendor but rather is available from any of several vendors in functionally identical and interchangeable form.

c_P—Specific heat.

CPAC—Center for Process Analytical Chemistry.

CPG—Consumer packaged goods.

CPI—Chemical process industries.

CP/M–Command Program for Microcomputers.

cpp—Characters per pica; in typographical composition of screen displays and printing, used in copyfitting calculations as the average number of characters in a specific point size and typeface that will fit in one pica of horizontal space.

cps—Characters per second in data processing; since a single character requires approximately eight bits to represent it, baud rate can be divided by eight to calculate cps (such as, 300 baud = 37.5 cps). *Also,* cycles per second. In electrical alternating current cps is now properly called hertz.

CPU—See *central processing unit. Also,* Central Propulsion Unit, the computer's engine; consists of a tiny spinning wheel that's powered by a running rodent, which is: a gerbil if the machine is a 286; a ferret if a 386; a ferret on speed if a 486; a Tasmanian devil with scalpel if Pentium. ☺

CR—Carriage return. *Also,* CEN Report.

cracking—In computers, breaking into computers through phone lines; see *hacking*.

CRC—Cyclic redundancy check; basic error-checking mechanism for link-level data transmissions, typically bit-oriented protocols. The integrity of the frame is checked using a polynomial algorithm based on the content of the frame and matched with the same calculation made and sent by the originating station.

crest value—Peak value (of voltage, current, or any alternating signal). See *peak value.*

Critical Path Method—In MES, the use of computers to determine the order operations that must be executed to complete some effort in minimum time and determine which operations have some "float" or capacity to be reprogrammed without affecting that minimum time.

CROM—Control Read-Only Memory.

crop—To cut off some part of an image, done in computer graphics.

crossed pinning—Physical configuration that allows two DTE devices or two DCE devices to communicate. See *DCE, DTE.*

crossover—Conductor that runs through cable and connects to differently numbered pin at each end.

crosstalk—Interference due to cross coupling between adjacent circuits or to the intermodulation of two or more carrier channels, producing unwanted signal(s) in one circuit when signal is present in the other.

crowbar—Action in power supply that effectively creates high overload on the actuating member of a protective device. Crowbar action may be initiated by a slight increase in current or voltage.

crowbar voltage protector—Separate circuit that monitors the output of power supply and instantaneously throws short circuit (or crowbar) across output terminals of the power supply whenever a preset voltage limit is exceeded; silicon controlled rectifier (SCR) is often used as crowbar device. See *SCR.*

CRT—Cathode ray tube (video screen), which is used to display information.

CRTL—C-language Run-Time Library

Crystalloluminescence—Light produced by the crystallization of chemicals.

C.S.—Carbon steel.

C/S—See *client/server.*

CSA—Canadian Standards Association; Canadian certification laboratory for testing equipment of different vendors to some common standard.

CSI—Current source inverter type of variable frequency drive; see *VFD. Also,* Control Systems Integrator.

CSIA—Control Systems Integrators Association; group formed by NEMA to address programs for control system engineer registration, ISO 9000 quality program, strategic alliances/joint ventures, business management, and business practices. Affiliated with System Integrators Group within Automation Products and Systems section of Industrial Automation Division.

CSIC—Customer-specific integrated circuit.

CSMA/CD—Carrier Sense Multiple Access with Collision Detection; media access method (ISO data link layer 2) for local area networks (LANs); IEEE 802.3-like standard by Intel, Xerox, and DEC in which contention between two or more stations is resolved by detecting the simultaneous transmission and causing each to retry after waiting a predetermined time; the time is different for each station on network and usually several microseconds.

CSN—Czech Office for Standards, Measurement, and Testing.

CSP—Computer-driven set point of process control loop.

CSS—Client/server solutions.

CSV—Comma-separated variable; format method of saving data to electronic memory expressly for sharing data between computers or applications. Often used to transfer columns of text and numerical data.

CT—See *computer telephony.*

CTD—Cumulative trauma disorder(s); physiological problems that can occur in users of equipment with ergonomically poor design; often used in reference to, but not limited to, the broad category of problems related to repetitive wrist movements linked to extensive data entry in computers. The problem occurs among many other occupations, but the highest rates are among meat packers (OSHA); accounts for 61 percent of all private-sector occupational illnesses in 1991 according to the Bureau of Labor Statistics; also called repetitive strain injury (RSI).

CTE—Coefficient of thermal expansion of materials.

CTS—Clear to send; modem interface control signal (typically, EIA RS-232/422) indicating readiness to accept data from DCE. *Also,* Carpal Tunnel Syndrome; the irritation of tendon sheath and lining involving the median nerve at the human wrist; can affect typists, computer operators, and anyone who uses hand tools. *Also,* Cubital Tunnel Syndrome, irritation of tendon sheath and lining involving median nerve at the human elbow; can affect phone operators, drivers, and those who keep arms in flexed positions or constantly lean on their elbows.

CUI—Common user interface; provides access to any applications that reside on the server or mainframe, regardless of any incompatibilities that exist between workstations or applications.

current—Rate of flow of electricity, measured in amperes (A or amps); 1 Ampere = 1 coulomb per second.

Current loop—In electronic communications, a method of interconnecting terminals and transmission signals; mark (binary 1) represented by current present: space (binary 0) represented by no current.

current proportioning—Output form of controller that provides current proportional to the amount of control required; normally 4 to 20 mA current proportioning band.

cursor—The tracking/selecting "locator symbol" on a video screen; manipulated with keyboard, mouse, trackball, touch screen, etc. and used to retrieve or enter data, command functions and actions.

CUSUM—Cumulative sum; used in statistical process control (SPC).

cutoff wavelength—For single-mode fiber-optic cable, the wavelength above which the fiber exhibits single-mode operation.

cutout alarm—Alarm designed to not function during state of other operating condition(s) or parameter(s), often during start-up, shutdown, or critical stages of process, etc.

cuts-only—In video development, editing system limited to direct edits from one clip to the next with no transitions between the scenes.

c_v—Flow efficiency factor; flow rate (United States gallons per minute) across a restriction (e.g. valves, fittings, etc.) at 1 psig pressure drop.

CV—See *controlled variable*.

CVD—Chemical vapor deposition.

CVT—Constant voltage transformer.

CWA—Clean Water Act; United States federal law passed in 1972 and updated in 1987, regulating discharges to surface waters and publicly owned treatment works.

CWT—Cold water temperature.

cyan—Color hue that transmits only blue and green light with no red from the screen view; reflects only green and blue light and absorbs red light on paper using four-color process inks.

cycle progress—Feature of a timer or counter that shows progression point in time or count cycle; can be shown by a digital display or pointer progressing through the scale on a dial.

cyclic redundancy check—Basic error-checking mechanism for link-level data transmissions, typically bit-oriented protocols. The integrity of the frame is checked using a polynomial algorithm based on the content of a frame and matched with the same calculation made and sent by originating station.

cycle time—Time usually expressed in seconds for controller to complete one on/off cycle.

CYS—Cyprus Organization for Standards and Control of Quality.

D

D—Derivative (rate) action in modulating process control in which the rate of change (speed) of correcting a force is proportional to the error signal. *Also,* Thermocouple type for tungsten 3 percent rhenium versus tungsten 25 percent rhenium. *Also*, formerly meant "density" (mass), or specific gravity when used in the first alpha character position of ISA process instrument function tag, still means "differential" in the modifier position. [see ANSI/ISA S5.1-1984 (R1992)]; *Also,* d (lowercase) in math is the abbreviation "deci-" for 10^{-1} (= 0.1).

D/A—Digital-to-analog conversion of signal.

DAC—Digital-to-analog converter. *Also,* Digital Audio Compression.

daemon—Computing process that runs in background, performing specified operation at predefined times or in response to certain events. UNIX term now used with other operating systems; comes from Greek mythology where dæmons were guardian spirits.

DAIS—Database Access Integration Services; profile for uniform access to computer data.

Daisy Chain—To connect one device to another in sequence.

DAL—Data Access Language; in computers, a database access standard that provides a transparent connection among a variety of databases and any applications depending on them.

DAQ—Data acquisition; the gathering of discrete and analog parameters from a process. Sometimes incorrectly called SCADA; see *SCADA*.

dark current—Thermally induced current that exists in photodiode in the absence of incident optical power.

DAS—Data Acquisition System.

DAT—Duration Adjusting Type process control output (time proportioning). *Also,* digital audio tape.

data—In computers and transmission, information represented in digital form, including voice, text, facsimile, and video. ***Also,*** character in Star Trek—The Next Generation. ☺

data abstraction—In object oriented programming (OOP), the reduction of an object description to unique and general characteristics that define a class.

data acquisition system—Any instrument or computer system designed to gather data from many sensors through amplifiers, multiplexers, etc., usually for presentation at some central location.

database—In computer systems, those stores of data placed into a system by the user and in DCS by the process being monitored; usually consolidates many records into a common pool of data records that serves as a single central file.

data file—Portion of computer memory allocated to a specific set of organized data, including codes that identify file name and sometimes file type.

data flow—View of the system as set of independent asynchronous processes, each communicating with each other via I/O streams; coined by Tom DeMarco, Yourdon Press.

datagram—Packet delivery service between nodes in a network, that is, provided by ISO layer 2 interface; has no acknowledge, no ordering, no retransmission.

data highway—Popular term used for a communication network of distributed control systems (DCS); a cable physically connecting various hardware items (devices) distributed along that control system over which the transfer of data is communicated. Usually proprietary to individual vendors because of the need to work with real-time data in a very dynamic process and requiring data transmission much faster than that available on LANs designed for business computers.

data integrity—Performance measure based on the rate of undetected errors.

data link—Any serial data communications transmission path, generally between two adjacent nodes or devices and without intermediate switching nodes. The data link includes the physical transmission medium, the protocol, and associated devices and programs, so it is both a physical and logical link.

data link layer—Second layer in the OSI model; the network processing entity that establishes, maintains, and releases data link connections between (adjacent) elements in a network. Controls access to physical medium (layer 1).

data mining—The process of discovering meaningful new correlation's, patterns, and trends by sifting through large amounts of data stored in repositories, using pattern recognition technologies, and statistical and mathematical technologies. Typically used in enterprise resource planning (ERP) systems to develop an optimum business plan.

data processing—The automatic or semiautomatic organization of numerical data in desired manner; any system that can receive, store, or transmit data as well as perform operations upon data and present results.

data rate—Average number of bits, characters, or blocks of information per unit of time being transmitted, such as bits per second, and which may or may not be equal to signal rate or baud rate.

data streaming—Capability to deliver time-based digital data as it's requested, much like on audio or video cassette, rather than to require the downloading of all the information before it can be used (or played).

data table—Organized form on which data is held in computer.

data warehouse—Repository of extremely large amounts of data generated both inside and outside of an enterprise (corporation), generally for the purpose of developing some business plan to cope with complex operations so as to make them profitable.

Daytona—Version 3.5 of Windows™ NT (not NT 94); much faster, leaner, more applications.

dB—Decibel, logarithmic unit of ratio; ratio can express power, voltage, or current difference between two signals. In signal-to-noise measurements, dB usually signifies the voltage difference between a desired signal and the root mean square (rms) value of noise. The higher the ratio, the less noise that is present in the signal. *Also*, a measurement developed to approximate the response of human senses, which is logarithmic; that is, the doubling of signal power, voltage, or current does not double the volume of the perceived sound or the brightness of the perceived light.

dBm—Measured signal power compared with standard signal power of 0.001 watt into 600 ohms.

DBMS—Database management system; a collection of hardware and software that organizes and provides access to a database, simplifying the management of additions and rearrangements.

dBmV—Measured signal voltage compared with 0.001 volts into 75 ohms.

DC (or dc)—direct current; electric current flowing in one direction only and generally constant in value. *Also,* device control; in data communications, a category of control characters intended to turn other (usually subordinate) equipment on or off.

DCC—Digital compact cassette; uses digital audio compression method (PSSC) for quality similar to a CD but with less "data." *Also*, duty cycle control.

DCD—Data carrier detect(ed); a modem interface control signal (typically, EIA RS-232/422) indicating that a device is connected from DCE; is also called "received line signal detector" (RLSD). See *DCE*.

DCE—Data communications equipment; sits between end devices and network (such as a modem) establishing, maintaining, and terminating connection in data conversation data between two digital devices. *Also,* data circuit-terminating equipment. *Also,* Distributed Computing Environment; software technology licensed by Open Software Foundation (OSF) that provides services for distributed computing; includes technologies for threads, remote procedure calls, directory service, security, time service, distributed file system, personal computer integration, and management.

DCOM—Distributed Common Object Model; extends the Common Object Model (COM) for the network communication of independent, interoperable software objects. See *COM*.

DCPDP—See *Direct Current Plasma Display Panel*.

DCS—Distributed control system; real-time, fault-tolerant system for continuous and complex batch process applications that evolved from central computer control of the 1960s and was developed initially for continuous flow processes that required loop, analog, and limited discrete control. A system that, while functionally integrated, consists of subsystems that may be physically separate and remotely located from one another. *Also,* in system network architecture, digital cross-connect systems.

DCT—Discrete cosine transform; data compression technique. *Also,* device-supported time code.

DCTV—Digital composite Television.

DCX—Intel file format for saving multiple PCX graphics in electronic memory; used for exchanging data between computers.

DD—Device description; in Fieldbus Foundation context, the definition and description of function blocks and their parameters.

DDAC—Digitally directed analog control; otherwise called supervisory control.

DDAS—Diagnostic data acquisition system.

D/DBP—Disinfectants and Disinfection By-Products rule; nationwide U.S. study designed to control the allowable levels of contamination in public water supplies caused by these factors.

DDC—Direct digital control; controlling the action on a process by digital device (generally central computer), which establishes a signal sent directly to the final controlling element.

DDCMP—Digital data communications message protocol; character-oriented protocol developed by DEC for the transmission of data between stations in point-to-point or multipoint data communications system where the physical method of transfer may be parallel, serial, synchronous, or serial asynchronous.

DDD—Direct distance dialing; telephone service in North America that permits the subscriber to call other subscribers in different areas without operator assistance and permitting computers to do the same.

DDE—Dynamic Data Exchange; Microsoft-developed interapplication communications protocol where data from one program automatically updates another; originally to move data from a spreadsheet to a word processor. DDE is the baseline protocol for OLE 1.0 but not for OLE 2.0 (it is supported there, however, to maintain upward compatibility). Has become more complex with the advent of Windows and Windows NT in industrial applications, causing wags to refer to it as "Different Dynamics to Everyone." ☺

DDES—Digital Data Exchange Specifications.

DDL—Data definition language; used in DBMSs. *Also,* device description language from InterOperable Systems Project and HART, and now called VDS. See *VDS.*

DDMC—Distributed Discrete Manufacturing Control.

DDP—Distributed data processing; network of geographically dispersed, logically connected processors that share common resources.

DDR—Digital data repeating; scheme on a single radio frequency that allows peer-to-peer communication between RTUs so as to share workload, compare output to inputs, monitor remote I/O, and relay data back and forth. ***Also***, Digital disk recorders, stand-alone devices that connect to host computer via Ethernet or SCSI interface so as to share files for video image processing and animation effects. See *RTU, SCSI.*

DDS—Dataphone Digital Service; AT&T-developed communication service in which data is transmitted in digital rather than analog form, thus eliminating the need for modems. *Also,* Digital Data Storage. *Also,* Digital Data Service by DEC.

DE—Digitally enhanced; proprietary, digital multidrop instrument protocol by Honeywell.

Dead band—Increment through which an input signal to a device or system is varied before action is detected; expressed as percentage of input span. ***Also***, a quite dull group of musicians. ☺

dead volume—Volume of pressure port of a transducer at room temperature and ambient barometric pressure.

debug—To find and correct mistakes in software or hardware; compare: *bug*.

DEC—Digital Equipment Corp.; *also,* Do Expect Cuts. ☺

Decibel—(dB) dimensionless unit used to express the ratio of two powers, voltages, currents, or sound levels; ten times common logarithm of power ratio: $n = 10\log^{10}({}^{\text{Output}}/_{\text{Input}})$; dBm = decibel referenced to milliwatt; dBμ = decibel referenced to microwatt.

decimation—In digital signal processing *(DSP)*, the process by which the sampled data rate of a signal is reduced by some factor (usually an integer). Its purpose is to reduce the number of samples that must be processed by the circuitry that follows.

DECNET—Digital Equipment Corporation *NETwork*; proprietary architecture to communicate between all of that company's equipment using peer-to-peer technique.

DED—Dark-emitting diode; converse of LED (think about it); no doubt used to show output state of WOM; see *WOM*. ☺

de facto standard—Standard that is widely adopted by the marketplace but has no official legal status; compare *de jure standard*.

default—Value(s) or option(s) that are assumed when not particularly specified; usually important in very flexible systems that require the user to make so many selections that most decisions can be extremely confusing, time-consuming, or just unnecessary. User is free to concentrate only on those selections appropriate for the use at hand.

default directory—In computers, black hole into which all files you need disappear. ☺

de jure standard—Standard that has recognition extended among various organizations, agreed upon by a consensus (substantial agreement, although not necessarily unanimous); usually administered by official organizations, such as ISO/IEC,ANSI, ITU, IEEE, etc. Compare *de facto standard*.

DEK—Dansk Elektroteknisk Komite; the Danish member of IEC.

delay distortion—In communications, distortion resulting from the nonuniform speed of transmission of various frequency components of a signal through the transmission medium.

delayed contacts—Output contacts that transfer when timer times out.

Delay on release—Mode of operation where a delay timing period begins when a control switch is opened.

delimiter—In digital communication, a character that separates and organizes elements of data.

DEMKO—Danmark Elektriske Materiellkontroll; Danish certification and testing laboratory for testing the equipment of different vendors to some common standard.

demodulation—Process of retrieving original signal from modulated carrier wave; this technique is used in data sets to make communications signals compatible with computer signals.

density—Mass per unit volume of substance (specific weight of fluid); often expressed in grams/cm^3 or pounds/ft^3.

derivative action—(Rate); process control response that speeds a correction based upon the deviation rate of change from set point, thereby eliminating overshoot in system.

DES—Data Encryption Standard; data security scheme approved by NBS and specified by FIPS. *Also,* distribution execution system; software packages for such functions as marketing and sales.

descender—In typography, that part of a lowercase letter extending below main body, as in characters p and g.

destination field—In digital communication, field in the message header that contains the address of the station to which the message is being directed.

detector—Optoelectronic transducer used in fiber-optics to convert optical power to electric current; in fiber-optics, usually a photodiode.

deterministic model—Mathematical model that, upon a given set of input data, will produce a single output or single set of outputs (will act in only one very predictable way).

deviation—Difference between the set point (SP; desired value) and process variable (PV; actual, measured value at present) being controlled.

deviation amplitude—Total variation from desired set point of system; sometimes called "closeness in control" and expressed as "closeness of control is ±2°C" or "system bandwidth of 4°C".

device description—In the context of Fieldbus Foundation, the definition and description of function blocks and their parameters.

device driver—Software program that controls how the computer interacts with devices such as a printer, mouse, monitor, etc.; enables the use of devices with the computer.

DeviceNet—"Open" network on top of CANbus created by Allen Bradley; now owned and operated by Open DeviceNet Vendors Association. See *CAN*.

DFA—Digital fault analysis; **also** Design for assembly; the discipline of synchronizing and optimizing fabrication and assembly techniques.

DFM—Design for manufacturing; the discipline of synchronizing and optimizing fabrication and assembly techniques.

DFS—Distributed file system; network version of UNIX that provides transparent file transfer capability by allowing files and other resources attached to one system on a network to be used by other systems as though they were local resources. ***Also***, Design for service; the design of equipment to economically allow easy access and repair.

DFT—Design for test.

DGIS—Direct Graphics Interchange Standard proposed and created by Graphics Software Systems, Inc. (GSS).

DHCP—Dynamic Host Configuration Program; network protocol that allows a workstation to be assigned an IP address dynamically from a centrally managed configuration server; used in Windows™ NT Advanced Server.

DHW—Data Highway for digital communications; see *data highway*.

DI—Dielectric isolation.

diagnostics—Messages to user automatically presented by the system to pinpoint failures in that system.

dialog box—Video screen pop-up window within a selected view that carries an appropriate message for the actions involved and usually into which a response can be made.

diaphragm—Flat or convoluted plate that deforms to provide displacement in response to applied pressure.

DIAT—Direction Impulse Adjusting Type process control output (pulsed signal).

DIB—Device independent bitmap format for saving graphics in electronic memory; used for exchanging data between computers. *Also,* directory information base, for directory services.

DIBIT—Group of two bits providing four possible states: 00, 01, 10, 11.

dichroic filter—Optical filter that transmits light selectively according to wavelength.

DIF—Data Interchange Format; method of saving data to electronic memory expressly for exchanging data between computers.

differential—For an on/off controller, refers to the difference between the point where the controller is triggered off and point where it is triggered back on; control dead band or neutral zone. If too narrow, it can cause "chatter," causing high wear on components; if too wide, it causes poor control. With proportional control, the differential effect is usually averaged out and is of little consequence.

differential pressure—Difference in static pressure between two identical pressure taps at the same elevation located in two different locations in a device.

diffuser—Device that attenuates any fluid flowing through it—gas, liquid, light, or even electric power.

digital—Referring to communications procedures, techniques, and equipment by which information is encoded as either binary "1" or "0"; the representation of information in discrete binary form, discontinuous in time.

digital backup—Alternative method of digital process control initiated by the use of special-purpose digital logic in the event of failure in computer system.

digital control—Automatic process control loops performed by digital control devices, such as computer, microcomputer, microprocessor. Compare: *analog control*.

digital scrubbing—In video development, usually refers to audio scrubbing—reading back and forth over a small portion of audio to locate precise edit point.

digitalization—Process of transforming analog (video) signal into digital information.

digitized typesetting—In typographic imaging, the creation of typographic characters and symbols by the arrangement of pixels.

DIIK—Darned If I Know. ☺

DILTDD41—Do It Like The Darned Drawing For Once! ☺

DIMM—Dual inline memory module.

DIN—Deutsches Industrie Norms, Deutsches Institut für Normung e.V. German industrial standards often used internationally.

dingbat—In typographical composition of screen displays and printing, an ornamental character used to enhance or draw attention to text, which is not part of the standard alphanumerical set. *Also*, Archie Bunker's pet name for his wife. ☺

DI/O, DIO—Discrete input/output.

diode—Any electronic device that has only two electrodes and a voltage characteristic that allows AC current to pass only in the forward direction (as in a flow check valve).

DIP—(sometimes **DIL**) dual inline packaging; standard for or package for integrated circuits ranging in size from 8 to 48 pins.

DIP switches—Miniature circuit switches in a DIP configuration for mounting on circuit boards.

DIR—Direct acting.

direct current plasma display panel (DCPDP)—Type of liquid crystal display (LCD) that relies upon the emission of photons from gas that has been ionized by electric charge where electrodes are exposed to working gas. DCPDPs have lower driving voltages than ACPDPs, but their luminescence diminishes over time because of electrode deterioration. Compare with *alternating current plasma display panel*.

direct digital control—Process or manufacturing control performed by digital device (such as computer, microcomputer, microprocessor), which determines the signal to the final control element.

directory—Computer software structure for organizing files into convenient groups; used to locate files.

DIS—Draft international standard (ISO standard status that has been registered and numbered but not yet given final approval).

discrete—Separate and distinct, such as a signal toggled on or toggled off.

discrete manufacturing—Production line for the assembly of specific hardware, such as is typically found in the automobile and electronic industries.

discrete part manufacturing—Manufacturing process that produces discrete parts in comparatively small lots or batches of one to perhaps fifty thousand.

discrete value—Variable with only two states: "1" (true, on) or "0" (false, off).

discriminator—Circuit that selects signals with a particular range of amplitude or frequency and rejects all others. *Also,* circuit that converts frequency modulated or phase-modulated signal into amplitude modulated signal.

disk—In computer-based devices, moving magnetic surface memory in a disk shape so as to provide faster recall access than magnetic tape reels.

disk operating system (DOS)—Set of programs that instruct disk-based computing system to operate equipment through applications programs and manage its resources, such as tracking, saving, retrieving files, allocating storage space, etc.

disk server—Mass storage device that can be accessed by several computers, providing common sharing of stored data.

DISOSS—Distribution office support system; server portion of client/server facility for handling e-mail.

dispersion—General term for those phenomena that cause the broadening or spreading of light as it propagates through optical fiber; the three types are modal, material, and waveguide.

display—In industrial applications, typically the dynamic representation of data and plant information in visible form through a CRT (video), LCD (flat panel), or other methods.

display station—The location of the video screen and keyboard, etc., from which the plant, portion of plant, or process can be monitored and perhaps operated.

dissipation constant—Ratio for thermistor that relates change in internal power dissipation to resultant change of body temperature.

dissolve—In video development, any of several transitions that involve the gradual decrease or increase in opacity of a clip relative to another clip, graphic, or matte.

distortion—Extent to which a system or component fails to reproduce accurately at its output the characteristics of the input. *Also,* in video displays, called pincushioning; distortion manifests itself at the sides of the screen image by an inward or outward bowing of vertical lines, such as those in spreadsheets and tables; can vary after a switch in resolution and tends to worsen as monitor ages.

distributed communications network—Communications link among various (hardware) components in distributed control system. See also *data highway.*

Distributed Computing Environment (DCE)—Software technology licensed by Open Software Foundation (OSF) that provides services for distributed computing; includes technologies for threads, remote procedure calls, directory service, security, time service, distributed file system, personal computer integration, and management.

distributed control—The use of multiple microprocessors to distribute the functions of DDC (central or host computer) for performing process control, thereby distributing the risk from component failure. Later techniques to minimize ground loops permitted physical distribution around a plant, placing microprocessors at various points in the process.

distributed control system (DCS)—Real-time, fault- tolerant system for continuous and complex batch process applications that evolved from central computer control of the 1960s and was developed initially for continuous flow processes that required loop, analog, and limited discrete control. A system that, while functionally integrated, consists of subsystems that may be physically separate and remotely located from one another.

Distributed Management Environment (DME)—Part of the Distributed Computing Environment (DCE) that unifies the system and network management of stand-alone and distributed systems in a heterogeneous computing environment. Consists of graphical user interface (GUI) and application services for software installation, software distribution, software licensing, printer services, and user group administration.

distributed processing—In computing, sharing application load (sometimes operating system load as well) among multiple processors within a device or along some network of devices.

distributed system—Group of connected computers sharing software, information, and/or load.

dithering—Electronic graphic technique of filling the gap between two pixels with another pixel that has an average value of those two so as to minimize the difference or to add detail to smooth the resulting line. Also the intermingling of dots of various colors to create a color not in the palette that supports the display being presented.

DLC—Data link control; rules (protocol) used by two devices on a communication network to perform the orderly exchange of information. *Also,* Distributed line carrier, see *PLC.*

DLL—Dynamic-link library; unlike static libraries in DOS, code for all functions of a program is not copied into an executable file at link time, but rather linking occurs at run time when library code is joined with program code. This allows a single DDL file to be shared by multiple applications without increasing memory or hard disk, so there is a standard interface independent of languages, compilers, and applications software, and so updating DDL does not require all applications to be relinked or rebuilt.

DLT—Digital linear technology; contains compressed digital data, generally for the creation of commercial CDs.

DMA—Direct memory access; method of moving data from a storage device to RAM without the need for CPU intervention.

DMAC—Direct memory access control.

DMACS—Distributed Manufacturing Automation and Control System.

DMC—Distributed Measurement and Control system.

DME—Distributed Management Environment; part of the Distributed Computing Environment (DCE) that unifies the system and network management of stand-alone and distributed systems in a heterogeneous computing environment; consists of graphical user interface (GUI) and application services for software installation, software distribution, software licensing, printer services, and user group administration.

DML—Data manipulation language for DBMSs.

DMM—Digital multimeter; multiple electrical signal tester that shows values in digital display.

DMOS—Double-diffused metal-oxide semiconductor.

DMS—Dynamic mapping system.

DMT—Dead man timer; time-out device built into equipment to prevent continued operation if equipment operates too long for the intended function (i.e. indicating a problem or malfunction).

DMT (BvS)—(Deutsche Montan Technologie); German certification and testing laboratory for testing the equipment of different vendors to some common standard.

DMUX—Demultiplexer.

DNA—Digital Network Architecture; Digital Equipment Corporation's layered data communication protocol.

DNC—Distributed Numeric Control; *Also,* direct numerical control.

DNP—Distributed Network Protocol; from Westronics, now Harris Controls Division; user's group formed in 1993.

DNS—Distributed Name Service.

DO—Dissolved oxygen.

document—In computers, some unit of printer output that must be printed contiguously, that is, no other output must be interspersed within it; the software application must define the start and end of each document.

Document management system—Provides storage, retrieval, and manipulation of (computer) documents in compact space.

DOE—(Department of Energy); U.S. agency responsible for research and development of energy technology.

domain name—Unique name that defines Internet site, such as "(company).com"; always has two or more parts, separated by periods (part to left is more specific, to the right more general).

DOS—See disk operating system; *also,* Defunct Operating System. ☺

dot—Individual element of a halftone; can be as small as a pixel in screen displays.

dot generator—Test generator used with video receiver to adjust the convergence of a picture tube.

dowatchados—Vendor-named category of control system specifications written by users and system consultants that are typified by sections such as "cabinets shall be metal," followed by six pages of paint specifications contributed by their paint expert; see also *druthers, expectifications, gotchas, ropushers, smokescreens, stick-its, stonecutters, wannagirls*. ☺

downloading—Process of sending configuration parameters, operating software, or related data to remote stations or devices from (usually central) configuration station.

downtime—Period during which manufacturing system, process, plant, computer system, control system, etc., is unavailable to users because of failure.

dp—differential pressure; ***also,*** draft proposal (ISO standard status).

DPDT—Double pole double throw; electrical switch action on a pair of wires that can be used to select one of two paths for the pair or used to reverse the direction of a single polarized pair; relay output contact form C.

dpi—Dots per inch; measure of screen image or printed page.

DPM—Digital panel meter.

DPMI—DOS protected mode interface; multitasking DOS extender, replaces VCPI. See *VCPI.*

DPS—Distributed processor system; term created by Sam Herb in 1994 to identify the newer architectures being developed for distributed control systems in light of connectivity to MES/ERP systems, emerging fieldbus capabilities, "smart" transmitters, "smart" valves, etc., as well as the blurring of the distinction between process controllers and programmable logic controllers; see *DCS.*

DPSK—Differential phase-shift keying; modulation technique used in Bell 201 modem.

DPST—Double pole single throw; electrical switch action used to interrupt flow through a pair of wires.

DPU—Distributed processing unit; *also,* differential pressure unit.

DQDB—Distributed Queue Dual Bus; implementation of reservation strategy in a Metropolitan Area Network (MAN) in which each station on a 150 Mbs twin bus records and maintains reservations in local queue. See *MAN.*

DRAM—[*pronounced* dee-ram] Dynamic random access memory is high speed but must be refreshed regularly.

drift—Variation over time of any electrical property or signal value of a circuit or apparatus, usually because of a change in ambient temperature, time, line voltage, etc.; an advantage of values held in digital memory is that there is no drift in value.

drive—In computers, used as noun for the disk drive mechanism; often identified with alphabetical letter (A-Z) followed by colon (:) to indicate logical disk drive.

driver—(hardware), circuit or device that provides input for another circuit or controls operation of that circuit. *Also*, (software), series of instructions to reformat data to transfer from one computing device to another; often the electrical, mechanical, and software requirements of various devices in system are quite different when they each come from different vendors, and driver packages are needed to allow them to interconnect; open systems considerably reduce, and even eliminate, this need.

droop—A common occurrence in time-proportional controllers, it refers to the difference in output requested by set point and where the system actually stabilizes due to time-proportioning action of the controller.

drop cap—In typographical composition of screen displays and printing, an enlarged, initial capital letter of a paragraph set into the first several lines of that paragraph.

drop-in—Character that appears erroneously (on display screen, printer, file, etc.) because disk or tape drive misstored or misread one or more bits.

drop-out—Character that vanishes (from display, printout, or file) because disk or tape drive misstored or misread one or more bits; in data transmission, momentary loss in signal, usually due to the effect of noise or system malfunction.

druthers—Vendor-named category of control system specifications written by users and system consultants that appears to assemble one best feature from ten different vendors to create an impossible specification for the same one system; see also *dowatchados, expectifications, gotchas, ropushers, smokescreens, stick-its, stonecutters, wannagirls*. ☺

DS—Dansk Standardiseringsråd; standards group in Denmark.

DSA—Directory Service Agent, for directory services.

DSL—Digital subscriber line; technology that uses special modems to send digital signals, rather than analog waveforms, over existing twisted-pair copper phone lines; see also *ADSL*.

DSM—Demand-side management; electric power industry term.

DSP—Digital signal processor or processing; a RISC microprocessor optimized to execute digital signal processing algorithms; an algorithm process by which a sampled and digitized data stream is modified to extract relevant information. See *RISC*.

DSR—Data set ready; modem interface control signal (typically EIA RS-232/422) that indicates that the terminal is ready for transmission from DCE.

DSS—Decision support system; a form of computer-based data warehousing and management using DBMS techniques to focus the retrieval of information for specific needs.

DSSS—Direct sequence spread spectrum; used for wireless communication systems.

DSVD—Digital simultaneous voice data; telephone connections that permit the simultaneous transfer of voice and data similar to ISDN.

DTE—Data terminal equipment; end point of communication link such as a device acting as data source, data sink, or both (workstation, repeater, file server, etc.); usually producing data in human-readable form, as with a printer or video screen.

DTL—Diode-transistor logic.

DTMF—Dual Tone Multiple Frequency; audio signaling frequency on Touch-tone, pushbutton telephones.

DTP—Distributed transaction processing; *also*, Desk-top publishing.

DTR—Data terminal ready; modem interface control signal (typically, EIA RS-232/422) that indicates that the terminal is ready for transmission to DCE.

DTV—Desktop video; combines animation, image metamorphosis, photography, etc., within common data manager.

DUA—Directory User Agent, for directory services.

dub—In video development, a copy of a master tape, usually at lower resolution, for offline editing.

dumb terminal—ASCII asynchronous terminals that do not use data transmission protocol and usually send data one character at time, such as a printer or VDT.

duplex cable—In fiber-optics, two fiber cables suitable for duplex transmission; with copper wire, a pair of wires insulated from each other and with an outer jacket of insulation around the inner insulated pair.

duplex transmission—Transmission in both directions, either one direction at a time (half duplex) or both directions simultaneously (full duplex).

DUT—Device under test.

duty—Statement of operating conditions and their durations to which a device or equipment is subjected, including rest and deenergized periods.

Duty Cycle—In digital transmission, ratio of high levels to low levels; in electrical apparatus, the pulse width times the frequency. In process control equipment, a group of variations of load with time, as with repetitious operation (such as two seconds on, six seconds off), often expressed as the energized percentage of total time cycle; the total time to complete one on/off cycle.

DV, DVCAM—Digital videocassette camera video format; potential emerging video production standard promoted by SONY. DVCPRO is a version by Panasonic; Digital-S is a version by JVC.

DVD—Digital video disk; also called digital versatile disk; a concept to bring the worldwide (consumer) electronics industry into one standard for both computer and entertainment industries (large CD-ROM, movie playback platform, game platform, large computer data drive and erasable memory). Five inch disk fits 3.7 GB of data on a single side using the size of pits and spacing between pit tracks and read the data using a red laser beam rather than the current infrared beam. A variation provides up to 7.4 GB on a single side by using two layers, a semireflective layer above a fully reflective one; another variation provides 5 GB on each side of a two-sided disk. A later format for an agreed-upon standard among audio, video, and computer industries exceeds 17 GB. See *MMCD*, *SD*, and *HDCD*.

DVD-ROM—Digital video (versatile) disk-read-only memory; provides 4.7 GB of memory, roughly seven times more than the 650 megabytes held by CD-ROMs.

DVI—Digital video interactive; brand name of Intel for a variety of product families involving digital video and audio.

DVM—Digital voltmeter.

DVR—Dynamic voltage restorer; turns a distorted waveform, including voltage dips, into a required waveform by interjecting a precise amount of voltage using a series-connected transformer into a distribution feeder between the power supply side and the load side.

DXF—Drawing file format by AutoCAD, adopted by others.

dynamic analysis—Study of data under changing internal and/or external conditions; can include static analysis, linear, or nonlinear.

dynamic calibration—Calibration in which the input varies over a specific length of time and the output is recorded against time.

Dynamic Data Exchange (DDE)—Microsoft-developed interapplication communications protocol in which the data from one program (application) automatically updates another. Originally to move data from a spreadsheet to word processor. Is the baseline protocol for OLE 1.0, but not for OLE 2.0 (it is supported there, however, to maintain upward compatibility). Has become more complex with the advent of Windows and Windows NT in industrial applications, causing wags to refer to it as "Different Dynamics to Everyone." ☺

dynamic dispatching—In real time (as it occurs); reporting to an MES system all status changes, such as work completed, an operational problem, priority changes, updates to entire plant floor, and the automatic rescheduling of all operations for all released jobs to reflect those changes.

dynamic memory—Solid-state memory in which stored information decays over a period of time, depending on the nature of the device and its physical environment. The memory must be refreshed often enough to maintain integrity; MOS random access memory and CCD memory are both dynamic. See *MOS* and *CCD*.

dynamic pressure—Difference in pressure levels from static pressure to stagnation pressure caused by an increase in velocity; increases by the square of the velocity.

dynamic range—Range over which an active device can produce a suitable output signal in response to an input signal. Often determined as the difference in decibels between the noise level of a system and the level at which output is saturated (overload level).

E

E—Symbol of ANSI thermocouple type for chromel versus constantan. *Also,* means "voltage" (EMF) when used in the first alpha character position of ISA process-instrument function tag; means "primary element" (sensor) in succeeding position [see ANSI/ISA S5.1-1984 (R1992)]. *Also,* voltage signal.

EAAUG—European Association of AutoCAD User Groups; EC-sponsored initiative to provide members with access to information and services in their native languages through a simple dial-up modem service. See *EC*.

EABI—Embedded Application Binary Interface; establishes object code standards for embedded applications of software so as to allow developers to easily migrate and reuse code from processor to processor.

EAPROM—Electrically alterable programmable read-only Memory; memory that can be selectively altered using an electrical field rather than ultraviolet (as with EPROMs); sometimes the field can be controlled so as to be selective, without erasing all the stored data (as with EPROMs). See *EPROM.*

early trip contacts—Independent set of contacts in timing equipment that will transfer at a set point that occurs before the end of a timing or count cycle.

earth—That electrical potential that is common to Earth; British term for the term *ground* in United States.

EBCDIC—Extended Binary Coded Decimal Interchange Code; 8-bit character code used primarily in IBM equipment that allows for 256 different bit patterns.

EBR(S)—Electronic batch record (system).

EC—European Community; group of European countries banded together for common agricultural and economic policies: Belgium, Denmark, France, Germany, Greece, Ireland, Italy, Luxembourg, The Netherlands, Portugal, Spain, United Kingdom; not to be confused with the *EU. Also,* electronic commerce, business environment integrating electronic transfer and automated business systems. See *EU*.

ECAD—Electrical computer-aided design.

ECC—Error checking and correction; form of "self-correcting" memory; see *error detection and correction*.

ECELAN—Hardware and software for VAX and PCs so as to provide file transfer over Ethernet at 10 Mbaud.

echo—To reflect received data to the sender, for example, keys depressed on keyboard are usually echoed as characters displayed on screen; as security check, transmitted message is repeated back to sender.

echo check, echoplex—A method for checking accuracy of the transmission of data in which received data are returned to the sending end for comparison with the original data.

ECISS—European Committee for Iron and Steel Standardization.

ECL—Emitter coupled logic.

ECMA—European Computer Manufacturers Association.

EDA—Electronic design automation.

EDC—See *error detection* and *correction*; form of "self -correcting" memory.

eddy current—Current induced when a conductor is subjected to a varying magnetic field; the causes energy loss, usually as heat, and becomes significant in high-frequency applications.

EDG—Electronic dot generation; method for producing halftones electronically on scanners.

EDI—Electronic data interchange; computer-to-computer exchange of structured transactional information between autonomous computers.

EDIF—Electronic Design Interchange Format.

EDIFACT—Electronic Data Interchange for Administration Commerce and Traffic.

editing suite—In video development, a collection of equipment for editing video.

editor—In computing, software for changing, adding to, or deleting programs.

EDL—Edit decision list; in video development, a text file created by an editing application that describes all edits in a piece; an online editing system can read EDL and create a finished piece, using original source tapes.

EDM—Engineering data management; controls access to online and archived engineering data. Prevents unauthorized users from getting information and erroneously making changes that others don't know about.

EDO—Extended data out; high-performance dynamic random access memory (DRAM).

EDP—Electronic data processor or processing.

EEA—European Economic Area.

EEC—European Economic Community.

EECS—Electrical Equipment Certification Service. British certification laboratory for testing the equipment of different vendors to some common standard.

EEMS—Enhanced Expanded Memory Specification in PCs.

EEPLD—Electronically Erasable Programmable Logic Device.

EE(P)ROM—Electronically erasable (programmable) read-only memory. A device that can be erased electrically and reprogrammed; can be written upon selectively within active system on byte-by-byte basis, like RAM, but is also nonvolatile like ROM.

EES—Enterprise execution system; software packages to help reconcile top-down business planning with bottom-up production execution requirements for such functions as planning, production, and distribution issues. See *MES, DES* (distribution execution system).

effective resistance—Alternating current resistance; measured as power in watts dissipated as heat divided by current in amperes squared; includes resistance to direct current and resistance due to eddy currents, hysteresis, and skin effect.

effective value—Root mean square value; virtual value.

EFL—Emitter follower logic.

EFT—Electrical fast transient; burst surge interference to electrical and digital signals.

EFTA—European Free Trade Association; Austria, Finland, Iceland, Norway, Sweden, Switzerland.

EFTS—Electronic funds transfer system.

EGA—Enhanced Graphics Adapter (Array); video standard (for IBM PC in 1984); allows sixteen out of possible sixty-four colors to be used; can emulate all modes of earlier CGA, adding 320 x 200, 640 x 200, and 640 x 350 pixels with sixteen colors; see *CGA, PGA, SVGA, UXGA, VGA, XGA*.

E-glass—In the construction of glass bulb-type pH sensors, this term is used for membranes of electrodes for processes where measurements are to be made in acid media. Suitable for use at higher process temperatures. See *G-, L-, S-glass*.

EIA—Electronics Industries Association; standards organization in United States specializing in the electrical and functional characteristics of interface equipment (such as the RS series, now EIA series).

EIA 485—Specifies electrical characteristics of generators and receivers for use in balanced digital multipoint systems.

EIA 1393A—User-level format and protocol for the bidirectional transfer of digitally encoded information in a manufacturing environment.

EIA-SP 1907B—International building wiring standard that formalizes cabling practices, distances, installation practices, and media types.

EIAS—Electric-Image Animation System; Macintosh-based 3-D rendering and animation system.

EIS—Enterprise information system; integrated computer database for all aspects of corporate business including process and materials management functions across many plant locations. *Also,* executive information software (system), same as above for plant-wide data, but sometimes the two terms are interchanged.

EISA—Extended Industry Standard Architecture; 32-bit adaptation of 8- and 16-bit buses originally developed by IBM and now standard in almost all PCs using Intel 8086, 80286, and 80386 microprocessors (jointly developed by several other PC manufacturers). Allows more than one CPU to easily share the bus (multiprocessing).

elastance—Reciprocal of capacitance.

elastoresistance—Change in the resistance of a material when it is stressed within its elastic limit; concept used in the design of some sensors.

EL, ELD—See *Electroluminescent Displays*.

electrode—Device that emits, collects, or deflects electric charge carriers, usually in the form of a solid plate, wire, or grid that controls the current into and out of electrolyte, gas, vacuum, dielectric, or semiconductor; used in sensor technology.

Electroluminescent Displays (EL, ELD)—Devices that emit phosphorous glow when excited with small voltage; only completely solid-state type of liquid crystal displays (*LCDs*) and typically come in two versions: direct-current thick-film devices usually used as lamps behind LCDs, and alternating-current thin-film ELs (ACTFEL) devices, which are more suitable for high-performance, high-information content displays. Most ELs used in control systems are ACTFEL devices.

electromagnetic compatibility (EMC)—Directive that took effect January 1, 1996, to ensure that no electronic system sold in any member country will generate sufficient electromagnetic field to disturb nearby systems and will also be immune from electromagnetic fields generated by other systems that comply with those same regulations. Covers frequencies between 9 KHz and 1 GHz. Initially intended to control the electromagnetic sensitivity of virtually all electric and electronic industry products from any EU member or countries included in the European Economic Area (EEA) so as to reduce nontariff barriers to trade. Does not mandate a single law for all countries but sets guidelines that as a result are open to interpretation.

electromigration—Phenomenon in solid-state microcircuits where atomic-scale hills and valleys grow in those thin metal conductors that carry electronic information. Problem is more acute with smaller, more densely packed chips. Perhaps atoms moving around in the same way that hammering, bending, or stretching malleable affects metal eventually causes conductors to melt.

electronic commerce (EC) —Business environment integrating electronic transfer and automated business systems.

electronic data interchange (EDI)—Computer-to-computer exchange of structured transactional information between autonomous computers.

electronic printing—Any technology that reproduces pages without the use of traditional ink, water, or chemistry.

electrophotography—Image transfer systems used in copiers to produce images using electrostatic forces.

elementary—In object-oriented programming (OOP), something consisting of a single object, not a compound.

ELF—Extremely low frequency radiation in CRT-based video monitors; see *VLF.*

ELOT—Hellenic Organization for Standardization.

ELSI—Extra large-scale integration. Integrated circuits that contain more than one million components on a chip.

em—In typographical composition of screen displays and printing, a unit of measurement exactly as wide and high as the point size of the type font; so-named because the letter m in early fonts was usually cast on a square body.

EMA—Enterprise Management Architecture; open network management system created by DEC.

E-mail—Electronic mail; a method of transmitting text messages and files digitally over communication links, such as the phone system. Sometimes used in plant floor Operator Stations to send messages to other parts of the business.

EMC—See *electromagnetic compatibility.*

EMD—Equilibrium mode distribution; steady modal state of multimode optical fiber in which the relative power distribution among modes is independent of fiber length.

EMF—Electromagnetic force of electricity; usually measured in volts.

EMI—Electromagnetic interference; unwanted "noise" created by current-producing devices such as electrical motors and fluorescent lights that affects the quality of signals passing through a data transmission medium.

emissivity—In temperature measurement, the ratio of energy emitted by an object to the energy emitted by a blackbody at the same temperature. The emissivity of the object depends upon its material and surface texture.

EMIT—Embedded micro-interface technology; based on web server chips embedded within devices and allowing users to access and control those devices from anywhere else on that Web to perform remote functions.

EMMUA—Engineering Equipment and Materials Users Association.

EMS—Element Management System, part of AT&T's UNMA. *Also,* Energy management system. *Also,* Expanded Memory Specification in PCs by Microsoft; *Also,* Enterprise Messaging Server by Microsoft for Windows NT mail server.

emulation—Imitation of all or part of a computer system, performed by a combination of hardware and software, which allows programs to run between incompatible systems.

EN—Européen Norms (standards).

en—In typographical composition of screen displays and printing, one-half the width of an *em*. See *em*.

encapsulation—In object-oriented programming (OOP), the inclusion of data structures and procedures in a single entity and the isolation (or hiding) of those workings, leaving interfaces clean and defined for modularity.

encoding/decoding—Process of organizing information into a format suitable for transmission and then reconverting it after transmission.

ENDEC—Encoder/decoder; term used in the disk industry for digital circuitry that performs manipulations similar to those a video codec does for video signals, in bits going to and from disk drive. See *codec*.

end element—(also final device, final control device); in process control, device that causes a change in a process, such as a valve, motor drive unit, SCR, etc.

endothermic—Condition in process that absorbs heat.

end points—Limits of full-scale calibration curve.

End-user interface—Device through which computer application program(s) and /or instrumentation and measurement device(s) provide information to theappropriate people. See also *HMI*, *GUI*.

engineering analysis system—Performs computer-based analyses for evaluating CAD designs and models.

ENIAC—Electronic Numerical Integrator And Computer; reported to be the first electronic computer; introduced at the University of Pennsylvania in 1945 by John W. Mauchly and J. Presper Eckert Jr. after Mauchly had visited John V. Atanasoff in 1941 to examine his 1939 prototype electronic vacuum tube computer, which was the first to use the binary system and could solve equations containing twenty-nine variables. ENIAC consisted of 30 tons of 18,000 vacuum tubes, 500,000 soldered joints, 70,000 resistors, and 10,000 capacitors.

ENQ—Enquiry; Digital transmission control character used as request for response from some remote station.

Enterprise Management Architecture—Open network management system created by DEC.

enthalpy—Sum of internal energy of a body and the product of its volume multiplied by the pressure.

entities—Design elements at the lowest stage of complexity, such as lines or arcs, that are joined to make symbols or groups; see also *primitives*.

ENV—European prestandard.

environmental conditions—All the conditions that equipment may be exposed to during shipping, storage, handling, and operation.

EOC—End of conversation.

EPA—Enhanced (Extended) Performance Architecture for MAP. **Also,** Environmental Protection Agency, primary agency responsible for enforcing U.S. federal environmental laws.

EPC—Engineering, procuring, and construction; a company that designs and builds process plants; formerly called A&E.

EPLD—Erasable programmable logic device.

EPP—Enhanced Parallel Port; digital communication that communicates in both directions.

EPR—Ethylene propylene rubber.

EPRI—Electric Power Research Institute; research consortium of 660 member utilities in the United States.

EPROM—Erasable programmable read-only memory; digital storage device that can have its contents modified by erasing them with ultraviolet light and reprogramming; can be done repeatedly.

EPS—Encapsulated PostScript; format for saving bit-mapped graphics in electronic memory; used for exchanging data between computers.

equalization—Compensation for the increase of attenuation with frequency; its purpose is to produce a flat frequency response.

ERA—(ERA Technology Ltd.); British certification laboratory for testing the equipment of different vendors to some common standard.

ergonomics—Everything related to human physiology and psychology concerning the design of a physical environment to better suit the human condition.

EROM—Erasable read-only memory; entire memory can be erased with exposure to ultraviolet light so that a new program can replace an old.

ERP—Enterprise resource planning; computer-based corporate planning system defined by Gartner Group, linked through Manufacturing Operations Management system to plant controls; counterpart to COMMS by Advanced Manufacturing Research (AMR). See *COM(M)S*.

error—Difference between the value indicated through a sensor and measuring device, and true value of the measurand being sensed; usually expressed in percentage of full scale.

error band—Allowable deviations of output from a specific reference norm. Usually expressed as percentage of full scale. *Also,* group of musicians with a style inappropriate to the occasion. ☺

error control—Arrangement that detects the presence of errors; in some systems, refinements are added that will correct detected errors, either by performing operations on the received data or by requested retransmission from the source.

error detection and correction—Term sometimes used for "self-correcting memory" (code, transmission); software that looks for specific rules of construction, detects expressions that do not conform and substitutes an equivalent form. See *Self-Correcting Memory*.

error message—In computing, some terse, baffling remark used by programmers to place blame on users for the shortcomings of a program.☺

ES—End system; one that implements all seven layers of the OSI model. *Also,* electric supply.

ES-IS—End system to intermediate system.

ESAC—Electrical systems and controls.

ESC—Escape; digital communication control character used to provide additional control functions, it alters the meaning of a limited number of continuously following bit combinations, usually so as to take control of a computer away from a program or to stop a program.

ESD—Electrostatic discharge. *Also,* Emergency Shutdown.

ESDI—Enhanced Storage Device Interface.

ES&H—Environmental, safety, and health.

ESPRIT—European Strategic Programme for Research and development in Information Technology.

ESR—Equivalent series resistance.

ESS—Electronic switching system.

Ethernet—Popular local area network (LAN) design, invented by Robert Metcalfe of Xerox Corporation in the mid-1970s, and used as a standard by DEC and Intel. Characterized by 10 Mbps baseband transmission over shielded coaxial cable and employing CSMA/CD as the access control mechanism. Standardized as specification IEEE 802.3. Uses error-detection procedures but no error correction, but unlike IEEE 802.3, has signal quality error/heartbeat signal from transceiver to node; allows audio and video information to be carried as well as computer data.

Ethernet **10BASE2**—Implementation of IEEE 802.3 standard known as thinnet; operates over thin coaxial cable at 10 Mbps baseband.

Ethernet 10BASE5—Implementation of IEEE 802.3 standard known as standard Ethernet or thicknet; operates over thick coaxial cable at 10 Mbps baseband.

Ethernet 10BASEFL—Implementation of IEEE 802.3 standard designed to operate over fiber-optic cable at 10 Mbps baseband.

Ethernet 10BASET—Implementation of IEEE 802.3 standard designed to operate over Unshielded Twisted Pair (UTP) cable at 10 Mbps baseband.

ETSI—European Telecommunications Standards Institute.

EU—European Union; group of European countries banded together for common security and defense policies; includes the countries of European Community (*EC*) but not to be confused with that organization. See *EC*.

EUI—See *End-user interface*.

EuroMAP—MAP option by ESPRIT that includes special architectures for process industries and Ethernet.

EUT—Equipment under test.

Eutectic Temperature—Lowest possible melting point of a mixture of alloys.

even parity—A "dumb" terminal data verification method in which each character must have an even number of on bits.

event—In process control, change of the status or condition of process loop, such as when some threshold of modulating value is reached, some sequence step occurs, some discrete switch happens (manually or automatically), when a point goes into or comes out of alarm condition. Generally not connected to a time frame but serves to mark the beginning and completion of activities or conditions and to relate activities to one another; in process control systems, should be recorded in history, but discretion should be made on which are cause to notify operator; events can be used to trigger automatic actions in response.

event-driven programming—The ability of a program to respond to events rather follow traditional, sequential code.

EWI—Enterprise-wide integration.

EWMA—Exponentially weighted moving average; method of SQC/SPC suited for continuous process production.

EWOS—European Workshop for Open Systems.

ExCA—Exchangeable Card Architecture; extension to the PCMCIA specification added by Intel to ensure PCMCIA card interoperability on host systems using Intel CPUs.

exception reporting—In digital communication, media access protocol method whereby a station in a network containing a particular item of information maintains a "subscriber's list" of all other stations needing that information, so when that information changes by some specified amount all those subscribers are then updated with this new data.

excess loss—In fiber-optic coupler, optical loss from that portion of light that does not emerge from the nominally operational ports of the device.

excitation—External application of electrical voltage/current applied to transducer or sensor for normal operation.

executive program—Program that controls the execution of all other programs in computer, based on establishing hardware and software priorities and real-time or demand requirements.

exothermic—Condition in process that gives off heat.

expanded type—In typographical composition of screen displays and printing, type font whose width is greater than normal.

expansion factor—In pressure and flow measurement, correction factor for change in density between two measured areas in a constricted flow.

expectifications—Vendor-named category of control system specifications written by users and system consultants that form heroic or epic poetry favored by engineers. Expectifications supply a collection of impossible conditions with loopholes that are loosely held together by wistful verbiage. See also *dowatchados, druthers, gotchas, ropushers, smokescreens, stickits, stonecutters, wannagirls*. ☺

expedite—To confound confusion with commotion. ☺

expert—A self-publicist. ☺

expert system—Computer program applying information, operational rules, and reasoning techniques derived from codified experience and the advice of human experts so as to solve problems.

explosion-proof enclosure—Enclosure that can withstand an explosion of gasses within it and prevent the explosion of gasses surrounding it caused by sparks, flashes, or the explosion of the container itself and that can maintain an external temperature that will not ignite surrounding gasses.

exposed junction—Form of construction of a thermocouple where the measuring junction is fully exposed to the process being measured; used for fastest response time if contamination is minimal.

expression—In mathematics and computing, general term for numerals with signs of operation, variables, and combinations of these, such as 8, 9 + 4, n - 12, etc.

extension—In digital data file identification, abbreviated code at end of file that tells user what kind of information that file contains: for example, .BAT, .COM, .EXE contain applications; .TIF, .WMF, .EPS contain illustrations, .DOC, .TXT contain word files.

external graphic—On the Internet, digital graphic that must be downloaded from the Web instead of being viewed directly from a Web page. See *inline graphic*.

Extnd—Extended data transfer.

extreme (operating) specifications—Environmental conditions over which equipment or system will operate but that may degrade performance and/or life span; see *operating* and *storage specifications*.

extrinsic loss—In optical fiber interconnection, that portion of loss that is not intrinsic to the fiber but is related to imperfect joining, which may be caused by connector or splice.

E-zines—Electronic magazines; generally found on the Internet, these publications are accessed via computer over some network and contain pictures, articles, sound bites, and video clips and are often focused on very specialized topics. Their advantage is that information can be updated on line rather than having to wait for a later edition to be printed.

F

F—In thermometry, degrees Fahrenheit. *Also,* means "flow rate" when used in first alpha character position of ISA process instrument function tag; means "ratio" (fraction) when used in modifier position [see ANSI/ISA S5.1-1984 (R1992)]. *Also,* f (lowercase) in math is abbreviation "femto-" for 10^{-15}.

FA—Factory automation.

factorial designs—Designs of experiments in which multiple input variables are varied simultaneously at two or more discrete levels in every possible combination.

factory calibration—Tuning or altering of control circuit or device by manufacturer to bring it into specification.

FAIS—[*pronounced* fice] Factory Automation Interconnection System. Initially a Japanese effort to commercialize a Mini-MAP subsystem optimized for manufacturing cell network applications. See *Mini-MAP*.

fall time—Time required for the trailing edge of a pulse to fall from 90 percent to 10 percent of its amplitude; time required for a component to produce such a result.

fan-in—Maximum number of electrical inputs acceptable by a logic circuit.

fan-out—Within a family of logic circuits, the maximum number of electrical inputs to other circuits that output or given circuit can drive.

FAQ—Frequently asked questions; term usually associated with the Internet.

farsang—Linear measure of about four miles used four thousand years ago in Babylon, also known as parasang(es). ☺

Fat Client—In client/server architecture, client that performs bulk of data processing operations; data itself is stored on server; usually refers to software, it can also apply to network computer that has relatively strong processing abilities; see *thin client* for contrast.

fault tolerant—Ability of a system to continue executing tasks regardless of the failure of strategic components but perhaps with less effectiveness or somewhat diminished performance and/or functionality.

FC—Fail closed; default mode of the final element in a process, typically a valve.

FCC—Federal Communications Commission; U.S. agency involved with any radio-transmitted communications and the equipment that can interfere them.

FCFS—First come, first served; the order of packet transmissions in multiple access to linear bus LANs, where stations may place reservations in a separate logical channel (as compared with round robin method).

FCS—Frame Check Sequence method of transmission error detection. *Also,* Field(bus) Control System; *Also*, see Fieldbus Communication Services.

FDA—Food and Drug Administration; U.S. agency involved with the validation of all systems and facilities manufacturing food, pharmaceutical, and medical-related products for human or animal use.

FDC—Final control device, such as valve, motor drive unit, SCR, etc.; see *final element*.

FDDI—Fiber Distributed Data Interface; ANSI standard for fiber-optic links with data rates to 100 Mbps; two 50 Mbs counter-rotational token rings, synchronous, prioritized; see *CDDI*.

FDDI-II—Variant to FDDI that supports isosynchronous traffic.

FDI—Failure detection and identification routines.

FDM—Frequency division multiplexer; device that divides available transmission frequency range into narrower banks, each of which is used for a separate channel. *Also,* fused deposition modeling, a form of rapid prototyping, see *RP, rapid prototyping*.

FDX—Full Duplex; mode of communication in which data may simultaneously flow in both directions (4-wire).

FEA—Finite element analysis software for design.

FED—See field emitter display.

Fed. Reg.—*Federal Register*; daily U.S. government publication detailing proposed and final rules and other federal business.

feedback—In process control, sensing change in the output of a processsor as to cause change in the control signal to one of the inputs to that same process; also called closed loop control. See *closed loop control*.

feedforward—In process control, sensing change in the input of process so as to cause change in the control signal to one of the other inputs to that same process; does not have self-correcting action as with closed loop (feedback) control; also called open loop control or anticipatory control. See *open loop control*.

feedthrough—Contact on printed circuit board that connects one physical layer of interconnections with the next, passing through the insulating material that separates them.

FEP—Front end processor; dedicated processor to perform communication functions to off-load other processors within same device; it is that portion of the system that first receives process or plant data, usually for signal conditioning and/or multiplexing.

ferrite—Low-density ceramic material with a composition that includes divalent metal, such as cobalt, nickel, maganese, or zinc. Cores made from these have very low eddy current loss and are useful in some mechanical-to-current transducers as well as in high-frequency circuits and as magnetic dust cores in computers.

ferroresonant power supply—Power supply using ferroresonant regulator consisting of ferroresonant transformer AC tuning capacitor, rectifier, and DC filter capacitor so as to provide reasonable line voltage regulation, which is the least expensive yet most reliable because of the simple circuit.

FET—Field-effect transistor; unipolar multielectrode semiconductor device in which current flows through a narrow conducting channel between two electrodes and is modulated by an electric field applied at the third electrode.

FF—Form feed. *Also,* flat faced. *Also,* means "flow ratio" when used in the first two alpha character positions of ISA process instrument function tag [see ANSI/ISA S5.1-1984 (R1992)]; *Also,* Fieldbus Foundation, a not-for-profit organization dedicated to developing a single, worldwide, interoperable fieldbus. Formed from the merger of WorldFIP North America and ISP Foundation in 1994.

FFT—Fast fourier transform; in digital signal processing *(DSP)*, an algorithm for reducing the amount of calculation needed to compute a Fourier transform.

FI—Fail indeterminate; default mode of a final element in a process, typically a valve.

fiber channel—Emerging optical communications standard by an ANSI working group; 100 Megabytes/second.

fiber loss—Attenuation (deterioration) of light signal in optical fiber transmission.

Fiber-optic Inter Repeater Link—Early implementation of subset of IEEE 802.3 10BASEFL standard designed to connect fiber-optic repeaters at 10 Mbps. Used by various Ethernet manufacturers to produce network and port interface cards as well as MAUs/transceivers. See *MAU.*

fiber-optics—Transmission technology in which modulated light wave signals, generated by laser or LED, are propagated along a (typically) glass or plastic medium, then demodulated to electrical signals by a light-sensitive receiver.

FIC—Fieldbus Implementation Consortium; to implement SP50 as it evolves.

FICIM—Fieldbus Integration into CIM; ESPRIT project group 5206.

field—In record keeping, a predetermined section of a record; that part of a computer record containing some specific portion of information.

fieldbus—Digital, serial, multidrop, twoway communication path between industrial field equipment such as sensors, actuators, controllers, and even control room devices. Specific ISA SP50 (Fieldbus Foundation) standard for digital communications operating at the lowest level of data communications (I/Os) in automation systems. It allows communication and interoperability among "smart" field devices and control system devices from multiple vendors; it also supports information access for monitoring, control, and alarm tasks during plant start-up, operation, and maintenance. As this standard is developing and gaining interest, two versions are emerging: H1 for linking sensors, and actuators to control devices and H2 for functioning more as a full-blown data highway on a more sophisticated scale.

fieldbus communication services—In the context of the Fieldbus Foundation, a messaging sublayer that the application layer provides so as to access to remote application process objects and their Object Directory descriptions.

field emitter display (FED)—Flat-panel display that works much like a CRT, shooting electrons at colored phosphors (pixels) so as to create an image on screen. But rather than illuminate the phosphors with a single electron gun, a "flat cathode" chip is placed behind each phosphor, allowing the use of a flat panel in lieu of bulky picture tube.

field/frame—In NTSC video development, each frame has two fields, one for every even scan line and the other for every odd scan line, so NTSC has 60 fields and 30 frames per second. See *NTSC.*

field of view—Volume in space defined by an angular cone extending from the focal plane of an instrument or video screen.

field programmable—Timers and counters that have user programmable parameters such as time/count ranges and output sequences. Units are often programmed by miniature rocker switches located inside the timer or by jumper wires to different connection points.

field tested—We don't have the equipment to test it at the factory. ☺

FIFO—First in first out.

file—In computers, a set of related records or data treated as single unit. *Also,* a document that has been saved with an unidentifiable name, and thought of as something stored in a file cabinet in foreign language folders—except when you try to remove the file, the file cabinet gives you electric shock and tells you that file format is unknown. ☺

file server—Digital mass storage device that can be accessed by several computers, thereby providing the common sharing of stored data.

film resistor—Type of resistor that uses a thin layer of resistive material deposited on the insulating core. For low-power applications these are more stable than composition resistors and smaller, less expensive than the more accurate wire-wound resistors.

Filter—In digital signal processing *(DSP)*, a circuit that reduces the noise and other unwanted elements of a signal.

filtering—Protection from "background noise" that could alter or destroy data transmission.

final element—(final device, final control Device). In process control the last device in a control loop that causes change in the process, such as a valve, motor drive unit, SCR, solenoid, etc.

Finger—Internet software tool for locating people on other Internet sites.

FInt—Fieldbus International; formed as the successor to Norwegian Fieldbus Consortium.

FIP—Factory Instrumentation Protocol; a French national field bus standard (1 Mbs) for linking sensing actuators and controllers in automation systems; supported by over 125 European companies.

FIPS—Federal Information Processing Systems.

FIR—Finite impulse response filter; in digital signal processing *(DSP)*, filter that has output determined by its coefficients and previous inputs and is characterized by having linear phase response; see *IIR*.

firewall technology—In computer-based networks, the security protection of a database and files from improper access through open networks such as the Internet.

firewire—Computer network technology that permits several electronic devices to communicate; made up of six individual cables—one for power, one for ground, two for data, and two for strobe—which synchronize the data; its assembly is shielded.

firmware—Computer program or software that constitutes a fundamental part of a specific system function and is stored permanently in PROM or ROM or semipermanently in EPROM; "software that acts like hardware."

FIS—Financial Information System; a computer database of customer and vendor accounts used in EIS. See *EIS*.

FIT—Failures in time. *Also,* failure units; the number of failures of a device in a given time; frequently expressed in failures per billion (10^9) hours.

fixed palette—In the context of the Internet, an established palette on a Web browser that converts graphic images to its own colors, rather than the colors from original image.

fixed point—Pertaining to a number system in which each number is represented by a single set of digits, and its base (position of radix point) is implied by the manner in which the numbers are used; see *floating point.*

FL—Fail locked; default mode of the final element in process, typically a valve.

flag—Any of various types of indicators used for the identification of a condition or event; for example, in communications, a bit pattern of six consecutive "1" bits (character representation is 01111110) used in many bit-oriented protocols to mark the beginning (and often end) of the frame.

flash memory—One of the first applications of PCMCIA cards; a Type I card (see PCMCIA) containing up to 20 MB RAM and a small battery so memory is retained when unplugged; alternative to floppy disks and much faster than floppy or hard disks. See *PCMCIA*.

flashover—Disruptive discharge in the form of arc or spark between two electrical conductors or between conductor and earth (ground).

flatbed scanner—Device that scans images in manner similar to photocopy machine where original art is positioned face down on glass plate.

flat tuning—Tuning with substantially equal response to the range of frequencies.

FLC—Fuzzy logic controller.

flicker—Flashing of a video screen as the electron beam that creates image follows its raster pattern.

flip-flop—Half-shift register; bistable multivibrator circuit that usually has two inputs corresponding to two stable states. So called because an appropriate pulse causes it to "flip" into and remain in one state, while a pulse on the other input will cause it to "flop" into the other state.

float—In process control, the amount of time between the completion of a task or activity and the start of the next. *Also,* in your checking account, same idea but with money. ☺

floating—In electrical circuitry, denotes a circuit or device that is not connected to any source of potential.

Floating Gate PROM—Optically erasable read-only memory.

Floating Point—Arithmetic notation in which the decimal point can be manipulated, values are sign, magnitude and exponent; this is a form of number presentation in which quantities are represented by a number called mantissa (significant digits) multiplied by the power of the number base; see *fixed point.*

floppy disk—In computers, a flexible disk carrying magnetic medium in which digital data is stored for later retrieval and use; usually iron-oxide coating on a flexible substrate.

flow—The travel of fluids (liquids or gasses) in response to force, such as pressure or gravity; is often used to indicate the movement of electrical energy (flow of electrons) and digital signals (flow of data).

flow cases—Known conditions of flow.

flowchart—Diagrammatic representation of the operations involved in an algorithm or automated system. Flow lines indicate a sequence of operations or the flow of data, and special standard symbols are used to represent particular operations.

flow control—In digital processing, a procedure for regulating the flow of data once the buffer of a specific device has reached capacity.

flow rate—Actual speed or velocity of flow movement.

flowmeter—Device used for measuring flow or the quantity of moving fluid.

flush left (or right)—In typographical composition of screen displays and printing, setting type so as to line up at the left (or right) margin.

flush paragraph—In the typographical composition of screen displays and printing, a paragraph with no indentation.

flying lead—Wire lead that exits in the back of the connector hood on the outside of the cable jacket; normally attached to the drain wire or shield and then connected to the chassis of the switch, modem, etc. *Also,* hardware control lead.

FM—Factory Mutual Research Corporation; organization that sets industrial safety standards, generally to protect the process; focused on fire safety and prevention. They test and approve products, and FM approval is recognized by OSHA as indicating a product that does not create a fire hazard. Compare with *UL*. Also, frequency modulation; a method of transmission in which the carrier frequency varies in accordance with the signal; *also,* in measuring devices, usually in the form of deviation from center frequency, where the deviation is proportional to applied stimulus. *Also,* in electronic publishing and screen displays, a digital screening process that converts images into very small dots of equal size and variable spacing. See *stochastic screening*, compare with *AM*.

FMEA—Failure Mode and Effects Analysis; a procedure by which every individual component is ranked with percentage failure values for each failure mode (i.e.; transistor short, open, drift, etc.) so as to determine their respective failures in time (FIT). Then, an overall impact is calculated for the device in which all of these components are used; used in developing MTTF. See *MTTF*.

FMS—Flexible manufacturing system. *Also,* Fieldbus Messaging Service; companion standard for Fieldbus application layer.

FNPT—Female National Pipe Thread.

FO—Fail open; default mode of the final element in the process, typically a valve.

focus—In video displays, the crispness of text and lines, the contrast of adjacent single-pixel-wide black and white lines.

FOF—First out fault; system to determine accurately the sequence of alarms in a process or plant.

FOIRL—Fiber-optic Inter Repeater Link; early implementation of subset of IEEE 802.3 10BASEFL standard designed to connect fiber-optic repeaters at 10Mbps. Used by various Ethernet manufacturers to produce network and port interface cards as well as MAUs/transceivers.

Foldback—In the current-limiting circuit of a power supply, the ability to reestablish a flow of current after overload has caused the interruption of current flow by exceeding the preset limits.

folio—In typographical composition of screen displays and printing, the page number.

font—In typographical composition of screen displays and printing, the complete assortment of letters, numbers, punctuation marks, etc., of given size and design.

footlamberts—Unit of brightness in video displays.

forceback—Back-calculation within algorithm function block to prevent signal "bump" during multitasking (switching between functions); particularly important in linking cascaded process control loops in microprocessor-based controllers.

form factor—Physical specifications of a device, such as rack mounts, etc.); evolved from relay terminology for contact configurations.

format—In typographical composition of screen displays and printing, the size, style, type page, margins, printing requirements, etc. *Also,* in computer disks, to prepare the disk so it can hold information in a form recognized by the computer operating system (Macintosh, PC, etc.). *Also,* in computer data object rendition, the form in which data is stored (saved) such as text, bit-mapped, etc.

FORTH—Computer language that should have been called FOURTH (4th-generation), but astronomer/developer Charles Moore's computer accepted only five-character names. This object-oriented language was created to control telescopes, but its extendability is the key to its ever-growing popularity; using "reverse Polish" notation, it contains applications useful in process control.

FORTRAN—Formula Translation; first high-level computer language, developed by IBM (1954); known as a scientific language because of its facility at "number crunching" and solving engineering, mathematical, and other scientific problems; is procedure-oriented and has good array-handling features.

forward channel—Data transmission channel in which the direction of transmission coincides with that in which the information is being transferred.

forward compatible—Designs that ensure compatibility with future versions.

Fourier transform—In digital signal processing *(DSP),* on algorithm for extracting frequency information from a signal.

Fourth-generation Language (4GL), Environment (4GE)—Computer language instructing the computer at a higher-level language abstraction than traditional high-level programming languages; any computer language that does not require traditional input process/output logic will fall into this category.

FOV—Field of view (of sensors, especially optical).

FPD—Flat-panel display; non-cathode ray tube (CRT) displays, generally dominated by liquid crystal displays (LCDs), electroluminescent displays (ELs), and plasma display panels (PDPs). Older, but still widely used, are field emitter displays (FEDs).

FP-EPSM—Functional Profiles for Electric Power Systems Messaging.

FPGA—Field-programmable gate array.

FPLA—Field-programmable logic array.

FPM—Feet per minute (flow velocity). *Also,* Fast Packet Multiplexing, a technology that integrates synchronous and asynchronous data with voice and fax signals over a composite channel, eliminating the delays associated with standard packet multiplexing by giving priority to voice and fax signals over data signals.

FPROM—Field-programmable read-only memory.

FPS—Feet per second, in flow velocity; frames per second in video and computer imaging.

FPU—Floating point unit; performs numeric calculations for the processor, specialized just for numeric calculations. Can boost screen redraws, image filtering effects, spreadsheet calculations, and similar operations by as much as 900 percent.

FQ—Means "flow quantity" when used in the first two alpha character positions of ISA instrument function tag [see ANSI/ISA S5.1-1984 (R1992)].

fractional factorial designs—Subclass of factorial designs that reduces the number of experiments to be performed by exploring only a fraction (such as one half) of the input variable space in a systematic manner.

FRAD—Frame relay access devices.

FRAM—Ferroelectric random access memory is high density with the high speeds of DRAM and SRAM and the nonvolatility of ROM; also called "Flash RAM;" see *flash memory.*

frame—Group of digits transmitted as a single unit, over which a coding procedure is usually applied for synchronization or for error control purposes; also called *block.*

Frequency—Number of cycles over specified time through which an event occurs; reciprocal is called the period.

Frequency division multiplexer (FDM)—Device that divides the available transmission frequency range into narrower banks, each of which is used for a separate channel.

frequency output—Output in the form of the frequency that varies as a function of applied measurand.

frequency phase control regulation—Regulation technique in power supplies that usually employs SCRs and can control the phase of either primary or secondary.

frequency response—Behavior of device output as a function of input, both with respect to time.

Fresnel reflection—A reflection that occurs at the planar junction of two materials having different refractive indices; this is not a function of angle of incidence.

front end—Enigmatic term used by some to mean the operator interface or the application-specific aspects of a computer program; defined by others to mean that part of the control system directly connected to the process sensors and instruments connected to the process.

front-end processor—Dedicated processor to perform communication functions so as to offload other processors within same device. It is that portion of the system that first receives the process or plant data, usually for signal conditioning and/or multiplexing.

FRP—Fiber-reinforced plastic; sometimes used for instrument enclosures.

F.S.—Full scale.

FSF—Fathom-stone-fortnight; a hypothetical system of fundamental units used to indicate the antiquity of someone's thinking; see *MKS*. ☺

FSK—Frequency-shift keying; method of data transmission using frequencies to indicate the state of the bit being transmitted, see *AM* and *PM*.

FTAM—File Transfer, Access, and Management; ISO protocol and part of MAP layer 7.

FT-IR—Fourier transform infrared-based analyzer.

FTP—File transfer protocol; upper-level TCP/IP service that allows files to be copied or moved across a network. *Also,* foil-screened, unshielded twisted pair (wiring for signals).

FTSA—Fault-tolerant system architecture.

FUD—Fear, uncertainty, and doubt; what some vendor sales people try to instill in customers about that vendor's competition. ☺

full bridge—In strain gauges, such as in force or pressure sensors, all four legs of Wheatstone bridge configuration are active in the development of a signal.

full duplex transmission—Simultaneous two-way communication between devices.

full-motion imaging—Video image that is completely smooth; see *raster imaging*.

full-scale output—Algebraic difference between minimum output and maximum output.

function—Characteristic actions, operations, or kinds of work performed by equipment (or people), such as the material handling function. The operation called for in a software instruction, such as "the PID function."

function block diagram—Graphical language of programmable controllers that allows program elements (such as PID and other algorithms) to appear as blocks "wired" together in a presentation similar to circuit diagram. One of five languages accepted under the IEC 1131 standard for PLCs. See *instruction list*, *ladder logic*, *structured text*, and *SFC*.

function blocks—Software modules, often firmware, that generally perform functions originally done in hardware elements and form the building blocks of control strategies; these are located in the user layer of fieldbus standard.

functional requirement—Requirement that specifies some function that a particular system or system component must be capable of performing; usually formally written, especially in process validation.

functional testing—In computer systems, also known as black box testing because source code is not needed. it involves the input of normal and abnormal test cases and then evaluating the outputs against those expected; can apply to computer software or to a total system.

furnace—Apparatus in which heat is liberated and transferred directly or indirectly to a solid or fluid mass; it generally operates at ranges higher than ovens.

futurebus+—Fast standard for scalable backplane interconnect; adapted by IEEE in September 1991 with 32- or 64-bit rate up to 175 MBps, no license fees.

fuzzy logic—Computing method used to model linguistic expressions (such as "somewhat more than") that have nonbinary truth values. It has been used with PID algorithms in process control, especially where process relationships have been nonlinear. Term coined by Lotfi Zadeh in his 1965 theory; used in feedback controller by E. H. Mamdani in 1974.

G

G—Thermocouple type for tungsten versus tungsten 26 percent rhenium. **Also,** formerly meant "gauging" (dimensional) when used in first alpha character position of ISA–instrument function tag; still means (sight) "glass" or "viewing device" when used in succeeding position [see ANSI/ISA S5.1-1984 (R1992)]. *Also*, G (uppercase) in math is abbreviation "giga-" for 10^9, once called kilomega (kM).

G-glass—In the construction of glass-bulb type pH sensors, this glass is used for membranes of electrodes for processes where the nominal pH value varies around pH 7. Since this type of glass has a wide application range it is also termed "general-purpose" glass; see *E-, L-, S-glass*.

G1—In equipment corrosion specifications, less than 300 Å/month copper corrosion (of electrical terminals) as one measure of *mild* environmental contamination, as defined in ISA standard S71.04.

G2—In equipment corrosion specifications, less than 1000 Å/month copper corrosion (of electrical terminals) as one measure of *moderate* environmental contamination, as defined in ISA standard S71.04.

G3—In equipment corrosion specifications, less than 2000 Å/month copper corrosion (of electrical terminals) as one measure of *harsh* environmental contamination, as defined in ISA standard S71.04.

gain—Increased signal power, usually a result of amplification; the opposite of attenuation; the ratio of output to input voltage, current, or power.

GAL—Generic array logic, same as programmable array logic device, but AMD made "PAL" a tradename; another term is *PEEL*. See *PEEL*.

gamma (γ)—In digital graphic video, measures the contrast that affects the midtones of an image. Adjusting gamma allows a change in the brightness values of middle-range gray tones without altering shadows and highlights.

gap loss—Loss resulting from end separation of two axially aligned optical fibers.

gateway—Conceptual or logical network station that serves to interconnect two otherwise incompatible networks, network nodes, subnetworks, or devices. Performs protocol conversion operation across numerous communications layers; much more complicated than bridge, ISO defines it as a device that traverses all seven layers. Current, sloppier definition describes it as any mechanism providing access to another system.

gauge factor—Ratio of resistance to relative change in length of piezo-resistive strain gauge.

gauge pressure—Force per unit area exerted by fluid using atmospheric pressure as zero reference; absolute pressure minus atmospheric pressure.

GAW—Guided Acoustical Wave type of touch screen, which channels acoustical energy into the full volume of screen material; compare with SAW.

GB—See Gigabyte.

Gb—Gigabit; 1,073,741,824 bits.

GC—Gas chromatography.

GCI—Guest computer interface.

GCR—Gray component replacement; color separation control technique in color screen displays and printing.

GDDM—Graphic data display manager for the presentation of graphics.

GDS—Graphic data system.

GDT—Gas discharge tube; used for overvoltage protection and energy transfer switches.

GE Genius—I/O protocol of GE-Fanuc.

GEMS—Global Enterprisewide Management System; beyond enterprise resource planning, (ERP) this includes connectivity from a corporation to the companies of suppliers as well as customers, often over the Internet, so as to manage the flow of business requirements and products among all of them. See *ERP*.

Generation—In analog editing of videotape, each copy creates another generation and loses signal quality, hence, the term *generation loss* or *to go down another generation*.

generator—Considered in EPA (U.S.) regulations as the person, group, or organization whose activities generate hazardous waste.

genetic algorithm—Reiterative computing method developed by John Holland in the 1970s to more quickly solve complex problems using the properties of natural selection found in biological evolution so as to adjust to changing environments. Uses simple encoding and reproduction mechanisms through the simple manipulation of chromosomes (strings of 1s and 0s) to develop "new genes" (solutions) through parent selection, mutation, and crossover so as to create children different than their parents. By constantly comparing the multiple solutions with the desired result, it will accept and reject various chunks of code and try new combinations from those chunks that remain, until it finds the optimum fit.

GFCI—Ground fault circuit interrupter, which protects humans from electrical shock.

GFLOPS—Giga floating-point operations per second.

GHIM—Good Heavens, It's Monday.

GIF—Graphics Interchange Format [*pronounced* jiff]; method of saving graphics in electronic memory; used for exchanging data between computers.

gigabyte—Gbyte, Gig, GB; 1,073,741,824 bytes; 1024 megabytes (2^{30} bytes); basic unit of measurement of mass storage. ***Also***, used in describing data transfer rates (primarily parallel) as a function of time (Gbps).

gigaflops—One billion (10^9) floating-point operations per second.

GIS—Graphic Information System; computer system for presenting data in graphic form. ***Also***, Geographic Information System, an emerging computer technology being used to manage industrial facilities.

GIW—Gain in weight; generally measured in processes that create change in the density of product or the volume of product in some vessel during operations on the product.

GKS—Graphical Kernel System; standard interface between application programs and graphics system; ANSI/ISO 2-D international standard.

GLP—Good laboratory practice; regulations by FDA (U.S.) for non-clinical laboratory studies.

GMC—General motion controller.

GMM—Graphical multimeter; multiple electrical signal tester that can display waveforms.

GMP—Good manufacturing practice; regulations by FDA (U.S.) for medical devices.

GMR—Giant magnetoresistive; changes in the electrical resistance in materials composed of alternating thin layers of metallic elements or magnetic metals separated by nonmagnetic "spacers." Used in memory storage devices for much more capacity in disk drives than offered by conventional magnetoresistive methods.

GND—Ground; usually chassis ground but can be used for earth ground electrical potential.

gopher—Internet protocol that directly preceded the World Wide Web, created by University of Minnesota; a more basic system than HTTP. *Also*, a software tool used for finding information over the Internet when the address holding the information is unknown using menu options that take the requester through hierarchical directories and in doing so will "go for" it. *Also*, person whose job is to "go for" it. ☺

GOSIP—Government Open Systems Interconnection Profile; U.S. Federal Information Processing Standard 146, which defines a set of open system communication protocols that allow different makes of computers to communicate and users of different applications on these systems to exchange information.

Gotchas—Vendor-named category of control system specifications written by users and system consultants that have the same effect as smokescreens but use some single detail to define the unique. See also *dowatchados, druthers, expectifications, ropushers, smokescreens, stickits, stonecutters, wannagirls*. ☺

gowpen—Amount of water you can hold by cupping your hands. ☺

GPD—Gas plasma displays that emit a glow when excited with small voltage; type of liquid crystal displays (*LCD*).

gph—Gallons per hour (volumetric flow rate).

GPIB—General Purpose Interface Bus; IEEE 488 standard; parallel, multiport, 300 Kbs to 1 Mbs, 15 to 28 stations on up to 50 feet. Originally developed by Hewlett-Packard as HP-IB for laboratory instrumentation.

gpm—Gallons per minute (volumetric flow rate).

graceful degradation— A method for keeping the process running though component failures may degrade the degree of automation and sophistication.

graded index fiber—Optical fiber whose core has a nonuniform index of refraction. Core is composed of concentric rings of glass whose refractive indices decrease from the center axis to reduce modal dispersion and thereby increase fiber bandwidth.

GRAFCET—Graphe Fonctionnel de Commande Etape/Transition (in English, "step transition function charts"); created in 1979 by French Association for Economical and Applied Cybernetics, GRAFCET is a popular subset of sequential function chart (SFC), providing a diagrammatic representation of program sequences and supporting alternative sequence selections and parallel sequences. Basic elements are steps and transitions; originally an enhancement to PLC ladders.

grapheme—Smallest unit of written language, generally, a single letter for a vowel or consonant; sometimes a combination such as "th" or "ch."

graphical user interface (GUI)—Operating system or environment that displays program choices and options on the screen as icons (pictures or symbols) and often windows. Selections are typically made with a mouse or trackball (point and click). Invented at Xerox in the 1970s, was first used on Apple Macintosh and later on Microsoft Windows, Digital Research GEM, and X-Windows.

graphics object—Visually oriented screen view item, such as a scroll bar, bit- map, icon that is used in the presentation of some application interface.

gravity convection oven—Oven in which there is no mechanical means for circulating air in the oven chamber.

gray balance—In composition of screen displays and printing, the dot values or densities of cyan, magenta, and yellow that produce neutral gray.

ground—Electrical connection or common conductor that, at some point, connects to earth; negative side of dc power supply; reference point for electrical system.

ground loop noise—Noise that results when equipment is grounded at points having different potentials and thereby creating an unintended current path.

grounded junction—Form of thermocouple construction where the measuring junction is electrically connected to its protective sheath so that both have the same potential.

group addressing—In transmission, the use of an address that is common to two or more stations. On a multipoint line, where all stations recognize addressing characters but only one station responds.

gry—Equivalent to 120th of an inch, comes from Greek word for speck of dirt under fingernail; proposed for use in England in 1813 as part of a plan to make all linear measurements decimal-based. ☺

GS—Gas supply.

GSM—Global System for Mobile communications; a digital wireless communications technology.

guest (computer)—In process control, the use of a computer that is not the primary or controlling computer nor used to configure some multiple-part system, but provides services auxiliary to the basic control. Such functions can be the collection of historical and archival data, the creation of a library of application programs, performing background calculations, etc. The term was originally used somewhat tongue in cheek by Sam Herb and Scotty Moore in the first edition of *Understanding Distributed Process Control* in 1981 for system with a computer that is connected but not required for a process control system start-up or operation. See *host*.

GUI—[*pronounced:* gooey] Graphical user interface; operating system or environment that displays program choices and options on the screen as icons (pictures or symbols) and often windows. Selections are typically made with a mouse or trackball (point and click). Invented at Xerox in the 1970s, was first used on Apple Macintosh and later on Microsoft Windows, Digital Research GEM, and X Windows.

Guided Acoustical Wave (GAW)—Type of touch screen that channels acoustical energy into the full volume of screen material; compare with *SAW*.

GX—In equipment corrosion specifications, equal to or greater than 300 Å/month copper corrosion (of electrical terminals) as one measure of *severe* environmental contamination, as defined in ISA standard S71.04.

H

H—Means "hand" (manually initiated) when used in the first alpha character position of ISA-instrument function tag; means "high" in succeeding position [see ANSI/ISA S5.1-1984 (R1992)]. *Also*, hydraulic signal.

H1—Emerging ISA SP50 (fieldbus) standard for communications between sensors, actuators, and control devices. Generally, lower speed and lower cost than H2.

H2—Emerging ISA SP50 (fieldbus) standard for more sophisticated "data highway" and level communications between controlling devices and operator interfaces, etc., of distributed process control systems. Generally, much higher speed and higher cost than H1.

hacking—In computers, computer communication. Due to misuse in the news media it has come to mean for some the indiscriminate accessing of other computers over public networks; see ***cracking***.

hairline register—In composition of screen displays and printing, register within ±1/2 row of dots.

half bridge—In strain gauges, such as in force or pressure sensors, when only two of four legs of Wheatstone bridge configuration are active in development of a signal.

half duplex transmission—"One way at a time" communication. Both devices can transmit and receive data but only one at a time.

halftone—In electronic publishing and screen displays, the reproduction of continuous-tone images through a screening process, which converts the image into dots of various sizes and equal spacing between centers (as with conventional printing). *Also* called amplitude modulated (AM) screening. See ***AM***.

HALT—Highly Accelerated Life Test; typically the rapid ramp-soak cycling of electronic equipment between the extremes of its temperature rating over two to three days to quickly identify failures that would otherwise take years to surface.

hand set—This term applies to timers that are set manually after each operation. The operator turns the set pointer to the required time interval, and during timing the timer motor drives the pointer back to zero.

handshaking—The exchange of predetermined signals between two devices establishing a connection; usually part of a communications protocol.

HAP—Hazardous air pollutant(s).

hard copy—Output in permanent (paper) form, usually through a printer or chart recorder, as compared with a disk or display terminal.

hard disk, hard drive—In computers, platter-shaped disk(s) rotate(s) very fast and have greater storage capability and quicker access than floppy disk; usually sealed and nonremovable, and unlike floppy disks, the disk and drive are inseparable; so proper term is hard drive.

hardware—Electrical, mechanical, and electromechanical equipment and parts associated with a system, as compared with ***software*** and ***firmware***. *Also*, collective term for any computer-related object that can be kicked or battered and will stop working when your favorite beverage is spilled on it. ☺

HART—Highway Addressable Remote Transducer; open "smart" field instrumentation protocol developed by Rosemount that has been adapted by several other companies, creating a *de facto* standard fieldbus. Not considered a true fieldbus, it imposes Bell 202 FSK, 1200 bps digital signal on twisted pair of wires carrying 4-20 mA input.

hazardous classifications—NEC ratings for hazardous atmospheres:

Division 1—Continuous hazard (>1000 hrs/yr): Zone 0 for gasses, Zone Z (10) for dusts; and intermittent hazard (10-1000 hrs/yr): Zone 1 for gasses, Zone Z (10) for dusts.

Division 2—Hazard under abnormal conditions (0.1-10 hrs/yr): Zone 2 for gases, Zone Y (11) for dusts.

Class I—Areas in which flammable gases or vapors may be present in air in sufficient quantities to be explosive.

Group A—Atmospheres containing acetylene.

Group B—Atmospheres such as butadiene, ethylene oxide, propylene oxide, acrolein, or hydrogen (or gases and vapors equivalent in hazard).

Group C—Atmospheres such as cyclopropane, ethyl ether, ethylene, or gases and vapors equivalent in hazard.

Group D—Atmospheres such as acetone, alcohol, ammonia, benzene, benzol, butane, gasoline, hexane, lacquer-solvent vapors, naptha, natural gas, propane, or gases and vapors equivalent in hazardous.

Class II—Areas made hazardous by the presence of combustible dust.

Group E1—Atmospheres containing combustible metal dusts, regardless of resistivity.

Group E2—Atmospheres containing combustible dust of similarly hazardous characteristics having resistivity of less than 100kΩ-cm.

Group E3—Atmospheres containing combustible, electrically conductive dusts.

Group F1—Atmospheres containing combustible carbon black, charcoal, or coke dusts having more than 8 percent total volatile material.

Group F2—Atmospheres containing combustible dusts having an explosion hazard with resistivity $<100\Omega$-cm and $\geq 1\times10^8\Omega$-cm.

Group G1—Atmospheres containing combustible dust having resistivity $\leq$100kΩ-cm.

Group G2—Atmospheres containing combustible electrically nonconductive dusts.

hazardous location—Area where the possibility of explosion and fire is created by the presence of flammable gasses, vapors, dusts, fibers, or flyings.

hazardous waste—Under the Resource Conservation and Recovery Act (U.S.), any solid, liquid, gas, or combination of wastes that because of its chemical, physical, or infectious characteristics, may pose a hazard when managed improperly.

HAZOP—Hazard and Operability studies.

HCFC—Hydrochlorofluorocarbon, a consideration in EPA (U.S.) regulations. Any of several substances used as alternatives to CFCs but also thought to cause the depletion of the Earth's protective ozone layer.

HCI—Human-computer interface.

HCS—Hybrid control system; a control system that includes both "classic" distributed control and programmable control components for processes or operations that need the benefits of each system connected onto the same network.

HD—Harmonization document; relating to international standards. *Also*, high density, such as with memory disks. *Also*, high definition, such as a higher number of scan lines on cathode ray tube. *Also*, hard drive or hard disk; used as memory media in computers.

HDC—Highly distributed control.

HDCD—High-definition compatible digital; for video data.

HDCD-ROM—High-density compact disk read-only memory; for digital data storage.

HDL—Hardware Description Language.

HDLC—High-level Data Link Control; international standard communications, bit-oriented protocol defined by CCITT for ISO and used in Open Systems Interconnection (OSI).

HDR—High data rate; usually in the context of digitizing video information.

HDTV—High-definition television; has a pixel resolution of 1920 × 1080.

HDX—Half duplex; mode of communication in which two-directional data will flow only one direction at a time (2-wire).

He/Ne—Helium-neon red laser.

head end—Passive component in broadband transmission network that translates one range of frequencies (transmit) to different frequency band (receive); allows devices on a single cable network to send and receive signals without interference.

header—In digital transmission, control information added to the beginning of a message. Contains destination address, source address, and message number.

headline, "head"—In typographical composition of screen displays and printing, the display type, usually at the top of the screen or document to identify the topic.

head loss—Loss of pressure in flow system, measured using a length parameter, such as "inches of water" or "inches of mercury." Presumed condition of some managers in a crisis. ☺

head margin—In typographical composition of screen displays and printing, unused space above the first line on a page.

head pressure—Pressure in terms of the height of fluid.

heartbeat—Signal Quality Error (SQE) in CSMA/CD communication media access method; a test between the transceiver/MAU and DTE to ensure the collision detection circuit in the transceiver/MAU is working.

heat—Thermal energy, expressed in units of calories or BTUs.

heat sink—In thermodynamics, a body that can absorb thermal energy. In mechanical design, a finned piece of metal used to dissipate heat from the components mounted on it.

heat transfer—Process of thermal energy flowing from a body of low energy. The means of transfer includes conduction where the two bodies contact, convection where the two bodies contact different phases (such as solid and gas), and radiation where the bodies emit infrared radiation.

help—Computer feature that assists in generating more questions; when used correctly, users navigate through a series of help screens to end up where they started, without learning anything. ☺

heuristic—Describes approach based upon common sense rules (rules of thumb) as well as trial and error, as opposed to being based on comprehensive theory found in algorithms using mathematically provable procedures. Heuristic programs are characterized by being self-learning, i.e., they get better through experience, arriving at a good result if not always the best result; often used in expert systems.

hex—Hexadecimal; refers to base 16 number system using characters 0 through 9 and A through F to represent values; often used in machine language programs.

H_F—Latent heat of fusion.

HFC—Hart Communication Foundation; formed in 1993 as an independent, non-profit organization specifically to carry on work of HART user group to provide overall coordination and support for the application of HART technology.

HGED—High-gain emissive display; flat LCD-like panel containing color phosphors similar to those of CRTs but modified to operate at extremely low voltage (under 100) and activated by a matrix grid instead of a beam-steered, high-voltage electron gun. Unlike LCDs, matrix needs no transistors to address pixels; phosphors are instead excited by electrons guided to the grid by a patented process by Telegren, Inc. Costs less than one-tenth of LCD and has no viewing angle restrictions. Has brightness, color palette, resolution, refresh rates needed for high-definition video, without the concern of X-ray emissions from near-field viewing.

hierarchical—Approach used in many technologies, including process control, machine vision, system networks, databases, sequence-of-video screen views, and planning, where actions, scope of work, etc. are arranged in hierarchies that establish priorities and appropriate routings.

high-level language—Problem-oriented programming language in which each instruction may be equivalent to several machine code instructions.

high-pass filter—In digital signal processing *(DSP)*, a filter that attenuates low frequencies and passes high frequencies.

high-level data link control—(HDLC); International standard communications protocol defined by ISO.

HiNIL—High Noise Immunity Logic.

HIS—Human resources Information System, a computer database of manpower scheduling used in EIS. *Also*, HDL (Hardware Description Language) Interactive Simulation.

histogram—Bar graph to show frequency distribution of various characteristics in statistical analysis (in SPC).

historical data—In process control, operating data saved within specific device, equipment, or system; see *archival*.

hit—Internet term for successful by gaining access to a file on a Web page.

HJBT—Heterojunction Bipolar Transistor.

H/L—High/low; alarm thresholds.

HMD—Head-mounted display; worn by engineer or operator, this fits on a pair of high-tech glasses and uses virtual imaging to present the illusion of a full-size video screen to the wearer while he or she is touring a plant to make modifications or adjustments to the process.

HMI—Human-machine interface.

holding time—Length of time communication channel is in use for each transmission.**hold station**—Usually circuit card(s) with capacitive elements to hold electrical charges representing values calculated by controllers, until some multiplexing operation sends those signals to the field; output signal conditioning circuitry may still be called this by some.

home page—First HTML page users generally see upon reaching the Internet/World Wide Web site of an individual or corporation.

HOOPS—Hierarchical Object-Oriented Picture System; emerging standard in 3-D graphics.

horsepower—Unit of ability to do work; equivalent to 33,000 pounds moving through one foot in one minute.

host (computer)—In process control, primary or controlling computer in multiple-part system, providing primary services such as computation, database access, special programs, command generations, or programming languages. In some earlier DCSs the system was configured by programming the host, then downloaded over the network to each controller file. The term host implies that the computer is required for the complete performance of the system; see *guest*.

hot junction—That thermocouple junction used to measure an unknown temperature (measuring junction).

hot-standby—In distributed control systems, this usually means a duplicate (redundant) device such as a controller that carries identical information and can be functionally switched into replacement service with essentially no interruption of those functions.

hotswapping—Ability to remove and replace electronics board or device without removing power from the equipment in which it resides. *Also*, hardware and software protocol defined by PCMCIA whereby PC cards can be removed and inserted into sockets without powering down or rebooting PC. See *PCMCIA*.

HPC—High Performance Controller; microcontroller chip by National Semiconductor.

HPI—Human-process interface.

HP-IB—Hewlett-Packard Interface Bus; IEEE 488 standard; parallel, multiport, 300 Kbs to 1 Mbs, 15 to 28 stations on up to 50 feet. Originally developed by Hewlett-Packard for laboratory instrumentation and later called GPIB.

HRF—Hazard Reduction Factor; inverse of PFD (probability of failure on demand), which are the chances of a control system failure in energized mode.

HS—Hand station to provide direct process control signal to final element; *also*, hydraulic supply.

HSB—See hot-standby.

HSLN—High-Speed Local Network.

HSM—Hierarchal Storage Management; digital memory and data backup system.

HSV—Hue-saturation-value (or brilliance or luminance); color space used in some graphic programs for screen displays.

HSWA—Hazardous and Solid Waste Amendments; 1984 amendments to the Resource Conservation and Recovery Act (U.S.) establishing land disposal and underground storage tank regulations for hazardous materials.

HTG—Hydrostatic tank gauging.

HTL—High threshold logic.

HTML—Hypertext Markup Language; computer authoring language for publishing documents through the World Wide Web on the Internet using both text and two-dimensional graphics.

HTTP—Hypertext transport protocol; Internet computer communication encoding standard for the exchange of multimedia documents across the Web.

hub—In digital communications, wiring concentrator or repeater that brings together connections from multiple network nodes in a star topology.

hue—In video screen displays and printing, the main attribute of a given color that distinguishes it from other colors.

H_V—Latent of vaporization.

HVAC—Heating, ventilation, and air-conditioning.

HVLC—High volume, low concentration; usually used in reference to pollutant measurement for EPA (U.S.) regulations.

HWT—Hot water temperature.

hybrid control system—Control system that includes both "classic" distributed control and programmable control components for processes or operations that need the benefits of each system connected onto the same network.

hydrophilic—Water receptive.

hydrophobic—Water repellent.

hygrometer—Instrument used for determining relative humidity.

hypercard—Programming environment that organizes information into what appears functionally to the user to be stacks of index cards. Theses stacks can then be manipulated and resorted to create new applications.

hyperlink—In networked computers, the path between two documents that allow the user to point and click on specific words in one document on the screen so as to move to some other document, wherever it physically is located.

hypermedia—Hypertext function expanded so that documents contain links not only to other pieces of text but also to other forms of media—sounds, images, and video. Images themselves can be selected to link to sounds or documents, etc.

hypertext—Basically the same as regular digital communication text—it can be stored, read, searched, or edited—but also with connections (links) within that text to other documents; for example, while viewing word or phrase in one document, user can access and retrieve any other document using that word or phrase.

hysteresis—Difference in a signal when the point to be measured is first approached with increasing values and then with decreasing values, usually expressed in terms of percentage of full scale during any one calibration cycle. The lagging in the response of a unit of a system behind an increase or a decrease in the strength of a signal. *Also*, physical phenomenon demonstrated by materials that makes their behavior be a function of the history of the environment to which they have been subjected.

Hz—hertz; a unit of frequency equal to one cycle per second.

I

I—Integral (reset) action in modulating process control, in which the amount of change of a correcting force is proportional to the error signal. *Also,* input signal in analog, discrete, or digital form. *Also,* means "current" (electrical) when used in the first alpha character position of an ISA instrument function tag; means "indicate" in successive position [see ANSI/ISA S5.1-1984 (R1992)].

IAE—Integral Absolute Error; performance criteria based on error during transient, sometimes used in the precise tuning of automatic controllers and/or adaptive control strategies.

IBM—I Blame Microsoft.☺

IBN—Institut Belge de Normalisation; standards group in Belgium.

IC—Integrated Circuit; very small, complete circuit of interconnected semiconductor devices like transistors, capacitors, and resistors printed on a single silicon chip.

ICAC—Integrated Communications Advisory Committee; advises industry on the development of open systems and interconnection protocols.

ICC—International Color Consortium; formerly called ColorSync Profile Consortium, an industry initiative led by Apple® to develop multi-platform color matching among scanners, output devices, and displays. Members include Agfa®, Eastman Kodak®, Microsoft®, Silicon Graphics,® and Sun Microsystems®.

ICCP—Intercontrol Center Communications Protocol by EPRI, published mid-1994.

ICE—In-circuit emulator.

ice point—Temperature at which pure water freezes (0°C or 32°F).

ICMP—Internet Control Message Protocol; TCP/IP process providing a set of functions for networking layer management and control.

icon—Graphic functional symbol display; graphic representation of a function or functions to be performed by the system.

ICR—Information Collection Rule; nationwide U.S. study designed to determine the best long-term solution for giving public the healthiest water possible.

I.D.—inside diameter.

IDAPI—Integrated Database Application Programming Interface; open standard.

IDEC—Inter-utility Data Exchange Consortium/Committee of eastern U.S. utilities.

identification—In instrumentation, sequence of letters, digits, or both that are used to designate an individual instrument or loop, sometimes called "tag name." See tag name.

IDL—Instrument Design Language; for batch processing.

IDP—Integrated Detector/Preamplifier; detector package containing pin photodiode and transimpedance amplifier.

IDS—Input Data Strobe.

IE—Information engineering.

IEC—Infused Emitter Coupling; *also*, (International Electrotechnical Commission), established in 1906 to facilitate the coordination and unification of standards among member nations and focused on electrical and electronic products. In 1994 it was composed of forty-four national committees that collectively represent

80% of world's population that produces and consumes 95% of electricity.

IEC 617-12—Graphical symbols standard for diagrams, binary logic elements.

IEC 617-13—Graphical symbols standard for diagrams, analog elements.

IEC 848—Standard for the preparation of function charts for control systems (SFCs).

IEC 1000-4-2 —Immunity Standard for Electrostatic Discharge (previously IEC 801-2).

IEC 1000-4-3 —Immunity Standard for Radiated Radio Frequency (previously IEC 801-3); EN Prestandard ENV50140.

IEC 1000-4-4 —Immunity Standard for Electrical Fast Transients (previously IEC 801-4).

IEC 1000-4-5 —Immunity Standard for Surge; EN Prestandard ENV50142.

IEC 1000-4-6 —Immunity Standard for Conducted Radio Frequency; EN Prestandard ENV50141.

IEC 1000-4-8,9,10,11—Immunity Standards for Magnetic Field, Voltage Dips & Interruptions.

IEC 61131—Standard for Programmable controllers:

IEC 61131-1 general information and guidelines

IEC 61131-2 equipment requirements and tests

IEC 61131-3 programming languages

IEC 61131-4 guidelines to integrate PLCs into automated systems

IED—Intelligent Electronic Device.

IEEE—Institute of Electrical and Electronic Engineers; international professional society that issues its own standards and is a member of ANSI and ISO.

IEEE 472—Electrical surge withstand test standard.

IEEE 488—Bus standard originally developed by Hewlett-Packard for laboratory instrumentation.

IEEE 754—Mathematical floating-point standard.

IEEE 802.2—Data-link layer (of ISO reference model) digital communication standard used with IEEE 802.3, IEEE 802.4, and IEEE 802.5.

IEEE 802.3—Ethernet LAN standard except for type field (10 Mbps); physical-layer standard that uses CSMA/CD access method on bus topology.

IEEE 802.4–Physical-layer standard using token bus topology LAN; nearly identical to MAP.

IEEE 802.5–Physical-layer standard using token ring topology LAN.

IEEE 802.6—Metropolitan Area Network (MAN) or High Speed Local network (HSLN) standard.

IEEE 802.11—Radio and wireless LAN.

IEEE 802.12—Draft standard for 100BASEVG

IEEE-P1451—Draft standard for Smart Transducer Interface for Sensors and Actuators.

IES—Integral Error Squared; performance criteria based on error during transient, sometimes used in the precise tuning of automatic controllers and/or adaptive control strategies.

IFC—International Fieldbus Consortium; made up of forty-six members from major control and automation suppliers, users, and consultants worldwide; created in 1990 to show the interconnectability among a variety of field devices in process control and automation; based on SP50.

IFD—Intelligent Field Device; sensor, final element, or transmitter using microprocessor(s).

IGBT—Insulated Gate Bipolar Transistor.

IGES—Initial Graphic Exchange Specification; commonly used for translating data for other software.

IGFET—Insulated Gate Field Effect Transistor.

IGOSS—Industry and Government Open Systems Specification.

IIL,I²L—Integrated injection logic.

IIR—Infinite impulse response filter; in digital signal processing *(DSP)*, a filter whose the output is determined by its coefficients, current output, and previous inputs and is characterized by its nonlinear phase response; see *FIR*.

IIS—Internet Information Server.

ILD—Injection Laser Diode; device that accepts electrical signals and converts energy to a light signal; often the light source for fiber optic transmission over longer distances (>1 km).

image maps—In the context of the Internet, portions of images that are hypertext links, allowing the user to "mouse click" on different parts of a mapped image to activate different hypertext links.

image processing—Techniques for filtering, storing, and retrieving images and for processing pictorial information by computer.

imagesetter—In computer imaging, a device that outputs type, line art, and photos composed in position.

IMC—Internal Model-based Control; alternative to the PID approach for self-regulating (non-integral type) processes.

IMES—Integrated Manufacturing Execution Systems.

impedance—Combined effect, usually in opposition, on the transmitted signal flow from resistance, inductance, and capacitance.

IMS—Intelligent Manufacturing Systems; initiative proposed by Japan and now supported in Europe, North America, and Australia to coordinate manufacturing research and development efforts among companies, universities, and research institutions.

in point—In video development, the first frame of a clip; see *Out Point*.

in situ—In the natural or original position; in process control applications generally refers to cleaning, treating or disposal methods that do not require the removal of vessels or contaminated material.

index of refraction—(n) Ratio of the velocity of light in free space to the velocity of light in a given material.

inductive load—Electrical devices made of wound or coiled wire so that the current passing through the coil creates a magnetic field that in turn produces mechanical work.

industrial hardened—Processing equipment installed to withstand the effects of the manufacturing environment, including dirt, heat shock, and vibration as well as insulating equipment from poor quality electrical power.

INERIS—Institut National de L'Environnement Industrial et des Risques; French certification and testing laboratory for testing the equipment of different vendors to some common standard.

infinite capacity scheduling—Loading plant or work center without regard to its capacity to show points of overload so they can be corrected.

infrared thermometer—Thermometer that measures emitted infrared radiation (heat) to determine the temperature of an object that generally is not suitable for contact measurement.

inheritance—In Object Oriented Programming (OOP), a sub-class contains characteristics of a super-class unless modified.

INIEX—Belgian certification and testing laboratory for testing the equipment of different vendors to some common standard.

initialization—The beginning of an operation; within the function blocks of cascaded PID loops inside microprocessor controller, this is the automatic balancing of signals so that the transfer of a loop from manual, automatic, or computer mode to cascade mode will not disturb the process. *Also*, within a token passing type data highway, the restarting of the token, usually to revisit every potential address so as to find and include any new station that may have been physically added.

inline graphic—Digital graphic that can be displayed directly on an Internet Web page; see *External Graphic*.

INMS—Integrated Network Management System, part of AT&T's UNMA. See *Unma*.

input impedance—Impedance measured across the input terminals of device due to circuitry within that device.

input signal—Signal applied to a specific device, element, or system, usually representing the value or status of a process as read by some sensor.

insertion point—In computer screens, the place where text will be inserted when typing;

usually identified with a flashing vertical line (cursor) that appears to the left of the insertion point and is pushed to the right as text is entered.

insertion loss—Loss of power that results from inserting a component such as a connector or splice into some previously continuous electrical path.

installation qualification—In process validation, documented verification that all key aspects of hardware installation adhere to appropriate codes and approved design intentions and that the recommendations of the manufacturer have been suitably considered.

installed flow—The true performance of a valve or flowmeter when it forms part of an actual processing line.

instance—In object oriented programming (OOP), the definition of a specific object according to its class and individual characteristics.

instantaneous contacts—Output contacts that transfer when a timer begins timing.

instruction list—Low-level language of programmable controllers similar to assembler language in which only one operation, such as storing a value in a register, is allowed per line, useful for smaller applications or for optimizing parts of an application. One of five languages accepted under the IEC 1131 standard for PLCs. See *function block diagram*, *ladder logic*, *structured text*, and *SFC*.

instrument—Term for any item of pneumatic, electromechanical, electrical, or electronic equipment designed to carry out a specific function or set of functions; usually measures the value of an observable attribute and may also control the value.

instrumentation—Systems of instruments used to observe and control a process or plant.

insulation resistance—Resistance value for the cover material of an electrical conductor; expressed in Ohms.

integral action—(Reset) process control action that changes proportional control depending upon the time deviation from set point, thereby eliminating droop (offset) in the system.

integrate—Seamless data exchange without a translator; to bring separate parts together to make a whole.

integration—State in which all aspects of a system or plant-wide operations are tied together in a continuous loop of function and information. Generally, data can be fed into and retrieved from an integrated system from anywhere in the system or plant.

integrator—Device that continually totalizes or adds up the value of a quantity for a given time.

intelligent terminal—Programmable terminal; sometimes called the "Intelligent Workstation" is any terminal that can provide the user with independent processing power and applications support, without the need for a central computer; example: personal computers.

inter-repeater link—In data communications, an electronically continuous piece of bus consisting of the same cable with only two devices in point-to-point configuration; *also* called *link segment*.

interactive processing—In data processing, describing time-dependent (real-time) data handling or communications; the user enters data and then awaits a response from the destination before continuing; conversational rather than batch processing.

interactive video—Fusion of video and computer technology; running a video program and a computer program in tandem under the control of the user; with interactive video, the user's actions, choices, and decisions genuinely affect how the program unfolds.

InterBus-S—High speed proprietary "fieldbus" by Phoenix Contacts® for sensors and actuators. InterBus-S Club was formed in Europe in 1993 to maintain and advance this as a standard, assist in the development of sensor/actuator products, and work with NEMA/IEEE organizations for a Unified Sensor/Actuator Standard.

interchangeability—In reference to fieldbus, the ability of a vendor's product to be fully replaceable by a similar product from another vendor. The functions must be identical but may not always include extensions beyond standard specifications; for example, some features may differ, such as the self- tuning technique of PID function block, while the PID function itself remains identical. Compare with *interoperability.*

interchangeability error—Measurement error that can occur if two or more sensors are used to make the same measurement; caused by a slight variation in the characteristics of those sensors.

interface—Shared boundary defined by common physical interconnection characteristics, signal characteristics, and meanings of interchanged signals; device or software making possible interoperation between two different functions/systems or between the function/system and human.

interim release—Computer programmer's feeble attempt at repentance.

interlaced—In video development, the alternating of horizontal scan lines, such as in an NTSC signal which delivers 30 frames per second of 525 lines; odd set is displayed in the first 1/60th second, the even set in the second 1/60th second in each frame.

interleave—In data communication, to send blocks of data alternately to two or more stations on a multipoint system or to put bits or characters alternately into time slots of Time Division Multiplexer. *Also,* on a video screen, to alternate raster scan lines so as to transmit higher resolution frames per second.

interlock—Physical device, equipment, or software routine that prevents an operation from beginning or changing function until some condition or set of conditions are fulfilled.

Internal model-based control - alternative to PID approach for self-regulating (non-integral type) processes.

Internet™—Digital communications network that interconnects many other networks; literally, a "network of networks," a global wide area hypermedia information retrieval initiative aiming to give universal access to a large universe of documents, using hypertext as its means for interacting with commercial users.

interoperability—In computers, the ability of computing systems to share application software; *also,* in reference to fieldbus, the ability of products from different vendors to coexist on the same network and to send, receive, and interpret messages, respond correctly to their instructions, and to even allow cascaded control functions to occur between devices; they share the same application software. Compare *interchangeability.*

interpreter—System program that converts and executes each instruction of a high-level language (user-written) program into machine code as it runs, before going on to the next instruction.

Interrupt—To stop a process in such a way that it can be resumed.

interval timer—Timer that has its output occur during timing state.

intranet—Internet digital communication network devised so that only a limited number of people have access, such as employees and field salesmen of a company who wish to exchange and have the ability to reference information worldwide but do not wish that access to be available to their competitors; usually involves "firewalls" to ensure this security. See *firewell technology.*

intrinsic safety—Method to provide safe operation of electric process control instrumentation where hazardous atmospheres exist; this method keeps electrical energy so low that the ignition of hazardous atmosphere cannot occur.

intrinsic safety barrier—Device inserted in an electric wire route between process control instrumentation and the point where the wire passes into hazardous area; it limits voltage and current on the wire to safe levels. Often, many barriers are mounted together on some barrier panel or in a common enclosure.

intrinsically safe—Condition that will not produce any spark or thermal effects under normal or abnormal conditions that will ignite a specified gas mixture.

inventory management—The systematic determination of items and quantities to be ordered; coordination of order release and order due dates; changes in required quantities; and the rescheduling of planned orders.

inventory turnover—Number of times that an inventory cycles during a year.

I/O—Input/Output; flow of data to and from some hardware or software function, in control systems, terminations between controllers and process for pneumatic, hydraulic, electrical signals in analog, discrete, or digital form.

IOP—Input/Output Processor.

IOS—Input/Output Subsystem; usually a digital real-time network of software, hardware, protocol, and diagnostics to manage process I/O with solid integrity. *Also*, International Organization for Standards, see *ISO*.

IP—Internet Protocol; used in gateways connecting networks at the OSI network layer. *Also*, Intellectual property (usually in reference to reusable knowledge encapsulated within some chip-based component like System-On Chip).

IPC—Interprocess Communication, from system V UNIX®.

IPDS—Intelligent Printer Data Stream; page description printer protocol that allows the complete page of text and graphics to be formatted and stored in printer's memory.

IPI—Intelligent Peripheral Interface.

IPM(S)—Inter-Personal Messaging (System); first application for MHS, uses P2 format of X.400. See *MHS*.

IPQ—Instituto Português da Qualidade; standards group in Portugal.

IP ratings—Ingress Protection codes; IEC enclosure classes *approximately* equivalent to NEMA ratings: IP 10 = NEMA 1, IP 11 = NEMA 2, IP 14/54 = NEMA 3/13, IP 52 = NEMA 5/12, IP 56 = NEMA 4, IP 67 = NEMA 7:
IP 00 = no protection from solid bodies or liquids;
First digit is protection from solid bodies:
0 = none
1 = objects > 50 mm
2 = objects > 12 mm
3 = objects > 2.5 mm
4 = objects > 1.0 mm
5 = dust-protected
6 = dust-tight
Second digit is protection from liquids:
0 = none
1 = vertically dripping water
2 = angled dripping water (-75° to 90°)
3 = sprayed water
4 = splashed water
5 = water jets
6 = heavy seas
7 = effects of immersion
8 = indefinite immersion

IPTS—International practical temperature scale; providing fixed points in thermometry as specified by the General Conference of Weights and Measures.

IPX—Internetwork Packet Exchange; operating system by Novell, Inc.

IR—Infrared; area in electromagnetic spectrum extending beyond red light from 760 nanometers to 1000 microns (10_6 nm); form of radiation used for making noncontact temperature measurements; it is also the signal range for some fiber-optic communications systems.

IRC—Internet Relay Chat; is used for real-time conversations over the Internet.

IRDS—Information Resource Dictionary System; emerging U.S. government-backed ANSI standard.

IRL—Inter-repeater link; in data communications, an electronically continuous piece of bus consisting of the same cable with only two devices in point-to-point configuration; *also* called link segment. See *link segment*.

IRQ—Interrupt request; prioritized demand for attention from a microprocessor.

IRS—Information retrieval services; *also*, Institut Român de Standardizare; standards group in Romania.

IS—International standard (by ISO); *also*, Information systems; computer network used to track the performance of plant at close to real time without excessive need for paper-based systems.

ISA—Instrument Society of America; organization now formally known as "ISA, the international society for measurement and control;" started in 1945 in the United States and made up of individual volunteers from all aspects of the instrumentation business, representing vendors and users, many types of industries, and nearly every job description. ISA traditionally provides education and develops international consensus standards and practices. *Also*, Industry Standard Architecture; a *de facto* personal computer, 24-bit bus standard used in IBM® PCs and compatibles; developed for extension cards in the first IBM PC, it originally supported only an 8-bit-wide data path (now called PC/XT bus); subsequently developed to 16-bit for the AT class of computers and called AT bus, supporting both 8-and 16-bit cards.

ISDN—Integrated Services Digital Network; standard for the high-speed digital transmission of voice, video, and data via standard telephone lines; works under X.25; requires electronic (digital) telephone switching offices. Computers with ISDN card do not need modem and run ten times faster. ***Also***, It Still Does Nothing. ☺

ISO—International Standards Organization; international organization for promoting the development of standards for computers.

ISO 9000—International Standards Organization standards for quality systems.

isochronous—Equally timed; in data communications, timing information is transmitted on a channel along with data, sending asynchronous data by synchronous means; this method involves synchronously sending asynchronous characters between each pair of start and stop bits.

isometric view—Drawing in which horizontal lines of object are drawn at an angle to horizontal and all verticals are projected at an angle from base.

isomorphic representation—Representation in which there is a one-to-one correspondence between a scene and its representation.

ISORM—ISO Reference Model.

isothermal—Process or area that is at constant temperature.

ISP—InterOperable Systems Project; group of companies formed in October 1992 and committed to accelerating the availability of products and systems using a standard international fieldbus. Based on the work of the IEC and ISA as well as other well-known fieldbus technologies including Fieldbus Foundation, a not-for-profit organization dedicated to developing a single, worldwide, interoperable fieldbus, formed from the merger of WorldFIP North America and ISP Foundation in 1994. ***Also***, internet services provider; a business that allows companies and individuals to connect to Internet by providing an interface to the Internet backbone.

ISV—Independent software vendors.

IT—Information technology; current methods and computer-based techniques for gathering and analyzing business information from manufacturing and process plant operating parameters and plant control parameters from business requirements.

ITAE—Integral time absolute error; performance criteria based on error during a transient and sometimes used in the precise tuning of automatic controllers and/or adaptive control strategies.

italic—In typographical composition of screen displays and printing, the style of letters that slant as distinct from upright, or roman, letters; generally used for emphasis within text.

ITB—Intermediate block character; digital transmission control character that terminates an intermediate block, a block check character usually follows; the use of ITBs allows for the error checking of smaller transmission blocks.

ITC—International Trade Commission.

ITI—Industrial Technology Institute.

ITM—Inspection du Travail et des Mines; standards group in Luxembourg.

ITO—Indium tin oxide; coating used on transparent metal substrates of resistive and capacitive-type membrane; used with some touch screen and digital pen technologies.

ITRC—Information Technology Requirements Council; formed in 1988 to promote consensus, integration, and coordination of requirements across the entire range of information technologies by establishing and funding requirements groups, such as the "North American MAP/TOP Users' group."

ITU-TSS—International Telegraphic Union—Telecommunications Standards Sector; replacement organization for CCITT. See **CCITT**.

ITV—Interactive television; beyond video reception, ITV allows the viewer to respond to multichannel made possible by the availability of media such as fiber optic cable; has industrial implications similar to videoconferencing.

ITVA—International TeleVision Association.

IVDS—Interactive Video Data Service; system where user both enters and receives information through a television set normally used for receiving entertainment programs; user can change camera angles, alter story endings, etc.; potential for control room functions.

IXC—Interexchange carrier; telephone service that connects local exchange carriers (LEC) for long-distance communication; compare ***LEC***.

J

J—Symbol of ANSI thermocouple type for iron versus constantan. *Also*, means "power" (joule) when used in the first alpha character position of ISA instrument function tag, means "scan" when used as modifier [see ANSI/ISA S5.1-1984 (R1992)].

jabber—In data communications, the error condition that occurs when a network device transmits packets larger than the maximum allowable size or will not relinquish token, etc. (depending upon the media access method being used).

jabberlock—In data communications, a device or technique in a specific device to prevent it from "jabbering," see ***jabber.***

Java—Software code which can rum on multiple platforms (UNIX, OS/2, NT, MACINTOSH, etc.); originally developed by Sun Microsystems Inc. as a platform for programming on small embedded devices such as cell phones, PDAs and sensors; claimed to be more simple than C++, it has significant implications for use on Internet applications.

Java Beans—Reusable chunks of Java software code that can be assembled as components in larger applications.

JEIDA—Japanese Electronics Industry Development Association; equivalent to PCMCIA. See **PCMCIA**.

JEMIMA—Japan Electric Measuring Instrument Manufacturer's Association.

JESSI—Joint European Submicron Silicon Initiative.

jetness—Darkness of a pigment, typically caused by the size of carbon black agglomerates (smaller causes darker films).

JFET, JUGFET—Junction field effect transistor.

JI—Junction isolation.

JIT—Just-in-time manufacturing; delivery approach that stresses the benefits of the "pull" system, wherein material is brought to the work site only when needed; requires close synchronization with all related activities.

jitter—In transmission, a slight movement of the signal in time or phase that can introduce errors and cause loss of synchronization in high-speed synchronous communication.

joule—Basic unit of thermal energy.

JPEG—Joint Photographic Experts Group; working committee under the auspices of the ISO that is attempting to define a proposed universal standard for the digital compression and decompression of still images for use in computer systems and for their exchange between computers. The JPEG algorithm reduces image size by as much as 65:1 while maintaining image integrity by eliminating imperceptible color information.

JSA—Japanese Standards Association; member of IEC.

JTAG—Joint Test Action Group.

JTM—Job Transfer and Manipulation; emerging ISO standard.

jumper—A patch cable or wire used to establish a circuit, often temporarily, for testing or diagnostics.

junction—Point in a thermocouple where two dissimilar metals are joined; point where any two or more wires are joined.

justify—In typographical composition of screen displays and printing, to space characters uniformly so that all line lengths are the same, flush to both right and left margins.

K

k—Abbreviation for kilo: K (upper case) in computing means multiple of 2^{10} (= 1024), often incorrectly assumed to be =1000; *also*, k (lower case) in math means multiple of 10_3 (=1000); *also*, k (lower case) in physics and instrumentation means Thermal conductivity; *also*, K (upper case) in thermal measurements is the symbol for kelvin; the absolute thermodynamic temperature scale based upon the Celsius scale with 0°C = 273.15K; *also*, K (upper case) is a symbol of the ANSI thermocouple type for chromel versus alumel™. *also*, means "time" or "time schedule" when used in the first alpha character position of an ISA process instrument function tag; means "time rate of change" when used as modifier; means "control station" in a succeeding position [see ANSI/ISA S5.1-1984 (R1992)].

kanban—Japanese methodology for achieving JIT, often involving the use of kanbans, or "cards," to indicate parts status.

KB—Keyboard; kilobyte.

Kbps—Kilobits per second; standard measurement of data rate and transmission capacity; but interestingly, kbps equals 1000 bits per second (a math quantity, not a memory capacity).

KEMA—KEMA Registered Quality Nederland B.V. Certification and testing laboratory for testing the equipment of different vendors to some common standard, based in The Netherlands.

kernel—In computer software, the core or central part of program or operation around which several other "shells" of programs or functions are built; compare ***shell***.

kerning—In typographical composition of screen displays and printing, subtracting space between two characters to bring them closer together for improved balance and appearance.

kilobyte (Kbyte)—Equals 1024 bytes (8-bit characters) of memory; standard measurement for disk, diskette, and other methods of memory storage.

kinematics—Branch of applied mathematics that studies the way in which the velocities and accelerations of various parts of moving system are related.

kinetic energy—Energy associated with mass in motion, i.e., half the density of the moving mass times its velocity.

Knowledge-based system—Software that uses artificial intelligence techniques and a base of information about a specialized activity to control systems or operations.

KPI—Key performance indicator

kVA—Kilovolt-amperes (= 1000 volt amps).

kW—Kilowatt (= 1000 watts).

kWh—Kilowatt hour (= 1000 watt-hours).

L

L—Means "level" when used in first alpha character position of ISA instrument function tag; means "light" (pilot) in succeeding position; "low" when used as modifier [see ANSI/ISA S5.1-1984 (R1992)].

l—lambda; closed loop time constant that specifies closed loop performance in process control.

LAD—Local area disk; access by Digital Equipment Corporation to virtual disks via Ethernet.

ladder logic—Traditional language of programmable controllers that originated with electricians and the electrical maintenance of electromechanical relay panels, symbolic representation that schematically illustrates the functions of a control circuit where the power lines form the sides of a ladderlike structure, with program elements arranged to form rungs. One of five languages accepted under the IEC 1131 standard for PLCs; see *function block diagram*, *instruction list*, *structured text*, and *SFC;* **see also** *state logic*. *Also*, a training program for firemen. ☺

lag—Time delay between the output of a signal and the response of the equipment to which the signal is sent, usually caused by conditions such as capacitance, inertia, resistance, and dead time, either separately or in combination; time relationship between two waveforms where the fixed reference point on one wave occurs after the same point on the reference wave.

laminar flow—Streamlined flow of fluid where the viscous forces are more significant than inertial forces; generally below Reynolds number of 2000.

LAN—Local area network; data communications network within a given area, such as a control room, office, specific work space, building, building cluster, etc.; up to six miles (ten kilometers), but not using common carrier.

land ban—Under the Resource Conservation and Recovery Act (U.S.), prohibits land disposal of certain hazardous wastes unless they meet applicable treatment standards.

LAP—Line Access Procedure; CCITT-specified data link protocol.

LAPB—Link Access Procedure, Balanced.

LAPI—Layered application programming interface.

LAPUT—Light-activated programmable unijunction transistor.

LASCR—Light-activated silicon controlled rectifier.

LASER—Light amplification by stimulated emission of radiation; intense light beam with very narrow band width that can produce images by electronic impulses from digital data.

laser disk—Optical medium capable of holding thirty minutes of moving video footage or up to 54,000 individual frames of still video per side; individual segments of frames can be accessed by computer.

LAT, (LAST)—Local Area Transport, (Local Area System Transport); protocol unique to Digital Equipment Corporation products for virtual terminal access across an Ethernet network.

latency—Time interval between when a network station seeks access to a transmission channel and when access is granted or received; equivalent to waiting time.

latent heat—Amount of heat needed (absorbed) to convert a pound of boiling water to a pound of steam; expressed in BTU per pound.

lateral displacement loss—Loss of power that results from lateral displacement from the optimum alignment between two optical fibers or between a fiber and an active device.

layer—Element of a digital communication stack; one level of a hierarchy of functions or segments of a protocol that perform specialized roles (physical, data link, application, user). In the OSI reference model, one of seven basic layers, referring to a collection of related network processing functions.

LCCA—Life cycle cost analysis; orderly selection/elimination method that includes all cost factors (fixed and variable) of a project, product, or endeavor.

LCD—See Liquid crystal display.

LCH—Luminance, chroma, hue; model for color correction software for digital scanning, output devices, and displays.

LCIE—French certification and testing laboratory for testing the equipment of different vendors to some common standard.

LCP—Liquid crystal polymer; material frequently used to make electronic connectors.

LD—Ladder diagram; type of programming for programmable logic controllers, see ***ladder logic***. *Also*, see ***laser disk***.

LDAP—Lightweight Directory Access Protocol; standard Internet access protocol embraced by many software vendors.

LDAR—Leak detection and repair; programs maintained by EPA (U.S) to assure extremely low valve stem leakage.

LDP—Laser disk player.

LDR—Land Disposal Restrictions, which are EPA-promulgated rules implementing the ***land ban***. See ***land ban***.

LD-RAM—Laser disk random access memory.

LD-ROM—Laser disk read-only memory.

LD-V—Laser disk video.

leaders—In typographical composition of screen displays and printing, rows of dashes or dots to guide user's eye across screen or page; used in tabular work, programs, tables of contents, etc.

leading—[*pronounced* ledding]; in typographical composition of screen displays and printing, the distance between lines of type measured in points.

leakage rate—Maximum rate at which fluid is permitted or determined to leak through (pipe, valve, vessel, etc.) seal; the type of fluid, differential pressure across seal, direction of leakage, and location of the seal must be specified.

leased line—Telephone line reserved for the exclusive use of leasing customers, without interexchange switching arrangements; also called "private line"; used to connect two or more locations (such as company plants) on a private WAN (wide area network).

least squares line—Straight line for which the sum of the squares of deviations is minimized.

LEC—Local exchange carrier; responsible for telephone service to the final user; compare ***IXC***.

LED—See *Light-emitting diode.*

legacy systems—Software and/or hardware systems that have existed for some time and yet are still viable, are often proprietary in nature, and cannot practically be removed from an operation, perhaps because of the volume of use or popularity; they usually need some interface to operate with more current systems.

letterspacing—In typographical composition of screen displays and printing, the placing of extra space between each letter of a word.

LF—Line feed.

L-glass—In the construction of glass bulb-type pH sensors, this is used for the membranes of electrodes for processes in which measurements are to be made in alkaline media with high process temperatures; see ***E-, G-, S-glass***.

LIC—Linear integrated circuit.

life—A whim of several billion cells to be you for a while ☺.

life cycle cost analysis—Orderly selection/elimination method that includes all cost factors (fixed and variable) of a project, product, or endeavor.

LIFO—Last in, first out.

light-emitting diode (LED)—Device that accepts electrical signals and converts the energy to light signal; semiconductor diode, the junction of which emits light when passing current in the forward (junction on) direction; often a light source for fiber-optic transmission and also used as annunciator lamps in red, amber, green, and blue.

LILO—Last in, last out.

LIM EMS—Lotus/Intel/Microsoft Expanded Memory System.

limit switch—Electromechanical device positioned to be actuated when a certain motion limit is reached, thereby deactivating the actuator causing that motion.

limits of error—Tolerance band for the thermoelectric response of thermocouple wire, expressed in degrees or percentage defined by ANSI specification mc-96.1 (1975).

LIMS—Laboratory information management system; used to integrate the analytical data from process control laboratory with the plantwide process control, manufacturing, and inventory systems for more rapid contribution to quality control, process optimizing, and operational costs.

linear—Motion, action of device (typically a sensor), or value of a signal where the effect is exactly in proportion to its cause. *Also*, in video development, an editing limitation that requires edits to be performed from the beginning to the end of a production piece in sequential order; changes cannot be made to previous edit decisions without the loss of quality or need to start over (compare with ***nonlinear***).

linear editing—In video development, central to the old paradigm of using tape: editing from data stored on media that is not instantly accessible because of the continuous and linear layout of the data and therefore slower than nonlinear editing.

linearity—Closeness of a calibration curve to a specified straight line; expressed as the maximum deviation of any calibration point on a specified straight line during any one calibration cycle.

linear power supply—Also known as series pass power supply, this style is the most commonly used power supply design, consisting of transformer, rectifiers, and filter capacitors, followed by a pass element that varies the voltage drop to maintain constant output voltage; provides the best performance in the regulation, ripple, transient response, output impedance and cost, but is larger, heavier, and has lower efficiency.

linear programming—Technique applied to problems in which linear function of several variables is subject to number of constraints in form of linear inequalities.

line driver—Signal converter that conditions a digital signal to ensure reliable transmission over an extended distance. *Also*, baseball player who regularly hits the ball so it travels close to the ground. ☺

line power—Main power source supplied by a power company or the central generator of self-sufficient site; U.S. equivalent to what in the United Kingdom is called "mains."

line regulation—In power supplies, a change in value of DC output voltage resulting from change in AC input over a specified range from low line to high line; normally specified as plus or minus change of nominal AC input voltage.

line spacing, line depth, line feed—In typographical composition of screen displays and printing, the distance from baseline to baseline between two lines of type.

line turnaround—In digital communication, the reversing of the transmission direction from sender to receiver or vice versa when half-duplex circuit is used.

link—Any specified relationship between two nodes in some network; communications path between two nodes.

link layer—Layer 2 of OSI reference model; see ***data link layer***.

link(s)—In the context of the Internet, emphasized (with underlines, color, etc.) words in hypertext document that act as pointers to more information on that specific subject; a "mouse click" on them can transport user to another Web site.

link segment—In data communications, an electronically continuous piece of bus consisting of the same cable with only two devices in point-to-point configuration; also called inter-repeater link.

liquid crystal display (LCD)—Reflective visual readout of alphanumeric characters, generally of two types: passive-matrix displays (PMLCDs) and active-matrix displays (AMLCDs), which refer to how the pixels in the display are controlled. See ***PMLCDs, AMLCDs***.

LIS—Logistics information system; computer database of sales, purchasing, production, plant maintenance, and quality control used in EIS. See ***EIS***.

LISP—List processing; computer language created by John McCarthy using data type list as its basic element; many artificial intelligence applications are written in LISP; some have also defined this as Logical Instruction Set Processing.

live object— In the context of the Internet, a term by Netscape for "plug-ins" that enable the browser to play image, cinema, and sound files as inline part of Web page.

LIW—Loss in weight; generally measured in processes that create change in the density of product or volume of product in some vessel during operations on product.

LLC—Link Layer Control; also called Logical Link Control, Link Level Control; protocol developed by IEEE 802 committee for data-link level transmission control; LLC addresses distinguish different applications within the same station; includes end system addressing, error checking.

LLSAP—Link Layer Service Access Point (ISO model for digital communication); different for particular applications in specific stations.

LNA—Low noise amplifier.

load—Electrical demand of a process expressed as power (watts), current (amps), or resistance (ohms).

load cell—Transducer for the measurement of force or weight; action is based on strain gauges mounted within cell on force beam.

loaded line—Communications line for analog signals, such as telephone, that is equipped with loading cells to add inductance so as to minimize amplitude distortion.

load impedance—Impedance presented to the output terminals of some device by associated external circuitry.

load regulation—In power supplies, change in the value of DC output voltage due to a change in load resistance from open circuit to some value that yields maximum rated output current, or from full load to open.

load sharing—In communication systems, distribution of a given load among several computers on a network.

LOC—Lines of code; lines of executable computer programming.

local—In instrumentation, the location of an instrument that is neither in nor on a panel or console, nor is it mounted in a control room; local instruments are commonly in the vicinity of the primary element or final control element; term's use is often synonymous with "field," or "field-mounted."

local panel—A panel that is not the central or main panel; local panels are commonly in the vicinity of plant subsystems or subareas; local panel should not be confused with "local instrument."

logarithm—Exponent that indicates the power to which a number is raised.

logical circuit—see ***virtual circuit***.

logical link control—Protocol developed by IEEE 802 committee for data-link level transmission control; LLC addresses distinguish different applications within the same station; includes end system addressing, error checking; also called link layer control. See ***LLC***.

logical port—A port specifically defined by a name (such as COM1, COM2, etc.) without a strictly defined physical port.

LOM—Laser object manufacturing; form of rapid prototyping; see ***RP***. *Also*, Spanish certification and testing laboratory for testing the equipment of different vendors to some common standard.

LON—Local Operating Network; by Echlon, Inc., used as an inexpensive, unsophisticated communication bus.

LonMark—LON interoperability testing program.

LonTalk—LON protocol.

LonWorks—LON hardware including neuron chip licensed to Toshiba and Motorola.

loop—In process control, the combination of process, sensor, controller, and final control element.

loopback—Type of diagnostic test in which transmitted signal is returned to the sending device after passing through all or part of the data communications link or network so that the returned signal can be compared with the transmitted signal.

LOSC—Londonderry Occupational Safety Centre; British certification and testing laboratory for testing the equipment of different vendors to some common standard.

loss—Reduction in signal strength, expressed in decibels. *Also*, attenuation, opposite of gain.

lossless—Digital data technique that reduces the size of the file without sacrificing any of the original data; this tool allows expanded or restored file to be the exact replica of the original file before compression.

lossy compression—Digital data compression technique in which some data is deliberately discarded so as to achieve massive reductions in the size of compressed file.

lower case—In typographical composition of screen displays and printing, the small letters in type, as distinguished from capital letters.

low pass filter—In digital signal processing (***DSP***), a filter that passes low frequencies and attenuates high frequencies.

Low Voltage Directive (LVD)—Establishes safety guidelines for electronic products that operate at 50 volts or above to ensure the customers can handle such products safely (no exposed voltages or other hazards that can cause injury); part of regulations set in January

1997 for companies selling electronic systems within the European Economic Area, comprised of the European Union and the European Free Trade Association.

LP—Linear programming; computation technique for finding the optimum combination of process variables where there may be no single best one.

LPM—Liters per minute.

LPT—Line printer.

LPTTL—Low power transistor-transistor logic.

LRC—Longitudinal redundancy check; error-detecting scheme consisting of bits calculated from odd and even parity for all characters in a block.

LRDCT—Linear rotary differential capacitive transducer; measures rotational movement more precisely than do linear differential transformers.

LRU—Least recently used.

LSB—Least significant bit.

LSC—Least significant character

LSD—Least significant digit; digit representing the smallest value.

LSI—Large-scale integration; multifunction semiconductor, such as a microprocessor, with high-density electronic circuitry on a single silicon chip (as high as 1000 equivalent gates).

LSP—Local set point; of process control loop; typically entered by control room operator.

LU—Logical unit; in systems network architecture, a set of protocols that provides peer-to-peer communication between applications.

LU 6.2—In systems network architecture, a set of protocols providing peer-to-peer communication between applications.

luminance—also brightness; in video displays, the greatest light a monitor can emit without losing focus; measured in units called footlamberts.

LUT—Lookup tables; in digital data handling, a method of comparing data that can often be used to simplify data communication, classify and analyze data for storage or retrieval, linearize digitalized analog signals, etc.

LVD—See Low voltage directive.

LVDT—Linear velocity differential transformer; sensor to measure rotational movement as linear displacement.

LVHC—Low volume, high concentration; usually used in reference to pollutant measurement for EPA (U.S.) regulations.

LVIT—Linear variable inductance transducer; linear measurement sensor based upon chemically etched planar coil technology.

LV-ROM—Laser video read only memory. **Also,** LaserVision ROM by Pioneer.

L-Z algorithm—Lossless data compression technique developed by two researchers named Lempel and Ziv.

LZH—Lempel-Ziv-Huffman; method of data compression that can reconstruct data exactly like the original with no loss.

LZSS—A refinement of the L-Z algorithm for data compression that can reconstruct data exactly like the original with no loss.

LZW—Lempel-Ziv and Welch; patented by Unisys, another refinement of the L-Z algorithm for data compression, which can reconstruct the data exactly like original with no loss.

M

M—(uppercase) Abbreviation for mega-, a prefix in math for multiple of 10^6 (= 1,000,000); ***also,*** in computing, a multiple of 2^{20} (=1,048,576) megabyte= 2^{20} bytes. *Also*, m (lower case), abbreviation for ***milli-***, a prefix in math for a submultiple of 10^{-3} (= 0.001). *Also*, formerly meant "moisture" (Humidity) when used in the first alpha character position of ISA instrument function tag; still means "momentary" as modifier; still means "middle" or "intermediate" when in succeeding letters [see ANSI/ISA S5.1-1984 (R1992)]. *Also*, mouse.

μ—Micro, in math (and often in computer terminology) is abbreviation for 10^{-6}, (0.000001).

μC—Microcontroller; microprocessor with timers, counters, RAM, and ROM included.

μP—Microprocessor; electronic integrated circuit, typically a single-chip package, capable of receiving and executing coded instructions; performs the functions of both CPU and ALU but excludes memory and I/O systems.

MAC—Media Access Control; media-specific access-control protocol within IEEE 802 specifications (lower sublayer of layer 2 of ISO model), which includes variations for token ring, token bus, and CSMA/CD.

MACE—Macintosh Audio Compression/Expansion; digital data compression standard developed by Apple and used in Macintosh's method for saving digital audio in electronic memory; used for exchanging data between computers in Audio Interchange File Format (AIFF).

machine language—Instructions written in binary form that computer can execute directly; also called machine code, object code, and object language.

machine vision—Computer perception of visually based sensory output used to produce a concise description of an image; devices used for optical non-contact sensing to receive and interpret automatically an image of an actual scene in order to obtain information or to control some process.

MACINTOSH–Most Applications Crash; If Not, The Operating System Hangs. ☺

macro—A kind of computer shorthand that reduces many programming commands to one, making it easy to activate functions that are used frequently.

MACT—Maximum Achievable Control Technology, usually used in reference to response to EPA (U.S.) regulations.

MAF—Mass air flow.

magenta—Color hue that transmits only blue and red light with no green from the video screen view; reflects only red and blue light and absorbs green light on paper using four-color process inks.

magnetic medium—Any data storage medium and related technology, such as core, drum, film, tape, and disk, in which different patterns of magnetization represent bit values.

magnetoresistive (MR)—Changes in the electrical resistance in materials composed of metallic elements, or magnetic metals used in memory storage devices.

magnitude—In digital signal processing *(DSP)*, square root of the sum of the squares of real and imaginary parts of a complex signal.

maillist—In e-mail systems, a (usually automated) method allowing a message to be sent to only one address, where it is then routed to specific other addresses.

mainframe—Large-scale computer system that can house comprehensive software and several peripherals; "opposite" of distributed system.

mains—Main power source supplied by power company or central generator of a self sufficient site; British equivalent to what in United States is called "line power."

make-to-order—Products manufactured to specific customer order configuration and delivery time specifications.

make-to-stock—Products manufactured to finished-goods storage before customer order arrives.

MAN—Metropolitan Area Network; 'stretched" LAN providing digital data communications over a distance of about 50 km; generally associated with IEEE 802.6 MAN standard.

Manchester encoding—Digital encoding technique (specified for IEEE 802.3, Ethernet) in which each bit is divided into two complementary halves; negative-to-positive (voltage) transition in the middle of the bit period designates binary "1," while positive-to-negative transition represents "0"; the technique also allows the receiving device to recover the transmitted clock from the incoming data stream (self-clocking).

manipulated variable (MV)—In process control, a quality or condition altered by control action in order to change the value of the regulated condition.

manual loading station, manual station, manual loader—Device or function having manually adjustable output that is used to actuate one or more remote devices; station does not provide switching between manual and automatic modes of control loop (see *Controller* and *Control Station*); station may have integral indicators, lights, or other features.

manual reset—Adjustment on proportioning controller that shifts the proportioning band in relation to the set point to eliminate droop or offset errors.

manual reset switch—Switch in limit controller that manually resets the controller after limit has been exceeded.

Manufacturing Message Specification (MMS)—ISO standard 9506, OSI application-layer protocol for messaging within and between industrial automation systems.

MAP—Manufacturing Automation Protocol; based on IEEE 802.4; General Motors originated networking protocol that follows the seven-layer OSI model. [Note: MAP-compliant means it conforms to specifications and will talk with other devices over the system; MAP-compatible means only that it will not interfere (physical and data link layers only) with "foreign" devices, but will only talk with like devices while sharing the timing with those foreign devices). *Also*, Manifold absolute pressure engine sensor.

MAP/EPA—MAP Extended Performance Architecture; dual architecture that supports both the full MAP seven layer communication architecture as well as architecture for time-critical communication that bypasses layers 3, 4, 5, and 6.

MAPI—Messaging Application Programming Interface; messaging API by Microsoft; in distributed client/server digital communication environments, MAPI treats the client and server components as independent applications; see *API*.

MAPI-WF— Messaging Application Programming Interface-Workflow Framework; proprietary messaging Application Programming Interface (API) by Microsoft as part of effort to create a de facto standard for workflow engine interoperability on the Internet.

mapping—In digital communication network operations, the logical association of one set of values, such as addresses on one network, with quantities or values of another set, such as devices on another network (that is, name-address internetwork route, protocol-to-protocol mapping).

margins—In typographical composition of video screen displays and printing, the white space surrounding the text area on a page.

mark—Presence of some signal; in current communication, such as telegraph, this represents closed condition or current flowing equivalent to binary 1.

marshaling cabinet—Cabinet, sometimes located outside the control or rack rooms, that houses terminal boards for plant or process field wiring, in which the wiring coming from or going to divergent locations is rearranged appropriately to control system I/O requirements, often with signal conditioning equipment, such as is needed for various transmitters and sensors; terminology comes from railroad marshaling yards (called switch yards in United States).

mass flow—The actual content of material in flow, correcting for pressure and temperature changes; volumetric flow rate times density, such as pounds per hour or kilograms per minute.

mass storage—Digital device like disk or magnetic tape that can store large amounts of data that are readily accessible to central processing unit.

master station—See *primary station*.

material dispersion—Dispersion resulting from the different velocities of each wavelength in an optical fiber.

matrix control strategies (MCS)—In process control, strategies that regulate the process from several inputs, usually involving unit severities and product compositions; also called multivariable predictive control strategies. See *multivariable control*.

MAU—Multistation access unit; wiring concentrator used in local area networks. *Also*, Media attachment unit; also known as transceiver and not to be confused with Token Ring MAU (media access unit), an Ethernet device for transmitting and receiving data that often provides data-packet collision detection as well; can either be an internal or a external feature of network device such as a network interface card, repeater, hub, or concentrator; multiport MAU, or transceiver, allows a number of computers or workstations to be attached to a single connection on Ethernet bus and each port performs standard transceiver functions.

maximum elongation—In strain gauges for force or pressure measurements, a strain value where a deviation of more than ±5 percent occurs with respect to mean characteristic (resistance change versus. strain).

maximum excitation—Maximum value of excitation voltage or current that can be applied to some device at ambient conditions without causing damage or performance degradation beyond specified tolerances.

maximum operating conditions—Maximum environmental conditions in which a device or system can operate safely but may limit life span of that device or system compared to operating in specified normal conditions.

MB—See Megabyte.

Mb—Megabit; 1,048,576 bits.

Mbone—Multicast backbone; a subset of the *Internet* that is capable of *multicasting*; started as "a wild idea" in 1992 when Allison Mankin, a researcher involved with the Internet Engineering Task Force (IETF), was too far along in her pregnancy to travel to San Diego for a needed meeting and suggested extending the experimental multicasting technology so she and others who could not attend could still fully participate; see *multicasting*.

MBPC—Model-based predictive control; similar to our own learning experience, a method of process control for use beyond the abilities of traditional PID type. Uses the correlation of training (or operating image [internal model]), target (or reference trajectory), action (computation of structured manipulated variable), and comparison of actual vs. expected (modeling error compensator).

Mbps, Mb/s—Million bits per second.

MC—Multivariable control; process control of many variables, generally based upon many inputs; usually, the term implies the need for some advanced control strategy.

MCA—Micro Channel Architecture; bus design of some PS/2 models.

MCAA—Measurement and Control Automation Association; develops standards for industrial process instrumentation and control; formerly called Scientific Apparatus Makers Association (SAMA).

MCC—Model correction coefficient; method of measuring process control loop tuning effectiveness.

MCGA—Multi-Color Graphics Array (or Adapter); created specifically for PS/2 models 25 and 30; does not work with EGA software.

MCI—Media Control Interface.

MCL—Maximum contaminant level.

MCM—Multichip modules.

MCR—Maximum continuous rating.

MCS—Matrix control strategies; in process control, strategies that regulate the process from several inputs, usually involving unit severities and product compositions; likewise called multivariable predictive control strategies.

MCU—Microcontroller unit, see *microcontroller*.

MD—MiniDisc; optical memory media that uses digital audio compression method (ATRAC) for quality similar to a CD but with less "data."

MDA—Monochrome Display Adapter; video standard introduced by IBM in 1982 for IBM PC, PC/XT and AT computers and compatibles, which handled only textual data and was eventually replaced by a card.

MDI—multiple-document interface; *Also*, medium-dependent interface; in data communications, a mechanical and electrical interface between a network segment and a Media Attachment Unit (MAU).

MDR—Magnetic disk recorder.

MDS—Microprocessor development system.

mean—Average of maximum and minimum values at (process) equilibrium.

measurand—The physical quantity, property, or condition that is measured.

measure—In typographical composition of screen displays and printing, the width of type, usually expressed in picas.

measured variable (MV)—In process control, that variable of process that is monitored by sensor to provide a signal to the controller; sometimes called process variable (PV).

measurement—Determination of the existence or magnitude of a variable.

measuring junction—That thermocouple junction referred to as the hot junction that is used to measure an unknown temperature.

media attachment unit (MAU)—Also known as a transceiver and not to be confused with a Token Ring MAU (Media Access Unit), an Ethernet device for transmitting and receiving data that often provides data-packet collision detection as well. A media attachment can either be an internal or external feature of a network device such as network interface card, repeater, hub, or concentrator. A multiport MAU, or transceiver, allows a number of computers or workstations to be attached to a single connection on the Ethernet bus, and each port performs standard transceiver functions.

media management—The ability to manage (the process of managing) different media used in the same network, such as coaxial cable, twisted-pair cable, and fiber-optic cable; involves cable performance monitoring, cable break detection, planning for cable routes, etc.

median—Middle value in a sample of rank-ordered data or measurements; there are as many values in this sample that are larger in a median as there are values that are smaller.

medium—Any material substance used for the propagation or transmission of signals, usually in the form of electrons, light, modulated radio, or acoustic waves such as optical fiber, metal wire, dielectric slab, air, water, free space, etc.

medium-dependent interface—MDI; in data communications, a mechanical and electrical interface between a network segment and a media attachment unit (MAU).

megabyte—Mbyte, meg, MB; 1,048,576 bytes; 1024 kilobytes (2^{20} bytes); basic unit of measurement of mass storage. **Also,** used in describing data transfer rates (primarily parallel) as a function of time (Mbps).

megaflops—One million floating point operations per second.

memory—In computing, a device into which data can be entered, in which it can be held, and from which it can be later retrieved. Usually considered to be kept electronically, as on chips (in RAM or ROM) rather than magnetically or optically on disks (stored media, usually referred to as storage). Of all computer components, it is the most generous in terms of variety and the skimpiest in terms of quantity. ☺

memory mapping—The duplication of all or part of the data in one memory location to the memory in another location or device.

MEMS—Microelectromechanical systems; micromachined integrated systems, usually on silicon chips, that perform some intelligent sensing function along with micromoving sensing diaphragms and beams, and actuating devices such as valves, motors, linear motors, cantilevers, switches, and gear trains.

menu—A method on workstation screens to select alternative functions displayed as a list and chosen through mouse, key, sequence of keys, touch screen hot spots, etc., rather than through the command language of the computer program.

MES— Manufacturing execution system; software packages for such functions as plant management, supervisory control and monitoring, plant engineering, and quality management. Model concept developed by Advanced Manufacturing Research (AMR), Boston, in the late 1980s with the intention of describing a system that, rather than focusing on measurements of material usage or process control, "centers on product itself as it moves through plant on way to customer." Intended to bridge the real-time information gap between planning (MIS) and controls (PCS) so as to link operators and managers with the current views of all processing resources; counterpart of MOM(s) model developed by Gartner Group. See MOM(s).

MESA—Manufacturing Execution System Association; Pittsburgh- based, not-for-profit consortium of twenty-five suppliers of MES software, services, and related technologies. Has the goal of educating potential users about the benefits of MES and to act as a resource for the media and public.

MESFET—Metalized Semiconductor Field Effect Transistor; an FET where a Schottky barrier is used for gate.

message box—In workstation screen views, a special dialog box within the application window that displays the information needed at some appropriate point of activity within that application. May alert the user when information is needed or display diagnostics when some error has occurred.

message switching—A method for handling messages over communications networks where the entire message is transmitted to an intermediate point (such as a switching computer), stored for a period of time (may be very short period), then transmitted toward its destination (each destination indicated by an address integral to the message). See also *circuit switching* and *packet switching*.

messaging—In object-oriented programming (OOP), objects communicating according to defined rules.

messaging application programming interface— System built into Microsoft Windows that enables different e-mail applications to work together for mail distribution. As long as both applications are MAPI-enabled, they can share mail messages with each other. MAPI confusion occurs because there are two very different kinds: first, MAPI of Microsoft Mail (MS Mail), which was a C-language API that allowed programmable access to those features; now called "Simple MAPI"; second, the "new MAPI" is a COM/OLE-based set of complex interfaces, sometimes called "Extended MAPI" or XMAPI, which includes Simple MAPI for compatibility with older software and also includes OLE Messaging, which is a set of OLE automation interfaces for messaging for use in Visual Basic, etc.

MFC—Microsoft Foundation Class; common computer software function libraries. *Also*, multifunction controller; term used by several process control systems vendors for a controller that contains software algorithms for loop, logic, and sequential process control within the same module.

MFD—Mode field diameter; diameter of optical energy in single mode optical fiber; because it is greater than core diameter, MFD replaces core diameter as a practical parameter.

MFLOPS—Million floating point operations per second (megaflops).

MFP—Multifunction printer; printer that will also scan, fax, and copy.

MFT—Main fuel trip; terminology that originated with the power generation industry.

MGA—Monochrome graphics adapter. *Also*, Murky Gray Area; reference by wags to the lack of a definitive line of responsibility between business planning software and process control software when these two operations are actually connected. This was a serious concern of the ISA SP95 effort to define enterprise/process functions. ☺

MHL—Microprocessor host loader.

Mho—In conductivity measurement, a unit of the conductance of solution, now called *siemens* (S); is reciprocal of its resistance in ohms.

MHS—Message Handling System standard defined by ISO and CCITT. *Also*, Message Handling Service, defined as something of a standard by Action Technologies Inc.; licensed and distributed by Novell.

MHSB—Monitored hot standby.

microcomputer—Based on the microprocessor, a computer that is physically small, usually fits on a small printed circuit board and works with a data word of 4, 8, or 16 bits; now often has all the power formerly found in minicomputers; also called personal computer.

microcontroller, μC—Microprocessor with timers, counters, RAM, and ROM included.

micron—One millionth of a meter (10^{-6}).

microprocessor, μP—Electronic integrated circuit, typically, a single-chip package, capable of receiving and executing coded instructions;

performs the functions of both the CPU and ALU but excludes memory and I/O systems.

middleware—Loosely defined as software for interconnecting application software from separate vendors, which are for different plant functions.

MIDI–Musical Instrument Digital Interface; industry standard connection for the computer control of musical instruments and devices. *Also*, what Mickey Mouse calls his girlfriend when he has a cold. ☺

MIF—Minimum networking functionality; general principle within OSI that calls for minimum LAN station complexity when interconnecting with resources outside the LAN.

milestones—Identified events to indicate the progression of a project.

MIL-STD—(U.S.) military standard.

MIMD—[*pronounced* mimdee] Multiple instruction multiple data stream computing, where at every instant each processor applies its own unique set of instructions on the data in its own local memory; see *SIMD*.

MIME—Multipurpose Internet Mail Extensions; Internet digital communication standard protocol that allows a message to contain textual, binary, or arbitrarily formatted data, such as sounds, cinema, and images.

MIMO—Multiple input multiple output; systems requiring complex control methods; see *SISO, MISO, TITO*.

minicomputer—Class of computer that has its CPU constructed of a number of discrete components and integrated circuits rather than being comprised of a single integrated circuit, as in microprocessor; a mini is larger than microcomputer and has a typical word length of 16 or 32 bits. It is a small, programmable, general-purpose computer typically used for dedicated applications.

MINI-MAP—Mini-Manufacturing Automation Protocol; version of MAP consisting of only physical, link, and application layers; intended for lower process control networks. Using MINI-MAP, a device with a token can request a response from an address device, and unlike the standard MAP protocol, the addressed device need not wait for the token to respond.

minus leading—In typographical composition of screen displays and printing, leading in which the baseline space is less than the point size (or less than solid leading).

MIP—Middleware Integration Platform; provides the capability to connect multiple control systems to multiple manufacturing and/or business applications. Integration functionality includes event handling, messaging, workflow transactions, systems management, dynamic configuration, some form of database management, etc.

MIPS—Million instructions per second (rough measure of processing power).

MIR—Micropower Impulse Radar; inexpensive, small sensor useful for motion detectors as well as flow and level sensors; works by way of its rapid-fire sampler, which enables it to analyze radio pulses that are much shorter than conventional radar, giving it tremendous accuracy at low power.

mirroring—In workstation screen displays, a display or creation of some graphic that portrays an image in the exact reverse orientation it originally had by flipping that graphic on its x-axis or y-axis.

MIS—Management Information System; computer network that allows managers to track the performance of a plant at close to real time without the excessive need for paper-based systems. Primarily used for the planning and scheduling of resources. *Also*, Metal Insulator Silicon.

misalignment loss—In fiber optics, a loss of power resulting from angular misalignment, lateral displacement, and end separation.

MISFET, MIST—Metal-Insulated Silicon Field-Effect Transistor; alternative name for MESFET. See *MESFET*.

MISO—Multiple input single output; systems requiring advanced control methods, such as fuzzy logic and neural networks; see *SISO, MIMO, TITO*.

MKS—Meter-kilogram-second; system of absolute units for length, mass, and time; now the basis of SI units.

MLA—Microprocessor language assembler.

MLB—Multilayer Board.

MLCC—MultiLayer chip capacitor.

MLE—Microprocessor language editor.

MLV—Multilayer varistor.

MMCD—Multimedia compact disk made by Sony/Phillips; now called DVD; see *DVD*.

MMFS—[*pronounced* Memphis] Manufacturing Message Format Standard; MAP layer 7 for numeric control, PLCs, robot control; replaced by MMS. See *MMS*.

MMG—Multibus Manufacturers Group

MMI—Man-machine interface; increasing use of the term HMI (human-machine interface) is occurring.

MMIC—Monolithic microwave integrated circuits.

MMS—Manufacturing Message Specification (part of MAP 3.0, layer 7); ISO standard 9506, OSI application-layer protocol for messaging within and between industrial automation systems; *also*, Maintenance Management System.

MMU—Memory management unit.

MMX—Multimedia extensions; performance-boosting technology that incorporated fifty-seven multimedia-centric instructions into Pentium processors by Intel so as to achieve 10–20 percent improvement on standard CPU benchmarks and up to 60 percent performance when running software specifically designed for the technology of audio, video and graphics. Involves a processing trick known as SIMD "single instruction, multiple data," which enables the MMX chip to package and process many pieces of information as one value, rather than in a one-at-a-time sequence that could cause bottlenecks. See *SIMD*.

MNCS—Multipoint Network Control System.

mnemonic—Technique used to aid human memory, such as a word or code (letters, symbols, etc.), for programming that is easy to remember or to suggest a correct response.

MNOS—Metal nitride-oxide semiconductor.

MNPT—Male National Pipe Thread.

MO—Model output; signal in the model correction coefficient (MCC) method for measuring process control loop tuning effectiveness. *Also*, magneto-optical, a technology that uses laser to heat a magnetic spot to 200°C within magnetic field so as to change data; allows millions of rewrites.

MOC—Management of change.

modal dispersion—Dispersion resulting from different transit lengths of different propagating modes in multimode optical fiber.

Modbus Plus—Popular Modicon master/slave protocol, owned by AEG Schneider Automation; inherently multidrop, has a communication rate of 1 Mbps.

Modbus RTU—Popular Modicon master/slave protocol, owned by AEG Schneider Automation; used by PLCs and specialty instrumentation such as analyzers, chromatographs, weigh scales, operator interfaces, RTUs, and DCSs.

mode—Method or condition of operation. *Also*, in fiber optics (and guided wave propagation), the distribution of electromagnetic energy that satisfies Maxwell's equation and boundary conditions; loosely, a possible path followed by light rays. *Also*, in SPC, the most frequently occurring value in a sample. *Also*, in controls, an output form or type of action, see *control mode*.

Model-based predictive control—Similar to our own learning experience, a method of process control for use beyond the abilities of the traditional PID type. Uses the correlation of training (or operating image [internal model]), target (or reference trajectory), action (computation of structured manipulated variable], and comparison of actual versus expected (modeling error compensator).

Modeling—Re-creation of event or object in a controlled environment so as to predict results from that event or object;

mathematically characterizing a process so that variables may be manipulated to determine their behavior in different situations.

model reference adaptive control—Method of self-adaptive control that compares real process parameters with a reference model.

Modem—Modulator/demodulator; interface device for data processing equipment to convert data to a form acceptable for sending and receiving on transmission facilities, most commonly telephone lines.

MODULA-2—Modular language-2; computer language designed by Niklaus Wirth to enhance Pascal; multiprocessing language with coroutines that may be executed simultaneously.

modulating control—To vary output signal based upon some variation of input (versus. on/off control).

modulation—Process by which the characteristic of one wave (the carrier) is modified by another wave (the signal), such as AM, FM, and PCM.

module—Separate and distinct unit of hardware and/or software; usually a card or subassembly of a larger device or the component of a larger system; a software segment (such as function block, subroutines) within a larger software program (or operation).

modulo—Mathematical function that yields that remainder of division; number x evaluated modulo n gives the integer remainder of x/n, for example, 200 modulo 47 equals the remainder of 200/47, or 12.

MOLAP—Multidimensional online analytical processing, see *OLAP*.

MOM(S)—Manufacturing Operations Management (System); software packages for such functions as plant management, supervisory control and monitoring, plant engineering, and quality management. Model concept developed by Gartner Group of Stamford, Connecticut, intended to bridge the real-time information gap between planning (MIS) and controls (PCS) so as to link operators and managers with current views of all processing resources. Counterpart of MES model developed by Advanced Manufacturing Research (AMR).

monitor—As a noun, general term for instrument or instrument system used to measure or sense the status or magnitude of one or more variables for the purpose of deriving useful information; the term is very unspecific, sometimes meaning analyzer, indicator, alarm, or CRT.

monitor light—See *pilot light*.

MOS—Metal-oxide semiconductor; uses a silicon dioxide layer as an insulator; is a special case of MIS transistors.

mosaic—In computer networks, user interface software for navigating, browsing, and accessing files across network (now used with the Internet); developed at National Center for Supercomputing Applications (NCSA) at the University of Illinois.

MOSFET, MOST—Metal-oxide semiconductor field-effect transistor; alternative name for MESFET.

motherboard—Printed circuit board of a computer that contains bus lines and edge connectors so as to accommodate other boards in the system; in a microcomputer, a motherboard often contains the microprocessor and expansion boards.

Motif—Graphical user interface defined by OSF and based largely upon DEC and others.

motion control—The application of moving parts in industrial settings including sequencing, speed control, point-to-point control, and incremental motion. Control options include timers and counters, chip-level and board-level computers, programmable logic controllers, (PLCs) and pneumatic sequencers.

motion JPEG—In video development, any of several proprietary implementations of motion video compression based on the JPEG standard, which produces outstanding quality video when the degree or amount of compression is not overdone.

MOTIS—Message-oriented text interchange system; ISO 10021.

MOU—Memoranda of understanding.

mouse—Handheld device developed by Doug Englebart in 1964 that is moved along a flat surface to drive and position a cursor on a workstation screen to direct the views or the operator inputs. *Also*, any of various small rodents with a pointed snout, slender body, and pointed tail and made to seem harmless by numerous cartoonists. ☺

MOV—Metal oxide varistor; device whose impedance changes appreciably in response to applied voltage. Used to limit the maximum voltage across an output device and protect vulnerable circuit components against transients by clamping the circuit to safe levels. *Also*, Motor-operated valves.

µP—See microprocessor.

MPC—Multivariable predictive control, in process control, strategies that regulate a process from several inputs, usually involving unit severities and product compositions; also called matrix control strategies. *Also*, Multimedia personal computer, which uses wavetable (FM) synthesis to generate complex frequencies, such as found in music. *Also*, Multimedia PC Council; a standards group.

MPEG—Motion Picture Experts Group; standards committee under the auspices of the ISO that is working on algorithm standards that will allow the digital compression, storage, and transmission of moving image information such as motion video, CD-quality audio, and control data at CD-ROM bandwidth. MPEG algorithm provides interframe compression of video images and can have an effective compression rate of 100:1 to 200:1.

MPEG 2—Proposed standard for ISO adaptation that allows for higher-resolution motion video compression than MPEG standard.

MPI—Metallized particle interconnect; component connection technology that consists of a proprietary polymer material embedded with metalized particles and formed into tiny microcolumns 0.025 inches in diameter and1 mm high. When mechanically compressed by frame holding microprocessor, the metallized particles within the compressed columns are joined to form a conductive path between contacts.

MPII—MAP in Process Industries Initiative.

MPP—Massively parallel processing; a type of computer architecture using a matrix of separate CPUs, each of which controls its own block of main memory and is linked in some way so as to communicate very quickly with each other.

MPR—Maximum power rating; maximum power in watts at which a device can safely operate.

mps, m/s—Meters per second.

MPU—Microprocessor unit, see microprocessor.

MR—See magnetoresistive.

MRA—Mutual recognition agreement.

MRAC—Model Reference Adaptive Control; a method of self-adaptive control that compares real process parameters with a reference model.

MRB—Management request broker; associated with Distributed Computing Environment by OSF.

MRP (MRP II)—Material Requirements Planning (and development phase II called Manufacturing Resource Planning); computerized method for planning a plant's use of resources, including raw materials, financial, vendors, production equipment, and processes.

MS—Manual station; provides process control signal directly to final element. ***Also,*** (lower case) millisecond; *also,* used by some to mean Microsoft.

MSB—Most significant bit.

MSD—Most significant digit; digit representing greatest value.

MSDB—Material safety data sheets; that carry information about what to do in emergencies when handling various specific, usually hazardous, materials.

MS-DOS—Microsoft Disk Operating System; developed for the IBM PC, it has become a de facto standard. Sometimes called PC-DOS, it designed to control and manage I/O devices and memory for personal computers (PCs).

MSHA—Mine Safety and Health Administration; U.S. agency.

MSI—Medium-scale integration; multifunction semiconductor, such as a microprocessor, with between twelve and one thousand equivalent gates.

MSN—Manhattan Street Network; refers to mesh architecture using wavelength division multiplexing in digital communication.

MS/TP—Master-slave/token-passing; data link protocol of BACnet that provides the same services to the network layer that ISO 8802-2 (IEEE 802.2) LLC does.

MSZH—Hungarian Office for Standardization.

MTA—Message Transfer Agent.

MTBF—Mean time between failures (since 1962) and calculated to be MTTF + MTTR; also Mean time before failure (prior to 1962 in U.S. military specification definition); the stated or published period of time for which the user may expect a device or system to operate before failure occurs (a computed arithmetic mean of the time, not a tested value).

MTC—MIDDI Time Code.

MTD—Mass tape duplicator/verifier; also, in PCMCIA technology, media technology drivers, which provide an effective method for making upper software layers independent of card technology; it is the intention that every PCMCIA have an associated MTD to contain programming algorithms for various devices on that card.

MTF—Modulation transfer function; video focus test to measure the contrast of adjacent single-pixel-wide black and white lines.

MTS—Message Transfer Service.

MTTF—Mean time to failure; used since 1962 as a calculated measure of overall reliability (a computed arithmetic mean of the time, not a tested value).

MTTFD—Mean time to failure (to) dangerous condition.

MTTFS—Mean time to failure (to) safe condition.

MTTR—Mean time to repair; average time required to perform corrective maintenance on a failed device or system.

muffle—Insulated enclosure of a furnace.

multicasting—Unlike

one-direction broadcasting in digital communications, this is entirely interactive, carrying audio, video, and a

"white-board" feature that enables participants to share text, images, and sketches; see *Mbone*.

multidrop—In fieldbus, the connection of multiple field devices to one pair of wires, usually “tee-connected.”

multimode—Essentially, optical fiber designed to carry multiple signals, distinguished by frequency or phase, at the same time.

multiplex—To interleave or simultaneously transmit two or more messages on a single channel.

Multiplexer—Device used for the division of a transmission facility into two or more subchannels, either by splitting the frequency into narrow bands (frequency division) or by allotting a common channel to several different transmitting devices one at a time (time division).

multipoint (multidrop) line—Single communications line or circuit interconnecting several stations; usually requires some kind of polling mechanism to address each connected terminal with a unique address code.

multiprocessing—The process by which an operating system allocates different programs and tasks to different processors without intervention by the operator to save considerable amounts of time.

multiprogramming—The ability to run multiple copies of an application program on a single computer.

multitasking—Concurrent execution of two or more tasks or applications by a computer at the same time, usually separate but interrelated; may also be the concurrent execution of a single program that is used by many tasks (not always real time); see *context switching*, *cooperative*, and *time-slice Multitasking*.

multivariable control (MC)—The process control of many variables, generally based upon many inputs; usually, the term implies the need for some advanced control strategy.

MUMS—Multiuser Management Systems; modern term for the role of SCADA systems, which give key decision makers the ability to analyze system operation so as to make it more efficient by providing access to spreadsheets, RDBMS, etc.

MUSIC—Management, user, system, information, communications.

MUX—Multiplexer; I/O device that routes data from several sources to a common destination.

MV—Measured variable; in process control, that variable of a process that is monitored by a sensor so as to provide a signal to the controller; sometimes called process variable (PV); *also,* manipulated variable; in process control, the quality or condition altered by a control action so as to change the value of the regulated condition.

MV/PC—Multivariable predictive control.

MXIbus—Multisystem extension interface bus; communications link designed by National Instruments to connect VXIbus systems.

N

N—Thermocouple type for omegalloy (nicrosil-nisil); *also,* n (lowercase) in math is the abbreviation "nano-" for 10^{-9}; once called millimicron (mμ) [see ANSI/ISA S5.1-1984 (R1992)].

NA—Numerical aperture; light-gathering ability of a fiber, defining the maximum angle to the fiber axis at which light will be accepted and propagated through that fiber; *also,* describes the angular spread of light from a central axis, as in exiting fiber, emitting from source, or entering detector.

NACCB—National Accreditation Council for Certification Bodies.

NAK—Negative acknowledgment; indicates that the previous transmission block was in error and that the receiver is ready to accept retransmission of the erroneous block. *Also,* the "not ready" reply to station selection in a multipoint operation or to the initialization sequence in a point-to-point operation.

NA mismatch loss—In fiber optics, the loss of power at a joint that occurs when the transmitting half has an NA greater than that of the receiving half, as when coupling light from source to fiber, from fiber to fiber, or from fiber to detector.

NAMUR—Norman Ausschultz für Messung und Regelung; committee founded in 1949 by several large chemical companies from Germany, The Netherlands, and Switzerland to standardize industrial practices in process measurement and control. A subcommittee published a set of guidelines for structured batch control in 1986, which were accepted throughout the European chemical industry with strong support worldwide. NAMUR looks at batch automation from the process activity viewpoint and views activities such as charge, mix, heat/cool, etc., as repeatable across many processes and industries. It therefore presents a hierarchy of structures, terminology, and definitions for classifying production facilities, processing equipment, recipe structure, as well as batch operational sequences and phases.

NAND—NOT-AND; an inverted AND gate.

nanometer—The unit in which wavelengths of light are expressed; one nanometer is one-billionth of one meter.

nanosecond—One billionth of one second.

narrowband channels—Subvoice-grade communication channels characterized by a speed range of 100 to 200 bps.

natural language—Any naturally evolved human language; usually used in comparison to a programming language.

NBS—National Bureau of Standards; now NIST.

NC—Normally closed (usually a switch or relay condition), allows flow until energized. *Also,* numeric control; a technique in operating machine tools or similar equipment in which motion is generated in response to numerically ordered commands. **Also** Network Computer, very inexpensive PC-like device that links to networks and contains minimum resident software, and no hard drives, but downloads whatever applications are needed for the task at hand only for as long as needed; contrasted with PCs, which must have everything resident within them to function.

NCAICM—National Center for Advanced Information Components Manufacturing; formed to develop considerably improved, high—resolution, flat-panel displays and advanced information components; participants include Los Alamos and Livermore Labs, thirty-nine industrial partners, and eight universities.

NCAP—Network-capable applications processor; provides "translation" of smart-transmitter data to/from network by STIM and TEDS, as defined by IEEE-P1451; see *STIM, TEDS, IEEE-P1451*.

NCB—National certification body; tests electrical equipment for safety standards to meet compliance requirements relevant to International Electrotechnical Committee IEC standard. There are thirty-four certification bodies in twenty-nine countries worldwide, five of which are in United States. Reciprocal certification among various countries reduces the delays of waiting for duplicate testing in each country before a product release there. See also *CB*.

NCG—Noncondensable gas.

NCGA—National Computer Graphics Association.

NCMS—National Center for Manufacturing Sciences in United States.

NDIS—Network Driver Interface Specification; standard created by Microsoft for writing hardware-independent drivers for third-party Ethernet adapters.

NDRO—Nondestructive readout.

nD_t—The refractive index of a substance using sodium light at a specific temperature.

NEC—National Electrical Code of regulations for the construction and installation of electrical wiring and apparatus; established by the NFPA, and suitable for mandatory application by a wide range of state and local authorities; classifications include the following:
Class I—Hazardous vapors
Class II—Combustible dust
Class III—Combustible fibers and particulated
Division 1—Flammable/combustible atmosphere generally present
Division 2—Flammable/combustible atmosphere present under abnormal conditions
Group A—Acetylene,
Group B—Hydrogen,
Group C—Ethylene, ether, other
Group D—Hydrocarbons (e.g., gasoline, natural gas)
Group E—Electrically conductive dust (e.g., magnesium)
Group F—Coal or coke dust
Group G—Agricultural dust

negative letterspacing—In typographical composition of screen displays and printing, the subtraction of space between characters individually or en masse; see *kerning*.

negative temperature coefficient—Decrease in resistance with an increase in temperature.

NEK—Norsk Elektroteknisk Komite; Norwegian member of IEC.

NEMA—National Electrical Manufacturers Association; trade association of electrical equipment manufacturers that develops many manufacturing specifications; included are cabinet ratings such as the following:
NEMA 1—Dust-resistant general-purpose,
NEMA 2—Drip-tight,
NEMA 3—Splash-proof (weather-resistant),
NEMA 4—High-pressure hose-proof,
NEMA 5—Dust-tight,
NEMA 6—Submersible,
NEMA 7—Hazardous indoor (NEC Class I Groups A,B, C, D),
NEMA 8—Hazardous indoor/outdoor (NEC Class I Groups A, B, C, D),
NEMA 9—Hazardous indoor/outdoor (NEC Class II Groups E, F, G),
NEMA 10—MSHA 30 CFR part 18,
NEMA 11—General purpose drip and corrosion-resistant from liquids and gases
NEMA 12—General-purpose indoor use drip-dust-rust-resistant
NEMA 13—General-purpose resistant to dust/rust and spraying of water/oil/noncorrosive liquids.
IEC enclosure classes equivalent to NEMA ratings: IP10 = NEMA 1, IP11 = NEMA 2, IP14/54 = NEMA 3/13, IP52 = NEMA 5/12, IP56 = NEMA 4, IP67 = NEMA 7.

NEMKO—Norges Elektriske Materiellkontroll; Norwegian certification and testing laboratory for testing the equipment of different vendors to some common standard.

NEPSI—National Supervision and Inspection Center for Explosion Protection and Safety of Instrumentation; Chinese certification and testing laboratory for testing the equipment of different vendors to some common standard.

nesting—To embed a programming subroutine or data block in a larger routine or data block; the organization of data in hierarchical structures for greater efficiency in the storing and processing of repetitive elements; thereby identical elements need be represented only once in the database.

NetBEUI—NetBIOS Enhanced User Interface; primary protocol used by Windows for Workgroups; supported in all of Microsoft's network products.

NetBIOS—Network Basic Input/Output System; high-level session-layer interface used by applications as a communications interface to PC-DOS applications.

NetPC—Network PC; more like a compact PC than a network computer (NC), contains minimum resident software and no hard drive and can download whatever applications are needed for the task at hand only for as long as they are needed; contrasted with PCs that must have everything resident within themselves to function. See *NC.*

network—Interconnected group of nodes; a series of points, nodes, or stations connected by communications channels; an assembly of equipment through which connections are made between data stations; in electrical pneumatic, or hydraulic circuit, any combination of circuit elements.

network architecture—Set of design principles, including the organization of functions and description of data formats and procedures, that is used as a basis for the design and implementation of a network (ISO).

network layer—Layer 3 in the OSI model; the logical network entity that services the transport layer; responsible for ensuring that the data passed to it from the transport layer is routed and delivered through the network.

network topology—The physical and logical relationship of nodes in a network; the schematic arrangement of links and nodes of a network; networks are typically star, ring, tree, or bus topology, or some combination.

neural computing—Adapts to repeated examples in order to recognize patterns; not based on algorithms; mathematical mapping between repeatable cause and effect is learned through pattern recognition; cannot handle constraints and cannot optimize.

neural network—Processing architecture derived from models of the neuron interconnections of the brain. Unlike typical computers, neural networks incorporate a form of learning rather than programming, and function using parallel rather than sequential processing.

neural network computer—Has no CPU, no memory; it has a learning algorithm and is not necessarily a state machine; each element (a neuron) is a system with a transfer function using a filter with a weight for each input.

neutral zone—Increment through which input signal to a device or system is varied before action is detected; expressed as a percentage of input span; see *differential.*

newsgroups—Somewhat like BBSs, these are discussion groups on the Internet with a global reach.

NFC—Norwegian Fieldbus Consortium; *also,* a French standards organization.

NFM—Near field monitor; one of several small audio monitors mounted in close proximity to listener(s) so the ratio of direct sound waves to waves reflected from surfaces in the room are quite high, meaning that sound is relatively unaffected by room acoustics.

NFPA—National Fire Protection Association; *also,* National Fluid Power Association.

NFS—Network file server; TCP/IP extension allowing files on remote nodes of a network to appear to be locally connected.

nibble—In digital computer communications, one half of a byte; four bits.

NIC—Network interface card.

NiCad—Nickel cadmium; usually plating on brass screws.

nicrosil/nisil—Nickel chrome/nickel silicone thermal alloy used to measure high temperatures.

NIOSH—National Institute for Occupational Safety and Health; independent U.S. federal agency charged with performing research on occupational disease and injury.

NIRD—Near infrared device, such as a spectrophotometer analyzer.

N-ISDN—Narrowband Integrated Services Digital Network.

NIST—National Institute of Science and Technology; formerly the NBS, a U.S. government agency that provides standard reference materials and calibration services; NIST-*certified* instruments are calibrated at NIST, whereas NIST-*traceable* instruments are factory calibrated against NIST-certified standards.

NMOS—N-channel metal-oxide semiconductor.

NMR(R)—See Normal mode rejection ratio.

NNC—Neural network computer; has no CPU, no memory; has learning algorithm; is not necessarily a state machine; each element (neuron) is a system with a transfer function using filter with a weight for each input.

NNI—Nederlands Normalisatie-Instituut; standards group in The Netherlands and a member of IEC.

NO—Normally open (usually in reference to a switch or relay condition); does not allow flow unless energized.

node—Point of interconnection to some network; normally the point at which a number of terminals or tail circuits attach to network.

noise—In electrical signals, the rms, a peak-to-peak alternating current component of DC signal in the absence of measurand; in general, any unwanted electrical interference or other disturbance superimposed on signal wires that will obscure information content. Noise comes from the very soul of the universe and occurs across the entire spectrum of electromagnetic communications. Any piece of electronics introduced into a circuit will introduce noise but usually "active" powered devices such as transistors, diodes, and integrated circuits are the noticeable offenders.

NOM—Natural organic materials; monitored in water supplies, especially for their reaction to disinfectant, which can cause damaging by-products.

Nonimpact printer—Electronic device like a copier or laser or inkjet printer that creates images on (usually paper) surface without contacting it.

nonlinear—In video development, the ability to edit scenes together in any order and make changes to previous edit decisions (compare with *linear*).

Nonprocedural programming language—Computer programming language used to express the parameters of a problem rather than the steps in its solution, for example, report writer or sort specification languages; see *procedural programming language*.

Nonswitched Line—Communications link that is permanently installed between two points; also called leased line or private line. See *leased line*.

nontransparent mode—The transmission of characters in a defined character format, such as ASCII or EBCDIC, in which all defined control characters and control character sequences are recognized and treated as such.

NOR—NOT-OR; an inverted OR gate.

normal mode rejection ratio—The ability of an instrument to reject interference, usually of the line frequency (50-60 Hz), across its input terminals (versus Common Mode). See *Common Mode Rejection Ratio*.

NOS—Network operating system.

Notch filter—In digital signal processing *(DSP)*, a filter that attenuates signals in a certain frequency band and passes all others.

NOx—Nitrogen oxides, a consideration in EPA (U.S.) regulations; compounds formed by the oxidation of atmospheric nitrogen under high-energy conditions, released primarily from burning fossil fuels.

NPDES—National Pollutant Discharge Elimination System; U.S. federal permitting program for discharging effluent to surface waters, required under the Clean Water Act; over fifteen thousand municipal and forty-eight thousand industrial facilities report monthly on the amount and content of discharge.

NPE—Normalized prediction error method of measuring process control loop tuning effectiveness.

NPL—National Priorities List of hazardous waste sites in the United States that will be addressed by the Comprehensive Environmental Response, Compensation, and Liability Act.

NPT—National Pipe Thread.

NRE—Non-recurring engineering.

NREN—National Research and Education Network (U.S.).

NREP—National Registry of Environmental Professionals; U.S. organization designed to implement programs for recognizing the quality and certification of environmental professionals.

NRFT—Not right first time; mathematical inverse of right first time (RFT), a technique for measuring error rates for the effectiveness for QA/QC. See *quality assurance, quality control.*

NRTL—Nationally Recognized Testing Laboratory; program that is part of OSHA's Directorate of Technical Support to recognize private-sector testing laboratories and designating that those laboratories have met the necessary qualifications specified in regulations for that program; leads to NRTLs from different international organizations so as to accept common standards with the same testing regimen.

NRZ—Nonreturn to zero; pulses in alternating directions for successive 1 bits; no change from existing bias for 0 bits.

NRZI—Nonreturn to zero inverted.

NS—Nitrogen supply.

NSAI—National Standards Authority of Ireland.

NSAP—Network service access point.

NSF—National Sanitation Foundation, nongovernment U.S. agency focused on health-related standards for products and services; approval indicates that the product is suited for applications such as food handling; *also,* Norges Standardiseringsforbund, standards group in Norway.

NSM—Network of systems management.

NSP—Native signal processing; Intel processor initiative for text-to-speech conversion.

NT—New technology; used for Microsoft computing platform, Windows NT.

NTC—Negative temperature coefficient, such as in "NTC resistor (thermistor)," which will make a large, abrupt change in resistance when an undercurrent or low temperature cools it below some specific point, thereby effectively "switching off," or in reality acting like a solid-state fuse.

NTL—Nonthreshold logic.

NTSC—National Television System Committee; sets video standards in the United States; 525 lines, 60 hertz, 110 volts, 30 frames per second in an interlaced analog signal; the world's first compatible color television service, started in 1953; became the standard for much of North America; sometimes referred to as "Never Twice the Same Color." ☺ See also, *SECAM, PAL, PAL-M.*

NTW—N(ext) t(echnology) workstation; Microsoft Windows NT workstation operating system.

NuBus—Bus used in the Macintosh computer by Apple.

null—Condition, such as balance, which results in minimum absolute value of signal.

null modem—Communication device that interfaces between some local peripheral that normally requires a modem and a computer near it that expects to drive a modem to interface to that device; an imitation modem in both directions.

NURBS—Nonuniform rational b-splines; b-splines for ensuring continuity among objects; a mathematical description of geometry that provides the easy manipulation of entities and surfaces.

NVLAP—National Voluntary Laboratory Accreditation Program; administered by NIST to accredit labs in the field of computer communications software; use of these accredited labs is required by the U.S. GOSIP testing program. See *GOSIP.*

NVP—Nominal velocity propagation (of signals within cables).

NVRAM—Nonvolatile random access memory.

NVT—Network virtual terminal.

Nyquist Rate—In digital signal processing *(DSP)*, the lowest sampling rate necessary to completely reconstruct a signal without distortion due to aliasing; equal to twice the highest frequency component of signal.

O

O—Output signal in analog, discrete, or digital form; **also:** means "Orifice," or "Restriction" when used as succeeding alpha character position of ISA instrument function tag [see ANSI/ISA S5.1-1984 (R1992)]; **also:** electromagnetic or sonic signal.

O/E—Or Equal; reference in system specifications when listing features needed and identified by specifics of given vendor equipment as form of description for that feature.

OA—Open Access.

OBIOS—Open, Basic Input/Output System; standard proposed by Real-Time Consortium.

Object—In Object Oriented Programming (OOP), software model or representation of a part of reality; **also:** set of data, such as bitmap image, text, trend graphs.

Object Dictionary—In Fieldbus Foundation context, schema-based approach for defining dictionary and directory information about devices and their function blocks.

Object Language—Also called object code, machine code; see *Machine Language*.

object linking and embedding (OLE)— in computers, a database feature of the Microsoft Windows and WindowsNT environments that treats data as collection of objects to be shared by applications supporting the OLE specification; enables several applications to be linked to accomplish a given task; allows user to keep information current across several software applications, simply by changing the information in one of them.

object oriented drawing—An approach in drawing and layout programs that treats digital graphics as line and arc segments (boxes, ellipses, etc.) rather than as individual dots; also called vector-oriented. See vector-oriented drawing.

object oriented programming—Computer programming based upon a package of information and descriptions of procedures forming a single object that can communicate with other objects.

object oriented system—System in which both data and procedures combine in software objects, message passing is used to communicate digitally with and between objects, similar objects are grouped into class structures, and both data and procedures are inherited through the class structure to specific instances (copies) of objects.

object request broker (ORB)—Architecture that defines interfaces by which objects transparently make and receive responses. Makes possible interoperability among applications on different machines and interconnects multiple objects, provided that the underlying computer infrastructure also supports ORB. See also *CORBA*.

OBS—Open business systems; term used by some for next-generation business system management packages where the hardware and software is not proprietary.

OC—Open controller; process controller that can communicate directly with other controllers, user interfaces, and other devices made by different vendors.

OCD—Open circuit detection.

OCR—Optical character recognition; scanning printed/written data into the text file of a computer.

OCS—Open control system; term used by some for the next generation of DCS where ideally hardware and software is not proprietary.

octal—Pertaining to the base 8 number system.

octet—Eight bits; whereas a byte is a "character" and may be six to eight bits.

OCX—OLE custom controls (extension); object-oriented software building blocks that save considerable amounts of programming time in the creation of applications; theoretically, can readily be plugged into Visual Basic, Visual C++, databases, spreadsheets, and word processors.

OD—Output driver; see **also,** object directory.

O.D.—Outside diameter.

ODA—Open document architecture; formerly, office document architecture.

ODBC—Open Database connectivity; in computers, a data access standard that provides a transparent connection among a variety of different databases (even across platforms) and any applications that depend on them; supports structured query language (SQL).

ODI—Open datalink interface; in computers, allows network users greater flexibility in moving files from one type of network to another; supports TCP/IP and SPX/IPX transport protocols concurrently with existing Ethernet, Token Ring, and ARCnet adapters.

ODIF—Open document interchange format; formerly office document architecture.

ODS—Output data strobe.

ODVA—Open DeviceNet Vendors Association; formed in 1995 by over a hundred developer-vendors in the United States after Allen-Bradley transferred intellectual property ownership so as to position DeviceNet the as non-proprietary international standard.

OEM—Original equipment manufacturer; one who provides final systems made from the assemblies and subassemblies of other manufacturers.

Off delay—Timer that begins when the power is removed completely from the unit.

off load(ing)—Relieving an intensive amount of data processing with a specific application from the CPU by performing those calculations in a dedicated or specialized processor.

offline—The condition in which a user, terminal, or other device is not connected to a computer or is not actively transmitting via a network, thus is operating independently from the main system; opposite of *on-line*. *Also,* in traditional video editing, stage at which most content and editing decisions are made, usually on less expensive equipment and using dubs (or work prints) of original source material; at this stage an edit decision list is often created to facilitate an on-line session.

offset—Difference between the set point and actual process value, sometimes called droop. See *droop*.

OFHC—Oxygen-free high-conductivity copper; industry designation of pure copper used in type T thermocouple.

OHIM—Oh Heck It's Monday. ☺

OI—Operator interface.

OLAP—Online analytical processing; software designed for ad hoc data access and analysis; allows the easy exploration of a database for patterns that assist in determining the significance of data (it obtains information from highly dimensional complex data).

OLE—Object linking and embedding; in computers, an application integration feature of the Microsoft Windows and WindowsNT environments that treats data as a collection of objects to be shared by applications supporting the OLE specification; enables several different applications to be linked so as to accomplish a given task; allows the user to keep information current across several different software applications simply by changing information in one of them. With the arrival of the Internet, Microsoft now prefers to use "ActiveX."

OLE-PC—Object linking and embedding for process control; OLE extensions to improve interoperability among different industrial automation devices and software; now frequently called OPC; see *OPC™*.

oleophillic—Oil receptive.

oleophobic—Oil repellent.

OLI—Open Link Interface; specification developed by Novell and Apple for DOS and OS/2 platforms.

OLP—Off line program.

OMAC—Open Modular Architecture Controller; concept a of system structure more than of hardware being developed by General Motors in conjunction with Ford Motor Co. and Chrysler Corp. to merge currently incompatible platforms of PLCs and motion-controlling CNCs; parallels the coexistence of PLCs and DCSs in process control; some technologies include IEC 1131-3 programming languages, Microsoft Windows environments, Ethernet, and VMEbus.

OMG—Object Management Group, 11 companies including IBM, H-P, Sunsoft who developed CORBA for programming object oriented software, which competes with de facto object standard COM by Microsoft.

OMT—Object Modeling Technique; of object-oriented design.

ON—Österreichisches Normungsinstitut; standards group in (former) East Germany.

on delay—Timer that starts when power is applied and output contacts transfer at the end the of timing period; this type resets during power failure.

on-line—Condition in which user, terminal, or other device is actively connected with the facilities of a communications network or computer; opposite of *off-line. Also,* in traditional video editing, the stage at which the final videotape is made, usually on more expensive equipment that reedits a piece using original or lowest-generation material for best quality and adds all finishing touches.

on/off Control—Process control response in which a function is either fully on or fully off, with no intermediate operating positions.

ONC—Open Network Computing; network computing environment developed by Sun Microsystems.

OOA—Object-oriented analysis.

OOD—Object oriented design.

OODBMS—Object-oriented database management system; reflecting the desire to organize data the way it is done in real world.

OOP—Object-oriented programming; programming based on objects that talk by message passing; an object is a package of information and descriptions of procedures so as to manipulate that information.

OPAL—Operational Performance-Analysis Language.

OPC—OLE-PC; object linking and embedding for process control; a task force of a consortium created to rapidly develop an OLE-based interface standard for manufacturing automation so as to improve interoperability among industrial devices and software. Includes AEG Schneider, Applied Automation, Aspen Technology, Fluke, Gensym, Hewlett-Packard, Honeywell, Siemens, USDATA, Hitachi, Moore Products, National Instruments, and Wonderware.

open loop control—In process control, sensing change in the input of a process so as to cause change in the control signal to one of the other inputs to that same process; does not have self-correcting action as with closed loop (feedback) control; also called feedforward control or anticipatory control.

open system—Hardware/software designs in which a degree of interchangeability and connectivity provides the user with choices: i.e., the ability to select multiple products from multiple vendors and integrate them seamlessly on powerful networks. Open systems make every resource on a network available to any authorized user who needs it. *Also,* but not limited to, a system that complies with the requirements of the OSI reference model.

operand—The quantity or data item that is operated upon.

operating specifications—operating range Environmental conditions over which equipment or a system will operate and maintain its specified performance without any degradation; see *condition (operating), extreme, storage* and *specifications.*

operating system—Computer software that controls the execution of programs, typically handling the functions of input/output control, resource scheduling, and data management. It provides application programs with the fundamental commands to control the computer.

operational qualification—In process validation, documented verification that an equipment-related system or subsystem performs as intended throughout its represented or anticipated operating ranges.

operator—In the description of a computing process, that which indicates the action to be performed on the operands.

operator interface—Shared boundary between human operator and computer system, typically consisting of a graphical representation (on CRT or LCD) and an input device (keyboard, touch screen, mouse, trackball, light pen).

operator station—The operator interface from which a process or plant is run.

OPI—Open Prepress Interface; desktop publishing standard that converts large, high-resolution images into smaller, more manageable bit maps for use during the layout of printed and screen images.

optical disk—Very-high-density information storage medium that uses light to read and write digital information (comes in read-only and write-once types). Unlike magnetic media, it is not inadvertently changed or erased due to EMI/RFI fields.

optical fiber—Any filament or fiber made of dielectric materials and consisting of a core to carry the light signal and surrounding cladding that reflects signal back into the core. A thin glass thread is most commonly used, but plastic fiber can also be chosen.

optical isolation—Two networks that are connected only through an LED transmitter and photoelectric receiver with no electrical continuity between the two networks.

ORB——Object request broker; architecture that defines interfaces by which objects transparently make and receive responses; makes possible interoperability among applications on different machines and interconnects multiple objects, provided that underlying computer infrastructure also supports ORB. See also *CORBA*.

ORP—Oxidation-reduction potential; often called *redox* in the process industries, which is directly related to the oxidative strength of a biocidal agent such as chlorine. The ratio of activities of the oxidized (loss—of- electron) and reduced (gain—of-electron) forms of various substances in solution, activities that generate millivolt potential similar to pH, depending on the substance.

orphan—In typographical composition of screen displays and printing, a word or short line ending a paragraph that is carried over to the top of the next column; frowned upon in good typography.

OS—Operator station; *also,* operating system.

OS/2—Operating System 2; multitasking third-generation operating system for PS/2 developed by IBM and Microsoft to use with Intel 80286 and 80386 microprocessors. *Also,* Obsolete Soon, Too. ☺

OS/2 EE—Operating System 2, extended edition.

OSF—(Open Software Foundation); not-for-profit coalition of DEC, IBM, Hewlett Packard, Apollo, Groupe Bull, Nixdorf Computer AG, and Siemens AG located in Cambridge Massachusetts, and founded in 1988 to develop and license core software technologies to develop alternative to UNIX because of AT&T's decision not to open UNIX for development. *Also,* Open Systems Foundation; organization created to define software specifications, develop software, and make available some open, portable environment.

OSHA—Occupational Safety and Health Act; U.S. federal law passed in 1970 specifying the requirements an employer must follow to guard against employee illness and injury. *Also,* Occupational Safety and Health Agency; responsible for enforcing that act.

OSI—Open Systems Interconnection; seven-layer reference model for network operations standardized within ISO to enable any two OSI-compliant devices to exchange information; the seven layers are physical, datalink, network, transport, session, presentation, and application.

OSI-RM—Open Systems Interconnection Reference Model; ISO IS7498.

OSI/NM—OSI/Network Management forum formed by eight companies in 1988 to accelerate standard on network management.

OSINET—Open Systems Interconnection NETwork; interoperability testing network, sponsored by NIST designed to provide vendors of products based on OSI model forum for doing interoperability testing.

OSPF—Open Shortest Path First; newly proposed routing standard.

OTD—Open Thermocouple Detection.

OTDR—Optical Time Domain Reflectometry; method of evaluating optical fibers based on detecting backscattered (reflected) light; used to measure fiber attenuation, evaluate splice and connector joints, and locate faults.

OTP—One-Time Programmable memory.

Out Point—In video development, last frame of a clip; see *In Point*.

Output—End result of process or system; information leaving a device, data resulting from processing; audio, electrical, mechanical, pneumatic, or hydraulic signal delivered by an instrument to a load.

Output Impedance—Impedance measured across output terminals of device due to circuitry within that device; in power supplies, equivalent dynamic series impedance of power supply output; normally derived from ratio of output voltage change for an output current change, as measured at output terminals; load line effect and termination must be considered for total impedance.

Output Noise—The RMS, peak-to-peak ac component of a device (typically a transducer) dc output in absence of signal variation.

Output Rating—Voltage and current carrying capability of equipment electrical output.

Output Sequence: OXO—Output switch is open during reset, closed during timing, and open during timed out condition.

Output Sequence: OOX—Output switch is open during reset, open during timing, and closed during timed out condition.

Oven—Heated enclosure for baking, heating, or drying; generally at temperatures considerably less than a furnace.

Overhead—Communications, all information such as control, routing, and error checking characters that are used in addition to transmitted data; includes routing information, operational instructions, and retransmissions of data that are received in error.

Overload Protection—Protection of equipment against excessive current, including short circuit current; in power supplies, protection circuitry is electronic with automatic recovery, current characteristic is normally a foldback type.

Overshoot—In process control, amount that process exceeds setpoint when dynamically approaching setpoint value.

Request Broker; architecture that defines interfaces by which objects transparently make and receive responses; enables interoperability among applications on different machines and interconnects multiple objects, provided that underlying computer infrastructure also supports ORB. (See also CORBA).

ORP—Oxidation-Reduction Potential; often called REDOX in the process industries, which is directly related to oxidative strength of biocidal agent such as chlorine; ratio of activities of oxidized (loss of electron) and reduced (gain of electron) forms of various substances in solution, activities which generate millivolt potential similar to pH, depending on the substance.

orphan—In typographical composition of screen displays and printing, a word or short line ending a paragraph which is carried over to top of next column, frowned upon in good typography.

OS—Operator Station; **also:** operating System.

OS/2®—Operating System 2; multitasking third-generation operating system for PS/2® developed by IBM® and Microsoft® to use with Intel® 80286 and 80386 microprocessors; **also:** Obsolete Soon, Too. ☺

OS/2 EE—Operating System 2, Extended Edition.

OSF—(Open Software Foundation); not-for-profit coalition of DEC®, IBM®, HP®, Apollo®, Groupe Bull®, Nixdorf Computer AG®, and Siemens AG® located in Cambridge Massachusetts, USA, founded in 1988 to develop and license core software technologies to develop alternative to UNIX® due to AT&T® decision to not open UNIX® development; **also:** (Open Systems Foundation) organization created to define software specifications, develop software, and make available some open, portable environment.

OSHA—Occupational Safety and Health Act; U.S. federal law passed in 1970 specifying requirements an employer must follow in order to guard against employee illness and injury; **also:** (Occupational Safety and Health Agency) responsible to enforce that act.

OSI—Open Systems Interconnect; 7-layer reference model for network operations standardized within ISO to enable any two OSI-Compliant devices to exchange information; the seven layers are Physical, Datalink,

Network, Transport, Session, Presentation, Application.

OSI-RM—Open Systems Interconnection Reference Model; ISO IS7498.

OSI/NM—OSI/Network Management forum formed by 8 companies in 1988 to accelerate standard on network management.

OSINET—Open Systems Interconnection NETwork; interoperability testing network, sponsored by NIST designed to provide vendors of products based on OSI model forum for doing interoperability testing.

OSPF—Open Shortest Path First; newly proposed routing standard.

OTD—Open Thermocouple Detection.

OTDR—Optical Time Domain Reflectometry; method of evaluating optical fibers based on detecting backscattered (reflected) light; used to measure fiber attenuation, evaluate splice and connector joints, and locate faults.

OTP—One-Time Programmable memory.

out Point—In video development, last frame of a clip; see *In Point*.

output—End result of process or system; information leaving a device, data resulting from processing; audio, electrical, mechanical, pneumatic, or hydraulic signal delivered by an instrument to a load.

output impedance—Impedance measured across the output terminals of a device due to circuitry within that device. In power supplies, the equivalent dynamic series impedance of power supply output. Normally derived from the ratio of output voltage change for an output current change as measured at output terminals. Load line effect and termination must be considered for total impedance.

output noise—The rms, peak-to-peak AC component of a device's (typically a transducer) DC output in the absence of signal variation.

output rating—Voltage and current-carrying capability of equipment's electrical output.

output sequence: OXO—Output switch that is open during reset, closed during timing, and open during timed-out condition.

output sequence: OOX—Output switch that is open during reset, open during timing, and closed during timed-out condition.

oven—Heated enclosure for baking, heating, or drying, generally at temperatures considerably less than that a furnace.

overhead—In communications, all information such as control, routing, and error-checking characters that are used in addition to transmitted data. Includes routing information, operational instructions, and retransmissions of data that are received in error.

overload protection—The protection of equipment against excessive current, including short circuit current. In power supplies, the protection circuitry is electronic with automatic recovery: the current characteristic is normally a foldback type.

overshoot—In process control, the amount by which a process exceeds the set point when dynamically approaching the set point value.

P

P—Proportion (gain) action in modulating process control that responds to the deviation from the set point within proportional band (corrective action is proportional to the amount of error). *Also,* means "pressure" (or "vacuum") when used in the first alpha character position of ISA instrument function tag, means "point" (test connection) in succeeding position. *Also,* P (uppercase) in math is the abbreviation "peta-" for 10^{15}. *Also,* p (lowercase) in math is the abbreviation "pico-" for 10^{-12}, once called micromicro (μμ) *also called,* mickeymikes [see ANSI/ISA S5.1-1984 (R1992)].

ΔP—Pressure drop (psig) across a restriction; inlet pressure minus outlet pressure.

P&ID—Piping and instrumentation Diagram.

P-I-N diode—Typically used for photodiodes, this semiconductor contains a depletion layer within the region of almost intrinsic (I-type) semiconductive material between its P-type and N-type regions.

P-P—Peak-to-peak.

packet—In digital communications, a group of bits, including data and call control signals, transmitted as a whole on a packet-switching network; usually smaller than a transmission block.

packet switching—Data transmission technique whereby physical resources on a path are switched on a per-packet basis, using control information in the header of each packet (the channel is occupied only for the duration of the transmission of the packet). In some data communication networks, the data may be formatted into a packet or divided and then formatted into a number of packets for multiplexing the transmission. See also *circuit switching* and *message switching*.

PACS—Picture archiving and communication system; the digital storage, retrieval, and presentation of input from video sensors.

PAD—Packet access device; an interface between the terminal or computer and the packet switching network.

PAL—Programmable array logic; trade name by AMD, see also *GAL* and *PEEL*; *Also,* phase-alternation line, in which a subcarrier derived from color burst is inverted in phase from one line to the next in order to minimize hue errors that may occur in transmission; has become a color video scan standard for Europe and other countries with 625 lines, 50 hertz, 220 volts; first introduced in Europe in the 1960s (the United Kingdom on July 1, 1967; Germany on August 21, 1967, the Netherlands on September 21, 1967), often referred to as "Peace at Last"; ☺ see also *NTSC, SECAM, PAL-M.*

PALC—Plasma-addressed liquid crystal; technology in which gas-plasma channels perform much the same pixel-triggering duties as thin-film transistors in active—matrix LCD panels, with standard LCD-style backlighting providing illumination.

palette—Collection of colors or shades available to a computer graphic system or program within a workstation.

PAL-M—Brazilian version of phase-alternation line; used only in Brazil, 525 lines, 50 hertz, 220 volts, often remembered as "Pay a Little More." ☺

panel—A structure that has group of instruments mounted on it to function as the operator interface to the process; panel may consist of one or more sections, cubicles, consoles, or desks.

Panel-mounted—Term for an instrument that is mounted on a panel or console and is accessible for normal operator's use; a function that is normally accessible to an operator in a shared display (video screen) system is the equivalent of a discrete panel-mounted device.

PANS—Process analytical systems.

PAR—Program aid routine.

paradigm—Set of rules and regulations, written or unwritten, that establish or define boundaries and govern how to behave inside those boundaries to be successful.

parallax—Optical illusion that occurs when the viewing eye is not in same plane (perpendicular) as the device being used; most noticed when a glass separates the eye from the target, such as when reading a meter or using a touch screen.

parallel processing—The oncurrent or simultaneous execution of two or more processes or programs within the same processor, as contrasted with serial or sequential processing.

parallel transmission—Transmission mode that sends a number of bits simultaneously over separate lines, such as 16 bits over 16 lines; usually unidirectional.

parameter—Arbitrary constant; a variable in an algebraic expression that temporarily assumes the properties of a constant.

parametrics—Geometry dynamically linked to a list of specific parameters, where changes to them result in changes to the overall system (such as a drawing in CAD system).

parasang(es)—See *farsang*.

Pareto chart—SQC diagram for correlating data that is used to help uncover the causes of quality variations.

Pareto's analysis—Technique for arranging data according to priority or importance and tying it to a problem-solving framework.

Pareto's Law—The 80/20 rule: 80 percent of problems arise from 20 percent of sources.

PARISC—Precision architecture reduced instruction set computing; see *RISC*.

parity bit—Bit that is set at "0" or "1" in a character so as to ensure that the total number of 1 bits in the data field is even or odd within digital communication between devices or components.

parity check—The addition of information bits that make up a transmission block so as to ensure that the number of 1s is always either even (even parity) or odd (odd parity); used to detect digital transmission errors. *Also,* satirical Czechoslovakian imitator. ☺

PAS—Publicly Available Standards; *Also,* Process Automation Systems; represents the emergence of a two-layer industrial automation model that consists of open business systems (OBS) and open control systems (OCS).

PASC—Precision Adaptive Subband Coding; coding method to create the Digital Compact Cassette, averaging 4 bits/sample as compared with the 16 bits used with compact discs.

Pascal—Computer language named after seventeenth-century mathematician Blaise Pascal; designed by Niklaus Wirth to teach students programming, it produces structured programs simple to follow and maintain.

pass band—In digital signal processing *(DSP)*, frequency band in filters that is attenuated less than some certain amount (usually 3 dB in analog filters); see *stop band*.

passive device—Any device, component, or circuit that does not introduce gain or does not have directional function; in practice, only pure resistance, capacitance, inductance, or a combination of these three is passive. In current loop applications, a device that is incapable of supplying current for the loop but must instead draw its current from connected equipment.

Passive-matrix liquid crystal displays (PMLCDs)—Liquid crystal display (LCD) technique in which the pixels on the screen are controlled by voltage signals applied in rows and columns and the crystals respond by reorienting along field lines to transmit or block light to create an image and return to their original orientation when the voltage drains away; compare with *active-matrix liquid crystal displays*.

pass through—Ability to gain access to one network element through another.

PAT—Position Adjusting Type control output; uses direct feedback to the controller algorithm from actual end element physical position (not from the positioner nor from simple feedback control from the process sensor).

path—In computer programs, the hierarchy of files through which control passes to find a particular file; designates one or more disk drives and/or directory paths to be searched sequentially for a specific program or batch file.

pathname—In computer programs, the description of the location of a directory or file within some system; usually includes the drive letter and a colon (:), followed by the directory and subdirectory names, followed by the file name, with each name separated from the previous by a backslash (\).

Pathworks—DEC replacement term for PCSA. See *PCSA*.

PB—Proportional band; that over which proportioning (gain) action occurs in modulating control.

PBP—Picture by picture; split-screen video display, with simultaneous adjacent views or channels.

PBX—Private branch exchange; user-owned telephone exchange.

PC—Printed circuit; *also,* programmable chip; *also,* programmable (logic) controller; *also,* proportional control; *also,* professional computer; *also,* personal computer (in reference to an IBM computer: Intel's 8088, 16-bit internal, 8-bit data bus, no internal memory protection); the processing speeds and memory capacity of PCs have been continually increasing.

PCA—Printed circuit assembly.

PC/AT—Personal Computer/Advanced Technology; PC with Intel 80286, 16-bit data bus, supports multiple displays.

PCB—Printed circuit board; electronic subassembly consisting of an insulating board or card and circuit components such as diodes and integrated circuits; *also,* Polychlorinated biphenyl, a consideration in EPA (U.S.) regulations; a colorless liquid used as insulating fluid in electrical equipment; a pathogenic and teratogenic.

PC card—Another name for PCMCIA; *also,* printed circuit card; *also,* politically correct humorist. ☺

PCD—Plasma display panel.

PCEbus—Personal Computer Eurocard bus; "open standard" architecture based on the ISA (Industrial Standard Architecture) electrical standard that provides PC software compatibility on the EU Eurocard format.

PCI—Peripheral Component Interconnect; bus architecture by Intel that increases the physical capacity for high-speed data transfer in graphically intensive applications such as HMIs and video systems on personal computers.

PCI-ISA—Peripheral Component Interconnect—Industry Standard Architecture; defines CPU card and backplane arrangement that allows PCI modules built for personal computers to operate in the more modular and rugged systems offered by passive plane ISA vendors.

PCM—Pulse code modulation; a technique in which an analog signal, such as a process sensor signal or a voice, is converted into a digital signal by sampling the signal's amplitude (slicing) and expressing the different amplitudes as binary numbers. The sampling rate must be twice the highest frequency in the signal; *also,* Plug-compatible manufacturer; provides interchangeable components for systems that can be built from products designed by many different vendors.

PCMCIA—Personal Computer Memory Card International Association; not-for-profit trade association of more than three hundred companies established in 1989 and chartered with establishing, marketing, and maintaining a series of hardware and software standards for credit-card-sized integrated-circuit PC cards. Its standard for memory cards, was not always consistent and is sometimes called Personal Computer Memory Card Interface Access; and PC card. Emerging uses for PCMCIA go beyond memory to include communication capabilities and I/O ports. PCMCIAs are available in three versions: Type I, Type II, Type III, all with the same 68-pin edge connector. Type I is 3.3 mm thick and typically used for memory enhancements such as RAM, OTP, EEPROM and flash memory. Type II is 5.0 mm thick, is the most common, and is also used for memory and increasingly as modems, sound cards, networking, I/O ports, and SCSI;. Type III is 10.5 mm thick, used for additional memory and I/O features needing a larger size such as hard disk drives, radio communication devices, etc. *Also,* **PCMCIA is** referred to by some wags as "Pretty Confusing, May Cause Intense Anxiety"; by others as "People Can't Memorize Computer Industry Acronyms." ☺

PC-MOS/386—Personal computer MultiLink Operating System for 80386 microprocessor.

PCN—Personal Communication Network; envisioned combination of MANs and wireless networks.

PCR—Phase-change rewritable optical disk system; developed by Panasonic to operate with quadruple-speed CD-ROM drives, and providing the ability to write to optical media as well as read from it.

PC/RT—Personal Computer/Risk Technology; using RISC with UNIX System V as its native operating system.

PCS—Plastic-clad silica; optical fiber having a glass core and plastic cladding; *also,* process control system; responsible for the manufacturing of product, as compared to MIS, in the context in which it is used by vendors of PLC systems (and some market research firms), i.e., as equivalent to DCS; *also,* Personal communications services; wireless communicators such as cellular telephones.

PCSA—Personal Computer System Architecture; by DEC.

PCTE—Portable Common Tool Environment.

PCX—Picture exchange; Intel bit map file format for saving graphics in electronic memory; used for exchanging data between computers.

PC/XT—Personal Computer extended architecture; PC with Intel 8088, 16-bit internal,

8-bit data bus, no memory protection, hard disk, no cassette support.

PD—Means "pressure differential" when used in the first two alpha character positions of ISA instrument function tag [see ANSI/ISA S5.1-1984 (R1992)]. ***Also:*** positive displacement; *also,* plasma display; *also,* Panasonic Drive, developed by Panasonic as a quadruple-speed CD-ROM with a phase-change rewritable (PCR) optical disk system.

PDA—Personal digital assistant; small hand-sized computer that acts as an appointment diary, to-do list, phone list, and for other functions; *also,* Power Distribution Assembly.

PDAS—Process Data Acquisition System.

PDC(S)—Plant Data Collection (System).

PDES—Product Definition Exchange Standard; ANSI standard for representing engineering data; recently formally changed to mean "Product Definition Exchange using STEP" from "Product Definition Exchange. Standard."

PDF—Portable Document Format; file format for saving literature layout with graphics in electronic memory; used for exchanging data between computers.

PDIF—Product Definition Interchange Format; formerly, Product Data Interchange Format.

PDLI—Physically distributed/logically integrated; engineering design team efforts through data management computer networking.

PDM—Positive displacement meter; generally used to measure flow; *also,* Product data management; a system that tracks product data creation, revision, and movement for the management control of engineering design information; *also,* see predictive maintenance.

PDN/VAN—Public data network/value-added network; such as X.25. See *X.25.*

PDP—See plasma display panel.

PDR—Preliminary design review; used to identify issues in design practicality; compare *CDR*.

PDT—Portable display terminal.

PDU—Protocol data unit; ISO term referring to a packet of information exchanged between two network layer entities.

peak value—Maximum value of impulse voltage, current, or any alternating signal; can be the positive or negative value of any alternating quantity during a given time interval; positive and negative components are not necessarily equal in value.

PECL—Positive Emitter Coupled Logic; a reference to 5V.

PEEL—Programmable electrically erasable logic; same as Programmable array logic device, but AMD made "PAL" a tradename; another term is *GAL*.

peer-to-peer—Digital communication directly between two autonomous devices on the same network without any intervening devices to "store and forward" messages.

Peltier effect—When current flows through a thermocouple junction, heat will either be absorbed or evolved, depending upon the direction of current flow.

percentage timer—The time cycle of this type of timer is fixed, with the percentage on time being adjustable; the cycle repeats.

performance qualification—In process validation, documented verification that the process and/or the total process-related system performs as intended throughout every anticipated operating range.

peripheral—A device external to the CPU and main memory, such as a printer, modem, terminal, etc. which are still connected into system.

permanent split capacitor motor—Low cost AC motor designed for low starting torque; start-up and running windings stay on during operation.

persistence—ability to continue to exist; often refers to the use of nonvolatile memory to retain information through a power outage or maintenance shutdown. *Also,* refers to the retention of screen images on a CRT due to phosphorus as well as images on the retina within the human eyeball, permitting a sense of smooth motion of rapidly changing views.

PES—Programmable electronic system; a system based upon one or more computers being connected to sensors and/or actuators in a process plant for the purposes of control, protection, or monitoring; *also,* Process Electrochemistry Systems.

PEX—Protocol that is the PHIGS extension to the X Windows system. See *PHIGS*.

PFD—Process flow diagram; *also,* probability of failure on demand; chances of failure in energized mode.

PFU—Programmable function unit; standard building block of field-programmable gate arrays (FPGA).

PG—Protective Ground; such as a shield or frame.

PGA—Professional graphics Adapter (Array); for PC/AT and PC/XT high-resolution graphics; see *CGA, EGA SVGA, UXGA, VGA, XGA*; *also,* pin grid array (packaging for ICs).

pH—Indication of the acidity or alkalinity of a solution; units range from 0 (most acidic) to 14 (most alkaline), with 7 as neutral. The term is used to describe the hydrogen ion activity (a_{H+}) of a system, so is equal to $-\log(H^+)$ (negative log of hydrogen concentration in moles per liter).

phase—Time-based relationship between periodic function and reference. In electricity, it is expressed in angular degrees to describe the voltage or current relationship of two alternating waveforms.

phase coherent—Single-channel communication signaling method that uses the frequency shifts of a signal to encode data. Frequencies are directly related to the data represented and are proportional to the data rate; changes between frequencies occur at 0 crossings.

phase difference—Time expressed in degrees between the same reference point on two periodic waveforms.

phase linearity—In digital signal processing *(DSP)*, the property of filters, meaning that all signals are delayed by the same amount of time, regardless of their frequency; this becomes a series of straight lines when plotting phase versus frequency.

phase modulation—One of three ways of modifying a sine wave signal to make it "carry" information; the sine wave or "carrier' has its phase changed in accordance with the information to be transmitted.

phase proportioning—A form of control, usually for electric heating, where the power supplied to a process is controlled by limiting the phase angle of line voltage.

phase shift—In digital signal processing *(DSP)*, the angular measure of shift between two signals.

PHIGS—Programmer's Hierarchical Interactive Graphics System.

photodetector—Optoelectric transducer, such as pin photodiode or avalanche photodiode.

photodiode—Semiconductor diode that produces current in response to incident optical power and is used as a detector in fiber optics.

photon—Quantum of electromagnetic energy; small "particle" of light.

physical layer—Within the OSI model, the lowest layer (layer 1) of network processing, below the link layer; concerned with electrical, mechanical, and handshaking procedures over the interface that connects a device to transmission medium; referring to an electrical interface, such as RS-232C.

physical port—Port specifically defined by an address that can take on almost any logical port name, for example, address 2F8H may normally be called COM2 but could be called COM1 if system "finds" only this COM port and initializes it first.

PI—Process information (system); ***also*;** Proportional-Integral (two-mode) modulating control.

PIA—Peripheral Interface Adapter.

PIC—Programmable interrupt controller.

pica—In typographical composition of screen displays and printing, a printer's unit of measurement, equals twelve points, approximately 1/6 inch.

Pi Characters—In typographical composition of screen displays and printing, characters not usually found in a typical font, such as reference marks, mathematical signs, accents, and symbols.

PICMG—PCI Industrial Computer Manufacturers Group; founded in May 1994 as a consortium of four and now over 122 computer products vendors to develop interconnection standards to peripherals.

PICSA—Protocol Implementation Conformance Statement; from MMS. See *MMS*.

PICT—Picture vector and bit mapped format by Apple in Macintosh for saving graphics in electronic memory; used for exchanging data between computers.

PID—Proportional-integral-derivative; (three-mode) modulating control, which combines the effects of an error signal with its integral and derivative to provide more responsive control system.

piezoresistance—Resistance that changes with (physical) stress, such as pressure in a sensor.

pilot light—A light that indicates which of a number of normal conditions of a system or device exists; it is unlike an alarm light, which indicates abnormal condition; also called a monitor light.

pilot plant—Smaller version of projected industrial plant; used to gain experience and data for the design and operation of final plant.

PIM—Personal information manager; *also,* process information manager; *also,* parallel inference machine, which contains many independent processors working simultaneously on pieces of the same overall problem for supercomputing capability.

pinout—List or diagram showing the location/definition of the individual wires in a cable or connector.

pin photodiode—Photodiode having a large intrinsic layer sandwiched between P-type and N-type layers.

PI/O, PIO—Parallel input/output.

PIP—Picture in picture; video screen with more than one simultaneous view or channel, usually one or more insets within a larger view.

PIXEL—picture element; smallest unit on video display screen that can be stored, displayed, or addressed; a computed picture is typically composed of an array of 450 × 300, 720 × 560, etc. In color video, a pixel contains red, green, and blue values, and the color depth refers to the number of bits of data used to define the pixels' color (8 bits = 256 colors, 16 bits = 65,535 colors, 24 bits = 16.7 million colors).

PKNMiJ—Polski Komitet Normalizacji; standards group in Poland.

PL/I—Thirty-year-old computer language by IBM intended to replace COBOL and FORTRAN without much success; is *not* an acronym for Programming Language 1.

PLA—Programmable logic array.

Plasma display panel (PDP)—Type of liquid crystal display (LCD) that relies on the emission of photons from a gas that has been ionized by an electric charge. Offered in two versions: direct current (DCPDPs) and alternating current (ACPDPs).

platform—In computers, a microprocessor and operating system.

Platinel—Nonstandard, high-temperature platinum thermocouple alloy whose thermoelectric voltage nearly matches that of a type K thermocouple; trademark of Engelhard Industries.

PLC—Programmable logic controller (sometimes called PC); a controller, usually with multiple inputs and outputs, that contains an alterable program, generally to perform high-speed repeatable tasks; *also,* power line carrier, see *DLC*; *also,* PROWAY Link Control.

PLCopen—Vendor- and product-independent international association founded in June 1992 to advance the IEC 1131-3 open software development standard for programmable controllers.

PLD—Programmable logic device.

plenum-rated cable—A cable that has flammability and smoke characteristics (and NEC rating) so as to allow routing between walls, under structural floors (plenums), and above drop ceilings without being enclosed in a conduit. Does not give off toxic fumes when it burns. Usually, this is only fiber-optic as metallic wire is for electrical energy, which has additional safety code restrictions.

pleslochronous—In multiplexing, a method used when not all the data flows have the same bit rates and they are adjusted by inserting or deleting bits.

PLL—Phase locked loop.

PLV—Production level video; video encoding using the oldest digital compression scheme, by Intel/IBM.

PM—Phase modulation; a method of transmission whereby the angle of phase of the carrier wave is varied in accordance with the signal; see *pm* and *fsk*; *also,* Permanent Magnet; **also:** Project Manager; *also,* see *preventive maintenance*.

PMC—PCI mezzanine card; peripheral component interface to PCs that allows a low-profile PCI attachment to larger format buses such as VME and MULTIBUS. *See VME*.

PM&C—Process management and control.

PMG—Permanent magnet generator.

PMLCD—See passive-matrix liquid crystal display.

PMOS—P-channel metal-oxide semiconductor.

PMS—Process Messaging Service; intended companion standard to MMS for process control. *See MMS.*

PNO—PROFIBUS NutzcrOrganisation; charter European group formed in 1987 to standardize the work of the Joint Fieldbus Project and embracing the German national standard for fieldbus protocol.

point—In typographical composition of screen displays and printing, a printer's unit of measurement used originally for designating type sizes (from the top of the ascender to the bottom of the descender); there are twelve points to a pica, approximately seventy points to an inch.

point-to-point (link)—Connection between two, and only two, pieces of equipment.

poke—In computer programming, instruction used to place a value (poke) into a specific location in computer's storage.

polarity—Any condition in which there are two opposing magnetic fields, voltage levels, or charges such as positive and negative.

Polish notation—Logical programming notation for series arithmetic operations in which no grouping symbol is used, for example, a*(b + c) is * a + bc; see *RPN*,p*Postfix*; developed by the Polish logician Jan Lukasiewicz in 1929.

polling—In digital communication, a media access method (ISO data link layer 2) for controlling devices on a bus (multipoint, multidrop) or ring (loop) communication network through a single network "master," sometimes called a "traffic director." The process of inviting another station or node to transmit data. Compare to *selecting*.

polymorphism—In object-oriented programming (OOP), different objects respond differently and appropriately to the same command.

POMS—Process Operations Management System; IBM software aimed at providing integration at the manufacturing execution level of third-party applications for quality, process engineering, and plant operations around a distributed relational database.

POP—Picture outside picture; simultaneous multiple view video screen, but without insets. *Also,* points of presence, term used by Internet providers to indicate the number or geographical locations of their access to Internet.

Port—Point of access into computer, network, or other electronic device; physical or electrical interface through which one gains access. Interface between process and communications or transmission facility. If digital, may be for serial or parallel transmission (for a mouse, modem, printer, etc.).

portability—In computing, the ability to use and migrate software across different platforms.

portable—Handles were added. ϑ

POS—Point of sale.

Positioner—see *valve positioner*)

positive temperature coefficient—Increase in resistance due to an increase in temperature.

POSIX—Portable Operating System Interface for UNIX; originated for computer environments as a means of standardizing the critical interfaces for the many divergent variations of the UNIX operating system. Living under the auspices of both IEEE and ISO, it has evolved into an entire family of standard interface definitions, no longer limited to UNIX. Specifies how software applications and operating system software should be implemented so that applications can be ported to other POSIX-compliant environments.

postfix—Programming notation system in which the operator follows operands, for example, the addition of x and y is xy+; see *RPN.*

postprocessing—Program that formats graphical or other data after it is processed on a system, so that data can be used elsewhere.

Postscript—Output protocol by Adobe Systems Inc. originally to be used by DEC with X windows. Sophisticated page description language used for printing high-quality text and graphics on laser printers and other high-resolution printing devices.

potential energy—Energy related to position from, or height above, the place to which fluid could flow or an object could relocate.

POTS—Plain Old Telephone Service.

POTW—Publicly owned treatment works; municipal wastewater treatment facility.

ppb, p/b—Parts per billion.

PPI—Plan-position indicator; *also,* programmed peripheral interface.

PPM—Pulse position modulation; digital communication method of modulating data by encoding its value as a position of pulse within a time interval.

ppm, p/m—Parts per million.

PPP—Point-to-Point Protocol; enables TCP/IP over asynchronous (regular telephone) lines (and modem); important to the UNIX and Internet communities; gradually replacing SLIP for this purpose. See *SLIP.*

PRACL—Page-replacement algorithm and control logic.

PRAM—Parameter random access memory; stores time and date settings as well as other information about the computer in which it is used; typically battery powered for use upon start-up.

precedence—In computer programming, rules that state which program operators should be executed first within an expression.

predetermined counter—Counter that accumulates pulses and compares the total to a preset value to determine when to initiate control action.

predictive maintenance (PDM)—To operate process or system until a predetermined condition indicates that controlled shutdown is appropriate and then makes necessary repairs. Usually, the least expensive method in the long run because shutdown occurs only when needed but before damage is done. Does require planning, thought, and proper monitoring; compare *corrective maintenance, preventive maintenance.*

preemptive multitasking—The ability to assign higher priority to certain tasks running on a computer so safety conditions are covered first, control actions second, advanced control third, reporting later, "bells and whistles" last.

preprocessor—Program that performs conversion, formatting, condensing, or other functions on input data prior to further processing.

presentation layer—Layer 6 of ISO reference model; provides standards for restructuring data into the required format, character set, or language.

pressure loss/drop—A reduction occurring in pressure from the start to finish of a processing operation.

pressure transducers—Three types are used to measure absolute pressure (total pressure at a point, including atmospheric), gauge pressure (difference between actual and atmospheric), and differential pressure (difference between two points); about 60 percent of differential types are used to measure flow, 30 percent to measure level.

preventive maintenance (PM)—To operate a process or system with a time-based shutdown schedule, then make necessary repairs; usually prevents loss and is therefore less expensive than corrective maintenance.

Compare *corrective maintenance, predictive maintenance*.

primary element, primary device—In process control, the actual sensing device that detects the measured parameter in the process, such as thermocouple junction, differential pressure capsule, etc.; also called sensor. See *sensor*.

primary standard—Standard reference units and physical constants maintained by the National Institute of Science and Technology (NIST) upon which all measurement units in the United States are based.

primary station—In communications system, the station that at any given instant has the right to select and transmit information to a secondary station and the responsibility to ensure information transfer; the station that has control of the data link at any given instant; the assignment of primary status may be temporary and governed by standardized control procedures.

primitives—Basic units of machine instruction; *also,* fundamental graphic entity called entities, these can also be design elements at the lowest stage of complexity, such as lines or arcs, which are joined to make symbols or groups.

printer—Created as a joke in poor taste and consisting of three main parts: the case, the jammed paper tray, and the blinking red light. ☺

print server—Intelligent device used to transfer information to a series of printers.

private network—Broadband service needed usually for video signals such as in conferencing, using leased, dedicated phone lines to avoid the switching done in normal phone service.

PRML—Partial-response maximum-likelihood read channel technology, as used in hard disk drives.

procedural programming language—Computer programming language used to express the sequence of operations to be performed by a computer, such as FORTRAN; see *nonprocedural programming language*.

process—Continuous and regular industrial production executed in a definite, uninterrupted manner; any operation or sequence of operations involving the continuous change of energy, state, composition, dimension, or other properties that may be defined with respect to a fixed point of reference; the art of making "stuff"; *also,* in computer technology, executing a program to perform some useful operations on data.

process colors—In printing, the subtractive primaries: yellow, magenta, and cyan, plus black in four-color process printing.

process control—The automatic monitoring and control of a process by instrument, computer, or a system of both, and designed to respond appropriately to signals returning from that process.

process control loop—All components in the controlling portion of a process: sensor, transducer, transmitter, controller, final element, and the process itself.

process simulation—The use of a mathematical model by a computer programmed to envision process design scenarios with real-time visual and numerical feedback; used for the optimization and prediction of potential problems.

process variable (PV)—Any variable property of a process other than instrument signals.

producer/distributor/consumer model—In digital communications, a method for data exchanging over fieldbus from any variable-producing device (producer) controlled by bus arbiter (distributor) and consumed by a subscriber (consumer).

productivity—A measure of effectiveness based on efficiency and utilization; production output per unit of input, such as units per labor man-hour.

production capacity planning—Determining the levels of activity that need to be sustained in the future with respect to sales forecasts and the availability of personnel, equipment, materials, and money.

production control—The systematic planning, coordination, and direction of all production activities to ensure that products are made on time, with the appropriate quality, and at reasonable cost.

PROFIBUS—Process field bus; German national field bus standard (DIN 19245), operational since 1989 to link sensors, actuators, and controllers in an automation system: supported by about one hundred companies and two hundred to three hundred, half outside Germany; based on OSI 7497.

profit velocity—Profit per hour per part.

program—A list of instructions that a computer follows to perform a task; a repeatable sequence of actions that defines the status of outputs as a fixed relationship to a set of inputs.

programmers—Computer avengers; once members of that group of high school nerds who wore tape on their glasses, played "Dungeons and Dragons," and memorized Star Trek episodes; now millionaires who create "user-friendly" software to get revenge on whoever gave them noogies. ☺

programming language—Artificial language that enables people to instruct machines; computer commands that form procedure by which software programmers design and implement computer software programs.

PROLOG—programming logic; computer language created at the University of Marseilles, France; used largely for artificial intelligence (applications as a logic-oriented language that arrives at problem solutions by the "reasoning" to the answer; it is declarative rather than procedural, solutions are based upon rules put in by programmer.

PROM—Programmable read-only memory; storage device in which data is accessed on demand but is not changed. *Also,* an event generally associated with final high school dances. ☺

proof pressure—A specified pressure that may be applied to a sensing element without causing permanent change in output characteristics.

propagation delay—Time it takes a signal (of electromagnetic energy) to travel from one point to another over a transmission channel.

proportional action (or control)—A control response proportional to the deviation from a set point within proportional band, also called "gain"; *also,* performance of a proportional band on stage (see next entry). ☺

proportional band—Range of values above and below the set point, where the control action is full on below the band, full off above the band, and proportional in between; *also,* a group of musicians who can play fast, slow, and in between. ☺

proprietary system—System (or devices) that operates only to the methods, standards, and protocols of the manufacturer, and is not able to be interchanged with, or to communicate with, devices or systems made by other manufacturers.

prosumer—Professional consumer.

protocol—Formal set of conventions governing the formatting, timing, sequencing, and/or error checking of message exchange between two digital communicating systems; it can exist on many levels within a network to establish, maintain, and control communications.

protocol analyzer—Device or software application that enables the user to analyze the performance of network data to ensure that the network and its associated hardware/software are operating within network specifications.

PROWAY—Process data highway local area network (LAN) standard for industrial process control systems developed through the International Purdue Workshop on Industrial Computer Systems; compatible with but a more restrictive standard than IEEE 802.2 and 802.4, and ISA S72.01; specified as part of MAP, layer 2.

proximity switch—Device that senses the presence of an object without having physical contact and in response closes or opens circuit contacts.

PRP—Potentially responsible party; under the Comprehensive Environmental Response, Compensation, and Liability Act, an individual, group, or organization legally liable in the United States for cleaning up National Priorities List sites.

PRT—Platinum resistance thermometer.

PRV—Pressure-regulating valve; pressure-reducing valve.

PS—Power supply.

P/S—See publisher/subscriber model.

PS/2—Personal System/2; family of IBM computers that along with OS/2 can provide a higher level of performance, capacity, and software consistency than earlier IBM PCs.

PSD—Position sensing diode.

pseudo A/B role—In video development, editing between two sources where the edited result shows one source visibly in motion against a constant image (usually the last frame of the preceding clip or scene).

psia—Pounds per square inch, absolute; pressure referenced to vacuum; the sum of atmospheric and gauge pressure.

psid—Pounds per square inch, differential; the pressure difference between two points.

psig—Pounds per square inch, gauge; pressure referenced to ambient air pressure.

psis—Pounds per square inch, standard; pressure referenced to standard atmosphere.

PSM—Process Safety and Management; OSHA standard covering more than 130 specific toxic, reactive, and hazardous chemicals in various threshold quantities.

psychrometer—Wet-dry bulb-type hygrometer for determining relative humidity.

PTB—Physikalisch-Technische Bundesanstalt German certification and testing laboratory for testing the equipment of different vendors to some common standard.

PTC—Positive temperature coefficient; as in "PTC resistor (thermistor)," which will make a large, abrupt change in resistance when an overcurrent or high temperature heats it above a specific point, thereby effectively "switching off," or in reality, acting like solid-state fuse.

PTFE—Polytetrafluoroethylene (Teflon); used in the packing of valves to control emissions below the EPA standard.

PTH—Plated through holes; on circuit boards.

PTO—PROFIBUS Trade Organization; North American sister group of PNO, dedicated to promoting the German standard (DIN 19245) as the worldwide protocol for industrial automation. See *PNO*.

public network—Network operated by common carriers or telecommunications administrations for the provision of circuit-switched, packet-switched, and leased-line circuits to the public.

publisher/subscriber model—In data communications, method for sharing data on a bus network in which each origin point for a datum for all interested parties (subscribers).

pulse spreading—The dispersion of an optical signal with time as it propagates through an optical fiber.

pulse width modulation—Output in the form of a duty cycle that varies as a function of an applied measurand.

push—In video development, a transition where a new scene moves into frame from a particular direction, for example "push right."

pushbutton timer—This type has a momentary start switch to begin timing action.

PUT—Programmable unijunction transistor.

PV—Process variable; usually the measured variable in process control.

PVC—Polyvinyl chloride; frequently used for cable covering and instrument enclosures; good high- temperature resistance with high-impact strength, and good overall chemical resistance; can be adversely affected by ultraviolet and cold temperature impact; appropriate for indoor, light-duty applications; however, produces toxic fumes when it burns; compare with *plenum-rated cable*.

PVDF—Polyvinylidene fluoride (Kynar); material used in place of stainless steel to reduce leaching contamination in some conditions.

PVGA—Paradise Video Graphics Adapter.

PVI—Peak inverse voltage.

PWB—Printed wiring board; electronic subassembly consisting of an insulating board or card and conductive circuit pathways (often "printed wiring"); sometimes the term is used interchangeably with printed circuit board (PCB), which additionally includes circuit components such as diodes and integrated circuits.

PWM—Pulse width modulation; *also,* pulse width modulated type of variable frequency drive, see *VFD*.

PWR—Pressurized water reactor.

Q

q—Flow rate (U.S. gallons per minute); *also,* means "quantity"; once meant "event" when used in first alpha character position of ISA instrument function tag; means "integrate" or "totalize" when used as modifier [see ANSI/ ISA S5.1-1984 (R1992)].

QA—See quality assurance.

QAD—Quarter amplitude damping; method espoused by Ziegler and Nichols for tuning PID loop response to a step change.

QC—See quality control.

QED—*Quod erat demonstrandum*; (Latin) that is what has been demonstrated.

QFD—Quality function deployment; discipline for synchronizing and optimizing fabrication and assembly techniques.

QFP—Quad flat pack; miniature IC package.

QIC—Quarter-inch compatibility standards group.

QML—Qualified Manufacturers List; usually refers to U.S. military specification quality-level approval for extreme conditions.

QNX—Real-time POSIX operating system based on microkernel technology by QNX Software Systems.

QRA—Quantitative risk analysis; used in the United States to develop safety factors for control systems.

qualification protocol—In process validation, prospective experimental plan that, when executed, is intended to produce documented evidence that a system or subsystem has been properly qualified.

quality—From the ISO 9000 standard, the total features and characteristics of a product or service that bear upon its ability to satisfy stated or implied needs.

quality assurance—From the ISO 9000 standard, all those planned and systematic actions necessary to provide adequate confidence that a product or service will satisfy given requirements for quality.

quality control—From the ISO 9000 standard, the operational techniques and activities that are used to fulfill requirements for quality.

quality loop—From the ISO 9000 standard, a conceptual model of the interacting activities that influence the quality of a product or service in various stages, ranging from the identification of needs to the assessment of whether these needs have been satisfied.

quality plan—From the ISO 9000 standard, a document setting out the specific quality practices, resources, and sequence of activities relevant to a particular product, service contract, or project.

quality policy—From the ISO 9000 standard, the overall quality intentions and direction of an organization as regards quality as formally expressed by top management.

quality surveillance- From the ISO 9000 standard, the continued monitoring and verification of the status of procedures, methods, conditions, processes, products and services, and analysis of records in relation to stated references so as to ensure that specified requirements for quality are being met.

quality system—From the ISO 9000 standard, the organizational structure, responsibilities, procedures, processes, and resources for implementing quality management.

quality system review—From the ISO 9000 standard, the formal evaluation by top management of the status and adequacy of a quality system in relation to quality policy and new objectives resulting from changing circumstances.

quantum efficiency—In a photodiode, the ratio of primary carriers (electron hole pairs) created to incident photons; a quantum efficiency of 70 percent means seven out of ten incident photons create a carrier.

query—A request for data initiated while a computer program is running.

queue—Any group of items, such as messages or computer tasks, waiting for service; this determines processing priority.

queuing—The sequencing of batch data sessions, or any other activities, such as storing events in the order of their occurrence.

QWERTY—First alpha characters (second line) of standard typewriter keyboard; identifies a somewhat universally accepted de facto standard computer keyboard layout of the alphabetic portion of key positions; as compared to placing keys in alphabetical order or in the order in which they are most frequently used.

R

r—Symbol of ANSI thermocouple type for platinum 13 percent rhodium versus platinum; symbol for Rankine, an absolute temperature scale based upon the Fahrenheit scale with 0°F = 459.67°*r*; *also,* means "radiation" when used in the first alpha character position of ISA process instrument function tag, means "record" or "print" in succeeding position [see ANSI/ISA S5.1-1984 (R1992)]; *also,* means "range of sample values" in SPC.

RAD—Rapid application development tools; computer software "toolkit" to allow the creation of powerful, easy-to-use, end-user applications, usually by using drag-and-drop methods into different databases; examples include Microsoft Visual Basic, Sybase PowerBuilder, and Oracle Developer2000.

radar—Radio detection and ranging; works by sending out radio waves and listening for their reflections; a principle used in several sensor designs, particularly for motion, flow, and level detectors.

radio buttons—Selectors within the operator (or configuration) screen view usually for responding to a choice of options; their form is a small empty circle in which a dot appears when the button is selected.

ragged left—In screen text and typesetting, type that is justified on the right margin and ragged or unjustified on the left.

ragged right—In screen text and typesetting, type that is justified on the left margin and ragged or unjustified on the right.

RAID—Redundant array of independent disks; provides a large amount of memory by "stacking" inexpensive hard disk drives. Formerly referred to as "redundant array of inexpensive disks."

RAID array level 1—Redundant array of independent disks; disk mirroring; actually, duplication of partition; some may refer to this as partition redundancy: Requires a minimum of two hard disks, but mirroring results in a 50 percent loss of available disk capacity (using two equally sized partitions to store the same information); really used for reliability rather than performance.

RAID array level 2—Redundant array of independent disks; in video development, with RAID level 2 sustained data throughput is enhanced by allowing drives to take turns reading or writing a high-speed stream of information; ideal for motion JEPG configurations.

RAID array level 5—Redundant array of independent disks; disk striping with parity distributed across multiple drives. A minimum of three drives is required to create a level 5 partition; if a single disk in the set fails, enough information is stored to allow the data to be completely reconstructed on the replacement drive. The total capacity of the disks is not available for data storage; the nut part is used to calculate and store parity information. Although slower than mirroring for disk- writing operations, it offers much better reading performance.

RALU—Register and arithmetic logic unit.

RAM—Random access memory; storage device into which data can be entered (written) and read while the system is operational; this type of memory is volatile, and data will be lost if power is removed.

range—Those values the sensor or transducer is intended to measure or over which equipment is intended to operate. Usually specifications by its upper and lower limits; see *operating, compensated range.*

renewability—Ratio of the maximum flow rate to the minimum flow rate of a meter or a valve.

rapid prototyping—Using ultraviolet-cured photopolymers to build up three-dimensional solid objects in layers from a 3-D CAD database; to give a designer the ability to have an accurate physical representation of a part in a matter of hours or days without expensive tooling.

raster—In the display on a video screen, a grid pattern of vertical and horizontal divisions outlining all the small elements that compose the picture.

raster imaging—Video image that stutters slightly when depicting motion; see *full-motion imaging*.

rate action—Another term for derivative control action in process control; the proportioning of output to the rate of change of input.

Rayleigh scattering—The scattering of light in fiber- optic cable that results from small inhomogeneities in material density or composition.

RBE—Report by exception; a method the rapidly reporting information in large process control communication systems by only communicating the data that change or for indicating anomalies rather than reporting everything.

RCF—Relative centrifugal force = (11.18×10^{-6}) (rotating radius in cm) (rotating speed in rpm).

RCM—Reliability-centered maintenance.

RCRA—Resource Conservation and Recovery Act; U.S. federal law passed in 1976 to regulate the management and disposal of solid and hazardous wastes.

RCTL—Resistor-capacitor-transistor logic.

RDA—Remote Database Access; on ISO draft standard that incorporates SQL.

RDBMS—Relational database management system; allows data access based upon relationships set up among several database files.

RDRAM—Rambus dynamic random access memory; developed by Rambus, Inc., in conjunction with Intel Corp. and other Rambus semiconductor partners for a high-performance memory interface in multimedia packages but migrated to main memory in process control system workstations.

real time—Current time or the moment when a process or event occurs; a computer operating mode that allows immediate interaction with data as it is created, as in process control systems or computer-aided design (CAD) system; in process control, necessary calculations and control functions are performed as inputs occur rather than by preprocessing or predetermining control response.

real-time process management—Integrating real-time process data from DCSs with business management information systems (MIS) so that activities and events report and respond as they happen.

record—A collection of related information that is treated as a single unit.

recovery time—The length of time that it takes a device to return to normal tolerances after an upset.

redox—Reduction-oxidation potential; process industries term for *ORP*. See *ORP*.

redundancy—Duplicate equipment or transmission path to prevent the failure of a function (versus *fault tolerant*).

redundancy check—In digital transmission, a technique of error detection involving the transmission of additional data related to the basic data so that the receiving terminal, by comparing the two sets of data, can determine probability if an error has occurred in transmission.

reference junction—Cold junction in thermocouple circuit that is held at a stable known temperature.

reference manual—Object that raises the computer monitor to eye level, *also* used to compensate for that short table leg.

refractive index—Ratio of the phase velocity of light in a vacuum to that in a specified medium.

regenerative repeater—Repeater designed for digital transmission that both amplifies and reshapes the signal.

register—Storage device with specific capacity, such as a bit, byte, or word; *also*, in screen display development and printing, the fitting of two or more images in exact alignment with each other.

relational database management system—Computing systems that allow data access based upon relationships set up among several database files; Structured Query Language (SQL) has been accepted as the "official standard" to retrieve information from these table-structured associations.

relative flow rate error—The margin of variation between design flow rate and actual flow rate for a given valve opening.

relay—Electromechanical device that completes or interrupts an electrical circuit by physically moving conductive contacts; solid-state switching device that performs the same function with no moving parts. Any electric, pneumatic, or hydraulic switch that is actuated by a signal. A relay allows a small signal to control a much larger one or to operate additional devices in the same or different circuits. In instrumentation, a device whose function is to pass on information in unchanged form or in some modified form; the term is often used to mean "computing device"; in this case, the latter is the preferred term.

RELMS—Residential energy and load management system of EPRI. *See EPRI.*

REM—Registered environmental manager (U.S.); a certified category listed by the National Registry of Environmental Professionals (NREP).

remote—Not hard-wired; usually communicating long distance over microwave, telephone, satellite, etc. Often refers to devices quite separated from the main portions of system, such as an RTU.

remote procedure call (RPC)—In computing equipment, to pass processing work from busy systems to less busy systems (often "remote") or from systems that lack specific functionality to systems that have that functionality.

REPA—Registered environmental property assessor (U.S.); certified category listed by the National Registry of Environmental Professionals (NREP).

repeatability—The ability of a sensor, transducer, meter, or other equipment (or system) to reproduce the same output, value, or action when the same stimulus is applied to it consecutively, under the same conditions, and in the same direction; usually expressed as the maximum difference between measurements.

repeat accuracy—Ability of a controller, timer, etc., to repeat results within tolerance limits.

repeater—In digital transmission, equipment that receives a pulse train, amplifies it, retimes it, and then reconstructs the signal for retransmission to extend the distance between stations. In fiber optics, a device that decodes a low power light signal, converts it to electrical energy, and then retransmits it via LED or laser light source. *Also,* a regenerative repeater; *also,* in Ethernet networks, repeaters link multiple segments in either the bus or star topology; fully IEEE 802.3-compliant repeaters regenerate and retime the signal of each packet of information and automatically partition and isolate faulty segments when collisions occur on the same network. Repeaters, hubs, and concentrators all technically perform the same basic function.

report by exception—A method for rapidly reporting information in large process control communication systems by only communicating data that change or for indicating anomalies rather than reporting everything.

reserved word—A word that has a defined function in the language and cannot be used as a variable name.

reset action—Another term for integral control action in process control; *also,* with timers, the time it takes to move from the time-out state to the reset state.

resistance temperature detector—(RFD); temperature- measuring device in which the resistance of the sensing element is an accurately known function of temperature.

resistance thermometer bulb—Temperature- measuring device in which the expansion and contraction of a fill, such as mercury and certain other gases and liquids, is calibrated to reflect the change in temperature.

resolution—In control, the smallest measurable magnitude of the output step changes as stimulus is continuously varied over the range; usually expressed as a percentage of full-scale output. When converting from analog to digital, resolution is usually limited by the number of bits used to quantify the signal (a 12-bit analog-to-digital converter can resolve to one part in 4096 or 2^{12}); *also,* in video, the number of pixels used in a screen display.

resonant frequency—Measurand frequency at which a system or device, such as transducer, responds with maximum amplitude.

response surface methodology—Statistical method in which data from suitably designed experiments is used to construct polynomial response models, the coefficients of which are determined by regression techniques.

response time—Length of time required for the output of a system or device to change to a specified percentage of its final value as a result of step change of input. *Also,* in computers, the lapsed time between the generation of the last character of a message at a terminal and the receipt of the first character of the reply; it includes terminal delay and network delay. *Also,* in power lines, how fast the surge protector responds to a block power surge, **also** known as "clamp time." See *clamp time.*

responsively—In fiber optics, the ratio of the photodetector's electrical output to its optical input in amperes/watt.

retinex algorithms—Video input image-defining algorithms that automatically compare images that combine dynamic range compression and color consistency with the correct lightness and color rendition. They overcome the discrepancy between what the natural eye sees and what the image camera acquires when lighting or illumination conditions change (as happens with the retina of eyeball).

retransmissive star—Star coupler; in fiber-optic transmission, a passive component that permits the light signal on the input fiber to be retransmitted on multiple output fibers. Formed by heating together one end of a bundle of fibers to near melting point; the other end is distributed to other locations in fiber-optic LANs.

retrofit—Backward integration of advanced capability into a device or program not originally intended for that purpose.

reusability—In object oriented programming (OOP), objects that can be reused.

REV—Reverse acting.

reverse channel—Channel used for the transmission of supervisory or error control signals; the direction of flow of these signals is opposite to that in which the information is being transferred.

reverse compatible—Designs that provide compatibility with earlier versions.

reverse start timer—Starts timing when the power is removed from the start circuit but does not reset during power loss. Rather it retains cycle progress and continues cycle when the power is restored. In electromechanical versions, clutch action is reversed so it is normally closed with the absence of input control power, and the clutch resets the timer upon the application of power.

reverse type—In typographical composition of screen displays and printing, a light typeface on a dark background.

Reynolds number—The ratio of inertial and viscous forces in a fluid; equals fluid density times velocity times the inside pipe diameter divided by viscosity.

RF—Raised face; *also,* radio frequency (above 10^4 Hz and below 3×10^{12} Hz).

RFC—Remote function call; in remote computing, generally to trigger the release of data, the translation of information, etc. **Also** request for comment, as when polling a group of people creating standards.

RFC1006—Specification for sending OSI application layer messages (such as MMS) via TCP/IP.

RFDC—Radio frequency data communication; in manufacturing industries, refers to data terminals with a built-in scanner to read bar-code symbols, a modem, an input/output interface, a radio, and a digital board; used usually for inventory management.

RFI—Radio frequency interference; unwanted "noise" created by field-producing devices such as "walkie-talkies" and citizen band (CB) radio transmission equipment, which affects the quality of signals passing through some data transmission medium.

RFID—Radio frequency identification; reader/transmitter protocol, usually proprietary with each vendor, along with a reader (antenna and decoder), a tag (transponder), and a host controller; usually used for factory automation, transportation, and personal access applications where bar-code labels are too vulnerable.

RFP—Request for proposal.

RFQ—Request for quote.

RFS—Remote File Sharing; developed by AT&T.

RFT—Right first time; mathematical inverse of not right first time (NRFT), a technique for measuring error rates and thus the effectiveness of quality assurance—quality control

RGA—Relative gain array; method for controlling processes with interactions of multiple variables.

RGB—Red—Green-Blue; analog NTSC video signal between commercial monitors and equipment such as VCRs and some computers. *Also,* a model or color space to convey color information. Combining differing amounts of these *additive* primary colors produces all the colors in the color space. Used by most monitors and most desktop scanners, it works by starting with no light (black) and then *adding* quantities of red, green, or blue light (a maximum of all three produces white). Compare with *CMYK*; see *additive primaries.*

RH—Relative humidity; amount of water vapor present, measured in percentage of absolute humidity divided by absolute humidity in saturation at the same temperature.

rheostat—A variable resistor.

RI—Ring indicator; indicates phone line "ring" between two computer telephone modems.

RIM—Read-in mode.

ring expansion—In digital communication, a media access protocol method whereby a station in the network monitors the message stream of all messages passing through it until it detects a lull in traffic, whereupon it inserts its own message while buffering and later retransmitting any additional incoming messages. So named because the method "expands" the ring of data by one message until the original message or acknowledgment by receiving station returns back to sender; *also* called carrier insertion. See *Carrier Insertion.*

Ring Network—Network topology in which each node is connected to two adjacent nodes, the entire network forming a closed ring; communication between any two points must include the intermediate points.

RIO—Remote input/output; direct wired or proprietary link from process sensors to controller; as compared with a digital system such as "standard" fieldbus.

RIP—Raster image processor; in computer imaging, the computerized process that results in an electronic bit map that indicates every spot position on a page in preparation for the actual printout. *Also,* routing information protocol (routing algorithm).

ripple—Periodic and random deviation of the output voltage of a power supply; this may be composed of line-related components and noise induced by other sources; specified in terms of rms value or peak to peak over the bandwidth.

RISC—Reduced instruction set computing; by IBM and Apple; an internal computing architecture with fewer processor instructions so that most functions can be performed in a single cycle, thus improving efficiency and speed; compare with *CISC.*

rise time—The time required for the leading edge of a pulse to rise from 10 percent to 90 percent of its amplitude; the time required for a component to produce such a result.

r/J—Reference junction, the "cold" junction of a thermocouple.

RJC—Reference junction compensation.

RLE—Run-length encoding; data compression technique that saves data by a single count byte and a repeat byte rather than through the use of memory to save a repetitive group of bytes (example: 777777 becomes "count of 6" with value of 7 [two bytes]).

RLL—Relay ladder logic; see *ladder logic.*

RMA—Reliability maintainability and availability.

RMI—Radio frequency interference; to electrical and digital signals.

RMM—Read mostly memory; *also,* read mostly mode.

rms—root mean square; alternating current value that corresponds to the same direct current value that will produce the same heating effect.

RO—Reverse osmosis; *also,* receive—only; a device that cannot transmit but only receive.

robotics—The study of the design and use of robots, particularly for use in manufacturing and related processes. Robots generally react to sensory input to perform high-precision or dangerous jobs. The term robot was coined by Isaac Asimov in his science fiction novel "*I, Robot.*"

ROC—Rate of change.

ROI—Return on investment.

ROLAP—Relational on-line analytical processing, See *OLAP.*

ROM—Read-only memory; storage device with permanent memory; cannot be written over and will not change during system operation.

room conditions—The ambient environmental conditions under which equipment must commonly operate.

ropushers—Vendor-named category of control system specifications written by users and system consultants, which require an itemized fixed- price quote valid for a year and based on preliminary specifications, estimated point counts, and drawings that will be added later; see *also dowatchados, druthers, expectifications, gotchas, smokescreens, stickits, stonecutters, wannagirls*. ☺

ROS—Return on sales.

ROSE—Remote Operations Service Element; ISO9072.

Routing—Process (performed by router) of selecting the correct circuit path for a message; employs the bottom three OSI layers to interconnect dissimilar networks. Routers are smarter than bridges and are unaffected by differences in access protocol or topology among subnetworks. A bridge will "know" the specific destination (address) of a data packet, a router can only "know" the next router. In manufacturing, a form that lists the sequence of operations required for the fabrication of a product. A list of instructions of the sequential operations needed to fabricate a part or perform a batch process.

RP—Rapid prototyping; using ultraviolet-cured photopolymers to build up three-dimensional solid objects in layers from a 3-D CAD database so as to give the designer the ability to have an accurate physical representation of a part in a matter of hours or days without expensive tooling.

RPC—Remote procedure calls; in computing equipment, to access other networked applications and, from an interactive window, view its files without "closing out" of the documentation system. Used to pass processing work from busy systems to less busy systems (often "remote") or from systems that lack specific functionality to systems that have that functionality.

RPG—Report program generator; a computer language created by IBM and generally considered nonprocedural for producing business reports.

RPN—Reverse Polish notation; programming form of postfix notation in which operands are entered before operators, for example, a • (b + c) in Reverse Polish notation is abc + • ; see *Polish notation* and *postfix*.

RPU—Remote processing unit; in which control and other actions are processed in various distributed locations, communicating these actions over a data highway to operators, a central information point, etc.

RS—Recommended standards (RS series specs) published by EIA that define various electrical and mechanical interfaces for use with data communications equipment; now identified as EIA series.

RS-232—Specifies the interface between data terminal equipment and data communications equipment employing serial binary data interchange.

RS-422—Specifies the electrical characteristics of balanced voltage digital interface circuits.

RS-423—Specifies the electrical characteristics of unbalanced voltage digital interface circuits.

RS-449—Specifies a general-purpose 37-pin and 9-pin interface for data terminal equipment and data circuit-terminating equipment employing serial binary data interchange.

RS-485—Specifies the electrical characteristics of generators and receivers for use in balanced digital multipoint systems.

RSI—Repetitive strain injury; another term for cumulative trauma disorder, see *CTD*; *also,* Romanian Standards Institute; a member of IEC.

RSLD—Received line signal detector; modem interface control signal (typically, EIA RS-232/422).

RSM—Remote switching module; *also,* Remote System Manager; a DEC product built on DECnet that allows Micro VAX IIs and VAX stations to perform file-sharing and electronic mail functions.

RSP—Remote set point; to a process control loop, this typically comes from an output of another device.

RT—See real time.

RTB—Resistance thermometer bulb; temperature-measuring device in which the expansion and contraction of a fill, such as mercury and certain other gases and liquids, is calibrated to reflect a change in temperature.

RTC—Real-time clock, typically battery backed; *also,* Real-Time Consortium; formed in 1990 for a proposed OBIOS standard.

RTD—Resistance temperature detector; temperature-measuring device in which the resistance of the sensing element is an accurately known function of temperature.

RTF—Rich Text Format; format or method of saving data to electronic memory expressly for exchanging data between computers.

RTL—Resistor-transistor logic; ***also***; run-time library.

RTOS—Real-time operating system; computer software that controls the execution of application programs that allow immediate interaction with data as it is created, as in process control systems.

RTPM—Real-time process management; the results of integrating real-time process data from DCSs with business management information systems (MIS).

RTS—Request to Send; modem interface control signal (typically, EIA RS-232/422) indicating readiness to send data to DCE.

RTSE—Reliable transfer service element.

RTU—Remote termination unit; cabinet for making field connections to transmitted data and to do remote discrete switching over some (often extreme) distance from the actual processing of control and operations. Usually associated with SCADA systems for power transmission and distribution, water, oil and gas pipelines. Recent usage includes of the term "smart" RTUs (with microprocessors) for local computing in the field with communications back to the plant via control system I/O channels or digital techniques.

RTV—Real-time video; in video development, a DVI or Intel i750-based algorithm for symmetric data compression. See DVT.

RTX—Real-time executive.

rugged—Too heavy to lift.

rule-based system—Functional system in which knowledge is stored as simple IF-THEN or condition, action rules.

run chart—In SPC, sometimes called the individual measurements chart, this shows the progress of a monitored characteristic or attribute (y-axis) as a function of time (x-axis).

run around—In typographical composition of screen displays and printing, the term describing type set to fit around a picture or other element of the design.

running head—In typographical composition of screen displays and printing, a headline or title repeated at the top edge of each page.

Run time—In computing, the time during which data is fetched by the control unit (CPU) and actual processing is performed in the arithmetic logic unit (ALU). *Also,* the time during which the program is executing.

Run-time controller—In process control, an implementation tool that includes a neural network model executor for prediction and a neural network model inversion engine for control or optimization; can be used to implement a prediction model.

RVI—Reverse interrupt; in digital communications, a control character transmitted by the receiving station to request the termination of the current transmission because of another high-priority message it must send.

R/W—Read/write.

RXD—Receive data; digital data signal input, usually to a receiver from a computer transmitter.

S

S—Symbol of ANSI thermocouple type for platinum 10 percent rhodium versus. Platinum. *Also,* means "speed" or "frequency" when used in the first alpha character position of ISA instrument function tag, means "safety" as a modifier, means "switch" when used in succeeding position [see ANSI/ISA S5.1-1984 (R1992)]. *Also,* solenoid actuator; *also,* standard deviation (Σ) in SPC; a mathematical measure of the variability or spread of a sample of data (is the square root of the average of squared deviations of each point from the mean).

SA—Standards Australia; Australian certification laboratory for testing the equipment of different vendors to some common standard.

SAA—System Application Architecture; set of standards developed by IBM that provides identical user interfaces for applications running on PCs, minicomputers, and mainframes. *Also,* Standards Association of Australia; a member of IEC.

SAMA—Scientific Apparatus Makers Association; develops standards for industrial process instrumentation and control. Now called Measurement and Control Automation Association (MCAA).

sample rate—In digital signal processing *(DSP)*, the frequency at which an analog signal is sampled by a digital system.

sampling—Measuring at regular intervals the output or variable(s) of a process to the estimate characteristics of that process.

Sanders 3-D plotting—Form of rapid prototyping; see *RP*.

sans serif—In typographical composition of screen displays and printing, a typeface without finishing strokes (serifs).

SAP—Service Access Point; ISO model; *also,* Systems, Applications, Products; Service Access Point, Aktiengesellschaft AG, a German company whose R/2 and R/3 software is used in enterprise information systems to link databases from all parts of the corporation to develop business solutions.

SAR—Successive Approximation Register; type of A/D converter found on board single-chip microprocessors that provides better speed but less accuracy than the "dual slope" technique.

SARA—Superfund Amendments and Reauthorization Act; U.S. federal law passed in 1986 that reauthorizes and expands the Comprehensive Environmental Response, Compensation, and Liability Act.

SASE—Specific Application Service Element; protocol of MMS.

saturable core reactor—Inductive "valve" that provides modulating control to a heavy inductive load such as the heating elements in furnaces.

SAW—Surface Acoustical Wave type of touch screen, which confines most of the acoustical energy to the surface of screen; compare with *GAW*.

SBC—Single board computer (*also,* controller).

SBE—Scan by exception; a way to rapidly report information in large process control communication systems by having the host poll all devices, but where devices will only communicate data that changed or indicate anomalies, rather than report everything. When there is nothing to report, the device will send a brief "all's well" signal.

SBM—Super bit mapping.

SBPC—Single board personal computer.

SBS—Silicon bilateral switch.

SC—Signal common; common ground for a cluster of signals that may not be at either chassis-ground or earth ground electrical potential, *also,* semiconductor.

SCA—Subchannel adapter; *also,* Single Connector Attachment; technology combines drive signal line with power lines in the same connector, making it possible to change out circuit boards and modules under power (called "hot-swap"). See *hot swapping.*

SCADA—Supervisory Control and Data Acquisition; generic name for a computerized system capable of gathering and processing data and applying operational controls over long distances, such as is used with power transmission and distribution and pipeline systems. Designed for unique communication challenges (delays, data integrity, etc.) resulting from the various media that must be used, such as phone lines, microwave, satellite, etc. Usually shared rather than dedicated.

scaleability—The ability to vary the information content of a program by changing the amount of data that is stored, transmitted, or displayed. In a video image, this translates into creating larger or smaller windows of video on screens. *Also,* in terms of a system, the ability to readily increase capacity and/or functions (sometimes by adding more devices to a network).

scan—In process control, to examine data from process sensors for use in calculations, alarms, etc., by intermittently sampling in a predetermined manner each of a number of variables. A single sweep of the applications programs in some computer, such as all functions of the process controller or PLC, based upon input status at the time so that functions can create new set of outputs or be placed into a historical database.

scanner—Electronic device used in making color and tone-corrected separations of images, usually to copy a photo or printed image into a computer for use in a video screen image.

scan time—The time it takes to perform all the appropriate functions of a (microprocessor-based) device or a set of specific functions within that device, such as "I/O scan time."

SCC—Standards Council of Canada; member of IEC.

sccm—Standard cubic centimeters per minute.

scfh—Standard cubic feet per hour.

scfm—Standard cubic feet per minute.

scheduled release date—Carefully calculated date determined by estimating the actual shipping date and subtracting six months from it. ☺

SCI—Serial Communications Interface.

SCIA—Steering Committee for Industrial Automation; within ISO/IEC.

SCM—Supply chain management; the process of all operations from your customer's customers to your supplier's suppliers are automated including Internet connections.

SCR—Silicon-controlled rectifier; a three-terminal PNPN device that normally blocks current flow in both directions until its gate is pulsed with a timed electrical signal, so that a modulation of a small electrical current can smoothly modulate a much larger one. *Also,* Saturable Core Reactor; an inductive "valve" to provide modulating control to a heavy inductive load such as the heating elements in furnaces. *Also,* Selective Catalytic Reduction system.

scroll—To move all or part of the material on a video screen up or down, left or right, so as to allow new information to appear.

scroll bars—Bars adjacent to a window in a workstation screen view that allow the user to scroll the contents within that window to display more information than can normally be shown.

scroll box—Small box within the scroll bar for moving the view by dragging it with the cursor.

SCS—Sira Certification Services, Ltd. British certification and testing the laboratory for testing equipment of different vendors to some common standard. *Also,* Silicon-controlled switch.

SCSI—[*pronounced* skuzy] Small Computer System Interface; ***also*:** System Can't See It.

SCSI CAM—Small Computer System Interface, Common Access Method extension.

ScTP—Screened twisted pair; wiring for signals.

SCTS—Secondary Clear to Send; modem interface control signal (typically, EIA RS-232/422) indicating the readiness of an alternate device to accept data from the DCE; see *CTS*.

SD—Super Density; compact disk made by SD Alliance; now called DVD; see *DVD*.

SDH—Synchronous Digital Hierarchy; networks on which multiplexing is done on a synchronous basis.

SDLC—Synchronous Data Link Control; bit-oriented standard protocol developed by IBM that supersedes bisynchronous transmission; uniform discipline for the transfer of data between stations in a point-to-point, multipoint, or loop arrangement using synchronous data transmission techniques.

SDRAM—Synchronous dynamic random access memory; used for high-performance main memory in computers and workstations; can handle bus speeds up to 100 MHz.

SDS—Smart Distributed System; a CANbus-based I/O communications systems for intelligent sensors and end elements by Honeywell MICROSWITCH.

SDWA—Safe Drinking Water Act (U.S.).

SECAM—Systeme Electronique Couleur avec Memoire; adopted as a television standard for France, Eastern Europe, Russia, and parts of Middle East on October 1, 1967; variations include SECAM "Vertical and SECAM "Horizontal"; commonly referred to as "Something Contrary to American Methods"; see *NTSC, PAL, PAL-M*.

secondary device—Part of flowmeter that receives from the primary device a signal proportional to the flow rate and then transmits it, displays it, records it, or performs any combination of these.

secondary standard—Standard of unit measurement derived from a primary standard; see *primary standard*.

secondary station—Station in a communications system that has been selected to receive a transmission from a primary station; the assignment of secondary status may be temporary and continues for the duration of a transmission.

SECS—Semiconductor Equipment Communications Standard; designed in the early 1980s to be a fully dynamic, nonfixed, variable-length, self-defining messaging protocol between equipment and the host control computer. The intent was to allow independent manufacturers of both equipment and host computers to connect to each other without specific knowledge of each other, a goal never achieved. Now being replaced by Computer Integrated Manufacturing Application Framework (CIM-AF); see *CIM-AF*.

SEC, SEA—Swiss Electrotechnical Committee of the Swiss Electrotechnical Association; member of IEC.

SECS-I—Early version of SECS designed for RS 232 serial communications then available between computers and equipment.

SECS-II—Later version of SECS designed for TCP/IP communication between computers and equipment.

Seebeck coefficient—Derivative (rate of change) of thermal EMF with respect to temperature; normally expressed in millivolts per degree.

Seebeck effect—When a circuit is formed by two junctions in two dissimilar metals and each junction is held at different temperatures, a current flows in that circuit that is caused by the difference in temperature between those two junctions.

Seebeck EMF—Open-circuit voltage caused by the difference between the hot and cold junctions of a circuit made with two dissimilar metals.

selecting—In communication, a process of inviting another station or node to receive data; compared to *polling*.

self-adaptive tuning—Technique within controller that watches the loop and tunes the controller when it thinks it should; does not require a process bump the in setpoint or controller output to perform, rather it uses normal loop changes. Upon start-up, it may need an initial bump or the programming of some loop conditions; see *auto-tinting*.

self-correcting memory (code, transmission)—Term sometimes used for error detection and correction. Software that looks for specific rules of construction, detects expressions that do not conform, and substitutes an equivalent form.

self heating—Internal heating of equipment as a result of power dissipation.

semantics—In computer programming, the actual meaning or use of a parameter, apart from its legitimate method of specification; see *syntax*.

semiconductor—The basis of all integrated circuits; any of a class of solids that have higher resistivity than a conductor but lower resistivity than an insulator, so that they will conduct electrical current in different amounts depending upon how they are affected by outside conditions (like the strength of external magnetic or electrical fields, pressure, temperature, light, etc.)

sensitivity—Minimum value of change in a signal so as to cause a change in the receiving device.

sensitivity shift—Change in the slope of a calibration curve due to a change in sensitivity.

sensor—(*s*ensing element) That part of a process measurement device that reacts in direct response to process change, providing some measurable output; *also,* known as a *detector* and as a *primary element*.

sensorbus—A cooperative effort "fieldbus."

sequence control—The control of a sequence of actions, with the completion of one movement or set of conditions initiating the next.

sequential access—Access mode in which records are retrieved in the same order in which they were written; each successive access to a file refers to the next record in that file.

sequential function charts—Originally formulated by Telemecanique as GRAFCET and standardized under IEC848 and NFC-03-190 to graphically represent a control system as a flow chart sequence of alternating steps and transitions so as to be better understood by all engineering disciplines. SFCs generally offer improved organization, modularity, and readability over free-form programming; see *function block diagram, instruction list, ladder logic,* and *structured text.*

sequential manipulation control—Advanced process control strategy whereby manipulated variables are managed in a prescribed order and on an "as needed" basis.

SERCOS—Serial real-time communication system; digital interface standard for distributed, multiaxis motion control.

serial transmission—The most common transmission mode, in which information bits are sent sequentially on a single data channel (wire, radio beam, etc.).

series (universal) motor—Noninduction-type motor utilized for small equipment; its speed will decrease as its load increases.

serif—In typographical composition of screen displays and printing, the finishing stroke at the ends of the main strokes of many letters in some type-faces.

server—A processor that supplies the network with specified service, such as a routing function, a common source of data, memory, or other functions, to be shared by many devices requesting these. See *client.*

servomechanism—Automatic device for controlling large amounts of power through the application of much smaller amounts of power.

servomotor—Power-driven mechanism that supplements the primary control operated a by much weaker force, as in a servomechanism.

session—Connection between two stations that allows them to communicate; in IBM SNA this is the logical connection between two network addressable units; *also,* the time period during which the user engages in dialog with an interactive computer. See *SNA.*

session layer—Layer 5 of the OSI reference model; provides protocols for assembling physical messages into logical messages.

set point—Value at which the controller is set to hold or drive the output signal for the control of a process; *also,* with the timers, the time or count value from which (or to which) the unit times or counts. It may be manually set, automatically set, or programmed.

set point control—Control technique in which the computer supplies a calculated set point value to an analog instrumentation control loop.

setting accuracy—The ability of equipment (controllers, timers, etc.) to be set within tolerance of a selected value.

seven-twenty four (7-24)—Seven days per week, twenty-four hours per day; a reference to operating around the clock every day.

SFC—Sequential function chart; not a stand alone language, but a language that pervades all of the IEC 1131 standard languages, see *function block diagram, instruction list, ladder logic,* and *structured text.* A way of organizing programs written in these languages to accomplish sequential control by partitioning them into sets of steps and transitions interconnected by directed links; see *also sequential function charts*; *also,* shop floor control.

SFID—Society for Information Display.

SFM—Scanning force microscopy; measures in angstroms; more powerful than scanning electron microscopes in locating the defects on integrated circuits.

SFMS—Shop floor management system; provides online data capabilities to capture such information as product progress, location, scrap, and relevant operator as well as machine, product, and quality data.

SFS—Suomen Standardisoimisliito r.y.

SG—Signal ground; electrical potential; usually called signal common (SC); a common baseline for signal reference. See *signal common.*

SGC—Solid ground curing; a form of rapid prototyping, see *RP.*

S-glass—In the construction of glass bulb-type pH sensors, this is a low ohmic glass used for membranes of electrodes for the processes where measurements are to be made in acid media and lower temperatures. At higher pH values alkaline error may be significant; see *E-, G-, L-glass.*

S/H—Sample and Hold.

shaded pole motor—Low-starting torque motor that depends on induced current to create a magnetic field necessary to start that motor.

shared controller—A controller containing preprogrammed algorithms that are usually accessible, configurable, and assignable; it permits a number of process variables, loops, and functions to be controlled by a single device.

shared display—Operator interface device, usually a video screen, used by a plant operator to display process control information from a number of sources.

sharpness—In video displays, the crispness of screen displays, like focus; generally due to the convergence of red, blue, and green electron beams into single white "dot" on the screen.

shear modulus—Ratio of shear stress and angular shear distortion.

shear stress—Where normal stress is perpendicular to a designated plane, shear stress is parallel to that plane.

shell—In computer software, a program or function created around some central kernel or core program and relying upon it for proper operation; compare with *kernel.*

shielding—Protective covering that reduces electromagnetic (EMI) and radio frequency interference (RFI) or leakage in a cable or device.

shot noise—Noise caused by random current fluctuations arising from the discrete nature of electrons.

SHTTP—Secure Hypertext transfer protocol; the implementation of secure information transmission through the Internet by Terisa Systems.

shunt— A conductor joining two points in an electrical circuit to form a parallel path; all or some portion of the current may pass through that shunt.

SI—System Internationale; Its full name is the International System of Units (le Systeme International d'Unites); *also,* system integrator.

siemens—In conductivity measurement, a unit of the conductance of a solution, formerly known as mho; the reciprocal of an electrical measurement called ohms (Ω).

sigma (σ)—In quality control, a statistical unit of measure that reflects capability. Example:

σ of 0.2 = 308,537 defects per million opportunities
σ of 3 = 66,807 defects per million opportunities
σ of 4 = 6,210 defects per million opportunities
σ of 5 = 233 defects per million opportunities
σ of 6 = 3.4 defects per million opportunities
With σ of 3 to 4, the cost of quality is about 10 percent of sales; moving toward 6σ offers a significant opportunity for savings in production!

sigma scale—In quality control, a measure that correlates directly to such characteristics as defects per unit (discrete production), parts-per-million defective (process production), or probability of failure/error.

signal—Electrical, pneumatic, hydraulic, or frequency transmittance (either input or output) that conveys information (analog or digital).

signal common—Common ground for a cluster of signals that may not be at either chassis-ground or earth-ground electrical potential; sometimes called signal ground.

signal conditioning—To process the form or mode of a signal so as to make it intelligible to, or compatible with, a given device, such as pulse shaping, pulse clipping, compensating, digitizing, and linearizing.

signal-to-noise ratio—The ratio of signal power to noise power, usually measured in decibels.

SIL—Safety integrity level; requirements for the safety instrumented system (SIS) based upon process hazard analysis and risk assessment.

silicon-controlled rectifier—Three-terminal PNPN device that normally blocks current flow in both directions until its gate is pulsed with a timed electrical signal, so that a modulation of a small electrical current can smoothly modulate a much larger one.

SIMD—[*pronounced* simdee] Single instruction multiple data stream computing where at every instant all processors carry out the same set of instructions on the data in its own local memory; see *MIMD*.

SIMM—Single inline memory module.

simplex cable—Term sometimes used for a single fiber-optical cable.

simplex mode—Operation of a channel in one direction, only with no capability of reversing.

simplex transmission—Transmission in one direction only.

SIMTARS—Safety in Mines Testing and Research Station; Australian certification and testing laboratory for testing the equipment of different vendors to some common standard.

simulation—In process control, using an analog or digital computer to represent the dynamics of the process itself; responding appropriately to all control signals from the instrumentation system so as to train operators and/or control techniques.

single mode—Describing an optical waveguide designed to propagate the light of only a single wavelength and perhaps a single phase. Essentially, optical fiber that allows for only one light beam or data-carrying lightwave channel and is optimized for that particular frequency.

single phase motor—Any motor energized by a single alternating voltage.

single shot—Mode of operation in a timer where the control switch (momentary or sustained) initiates the timing period during which output is energized; after the timing period the output is deenergized and the timer resets.

SI/O, SIO—Serial Input/Output.

SIP—Single in-line packaging of circuit chips; *also,* sterilize in place, typically used in food/pharmaceutical processing vessels where parts are not removable.

SIPAI—Shanghai Institute of Process Automation Instrumentation. Chinese certification and testing laboratory for testing equipment of different vendors to some common standard.

SIS—Standardiseringskommissionen i Sverige; Swedish member of IEC; *also,* Strategic Information System; *also,* Safety instrumented system; all the sensors, processors, and final elements that have an impact upon process safety.

SISO—Single input single output; systems requiring relatively straightforward feedback and/or feedforward control methods. See *MIMO, MISO, TITO.*

SiTVS—Silicon transient voltage suppressor.

SLA—Stereolithography, a form of rapid prototyping; see *RP.*

slave—Remote system or terminal whose functions are controlled by a central "master" system; it is similar in concept to a host system in that it responds to remotely generated requests, but unlike the host system is usually capable of performing only a limited range of operations.

SLC—Subscriber loop carrier; ***also*** single loop controller.

slew rate, slue rate—Rate at which the output of a device can be driven from one limit to another over its dynamic range.

SLIC—Subscriber line interface circuit.

slide—In video development, a transition where the old scene exits from the frame in a particular direction, for example "slide left."

slider—"Device" adjacent to a function within a workstation screen view to make analog changes to some application, such as a trend cursor, scaling value, or page selections.

SLIP—Serial Line Internet Protocol; enables TCP/IP over asynchronous lines: important to the UNIX and Internet communities.

slm, slpm—Standard liters per minute.

slope adjustment—In the measurement of pH, a correction within the pH meter for changes in response of an electrode compared to an ideal response.

SLS—Selective laser sintering: a form of rapid prototyping; see *RP.*

SLV—Single layer varistor.

SM—See system management; used in the context of the Fieldbus Foundation.

small caps—In typographical composition of screen displays and printing, an alphabet of small capital letters available in most roman typefaces; approximately the size of lowercase letters and often used in combination with larger capital letters.

smart hub—Type of twisted-pair concentrator used in either Ethernet or ARCNET networks; has built-in programmed firmware for network management facilities.

smart transducer—Processor-based transducer that connects the sensor or actuator with the digital network to communicate peer to peer with other devices on that network (typically one of the fieldbuses); performs data management within and may do computations and even control algorithms.

SMB—Server message block; protocol for dividing tasks between DOS-based PCs and UNIX systems.

SMD—Surface-mounted device.

SMDS—Switched Multimegabit Data Services; high-speed data transfer standard developed by BellCore for public carriers.

SME—Society of Mechanical Engineers.

SMIS—Standards and Metrology Institute of Slovenia.

smokescreens—Vendor-named category of control system specifications written by users and system consultants that describes in disguise a one-and-only item in great detail but asks several vendors for quotations (many are called but only one can be chosen); see *also dowatchados, druthers, expectifications, gotchas, ropushers, stickits, stonecutters, wannagirls.* ☺

SMOP—Simply a matter of programming (usually preceded by the phrase, "There's nothing to it, it's"). ☺

SMP—Symmetric multiprocessing; a type of computing architecture that allows a large number of users and transactions that can be supported in parallel.

SMPTE—Society of Motion Picture and Television Engineers.

SMPTE time code—In video development, a system for giving each frame of a video a unique number so as to allow indexing and precise tape control for synchronous timing.

SMT—Surface-mount technology; a method for mounting elements on a printed circuit boards; see *THT.*

SMTP—Simple Mail Transfer Protocol; part of TCP/IP suite.

SMU—Source measure unit; four instruments in one: a voltage source, a voltmeter, a current source, and a current meter.

SNA—Systems Network Architecture; for communication between IBM and other devices.

SNAcP—Subnetwork Access Protocol.

SNADS—System Network Architecture Distributed System; developed by IBM.

SNAP—Specifications for Nonheat Advertising Printing; standard for the printing industry used by some color printers.

SNDCP—Subnetwork Dependent Convergence Protocol.

SNICP—Subnetwork Independent Convergence Protocol.

SNMP—Simple Network Management Protocol; used to manage and monitor networks based on TCP/IP; this protocol runs at the transport layer of the OSI network model and provides components for vendor-developed network management utilities.

SNOBOL—String-Oriented Symbolic Language; computer language developed at Bell Labs and still used for text applications, including databases and editors.

SNPA—Subnetwork point of attachment.

SNR—Signal-to-noise ratio; the ratio of signal power to noise power; usually measured in decibels.

SNV—Schweizerische Normen-Vereinigung; standards group in Switzerland.

SOC—System on chip; A component designed with millions of electronic gates on a single chip; gate-based designs are replacing transistor-based ASIC designs. See ASIC.

SOE—Sequence of events.

softcontrol—PC-based process controller.

softlogic—PC-based logic controller.

software—Nonhardware portion of computer, which causes that computer to perform specific functions, depending on how it was programmed. Often defined as the entire set of programs, procedures, and related documentation associated with a computer.

software sensor—In analytical measurements, an analyzer that replaces or supplements a hardware analyzer or laboratory measurement for closed loop process control. Using neural network computing, it includes prediction net and sensor validation net.

soft wiring—The interconnection of software function blocks to create a system, control strategy, or some operation. Implemented within DCS in a way analogous to wiring physical hardware components as part of system configuration.

solenoid valve—On/off (shut off) valve whose position is determined by the current flow to a coil.

solid leading—In typographical composition of screen displays and printing, when no additional white space is added between lines of type.

solid modeling—Three-dimensional modeling in which the solid characteristics of an object are built into the database so that complex internal structures can be realistically represented.

solid-state (device)—Any element that controls current without moving parts, heated filaments, or vacuum gaps.

solid-state output—Output signals from triacs, transistors, field effect transistors, and other semiconductors.

SONET—Synchronous Optical Network; sends signals over optical fiber and complements ATM by providing standardized interfaces, high rates of data transmission, and high reliability.

SOS—Silicone-on-sapphire.

source—Light emitter, either LED or laser diode, in a fiber-optic link.

source code—Nonexecutable program written in a high-level language; a compiler or assembler must translate source code into object code (machine language) that the computer can understand and process.

SP—Set point; of process control loop; it determines the desired value at which the process will operate.

SP50—Standards and Practices group 50 of ISA, which has been developing a fieldbus standard since about 1985; also the Fieldbus Foundation, a not-for-profit organization dedicated to developing a single, worldwide, interoperable fieldbus and formed from the merger of WorldFIP North America and ISP Foundation in 1994.

SP72.01—Standards and Practices group 72 of ISA, dealing with PROWAY-LAN industrial data highway and link control (ANSI/ISA).

SP72.02—Standards and Practices group 72 of ISA, dealing with Process Messaging Service, an MMS companion standard. for process control. See *PMS.*

SP72.03—Standards and Practices group 50 of ISA, dealing with Process Communication Architecture standard to enable the digital transmission of voice and data via standard telephone lines.

SP88—Standards and Practices group 88 of ISA, which has been developing a batch standard since about 1988.

SP95—Standards and Practices group 95 of ISA, formed in October 1996 to develop a standard for the boundary between the corporate (enterprise) business plan and the plant floor, especially dynamic, real-time process control systems.

space—Absence of a signal; an open condition; no current flowing; in transmission, a space impulse is equivalent to a binary "0."

SPAG—Standards Promotion and Applications Group.

span—Algebraic difference between the limits of the range of a measuring or controlling device.

SPARC—Scalable Processor ARChitecture (Sun Microsystems); *also,* Scalable Processor Architecture reduced instruction set Computer, a very powerful workstation using RISC technology.

SPARCL—Smart pixel array cellular logic; pixel arrays through which two-dimensional frames of data are moved optically to perform digital operations on those incoming data frames and/or data frames stored within that pixel array. Multiple pipelined optical processors constructed as SIMD to speed image processing from optical sensors. See SIMDO.

SPC—Statistical process control; quality control method employing online (continuous) statistical procedures for immediate analysis to improve the management of continuous processes, often by using patterns of alarms and other discrete events. Usually open loop form of control: SPC often follows SQC analysis for quality control.

SPDT—Single pole double throw; electrical switch action on a wire that can be used to select one of two paths for the flow of signal or power.

specific gravity—Comparison of the mass (or weight) of a substance to that of an equal volume of water.

specific heat—Ratio of thermal energy required to raise temperature of a body 1° to the thermal energy required to raise an equal mass of water 1°.

SPI—System programming interface; *also,* serial parallel interface.

splash screen—On the Internet, the main menu screen, or the opening graphic to a Web page; in computer systems, same idea, but may *also* be a point of security code entry, showing copyright and revision-level information, etc.; usually used only upon initial start-up.

spline—Term used to describe irregular curve concept in conventional drafting; often performed with a French curve tool to assure that the curve passes through a series of defined points.

split-phase motor—Inexpensive AC motor generally used for easy-starting loads; it features two sets of windings, one for start-up and one for running the motor; once the motor has attained full speed, the current to the starting windings is switched off.

SPOOL—Simultaneous Peripheral Operation On Line; program or piece of hardware that controls the data going to an output device.

spooler—See b*uffer memory.*

spreadsheet—Computer program that arranges data and formulas in a matrix of cells.

spread spectrum radio technology—Digital communication technique where the signal is created by modulating the radio frequency signal with a spreading sequence code or by "hopping" the frequency of the carrier signal; developed for the U.S. military to prevent jamming.

sprite—In digital graphic displays, an individual component of animation, such as a character, icon, or graphic, that moves independently.

SPST—Single pole single throw; electrical switch action used to interrupt flow through a wire; on/off.

spurious error—Random or erratic malfunction.

SPX—Sequenced Packet Exchange; an operating system by Novell, Inc.

SQC—Statistical Quality Control; employing the laws of probability and statistical procedures for offline analysis to maintain an acceptable level of product quality, often by using predetermined discrete samples over a period of time in order to specify aims, goals, and quality parameters.

SQE—Signal Quality Error; in the CSMA/CD communication media access method, a test between the transceiver/MAU and DTE to ensure that the collision detection circuit in the transceiver/MAU is working; *also* known as "heartbeat."

SQL—Structured Query Language [*pronounced* "see quill"]; ISO database access standard for communicating (querying, updating, and managing) with various relational databases; allows the client to access only that data required to satisfy a specific request, reducing network traffic and improving performance. Derived from an IBM research project that created Structured English Query Language in the 1970s; now an accepted standard in database products.

SRAM—Static random access memory.

SRP—Source Routing Protocol; routing specification by IBM.

SS—Steam supply; *also,* stainless steel.

SSFDC—Solid-State Floppy Disk Card; flash memory media made by Toshiba.

SSI—Small-scale integration; multifunction semiconductor, such as a microprocessor, with fewer than twelve equivalent gates.

SSL—Secure Sockets Layer; implementation of secure information transmission through the Internet developed by Netscape Communications.

SSOLR—Solid-state overload relay; used in motor protection technology.

SSOP—Shrink Small Outline Package.

SSR—Solid-state relay.

SSU—Saybolt Seconds Universal.

stability—The ability of equipment or the system to retain all of its performance specifications throughout its life span; *also,* in power supplies, the change in DC output as a function of time at constant line voltage, load, and ambient temperature, and normally specified for an eight-hour period after a thirty minute warm-up; *also,* in SPC, when only normal variation is present (called statistical control).

stagnation pressure—The sum of static and dynamic pressures.

standardization—In pH measurement, a method of compensating for the inaccuracy of the pH electrode in which the meter is "standardized" or adjusted to give an ideal response to the standardizing solution (buffer) so that the pH of other solutions can then be more accurately measured.

star—In LAN topology, a configuration of computing devices in which each user is connected by communication links radiating out of a central hub that handles all communications.

state logic—Alternative to ladder logic as an implementation format, developed by Adatek, Inc., of Sand Point, Idaho. It is gaining popularity and may be more efficient for process control because it is event or time driven, rather than sequence driven or rule based. Its advantages include expedited program development, the ability to implement multiple tasks simultaneously, and virtually automatic program documentation.

statement—The expression of an instruction within some computer language.

static calibration—Calibration of equipment or system at fixed points in ambient conditions.

static error band—Error band in ambient conditions.

static pressure—Pressure of fluid whether in motion or at rest.

station—"Drop" on communication system to process data, such as input/output signals to and from the plant, information interface with an operator, history collection, etc.

statistical multiplexer—Device that allows a single channel to carry information from multiple devices simultaneously.

statistical process control (SPC)—Employing online (continuous) statistical procedures for immediate analysis to improve the management of continuous processes, often by using patterns of alarms and other discrete events. Usually an open loop form of control: SPC often follows an SQC analysis for quality control.

statistical quality control—Employing laws of probability and statistical procedures for offline analysis to maintain an acceptable level of product quality, often by using predetermined discrete samples over a period of time in order to specify aims, goals, and quality parameters.

STC—Self-tuning controller; allows the automatic retuning of PID controllers in changing environments, for slowly changing process conditions, and during the dynamics of start-ups.

steady flow—Flow rate in the measuring section of a flow line that does not vary significantly with time.

steady state—A system in equilibrium, when all the potential opposing forces are at rest or balanced; in fiber optics, equilibrium mode distribution.

STEP—Standard for exchange of product model data; European version of PDES by ANSI that enables companies to digitally represent product information between departments and manufacturing partners. See *PDESO*.

step index—A type of optical fiber with uniform refractive index at its core and a sharp decrease in refractive index at its core/cladding interface.

stickits—Control system specifications that say that user mistakes will be repaired by the vendor for free but stated in much finer language; see also d*owatchados, druthers, expectifications, gotchas, ropushers, smokescreens, stonecutters, wannagirls*. ☺

STIM— Smart Transducer Interface Module, defined by IEEE-P1451 to perform its own control or data manipulation task within a processor-based (smart) transducer, located closest to the actuator; see *NCAP, TEDS*.

STL—Standard Template Library; emerging international ANSI/ISO standard for the C++ programming language; originally designed by Alexander Stepanov and Meng Lee of Hewlett-Packard Company.

STN, STNLCD—Super-Twisted-Nematic; passive color liquid crystal display (LCD) technology; less expensive than active color TFT displays, but improving on them in contrast and brightness. See *PMLCD* and *AMLCD*.

STO—Seriple Technology Organization; formed to advance Seriplex control bus technology, broaden its applications and acceptance, and promote additional product development. Purchased by Square D and its parent company Groupe Schneider in 1995, supported by more than fifty companies, and now being offered as an open system, low-level distributed I/O control bus.

stochastic screening—In electronic publishing and video screen displays, a digital screening process that converts images into very small dots (14–40 microns) of equal size and variable spacing. Second-order screened images have variable size dots and variable spacing; *also* called frequency modulated (FM) screening.

stonecutters—Vendor-named category of control system specifications written by users and system consultants that changes the date on that 1952 specification, but not always on drawings or possibly they really want vacuum tubes. See *also* d*owatchados, druthers, expectifications, gotchas, ropushers, smokescreens, stickits, wannagirls*. ☺

stop band—In digital signal processing *(DSP)*, a frequency band in filters that is attenuated more than a certain amount; see *pass band*.

stop bit—A signal following a character or block that prepares the receiving device to receive the next character or block.

storage—In computing, a device into which data can be entered, in which it can be held, and from which it can be later retrieved. Usually considered as being kept magnetically or optically on disks rather than electronically on chips (in RAM or ROM), which is usually referred to as *memory*.

storage specifications—Environmental conditions over which equipment or a system can be stored without degrading the ultimate operating performance or life span; see *extreme(operating) specifications* and *operating specifications*.

storyboard—In video and other presentation media development, a visualization of the order of a piece, using representative frames from each shot or sequence to show a visual skeleton or outline of that piece. A useful concept in developing operator screen sequences for various process actions.

STP—Spanning tree protocol; routing specification for IEEE 802.1; *also,* standard text programming; *also,* shielded twisted pair, wiring for signals with at least two conductors twisted together, six twists per inch, to minimize the effects of electromagnetic radiation between them and covered with metal-backed Mylar, plastic, PVC, or metal-woven sleeve for protection from external EMI and RFI (compare with *UTP*).

STR—Self-tuning regulator; generally refers to a class of self-adaptive control systems, forerunner (1970s) of the self-tuning controller (STC).

strain gauge—Measuring element for converting force, pressure, tension, etc., into an output signal.

strength member—That part of fiber-optic cable composed of Kevlar aramid yarn, steel strands, or fiberglass filaments that increases the tensile strength of that cable. *Also,* anchor person on tug-of-war team. ☺

STRI—Technological Institute of Iceland.

string—In a computing, a sequence of characters or bits treated as a single item.

Strouhal number—Nondimensional parameter important in vortex meter design; equals frequency times reference length divided by velocity.

structural testing—In process validation, examining the internal structure of source code; includes low-level and high-level code review, path analysis, the auditing of programming procedures and standards actually used, inspection for extraneous dead code, boundary analysis, and other techniques. Generally, structural testing requires expertise in specific computer science and programming.

structured query language (SQL)—ISO database access standard for communicating (querying, updating, and managing) with various relational databases. Allows the client to access only that data required to satisfy a specific request, reducing network traffic and improving performance. Derived from an IBM research project that created Structured English Query Language in the 1970s; now the accepted standard in database products.

structured text—High-level, block-structure language of programmable controllers that has a syntax that resembles Pascal. Used to express complex statements involving variables representing a wide range of different types of data, including analog and discrete values as well as the management of time, dates, and durations. One of five languages accepted under the IEC 1131 standard for PLCs; see *function block diagram*, *instruction list*, *ladder logic*, and *SFC*.

subdirectory—In computer programming, directories located within directories as a convenient structure for organizing files into easily found groups; like having an address showing where files are located.

subhead—In typographical composition of screen displays and printing, subheads are usually located beneath the headline as secondary information or as a summarizing phrase between sections of text.

sublayer—Subdivision of an OSI layer; for example, the data link year is subdivided into LLC and MAC sub-layers.

subsystem—A group of hardware and/or software components that perform a distinct function or operation as part of some overall system.

subtractive primaries—In color reproduction, yellow, magenta, and cyan; hues used for process color printing inks.

SuperTwisted-Nematic (STN)—Passive color liquid crystal display (LCD) technology; less expensive than active color TFT displays but improving on them in contrast and brightness. See *PMLCD* and *AMLCD*.

supervisory control action—Control action in which control loops operate independently but are subject to intermittent corrective action, such as through set point adjustment or from a computer or similar external source. Generally used to gain some degree of coordination over the overall production of a plant.

supervisory programs—Computer programs that have the primary function of scheduling, allocating, and controlling system resources rather than processing data to produce results.

Surface Acoustical Wave (SAW)—Type of touch screen that confines most of its acoustical energy to the surface of the screen; compare with GAW.

surfaces—In CAD systems, wireframe models with "skin"; can cast shadows or exhibit shades.

surge current—Current of short duration that occurs when power is first applied to capacitive loads or to temperature-dependent resistive loads.

SUS—Silicon unilateral switch.

SVGA—Super Video Graphics Adapter (Array); introduced in 1988 as a refinement of VGA that offers higher resolution of at least 800 × 600 pixels and greater color compatibility of at least sixteen colors compared with VGA; see *CGA, EGA, PGA, UXGA, VGA, XGA*.

SVID—System V Interface Definition; in AT&T, UNIX.

S-video—In video development, a way of dividing the signal so luminance is on one wire or signal while the red-green-blue (RGB) mix is on another and is of higher quality than the composite. Is *also* called Y/C video for luminance/chrominance (lumination/color); compare with *composite video* and *component video*). Used in prosumer equipment but available on some consumer-grade video products. See *Y/C video*.

switch—Device that connects, disconnects, selects, or transfers one or more circuits and is not designated as a controller, relay, or control valve.

switched line—In communications, a link for which the physical path may vary with each use, such as telephone networks.

switching regulated supply—Power supply that uses one of several duty cycle control formats to maintain constant output voltages instead of linear control. Duty cycle control can be achieved by pulse width or pulse frequency modulation. Typically, switching regulated supply is more expensive because of its circuit complexity and component quality, but offers greater efficiencies and good size, weight, and cooling characteristics.

SWOP—Specifications Web Offset Publications; color standard for the printing industry used in some electronic printers.

symmetrical compression—System that requires equal processing capability for the compression and decompression of an image. This form of compression is used where both compression and decompression is used frequently.

synchronous—Logic or communications in which all operations are controlled by clock pulses; synchronous transmission eliminates the need for "start" and "stop" bits, everything is sent at a fixed rate.

Synchronous Data Link Control—(SDLC) IBM standard protocol superseding bisynchronous transmission; uniform discipline for the transfer of data between stations in point-to-point, multipoint, or loop arrangements, using synchronous data transmission techniques.

syntax—The rules governing the structure of a language; *also,* in computers, grammatical rules for software programming that specify how instructions can be written. *Also*, in computers, the legitimate way to specify something apart from its actual meaning; see *semantics*.

system chip—Component designed with millions of electronic gates on a single chip; gate-based designs are replacing transistor-based ASIC designs.

system management—In the context of the Fieldbus Foundation, provides a basic level of integrated operation access devices.

system software—Software designed for a specific computer system or family of computer systems to facilitate the operation and maintenance of that system and associated programs, e.g., operating systems, compilers, utilities, etc.

system specifications—They formally describe how the system will meet its functional requirements.

systems integration—The ability of computers, instrumentation, and equipment to share data or applications with other components in the same and other functional areas.

T

T—Symbol of ANSI thermocouple type for copper versus constantan; *also,* means "temperature" when used in first alpha character position of ISA process instrument function tag; means "transmit" in succeeding position [see ANSI/ISA S5.1-1984 (R1992)]; *also,* T (uppercase) in math is the abbreviation "tetra-" for 10^{12}; *also,* trap.

ΔT—temperature rise.

tag—In manufacturing, a unit of information whose composition differs from that of other members of the set so that it can be used as marker or label. *Also,* in process control, alphanumeric code that identifies each instrument device in a system. *Also,* in the SCADA system for power distribution, a flag or icon on the video screen that identifies that a person is working on a power line, which should prevent that line from being activated. *Also,* in computer programming, ACSII text indicators with which the user surrounds text and images so as to designate certain formats or styles.

tag name—In computing, the name assigned to some variable in a database; *also,* in process control, the identification of elements in control loops.

tail circuit—Feeder circuit or an access line to a network node.

talking heads—In video development, term commonly applied to a video scene with no action; comes from commercial TV where scenes often show only a person speaking or reporting.

tap—In digital signal processing *(DSP)*, a circuit in digital filters that multiplies a coefficient by a data sample; ***also***: in cable based LANs, connection to main transmission medium.

tape—Recording media for data or computer programs such as "permanent" perforated paper tape or erasable magnetic tape. Magnetic tape has had much higher storage capacity than disk storage but takes much longer to search for data to be written or recovered.

TAPPI—Technical Association of the Pulp and Paper Industry U.S.

task—In computer operations, an executing application.

TB—Trackball; *also,* terminal board; *also,* terabyte, one trillion bytes.

TBC—Time base corrector; electronic device that corrects inconsistencies in the rhythm of a video signal.

TBMT—Transmitter buffer empty.

TC—Time constant.

T/C—See *thermocouple*.

TCF—Totally chlorine free; a consideration in EPA (U.S.) regulations.

TCLP—Toxicity characteristic leaching procedure; test required under the Resource Conservation and Recovery Act (U.S.) to determine the toxicity and characteristics of hazardous waste and their potential for migration.

TCO—Total cost of ownership; more than selling price, includes the cost of total services and parts to keep a system operational over its lifetime.

TCP—Transmission Control Protocol; layer 4 of ISO model.

TCP/IP—Transmission Control Protocol/ Internet Protocol; originated by the U.S. Department of Defense, this standard allows the sharing of applications among different vendors' computing devices in a high-speed environment. Corresponds to the transport and network layers of the OSI model; breaks the data stream into packets and gives each an address and sequence number. IP gets its packets from the sender to the receiver in the shortest time possible. TCP manages flow and ensures that data is correct.

TD—Means "temperature differential" when used in first two alpha character positions of ISA process instrument function tag [see ANSI/ISA S5.1-1984 (R1992)].

TDEL—Thick dielectric electroluminescent; display media that produces bright, true-blue light using a purer strontium sulfide and a combination of thick-film and thin-film to improve brightness. Has advantages over LCD, including broader temperature range and wider viewing angle without fading or color loss across the whole spectrum.

TDM—Time division multiplexer; device that accepts multiple channels on a single transmission line by connecting terminals one at a time, at regular intervals, interleaving bits (bit TDM) or characters (character TDM) from each terminal.

TDMA—Time division multiple access; in digital communication, a media access protocol (data link layer) using TDM, see *TDM*

TDR— Time domain reflectometry; method of finding cable faults by sending out high frequency pulses, when the signal reaches problem point, it bounces back to tester.

TDS—Total dissolved solids.

TE—Thermoelectric.

technology—A "toolbox" of current applied science that can be used to develop automation (in our context here).

TEDS—See Transducer Electronic Data Sheet.

tee coupler—Three-port optical or electrical coupler, often used on multidrop data highways (communication systems).

telecommunications—Term encompassing both voice and data communications in the form of coded signals over media.

telemetry—Transmission of coded analog data, often real-time parameters from some remote site; today usually in digital formats.

telenet—Part of TCP/IP suite that supports virtual terminals for remote log-on.

telnet—In communications, software service packaged with many operating systems that allows the user to get onto the system over a network in the same manner as if a terminal were attached to the system.

temperature coefficient—In power supplies, the change in output voltage per degree centigrade or the change of ambient temperature when AC line voltage, output voltage setting, and load resistance are constant.

temperature compensation—Correction for the influence of temperature on a measurement to a standard temperature reference.

temperature error—Maximum change value of measurand within a specified range when the ambient temperature of a device or system is changed from room temperature to specified extremes.

terminal—In communications, the point in the network at which data can either enter or leave; *also*, in communications, a device, usually equipped with a keyboard and often with a display, that is capable of sending and receiving data over a communications link. *Also*, in hardwiring, the point where conductors meet to exchange electrical energy.

terminal server—A device that allows one or more terminals or other devices to connect to a common bus.

terminated line—A circuit with resistance at the far end, equal to the characteristic impedance of that line so no reflections or standing waves are present when a signal is entered at the near end.

termination—Placement of a connector on a cable.

terminator—Electronic hardware used at the end of some digital signal lines to provide balanced resistance so as to prevent those reflections or standing waves that can cause errors in data; *also,* character played by Arnold Schwarzenegger in a popular movie. ☺

test point—Process connector to which no instrument is permanently connected but that is intended for the temporary or intermittent connection of an instrument.

tetraflops—trillion (10^{12}) floating point operations per second.

text—Sequence of characters forming part of a transmission that is sent from a data source to a data sink and contains the information to be conveyed. It may be preceded by a header and followed by an "end-of-text" signal. In ASCII as well as in general communications usage, text is a sequence of characters treated as an entity if preceded by a "start-of-text" and followed by an "end-of-text" control character.

text box—Workstation screen view box where the user can type information or a command requested by the application; usually appears within a dialog box.

TFLOPS—Tera floating point operations per second.

TFT—Thin film technology; allows low-power operator interfaces that are resistant to shock and vibration, immune to electrical fields and X-rays, diminutive in size, offer ease of portability, and have bright, high-color intensity VGA resolution. As good as but expensive alternative to CRTs; *also,* thin film transistor-type active color liquid crystal display; alternative to STN technology. See *STN.*

TGA—Targa; format from TruVision, Inc., for saving graphics in electronic memory; used for exchanging data between computers.

TGIF—Thank Goodness It's Friday (or Finished). ☺

THD—Total harmonic distortion.

theory—System of ideas meant to explain something and chosen with a view to originality, controversialness, incomprehensibility, and how good it will look in print. ☺

thermal conductivity—Heat conducting property of a material in the form of thermal energy.

thermal expansion—Increase in size due to an increase in temperature expressed in units of an increasing dimension per degree.

thermal gradient—The distribution of a differential temperature through a body or across a surface.

thermal noise—Usually electrical noise resulting from thermally induced random fluctuation in the current in the receiver's load resistance.

thermal printer—Printer design that uses transfer sheet, which carries ink in contact with the paper or transparency, and a heated print head driven by digital data that touches that transfer sheet so as to attach images to the appropriate portions of page.

thermal sensitivity shift—Sensitivity shift within equipment due to changes of ambient temperature from room temperature to specified limits of the compensated temperature range.

thermistor—**Thermal resistor**; resistive circuit component having a high negative temperature coefficient of resistance, so that its resistance decreases as the temperature increases.

thermocouple—Device consisting of two dissimilar metals joined together at both ends. The voltage developed between these two junctions is proportional to the temperature difference between those junctions; used to measure temperature at one end while the other is held fixed as the reference (cold) junction.

thermopile—The arrangement of thermocouples in a series such that alternate junctions are at the measuring temperature and the reference temperature so as to amplify the thermoelectric voltages; often used in radiation pyrometry.

thermowell—Closed-end tube designed to protect temperature sensors from the harsh environments of the process.

THF—Time horizon to failure.

Thicknet—Implementation of IEEE 802.3 standard known as standard Ethernet or Ethernet 10BASE5; operates over thick coaxial cable at 10 megabits per second baseband.

thin client—In client/server applications, client designed especially small so that bulk of data processing occurs on server; although usually refers to software, it is increasingly used for computers, such as network computers and Net PCs, that are designed to serve as clients for client/server architectures; network computer without hard disk drive, whereas *fat client* includes disk drive.

thinnet—Implementation of IEEE 802.3 standard known as Ethernet 10BASE2; operates over thin coaxial cable at 10 megabits per second baseband.

thin space—In typographical composition of screen displays and printing, usually equal to one-fifth of an em, the thin space corresponds to a period or comma in column alignment.

Thomson Effect—When current flows through a conductor within a thermal gradient, a reversible absorption or evolution of heat will occur in that conductor at the gradient boundaries.

thread—Order of the software action of a specific task within a device, independent of its priority in multitasking environment, which continues in that order through multiple interruptions by higher priority functions.

three mode control—Modulating process control action using proportional, integral, and derivative actions.

three phase motor—Relatively inexpensive, self-starting motor, with no starting winding or capacitor, for starting heavy loads; requires three-phase AC power supply.

throughput—Material or product passing through an industrial process; *also,* the rate at which work passes through a manufacturing operation; ***also,*** the rate at which information is processed through a computer.

throughput loss—Ratio of power output divided by power input.

THT—Through-hole technology; a method of mounting elements on printed circuit boards; see *SMT.*

TIA—Telecommunications Industries Association.

TIFF—Tagged Image File Format; for saving bit mapped graphics in electronic memory; used for exchanging data between computers.

TIGA—Texas Instruments Graphics Architecture.

time base—Cadence of video signals that controls the scanning of the image, maintaining its stability.

time base corrector—Electronic device that corrects inconsistencies in the rhythm of a video signal; often used to make a video recorder playback stable.

time base error—Flutter in the horizontal sweep rate of a video signal; in videotape recorders this can be caused by tape stretch or inherent imperfections in the transport mechanism.

time boxing—In planning techniques, to limit a long-term vision or project into more practical lengths, often identified by "milestones."

time division multiplexer—(TDM) A device that accepts multiple channels on a single transmission line by connecting terminals one at a time, at regular intervals, interleaving bits (bit TDM) or characters (character TDM) from each terminal.

time-out—Expiration of a predefined time period at which point some specified action occurs; in communications, time-outs are employed to avoid unnecessary delays and improve traffic flow.

time proportional—Process control response that is either full on or full off, but the on duration and off duration are proportional to the deviation from set point.

time sharing—Method of computer operation that allows several interactive terminals to use one computer; although terminals are actually served in sequence, the high speed of the computer makes it appear as if all terminals were being served simultaneously.

time slot—Some assigned period of time, or an assigned position in some sequence, for operation usually of microprocessor.

time-slice multitasking—Truest form of multitasking; found on sophisticated workstations, where each task has the microprocessor's attention for a fraction of a second. Tasks are then performed in sequential order by priority; compare *context switching multitasking* and *cooperative multitasking*.

tints—In video screen displays and printing, the various even tone areas (strengths) of a solid color.

tip and ring—Traditional telephone terminology (U.S.) for "positive" and "negative" polarities based on old style telephone switchboards; "tip" wire, connected to tip of plug, "ring" wire connected to slip ring in the jack.

TI'T—*"Therrre it 'tis"*; phrase an old Irish math teacher of mine used instead of QED; see *QED*. ☺

TITO—Twin input twin output; systems requiring more sophisticated control methods than single loop controllers; see *SISO, MIMO, MISO*.

TMR—Triple modular redundant; three devices in a voting mode of two out of three to assure system availability.

TOC—Total organic carbon; a measurement that with the proper interpretation can be an indicator of the pollution level in a wastewater stream.

TOE—Time of event.

toggle—Pertaining to any device that has two stable states, such as forward/back, on/off, etc.

token bus—In digital communication, a LAN standard that uses the token-passing media access method (ISO data link layer 2), where the right to transmit is passed from device to device by way of a logical ring on a physical bus configuration.

token passing—In digital communications, media access method (ISO data link layer 2) for peer-to-peer communication bus nodes. The token is passed around to each node on a regular schedule, making throughput and response time predictable (deterministic). Only one node has the token at any one time, and during that time it has complete control of the network.

token ring—In digital communications, LAN standard that uses the token-passing media access method (ISO data link layer 2), in which a special data packet (called a token) is passed from one station to another along a (physical) electrical ring. When the station wants to transmit, it takes possession of the token, transmits its data, and then frees the token after data has made a complete circuit of the electrical ring.

tolerance—Maximum allowable deviation of the electrical, environmental, or dimensional parameters of a device, equipment, or system; usually given in percent.

tools—In the context of data processing, software programs to aid in the planning, design, implementation, maintenance, and diagnosis of computer systems.

TOP—Technical and Office Protocols; Boeing version of the MAP protocol that is aimed at office and engineering applications so as to enable MAP devices on IEEE 802.4 to interface with office systems on IEEE 802.3; closely associated with GOSIP being developed by NIST.

TOPFET—Temperature and overload protected field effect transistor; power-protected MOSFET.

topology—The logical and/or physical arrangement of stations on a network, such as star, ring, multidrop, tree.

total cost of ownership—More than the selling price, includes the cost of total services and parts to keep a system operational over its lifetime.

total productive maintenance (TPM)—Combines the preventive maintenance and predictive maintenance concepts with personnel assets for a team approach to ensuring continuous plant improvement and eliminating bureaucratic and organizational lines between production and maintenance departments; Intended to promote total quality control and employee involvement.

total quality—Holistic approach to quality control that stresses the building of a manufacturing process that its their users to confront quality problems rather than pass them on.

touch screen—A video screen (CRT) the operator can interact with by touching icons on the screen display, rather than through a keyboard or mouse.

TOX—Total organic halide; a measurement that with the proper interpretation can be an indicator of the pollution level in a wastewater stream.

TP—Twisted pair; wiring for signals.

TPG—Test pattern generator.

TPM—See total productive maintenance.

TQC—Total quality control.

TQM—Total quality management.

TR—Technical report.

traceability—Documentation of the existence of a calibration chain between an instrument and a primary standard.

track—Ring shaped portion of magnetic disk surface area for digital memory, defined by minimum and maximum distance from disk center.

trackball—Input device for a video screen (CRT) that has a ball recessed in its surface that the user rotates to control the position of the cursor. *Also*, unusual game dangerously played along railways. ☺

traffic director—In digital communications, network "master" station that performs "polling" as a media access method for controlling devices on bus (multipoint, multidrop) or ring (loop)-type network. Using the process of inviting another station or node to transmit data; compare to *selecting*.

transaction—In communications, a message destined for an application program; a computer-processed task that accomplishes a particular action or result. In interactive communications, an exchange between two devices, one of which is usually a computer; in a batch or remote job entry, a job or job step.

transceiver—Device that can both transmit and receive data communications; *also* known as media attachment unit (MAU) and not to be confused with a Token Ring MAU (Media Access Unit), which is an Ethernet device for transmitting and receiving data that often provides data packet collision detection as well. A transceiver can either be an internal or an external feature of a network device, such as network interface card, a repeater, a hub, or a concentrator. A multiport MAU, or transceiver, allows a number of computers or workstations to be attached to a single connection on the Ethernet bus, and each port performs standard transceiver functions.

transducer—A device for converting energy from one form to another, such as pneumatic to electric, mechanical to pneumatic, optical to electrical, etc. General term for a device that receives information in the form of one or more physical quantities; modifies that information and/or its form, if required; and produces a resultant output signal. Depending on the application, a transducer can be primary element, a transmitter, a relay, a converter, or other device. Because the term is not specific, its use for specific applications is not recommended.

transducer electronic data sheet (TEDS)—Digitally accessible specifications within the transducer itself (smart transducer), communicated over a digital connection to other devices (such as on an IEEE-P1351 defined fieldbus) to ensure that the appropriate device has been installed and is compatible, or even on some devices adjusting their compatibility. In combination with NCAP and STIM, a newly installed transducer can effectively announce and define itself to others on the same network; see *STIM, NCAP*.

transient—An abrupt change in voltage, of short duration, such as a brief pulse induced by the operation of a switch; sometimes called "spike."

transient response—The time required for output voltage to return within the DC regulation envelope for a step change of input voltage or DC output current; normally specified in microseconds for a 50 percent load change from one-half to full load.

transitional flow—Flow between laminar and turbulent flow, usually between a pipe Reynolds number of 2000 and 4000.

transmission—The sending of a signal, message, or other form of information over some medium; a series of characters, messages, or blocks, including control information and other user data.

transmission mode—Technique by which device recognizes beginning and end of character clocking in synchronous transmission; start and stop bits in asynchronous.

transmitter—Device that translates the low-level output of a sensor or a transducer to higher-level signal suitable for transmitting it to a site where it can be further processed; the sensor may or may not be integral with the transmitter.

transparent GIFFs—In digital graphics, a subset of the original GIF file format that adds header information to a GIF file, that signifies that color will be masked out.

transparent mode—The transmission of binary data with the recognition of most control characters suppressed. In binary synchronous communications, entry to and exit from transparent mode is indicated by a sequence beginning with a special data link escape (DLE) character.

transport layer—Layer 4 in the OSI reference model; provides a logical connection between processes on two machines.

tree—LAN topology that recognizes only one route between two nodes on the network; the "map" resembles a tree or the letter *T*.

TRI—Toxic Release Inventory; required by companies in the United States by the EPA to control industrial environmental releases.

triac—Solid-state switching device used to switch alternating current waveforms.

triboluminescence—The light emitted when particles bump into one another.

trim—In video development, adjusting the length of a video clip or other element. This feature allows editors to quickly, precisely, and only slightly change the in or out points of a clip. *Also*, in process modulating valves, the port and plug components, which are the controlling surfaces.

triple point—Temperature and pressure at which the solid, liquid, and gas phases of a given substance are present simultaneously in varying amounts.

TRMS—True root mean square.

Trojan Horse—Apparently innocuous software which, when loaded into network or system, allows access to virus or specific "cracker;" see *Cracker*.

trunk—Single circuit, usually of multiple channels, between two points, both of which are switching centers or individual distribution points; usually handles many channels simultaneously.

TS—Touch screen.

TSCA—Toxic Substances Control Act; U.S. federal law passed in 1976 authorizing the EPA to collect information on chemical risks; the basis for regulating such toxic substances as PCBs.

TSE—Turkish Standards Institution.

TSR—Terminate and stay-resident (MS-DOS).

TSS—Total suspended solids; a consideration in EPA (U.S.) regulations.

TTL, T^2L—Transistor-transistor logic; form of solid-state logic that uses only transistors to form logic gates.

TTY—Teletypewriter.

TU—Termination unit.

tuning adjustments—No two systems require the same tuning adjustments for optimum control, nor does any one system require the same tuning adjustments under all possible operating conditions; so controllers (and control algorithms) have adjustable settings to ensure optimum operation.

turbidity—Measurement to quantify the deviation between clear water and water containing suspended solids, usually through the measurement of the loss of light caused by absorbence and scattering.

turbochannel—100 MB/sec bus in DECstation 5000/200 by Digital Equipment Corporation with no license charge or royalty.

turbulent flow—When forces due to inertia are more significant than the forces of velocity; typically occurs with a Reynolds number in excess of 4000.

turn on time—Rise time, which is sometimes measured between the 20 percent and 80 percent points; see *rise time*.

turnaround time—Elapsed time between the submission of a job to the computer and the return of results; *also*, in communications, the actual time required to reverse the direction of a transmission from the sender to the receiver or vice versa when using the half-duplex method (time is required by line propagation effects, modem timing, and computer reaction).

turnkey system—Equipment or computer system that is delivered complete, installed, and ready to operate.

turnoff time—Fall time, which is sometimes measured between the 80 percent and 20 percent points; see *fall time*.

TÜV—Technischer Überwachungs Verein; German national electrical safety body.

TVS—Transient voltage suppressor.

twinax—Twinaxial cable; uses a twisted pair of conductors within shielding to improve resistance to RFI/EMI over coaxial cable; see *coax*.

twisted pair—Two insulated copper conductors that are wound around each other to cancel the effects of electrical fields (noise in signal).

Two-mode control—Modulating process control action using proportional and integral actions.

TWT—Traveling wave tube.

TXD—The transmit data; digital data signal output, usually from the computer transmitter to the receiver.

typical measurement—Error of a value is within plus or minus one standard deviation (±1%) of nominal specified value, as computed from the total population of values.

U

U—Means "multivariable" when used in first alpha character position of ISA-instrument function tag, means "multifunction" when used in succeeding positions [see ANSI/ISA S5.1-1984 (R1992)].

UA—User agent.

UART—Universal asynchronous receiver-transmitter; MOS/LSI device that is a complete subsystem that simultaneously transmits and receives asynchronous data in duplex or half-duplex operation.

UCA—Utility Communication Architecture.

UCR—Under color removal; color separation control technique in color screen displays and printing.

UDP—User Datagram Protocol; TCP/IP transaction protocol used for applications such as remote network management and name service access; allows users to assign a name to a physical or numbered address.

UEC—User Environment Component; part of X/Open environment. See *X/Open*.

UHF—Ultrahigh frequency.

UI—UNIX International; consortium to establish a standard UNIX; *also*, user interface.

UIL—User interface language.

UL—Underwriters Laboratories, Inc.; independent laboratory in the United States that establishes standards for commercial and industrial products, generally to protect the people using them. A UL listing indicates compliance with UL safety standards for electrical, mechanical, and fire hazards; compare with *FM*.

ULSI—Ultra—large-scale integration; over one million components on single multifunction chip.

ULTRIX—Operating system that is Digital Equipment Corporation's answer to UNIX.

UMS—Utilities management system.

unbalanced line—Digital transmission line in which the magnitudes of the voltages on the two conductors are not equal in respect to ground, such as a coaxial line.

UNC—Uniform Naming Convention; used for logon commands to a communication network, especially the Internet.

underscan—Video display effect where image is shrunk so that it does not fill entire screen.

undershoot—Difference between the value to which a signal goes below the set point, and the value of the desired set point.

ungrounded junction—The form of construction of a thermocouple probe where the hot, or measuring, junction is fully enclosed but electrically isolated from the sheath.

UNI—Ente Nationale Italiano di Unificazione.

uniformity—In video displays, the evenness of brightness across the screen display, without which the view appears dirty and the colors distorted.

union—Pipe-fitting type where two pipes are joined by a separable flangelike coupling, that requires neither pipe to be rotated.

uniqueness—In object oriented programming (OOP), each object that has a unique identification.

UNIX—Unified multitasking; a time-sharing operating system designed originally by (and a trademark of) AT&T for communicating between multiuser, 32-bit minicomputers. It has become widely accepted because of its versatility; the trade name now belongs to X/Open Corp. Ltd.

unloaded line—Analog transmission line that has no loading coils to reduce line loss; typically used at audio frequencies as with telephone lines.

UNMA—Unified Network Management Architecture, by AT&T.

UPS—Uninterruptible power supply; used to ameliorate the effects of poor electrical power quality, including voltage anomalies, high-frequency noise, or ground loops. Especially applicable where power outages of over half a second duration are possible.

URC—Universal raster coordinates.

URCLK—Universal receiver clock.

URL—Uniform Resource Locator; a World Wide Web Internet address for sources of information, which *also* indicates what kind of information the source contains and where it is located within that source.

USART—Universal synchronous-asynchronous receiver-transmitter.

US/AS—Unified Sensor/Actuator Standard international standard being developed by NEMA/IEEE for sensor and actuator network products and services.

USB—Universal serial bus; designed to allow the user to easily plug in additional devices onto a relatively short computer network without the need to reboot the computer; relies on a computer microprocessor for operation.

user-friendly—Pertaining to any feature, device, or concept that makes perfect sense to some computer programmer. ☺

users—Collective term for those who stare vacantly at a computer monitor; users are divided into three types: novice, intermediate, and expert. Novice users are people who are afraid that simply pressing a key may break their computer. Intermediate users are people who don't know how to fix their computer after they've just pressed a key that breaks it. Expert users are people who break other people's computers. ☺

USL—UNIX Systems Laboratories; an AT&T spin-off.

USNC/IEC—United States National Committee for International Electrotechnical Commission.

USOC—Universal Service Order Code; set of phone company standards (U.S.) for equipment, including connectors and interfaces.

USRT—Universal Synchronous Receiver-Transmitter.

UST—Underground Storage Tank; under RCRA (U.S. federal law), a tank with more than 10 percent of its volume (and connected piping)

USTAG—U.S. Technical Advisory Group; committee formed to work with IEC (International Electrotechnical Commission).

utility software (program)—Programs that make the operation of PC or LAN more convenient, including programs to move disk files more easily, diagnostic programs, etc.

UTP—Unshielded twisted pair; wiring for signals that consists of at least two conductors twisted together, six twists per inch, to minimize the effects of electromagnetic radiation between them, but without a metal covering to protect it from external EMI or RFI; compare with *STP.*

UUCICO—UNIX-to-UNIX copy in/copy out; program that oversees remote connections in lieu of the shell.

UUCP—UNIX-to-UNIX system copy service.

UUT—Unit under test.

UV—Ultraviolet; that portion of the electromagnetic spectrum below blue light (380 nanometers).

UXGA—Ultra extended graphics adapter (Array); video standard introduced as a refinement of SVGA that offers a higher resolution of at least 1600 x 1200 pixels; see *CGA, EGA, PGA, SVGA, VGA, XGA*.

V

V—Once meant "viscosity," now means "vibration" or "mechanical analysis" when used in the first alpha character position of ISA process instrument function tag; means "valve" (damper, louver) when used in succeeding position [see ANSI/ISA S5.1-1984 (R1992)].

value engineering—Total approach to design that achieves improved performance and quality by stressing simplicity and the integration of design and manufacturing techniques.

valve positioner/controller—Signal-operated device installed to control valve operation; designed to assure that a given signal obtains the desired action regardless of changes in friction or process pressures. That is, when a controller outputs a signal representing a specific valve opening to a positioner, a physical measure on the valve stem determines the actual position and changes the positioner signal to the actuator until that position matches the request.

valve travel—Distance over which a valve is turned between its full-closed and full-opened positions.

VAN—Value-added network; network whose services go beyond simple switching, often including store and forward (mailbox) services for managing high-volume message traffic and usually leased high-bandwidth networks between different geographical locations.

vaporware—Computer software that is announced or advertised, but never shipped. ☺

VAR—Value-added remarketer (or reseller).

VAT—Voltage adjusting type; process control output.

VAV—Variable air volume.

VAX—Virtual address extension; a product series from Digital Equipment Corp.

VB—Visual Basic; software programming that provides macro-type language and graphical environment; originally designed by Microsoft as an application-development environment that allows a standard GUI to be bolted on to some existing library.

VBX—Visual Basic extension; specialized applications typically written in C or C++ that embed themselves into the Visual Basic (VB) environment. VBX allows a VB programmer to plug another software component into an application without requiring any understanding of the inner workings of that component. Limitations include memory access, platform dependency, and speed.

VC—Virtual component; usually some system with reusable intellectual property (software) embedded within a chip but capable of being combined with others to create various different combinations of systems.

VCF—Voltage controlled frequency.

VCG—Voltage controlled generation; mode of function generator.

VCO—Voltage controlled oscillator.

VCP—Video control panel; term of reference from PLC operator interfaces.

VCPI—Virtual control program interface; single-tasking DOS extender; replaced by DPMI. See *DPMI.*

VCR—Videocassette Recorder; *also,* see *virtual field devices.*

VDE—Verband Deutscher Electrotechniker; association of German electrical engineers who *also* act as a European regulation and standards agency focused on electrical and electronic products; member of IEC as VDE-Verlag GmbH.

VDF—Vacuum fluorescent display.

VDI—Virtual device interface; *also,* Verein Deutscher Ingenieure; Association of German Engineers that provides engineers from different fields of study with a common representative body for promoting positive cross-disciplinary interaction.

VDMAD—Virtual direct memory access driver; see *DMA*.

VDP—Video disk player.

VDR—Video disk recorder.

VDS—Variable definition syntax; this is DDL renamed with the copyright granted to the SP50 committee by ISP Foundation; *also,* Video direct slot; provides a port for additional video monitors using a common signal source in a workstation.

VDT—Video display terminal.

VDU—Video display unit.

Vector-oriented drawing—An approach in drawing and layout programs that treats graphics as line and arc segments rather than as individual dots; *also* called object- oriented.

vectorscope—In analog video development, equipment used to precisely analyze various parts of a video signal.

verbose format—Displaying meaningful words rather than alphanumeric code.

VESA—Video Electronics Standards Association.

VF—Vacuum fluorescent type of liquid crystal displays (*LCD*).

VFD—Variable frequency drive; helps save energy and provide variable speed control with standard three-phase motors; these motors cut down on the inrush of current and mechanical stress during starting and can improve the power factor; *also,* Vacuum fluorescent displays that emit fluorescent glow when excited with a small voltage; a type of liquid crystal display (*LCD*); *also,* see *virtual field device.*

VFW—Video for Windows; Microsoft package for integrating video clips into other computer applications.

VGA—Video Graphics Adapter (Array); video standard introduced in 1987 for IBM PS/2 series that can emulate CGA and EGA modes and additionally provide 640 x 480 pixels with 16 colors and 320 x 200 pixels with 256 colors; see *CGA, EGA, PGA, SVGA UXGA, XGA*.

VHDL—VHSIC hardware description language.

VHF—Very high frequency.

VHLL—Very-high level language; very application-oriented computer programming language in which the burden on the user is shifted away from understanding computers and learning codes to simply understanding the problem to be solved. While dramatically faster and easier to use and providing a "top-down" focus on thinking, they generally work well for only a narrow class of problems for example, the spreadsheet for an accountant is not a useful word processing package for a fiction writer).

VHS—Video Home System; Matsushita videotape standard.

VHSIC—Very—high-speed integrated circuit.

vibration error—Maximum change in equipment or system performance when a specific amplitude and range of frequencies are applied to a specific axis at ambient conditions.

video card—Computer interface card that processes video data.

videodisk—Optical storage medium for storing high-quality audio information with random access capability.

Video for Windows—In digital graphics display, a multimedia architecture and application suite that provides an outbound architecture that lets applications developers access audio, video, and animation from many different sources through one interface. As an application, it primarily handles video capture and compression, as well as video and audio editing.

Video RAM—Random access memory with parallel-to-serial conversion for video display signal generation.

viewing area—That part of a video screen display that can be used in a given application; sometimes called w*orkspace*.

VIL—Vertical injection logic.

VINES—Virtual Network Software; operating software for LAN made by Banyan.

virtual circuit—In packet switching, a network facility that gives the appearance to the user of being an actual end-to-end circuit; a dynamically variable network connection where sequential data may be routed differently during the course of a "virtual connection." Virtual circuits enable transmission facilities to be shared by many users simultaneously; *also* called logical circuit.

virtual communication relationships—In the context of the Fieldbus Foundation, application-layer communications channels.

virtual field devices—In the context of the Fieldbus Foundation an abstract model for the description of data and the behavior of an automation system as seen by a communication partner.

virtual memory (storage)—Storage space that may be viewed as addressable main storage but is actually auxiliary storage (usually peripheral storage) mapped into real addresses. The amount of virtual storage is limited by the addressing scheme of the computer.

VISCA—Video Systems Control Architecture; protocol by Sony for controlling its own Vdeck line of tape drives and Vbox, which connects to control L and other devices; VISCA's open architecture allows third-party development as well, which is supported by numerous software applications.

viscosity—Inherent resistance of a substance to flow.

VISRD—Virtual interrupt service routine driver; used to reduce interrupt latencies as a very effective way to avoid performance degradation in Windows.

Visual Basic (VB)—Software programming that provides a macro-type language and graphical environment; originally designed by Microsoft as an application-development environment that allows a standard GUI to be bolted to some existing library.

visual engineering—Process of creating photorealistic images and animations from geometric and analytical data. Used for product design, testing, and manufacturing directions; for analysis of complex mathematics or physics such as thermal dissipation and stress; and for ergonomic studies of human interaction with designs.

VIW—Video in Window; placing a continuous video image (from, say, an RGB input) into a computer (typically, a VGA) screen view.

VLAN—Video local Area Network, created by Videomedia.

VL bus—VESA local bus; extension to the 486 bus system.

VLDB—Very large databases; generally corporatewide data from all parts of an enterprise and including all activities.

VLF—Very low frequency; radiation in CRT-based video monitors; see *ELF*.

VLM—Very large memory; with a capacity of up to fourteen gigabytes.

VLSI—Very—large-scale integration; high-density multifunction semiconductor device with 1,000 to 1 million components on a chip.

V-Mail—Video Mail; video counterpart of Electronic Mail; method of transmitting video as well as text messages and files (brochures, presentations, etc.) digitally over communication links, such as the phone system.

VME—Versa Module European; a 32-bit bus and component system (IEEE -1014 1987).

VMS—Virtual memory system.

VMX—Versa Module (European) extended; private bus.

VOC—Volatile organic compounds; a consideration in EPA (U.S.) regulations; highly evaporative organic material frequently found in paints, solvents, and similar products, and contributing to the formation of smog.

VOD—Video on demand; commercial capability to select "private programming" independent of broadcast schedules because of the multichannel availability of media such as fiber-optic cable; its industrial implications in plant simulation exercises during operation.

voice grade channel—Channel used for speech transmission, usually with an audio frequency range of 300 to 3400 Hz; *also,* used for the transmission of analog and digital data, up to 10,000 bps.

volatile memory—Storage medium that loses all data when power is removed.

volume(tric) flow rate—Calculated using the area of a full closed conduit (A) and the average fluid velocity (V) to arrive at total volume quantity of flow (Q); Q = V × A.

VPICD—Virtual Programmable Interrupt Controller Device; used by Window to manage the interrupt controller resources for multiple virtual machines (or tasks).

VPN—Virtual private network; software-defined, switched-based network that emulates a private network but on a nondedicated (not leased) public phone system, typically for video conferencing (which normally needs dedicated lines).

VR—Virtual reality; three-dimensional (3-D) computer simulation of real-world activities and events that allows the "walk-through" of various proposed designs or situations; becomes a 3-D doorway versus the 2-D window (video screen).

VRAM—Video random access memory; provides the capacity for a number of colors and resolutions (amount of pixels); optimized for video processing.

VRC—Vertical redundancy check; error-detection scheme in which the parity bit of each character is set so that the total number of "1" bits in each character is odd (or even).

VRML—[*pronounced* vermal] Virtual Reality Modeling Language; computer authoring language for publishing documents on the World Wide Web on the Internet using both text and three-dimensional graphics and thus allowing the user to shift direction, rotate, even "fly through" different views of objects using ordinary hardware and (mostly) free software.

VSD—Variable speed drive.

VSI—Virtual Socket Interface; industry standard methodology for allowing various predictable and preverified intellectual properties (IPs), generally in the form of software available so as to interconnect to create various systems, usually on chips, for specific user requirements.

VSS—Very small sensor; ultrasonic microtransducer- and microprocessor-based electronics.

VT—Virtual terminal; *also,* vertical tabulation; in data communication, a format effector that advances the active position to the same character position on the next predetermined line.

VTP—Virtual terminal protocol; emerging OSI standard to support terminal emulation.

VTR—Videotape recorder.

VVI—Variable voltage input; a type of variable frequency drive; see *VFD*.

VXI—VME extensions for instrumentation; open architecture multivendor standard for implementing modular instruments.

V.xx standards—A series of standards covering data communications over telephone circuits; established by CCITT.

W

W—Means "weight" or "force" when used in first alpha character position of ISA instrument function tag, means "well" in succeeding position [see ANSI/ISA S5.1-1984 (R1992)].

w/in²—Watt density; the watts emanating from each square inch of heated surface area of a device.

W3, WWW—World Wide Web.

WABI—Windows Application Binary Interface.

WAIS—[*pronounced* wayz] Wide Area Information Servers; the more sophisticated search indexes, which can find information based on subjects or descriptions rather than just keywords; helpful in accessing whole groups of documents that relate to the topic is being researched.

WAMM—Wide area mail management; used to collect messages, statistics, and reports over a network.

WAN—Wide area network; network linking data processing and telecommunications equipment over a larger geographic area than a single work site or a metropolitan area. Typically links cities and is usually based on X.25

packet switching; may be implemented by a private or a public telecommunications operator.

wands—Portable or tethered digital computer input device that reads bar codes.

wannagirls—Vendor-named category of control system specifications written by users and system consultants, which are immediately recognizable by the O/E (or equal) symbol ending every statement; like the song, "Mom epitomizes everything I want in a girl". see *also* d*owatchados, druthers, expectifications, gotchas, ropushers, smokescreens, stickits, stonecutters*. ☺

WAO—Wet air oxidation.

waveform—In video development, same as *vectorscope*.

wavelength—Distance between the successive peaks of a sine wave (or two equivalent points on any adjacent waves); the time required for a wave to complete a cycle.

wavelet—In video development, proprietary data compression developed by ImMIX that uses variable compression for individual frames to achieve the desired data rates.

WBT—Wet bulb temperature.

WC—Windows Connection; developed by Microsoft to allow non-Windows DOS to access files, data, and E-mail from Windows for Workgroups machines.

WCS—World coordinate system.

WD—Means "weight deviation" or "force deviation" when used in first two alpha character positions of ISA instrument function tag [see ANSI/ISA S5.1-1984 (R1992)].

WDM—Wavelength division multiplexing; transmission technique by which separate channels, distinguished by wavelength, are multiplexed through a transmission media.

WDT—Watchdog timer; time-out device built into equipment to prevent continued operation if the equipment operates too long for its intended function (thus indicating a problem or malfunction).

Web page—HTML document on the Internet versus World Wide Web, usually one of many that together make up a Web site.

Web server—System capable of continuous access to the Internet or to an internal network retrieving and displaying documents via hypertext transfer protocol (HTTP); files can be audio clips, video, graphics, or text.

weight—In typographical composition of screen displays and printing, the thickness of the stroke in a typeface.

WFI—Water for injection.

WfMC—Workflow Management Coalition; organization developing interoperability tools for digital communication applications over the Internet.

WFW–Windows for Workgroups; developed by Microsoft to directly support networking.

wideband—System in which multiple channels access a medium (usually coaxial cable) that has a large bandwidth, greater than that of a voice-grade channel; typically offers higher-speed data transmission capability (10,000 to 500,000 bps).

widow—In typographical composition of screen displays and printing, a single word in a line by itself, ending a paragraph or starting a page; usually frowned upon in good typography.

Win32—Windows NT/95 32-bit application programming interface (API) that allows programs to operate on both platforms.

winchester disk—A type of smaller hard disk.

window—In computer graphics, area defined in system not bounded by any limits; structured viewing area that can appear on monitor and provide functional application workspace.

Windows—GUI environment developed by Microsoft that permits users to run more than one application on a desktop computer simultaneously.

Windows CE Windows Compact Edition; developed by Microsoft as a less expensive version of Windows for a broad range of portable business and consumer devices (OEMs); allows mobile interconnectivity, as well as roving, monitoring, and controlling. An entirely new operating system that enables business and consumer non-PC devices to communicate with each other, share information with Windows-based PCs, and connect to the Internet.

Windows NT—Windows New (or Next) Technology; developed by Microsoft as a significant upgrade to Windows.

WINS—Windows Internet Naming Service; maps computer names to IP addresses.

WIP—Work in process.

wipe—In video development, a transition between two fully opaque sources that is defined by a shape.

Wire-frame—In a CAD system, the representation of an object with line segments.

wiring closet—A central location for terminating and routing on-site wiring systems; see *marshaling cabinet*.

wizard—Software tool that permits the user, without programming, to set up some application through a guided interrogation using selections and following prompts by the computer. Term made popular by Microsoft Office Suite of products for the setting up of slide shows, spreadsheets, and word processing applications. But the concept has been used for decades by various vendors of microprocessor control systems in one form or another.

WMF—Windows Metafile; format for saving graphics in electronic memory; used for exchanging data between computers.

WMS—Warehouse management systems; a class of software application designed to help manufacturers reduce distribution labor costs, lower inventory costs, improve warehouse space utilization, and enhance customer service.

WOM—Write-only memory (think about this). ☺

word—Number of bits treated as single a unit by the CPU; can be as small as two bits. In a 16-bit machine, a word's length is usually 16 bits and so on.

workgroup—Group of people working on same project, especially when connected to each other with some dedicated network.

working standard—Standard of unit measurement calibrated from either a primary or secondary standard that is used to calibrate other devices or make comparison measurements.

work space—That part of video screen display that can be used in a given application; sometimes called *viewing area*.

workstation—Human-machine interface (HMI) for computer-based system like that used for distributed process control; usually refers, but is not limited, to high-end machines using RISC processors and running on UNIX.

WorldFIP—Global organization dedicated to developing an open, universal fieldbus specification built upon robust, field-proven technology and embracing basic FIP protocol structure: formed six months after the formation of ISP, leading to the opinion by some that this was a commercial response by companies competing with those in ISP. *Also*, the Fieldbus Foundation, a not-for-profit organization dedicated to developing a single, worldwide, interoperable fieldbus; formed from the merger of WorldFIP North America and ISP Foundation in 1994. See *FIP*.

WORM—Write once, read many; common type of optical disk drive to which data can be written only once for permanent storage but can always be read. *Also*, (in lowercase letters); a self-replicating program that consumes processor time but cannot destroy data, software, or other system resources.

WOSA—Windows Open System Architecture.

write—To record data into a storage device or onto a data medium.

WS—Workstation; *also,* water supply.

WSCC—Western Systems Coordinating Council; group of power utilities.

WSP—Working set point; of a process control loop, where several set points may be selected.

W_T—Weight of material.

WV—Wild variable in ratio control.

WWV—Radio call letters for a time synchronization broadcast signal in the United States.

WWW—World Wide Web, *also* called W3, or merely the Web: Internet feature that allows even the uninitiated to access diverse resources (e-mail, newsgroups, FTP, etc.) in a user-friendly environment that can be browsed using a special front-end program. A mechanism developed by Tim Berners-Lee so CERN physicists would be able to share documents via the Internet, while sharing computer access in different locations in the world, by using URLs to identify files and systems and using hypertext links to move between files on the same or different systems. The concept originated when one member of the team became pregnant and the team worked together to find for a way for her to stay involved in their work. ***Also;*** World Wide Wait. ☺

WYSITB—[*pronounced* wissytib] "What you see is totally bizarre"; a wag's interpretation of the results of using certain software combinations that produce very random and erratic product. ☺

WYSIWYG—[*pronounced* wissywig] "What you see is what you get"; what shows on the video screen when creating views, is what will show in the end product, which is usually printouts, but is not limited to that media.

X

X—Means "unclassified" when used in first alpha character position or any succeeding position of ISA instrument function tag; means "x-axis" when used as modifier [see ANSI/ISA S5.1-1984 (R1992)].

X.21—CCITT standard governing the interface between DTE and DCE for synchronous operation mode on public data networks.

X.25—CCITT standard governing interface between DTE and DCE for terminals operating in the packet mode on public data networks.

X.25 PAD—Device permitting communication between non-X.25 devices and devices in an X.25 network.

X.400—ISO standard for session layer; CCITT standard for messaging and document distribution protocol; *also* used to connect different e-mail systems.

x-axis—Horizontal axis on coordinate plane.

XbarR chart—In SPC, a plot showing the range of sample values along with the arithmetical mean of the average for the sample of data.

XENIX—Microsoft trade name for a 16-bit microcomputer operating system derived from Bell Laboratories' UNIX.

XGA—Extended Graphics Adapter (Array); faster than VGA and causes less eyestrain but works only on Micro Channel 386SX or better PCs; resolution is 1024 x 768 pixels and 256 colors are supported; see *CGA, EGA, PGA, SVGA, VGA, UXGA.*

X-height—In typographical composition of screen displays and printing, the height of lowercase letters, not including ascenders and descenders.

XIP—Execute in place; technique by which software placed on a PCMCIA-compatible ROM card can be executed directly from the card itself instead of first being loaded into RAM.

XMAPI—Extended MAPI; see *messaging application programming interface.*

XML—Extensible Markup Language; computer authoring language for publishing documents through World Wide Web on the Internet, providing significantly greater flexibility and automation potential over HTML.

XNS—Xerox Network System; peer-to-peer protocol developed by Xerox that has been incorporated into several local area networking (LAN) schemes.

X/Open—Formed in 1984 as a consortium to develop a Common Applications Environment (CAE) to test and label for conformance; strong in Europe; now holds the UNIX trade name.

XON/XOFF—Xmitter (transmitter) on/ Xmitter off"; control characters used for data flow control between two digital devices, instructing a terminal to start transmission (XON character, usually a "control-Q") and end transmission (XOFF character, usually a control-S).

XOR—Exclusive *OR*; logic gate.

XPG—X/Open Portability Guide.

X terminal—Dedicated platform (terminal) that is transparent to the user and designed to run X-server software; used with powerful machines that run 680x0 processors such as RISC computers; X is a standard base-level windowing architecture for UNIX machines and their terminals.

X Windows—(trademark of Massachusetts Institute of Technology). Major element of the open systems concept, it is a technique that allows video terminals in one vendor system to present views and operate as if they were video terminals in other vendor systems that reside on same network.

Y

Y—Means "event," "state," or "presence" when used as first alpha character position of ISA instrument function tag, means "y-axis" when used as modifier; means "relay" or "compute" when used in any succeeding alpha character position [see ANSI/ISA S5.1-1984 (R1992)].

y-axis—Vertical axis on coordinate plane.

Y2K—Year 2000; usually used in reference to the clock rollover at midnight of the new millennium, which could cause some older computer programs to "bomb" because of their inability to distinguish between the year 1900 and the year 2000. This is because only the last two digits were used to implement the date code due to memory limits. Likely to be more of a serious problem with information-intensive business applications; much less likely to be problem with navigational-type process control systems.

Y/C Video—Y (luminance) and C (color) Video information on separate signals. Is of higher quality than composite video but not as high as component RGB video. Available on prosumer and some consumer-grade video products; same as S-video; see *composite video* and *component RGB video*.

Yo-yo—Something that is occasionally up, but normally down; see *also Computer*. ☺

Z

Z—Means "position," "dimension" when used in first alpha character position of ISA instrument function tag; means "z-axis" when used as modifier; means "driver," "actuator," or "unclassified final control element" when used in any succeeding position [see ANSI/ISA S5.1-1984 (R1992)]. *Also,* in electrical devices and systems it means electrical impedance.

ZD—Means "gauging deviation" when used in first two alpha character positions of ISA instrument function tag [see ANSI/ISA S5.1-1984 (R1992)].

zeal—Human enthusiasm, which is always at its height at the commencement of an undertaking (from Thucydides, *The Peloponnesian War*, book II, chapter 8). ☺

zero insertion—In SDLC digital transmission, the process of including a binary 0 in a transmitted data stream to avoid confusing data and SYN characters and of removing the inserted 0 at the receiving end.

zero offset—Difference expressed in degrees between true zero and an indication given by the measuring device.

zero power resistance—Resistance of a thermistor or RTD element with no power being dissipated.

zero shift—Error due to changes in ambient conditions in which zero output shifts; thus the entire calibration curve moves in a parallel displacement.

zero suppression—Span of indicator or recorder may be offset from zero (zero suppressed) such that neither limit of the span will be zero; for example, a temperature indicator that displays 100° span from 200° to 300° is said to have 200° zero suppression.

zero voltage switching—The making or breaking of a circuit that is timed so that the transition occurs when voltage waveform crosses zero voltage; typically found only in solid-state switching devices.

ZIF—Zero insertion force socket; standard integrated circuit socket design in which the user moves a lever to add or replace chips, reducing the chance of damage to pins.

Zin—In instrumentation devices, means input impedance, which generally should be very high so as to prevent signal loss across input transducer. Consists of a parallel combination of input resistance and input capacitance, which at frequencies over a few hundred hertz causes capacitance to dominate.

ZOH—Zero order hold; in sampled data systems, a device that maintains memory of control signal values between samples, as in digital-to-analog output to control valve.

zooming—In computer graphics, causing an object on the video screen to appear smaller or larger by moving the window and specifying various window sizes.

Vendor-Specific Acronyms: DCS

Some of the mysterious acronyms used by [their DCSs in brackets]:

ABB	Asea Brown Boveri (Taylor) [MOD III, MOD 30, MOD 300]
Bailey	Bailey Controls (Elsag Bailey) [Network 90, INFI-90]
F & P	Elsag Bailey Fischer & Porter [DCI-4000, DCI-5000, DCI System Six]
H-B	Elsag Bailey Hartmann & Braun [Digimatik Freelance 2000]
Fisher	Fisher Controls [PRoVOX]
Foxboro	Foxboro [Intelligent Automation]
FRSD	Fisher-Rosemount Systems Division (FRSD)
GSE/System	GSE Systems (formerly EMC, then Rexnord, then Texas Instrument) [D/3]
Honeywell	Honeywell [TDC2000, TDC3000]
JYC	Johnson Yokogawa (JYC) [m XL, CENTUM-XL]
L & D	MAX Control Systems, Inc., formerly Leeds & Northrup [MAX 1, MAX 1000]
Moore	Moore Products [MYCRO, MYCRO II, APACS]
Rosemount	Rosemount [System 3, RS-3]
Westinghouse	Westinghouse [WDPF, WDPF-II]

AASP—Advanced Applications Support Package (ABB)

ABU—Analog Backup Unit (F&P)

AC—Application Computer (Fisher)

ACIDP—Advanced Control Interface Data Point (Honeywell)

ACM—Advanced Control Module (Moore)

ACS—Analog Control Station (Bailey); Area CRT Station (Moore)

ADC—Automatic Data Capture (Foxboro)

ADP—Annunciator Display Panel (Bailey)

ADS—Annunciator/Display Select panel (Bailey); Automatic Data capture configuration Software (Foxboro)

AEM—Automation Equipment Manager (Foxboro)

AFEG—Area-Facility-Equipment-Generic name configuration method (L&N)

AI/ES—Artificial Intelligence/Expert Systems (ABB)

AIINT—Analog Input Intrinsically safe Terminal panel (GSE Systems)

AIS—Application Interface Software (Foxboro)

AITP—Analog Input Terminal Panel (GSE Systems)

AIV/F—Analog Input Voltage to Frequency board (GSE Systems)

ALG—ALGorithm card in controller (Honeywell, L&N)

AM—Application Module (Honeywell)

AMC—Advanced Multifunction Controller (Honeywell)

AMM—Analog Master Module (Bailey)

AMPL—ABB MasterPiece Language (ABB)

AM/R—Redundant Application Module card (Honeywell)

AMS—Asset Management Solutions (FRSD)

AMW—Alarm Mode Word (L&N)

ANK—AlphaNumeric Keyboard (ABB)

AOM—Analog Output Module (Bailey)

AP—Applications Processor (L&N, Foxboro)

APACS—Advanced Process Automation and Control System (Moore)

API—Application Programming Interface (ABB)

APM—Advanced Process Module [*also* Manager], Application Process Module [*also* Manager] (Honeywell)

ASDF—Active Station Data File (active memory in Operator Station) (L&N)

ASM—Analog Slave Module (Bailey)

ATB—Analog Terminal Buffer [*also* Board] (L&N)

AUX—AUXiliary CRT Station (Moore)

AWS—Area WorkStation (Moore)

BC—Basic Controller (Honeywell)

BCM—Batch Data Manager (FRSD)

BCS—Basic CRT Station (Moore)

BDM—Batch Data Manager (Fisher)

BIM—Bus Interface Module (Bailey)

BM—Bubble Memory (Rosemount)

BMI—Backup Multiplexer Interface (GSE Systems)

BMM—Backup Memory Module (ABB)

BPOL—Batch Problem—Oriented Language (Westinghouse)

BPU—Batch Processing Unit (Westinghouse)

BSM—Bus Switching Module (ABB)

CAPE—Computer-Aided Plant Engineering (ABB)

CAT—Current Adjusting Type control (L&N); Custom Application Toolkit (Bailey)

CB—Basic Controller (Honeywell)

CBC—Batch Command Module (Bailey)

CBU—Contact Backup Unit (F&P)

CCF—Configurable Control Function (ABB); Continuous Control Function (ABB)

CCL—Configurable Control Language (F&P)

CCM—Critical Control Module (Moore)

CCS—Configurable CRT Station (Moore)

CDM—Critical Discrete Module (Moore)

CEB—Computer Expansion Backplane (Moore)

CEM—Computer Expansion Module (Moore)

CEU—Customer Engineering Unit (F&P)

CF—Control File (Rosemount)

CG—Computer Gateway (Honeywell)

CHIP—Computer/Highway Interface Package (Fisher)

CIA—Communications Interface Assembly (Fisher)

CINP—Configuration INput Pointer (for "softwiring" algorithms) (L&N)

CIS—Controller Interface Slave Module (Bailey)

CIU—Computer Interface Unit (Bailey)

CKU—Checkpoint Unit for back-up units (F&P)

CL/AM—Control Language/Application Module (Honeywell)

CLC—Loop Command Module (Bailey)

CL/MC—Control Language/Multifunction Controller (Honeywell)

CL/PM—Control Language/Process Module (Honeywell)

CLS—Configuration and Loading System (Bailey)

CM—Computing Module (Honeywell); Control Module (ABB)

CMP—CoMmunication Processor Family (Foxboro)

COM—COntroller Module (Bailey)

COP—Central Operator Panel (F&P); COordinator Processor (Rosemount)

CP—Control Processor (Foxboro, Rosemount), Communication Processor (Foxboro), Coordinator Processor card (Rosemount)

CPC—Critical Process Controller (Honeywell)

CRDP—Calculated Result Data Point (Honeywell)

CSC—Sequence Command Module (Bailey)

CTB—Customer Termination Board (F&P)

CTM—Configuration Tuning Module (Bailey)

CTT—Configuration and Tuning Terminal (Bailey)

DAC/POL—Data Acquisition and Control Problem-Oriented Language (Westinghouse)

DAI—Digimatik Analog Input module (H-B)

DAO—Digimatik Analog Output module (H-B)

DAQA—Data AcQuisition Analog controller card (L&N)

DAQD—Data AcQuisition Digital controller card (L&N)

DAS—Data Acquisition Station (Moore)

DAT—Duration Adjusting Type control (L&N)

DAV—Dot Addressable Video card (L&N)

DBU—Digital BackUp controller board (F&P)

DC—Data Computing drop (Westinghouse)

DCD—Discrete Control Device (Fisher)

DCI—Distributed Control Instrumentation (F&P)

DCM—Display Control Module (GSE Systems)

DCM/C—Display Control Module/Configurator (GSE Systems)

DCN—Distributed Communication Network (ABB)

DCO—Digimatik COmmunication module (H-B)

DCS—Digital Control Station (Bailey)

DCT—Display Center Terminal (F&P)

DCU—Distributed Control Unit (F&P)

DDI—Digimatik Digital Input module (H-B)

DDO—Digimatik Digital Output module (H-B)

DDP—Detail Display Parameter (Fisher)

D-E-B—Direct Energy Balance technique of boiler/turbine control (L&N)

DEM—Democratic or Demand Multiplexing (Westinghouse)

DEP—Data Entry Panel (Honeywell)

D-ES—Digimatik Engineering Station (H-B)

D/F—DCN-to-File Bus module (ABB)

DH—Data Historian (FRSD)

DHC—Data Highway Controller (Westinghouse)

DHI—Data Highway Interface (Fisher)

DHP—Data Hiway Port (Honeywell)

DHS—Distributed Historian Station (Moore)

DHW—Data Highway (Honeywell, L&N)

DIAT—Duration Impulse Adjusting Type (L&N)

DILTP—Digital Input Lowlevel Terminal Panel (GSE Systems)

DIOB—Distributed I/O Bus (Westinghouse)

DIS—Digital Indicator Station (Bailey)

DLC—Dual Local operator Console (F&P)

DLS—Digital Logic Station (Bailey)

D/M—DCN-to-Multibus module (ABB)

DMC—Data Management Center (F&P)

DMM—Dynamic Maintenance Management (Foxboro)

DMTP—Digital Module input/output Terminal Panel (GSE Systems)

DOC—Distributed Operator's Console (F&P)

DORTP—Digital Output Relay Terminal Panel (GSE Systems)

D-OS—Digimatik Operator Station (H-B)

DP—Data Points in controller or data processor unit (L&N)

D-PS—Digimatik Process Station (H-B)

DPU—Data Processing Unit equipment (L&N, Westinghouse)

DPW—Digimatik Power supply (H-B)

DSM—Digital Slave Module (Bailey)

DSR—Historical Data Storage and Retrieval drop (Westinghouse)

DTB—Digital Terminal Buffer [*also* Board] (L&N)

DTS—Digital Test Set (Westinghouse)

EAM—Enhanced Analog Module (Moore)

EC—Extended Controller (Honeywell)

EFCD—Field Control unit, Dual processor, Centum-XL (JYC)

EFCS—Field Control unit, Single processor, Centum-XL (JYC)

EDFS—Single electronics packager., remote console, Centum-XL (JYC)

EDFW—Dual electronics packager., remote console, Centum-XL (JYC)

EFGW—Field Gateway, Centum-XL (JYC)

EFMS—Field Monitor System, Centum-XL (JYC)

EFUD—Field control station, Dual processor, Centum-XL (JYC)

EFUS—Field control station, Single processor, Centum-XL (JYC)

EHM—Event History Module (Honeywell); Equipment Health Management (Honeywell)

EIC—External Interface Card (Fisher)

EMCD—Master Control station, Dual, Centum-XL (JYC)

EMCS—Master Control station, Single, Centum-XL (JYC)

EMX—Expanded MultipleXer controller (Fisher)

ENGS—ENgineering Station, Centum-XL (JYC)

EOS——Enhanced Operator Station (Honeywell)

EOPC—Primary Operator Console, Centum-XL (JYC)

EOPS—Operator Console without electronics, Centum-XL (JYC)

EPUS—Engineering Personality Universal Station (Honeywell)

ES—Engineering Station (Westinghouse)

ETCS—Emulation Test Control Station, Centum-XL (JYC)

EWS—Engineering WorkStation (Bailey, L&N, Moore)

EXCEL—EXtended Control Engineering Language (software) (L&N)

FBI—Field Bus Isolator (Foxboro)

FBM—Field Bus Module (Foxboro)

FBT—Field Bus Terminator (Foxboro)

F-Bus—File-Bus (ABB)

FCE—Function Chart Editor (ABB)

FCM—Function Class Modules (ABB)

FDGP—Foreign Device Gateway Processor

FDI—Foreign Device Interface (Moore)

FEM—Front-End Module (Rosemount)

FIC—Field Interface Card (FRSD)

FIM—Field Interface Module (FRSD)

FOE—Fiber-Optic Extension (Moore)

FOL—Fiber Optic Link (Honeywell)

FST—Function Sequence Table (Fisher)

FTA—Field Termination Assembly (Honeywell)

GAK—Group Annunciator Keyboard (F&P)

GCI—Graphical Configuration Interface (FRSD)

GEDIT—Interactive software for building graphic displays (Westinghouse)

GES—Global Expansion Satellite (Moore)

GP—Graphics Processor (L&N); Gateway Processor (Foxboro)

GPCI—General-Purpose Computer Interface (Honeywell)

GPI—General-Purpose Interface (Moore)

GTY, GWY—Gateway (F&P)

GUS—Global User Station (Honeywell)

HART—Highway Addressable Remote Transducer (Rosemount)

HCI—Host Computer Interface equipment (L&N)

HCM—Host Computer Module (GSE Systems)

HDI—Highway Direct Interface circuit card (L&N)

HDL—Highway Data Link (Fisher)

HDP—Historical Data Processor equipment (L&N)

HDP/VT—Historical Data Processor/Virtual Terminal (L&N)

HDR—Historical Data Reporter (Westinghouse)

HF-Bus—Proprietary communication in m XL (JYC)

HFM—HART® Fieldbus Module (Moore)

HG—Hiway Gateway (Honeywell)

HIA—Highway Interface Adapter (Rosemount)

HIM—Hiway Interface Module (Honeywell)

HL—Host Link (L&N)

HLL—High-Level Link (Moore); High-Level Language (Westinghouse)

HLPIU—High-Level Process Interface Unit (Honeywell)

HM—History Module (Honeywell)

HPC—Honeywell Programmable Controller; Horizon Predictive Controller; High-Performance Controller [later called HPM] (Honeywell)

HPM—High-performance Process Manager (Honeywell)

HPPC—High-Performance Programmable Controller (Westinghouse)

HSPCI—High-Speed Pulse Counter Input (GSE Systems)

HSR—Historical Storage and Retrieval unit (Westinghouse)

HST—Hydrostatic Tank gauge (Foxboro)

HTD—Hiway Traffic Director (Honeywell)

I/A—Intelligent Automation (Foxboro)

ICI—Independent Computer Interface (Moore); Intelligent Computer Interface (Bailey)

ICM—Industrial Computer Module (Moore)

ICN—Instrument Communications Network (ABB)

ICS—Industrial CRT Station (Moore)

IDM—Input Discrete Module (Moore)

IFC—Integrated Function Controller (Fisher)

IGAP—Initialize Go-Ahead Pointer (L&N)

IGP—Instrument Gateway Processor (Foxboro)

IIL—INFI-NET to INFI-NET Local interface (Bailey)

IIR—INFI-NET to INFI-NET Remote interface (Bailey)

IIS—Instrument Information System (FRSD)

IMS—Information Management Station (ABB)

INIP—Information Network Interface Processor (Foxboro)

IPL—INFI-NET to Plant Loop local interface (Bailey)

LANI—Local Area Network Interface (Foxboro)

LEPIU—Low-Energy Process Interface Unit (Honeywell)

LES—Local Expansion Satellite (Moore)

LCM—Loop Class Modules (ABB)

LCN—Local Control Network (Honeywell)

LCP—Logical Control Points (Fisher)

LCT—Local Configuration Terminal (Moore)

LCTB—Local Customer Termination Board (F&P)

LEPIU—Low-Energy Process Interface Unit (Honeywell)

LES—Local Expansion Satellite (Moore)

LIL—Local Instrument Link (Moore)

LIM—Loop Interface Module (Bailey); Link Interface Module (Moore)

LIP—LAN Interface Processor (Foxboro)

LLL—Low-Level Link (Moore)

LLPIU—Low-Level Process Interface Unit (Honeywell)

LM—Logic Manager (Honeywell)

LMM—Logic Master Module (Bailey)

LOC—Local Operator's Console (F&P)

LOG—LOGging definition language (Westinghouse)

LOP—Local Operator Panel (F&P)

LOS—Loop Operator's Station (Moore)

LPM—Loop\Power Module (FRSD)

LPU—Local Processing Unit (L&N)

LSC—Logic and Sequence Controller (Moore)

LTD—Local Traffic Director (Fisher)

LU—Logging Unit (Westinghouse)

LWS—Local WorkStation (Moore)

MAIO—Multipoint Analog Input/Output panel (FRSD)

M&M—Multibus and Modems card cage in Operator Station (L&N)

MAOTP—Multiple Analog Output Terminal Panel (GSE Systems)

MBA—Modular Batch Automation (Honeywell)

MBC—Modular Batch Controller (Moore)

MBI—MODULBUS Interface module (Moore)

MBU—Multis interface to DIOB (Westinghouse)

M-BUS—MODULBUS (Moore)

M-bus—Multibus (ABB)

MBX—MODULBUS expander module (Moore)

MC—Multifunction Controller (Honeywell)

MCS—Management Command Station (Bailey)

MCU—MicroComputer Unit (GSE Systems)

MDAS—Modular Data Acquisition Satellite (Moore)

MDIO—Multipoint Digital Input/Output termination panel (FRSD)

MDS—Multipoint Display Station (Moore)

MFC—MultiFunction Controller (Bailey, Fisher)

MFCD—Field Control unit, Dual processor, m XL (JYC)

MFCU—Field Control Unit, single processor, m XL (JYC)

MFMS—Field Monitor unit, m XL (JYC)

MFP—MultiFunction Processor (Bailey)

MHPC—Multivariable Horizon Predictive Controller, (Honeywell)

MIO—Multipoint Input Output panel (FRSD)

MIS—Management Information System in Operator Station (L&N)

MLC—MultiLoop Controller (Moore)

MM—Memory Module (ABB)

MMLC—Modular MultiLoop Controller (Moore)

MMU—Module Mounting Unit (Bailey)

M-NET—MODULNET (Moore)

MNI—MODULNET Interface card (Moore)

MODEL—Management Of Database ELements (GSE Systems)

MOPL—Freestanding Operator station, m XL (JYC)

MOPLS—Tabletop 20 inch Operator station, m XL (JYC)

MOPS—Tabletop 14 inch Operator station, m XL (JYC)

MOS—Modular Operator Station (Moore)

MP—MasterPiece controller series (ABB)

MPC—Programmable Controller (Bailey); MultiPurpose Controller (Rosemount); Model Predictive Controller (FRSD)

MPU—MicroProcessor Unit card (Fisher)

MPUS—Maintenance Personality Universal Station (Honeywell)

MSJP—Manual Station Junction Panel (L&N)

MTA—Marshaled Termination Assembly (Moore)

MTCC—MultiTube Command Console (Rosemount)

MUX—MUltipleXer controller (Fisher)

MV—Master View operator console series (ABB)

MYCAD—MYCRO Configuration And Documentation (Moore)

MYSL—MYCRO Sequence Language (Moore)

M/11—MYCRO/11 computer system (Moore)

NB—NodeBus (Foxboro)

NBE—NodeBus Extender (Foxboro)

ND—Network Device (Fisher)

NIM—Network Interface Module (Honeywell, Moore)

NIP—Nodebus Interface Processor (Foxboro)

NIS—Network Interface Slave (Bailey)

NIU—Network Interface Unit (Bailey, Fisher)

NOS—Network Operations Server (FRSD)

NPM—Network Processing Module (Bailey)

NPU—Network Processing Unit (Bailey)

NTD—Network Traffic Director (Fisher)

NVM—Non-Volatile Memory (Rosemount)

OAP—Open industrial Platform (Foxboro)

OBU—Output Bypass Unit (Rosemount)

OCM—Operator Control Module (GSE Systems); Optical Communication Module (ABB)

OCP—Operator Control Panel (ABB)

ODM—Output Discrete Module (Moore)

ODMS—Open Data Management System (Bailey)

OEI—Optical/Electrical Interface hardware module (L&N)

OIM—Operator Interface Module (Westinghouse)

OIP—Open Industrial Platform (Foxboro)

OIS—Operator Interface Station (Bailey); Open Industrial Server (Foxboro)

OIU—Operator Interface Unit (Bailey)

OM&S—Oil Movements and Storage (Honeywell)

OMC—Open Modular Controller (Foxboro)

OS—Operator Station (L&N)

OSM—Open Systems Manager (Bailey)

OWP—Operator WorkPlace (Fisher)

PAT—Position Adjusting Type control (L&N)

PBS—Parallel Bus Slave module (Bailey)

P-Bus—Parallel Bus (ABB)

PCI—Pulse-Count Input (FRSD)

PCIU—Programmable Controller Interface Unit (Fisher)

PCL—Programmable Control Link (FRSD)

PCM—Programmable Controller Module (Westinghouse); Process Control Module (GSE Systems)

PCN—PeerWay Control Network (Rosemount)

PCS—Programmable Sequence Controller (Moore)

PCSI—Personal Computer Serial Interface (Honeywell)

PCU—Process Control Unit (Bailey, F&P)

PCV—Process Control View (Bailey)

PDA—Power Distribution Assembly (Moore)

PDS—Process Data Server (FRSD)

PF—Programmable Functions (L&N)

PFC—I/O processor board (F&P)

PFI—Programmable Functions Interpreter (L&N)

PG—Processor Gateway (Honeywell)

PIB—Programmable Interface Board (ABB)

PIM—Process Interface Module (GSE Systems)

PIO—Parallel Input/Output (GSE Systems)

PIU—Process Interface Unit (F&P, Honeywell)

PLCG—Programmable Logic Controller Gateway (Honeywell)

PM—Process Manager (Honeywell); Processor Module (ABB); Plant Management area (Fisher)

PMI—Process Management Information system (FRSD)

PMM—Process Manager Module (Honeywell)

POET—Package Of Engineering Tools (GSE Systems)

POL—Problem-Oriented Language (Westinghouse)

POPUS—Process Operator Personality Universal Station (Honeywell)

PPA—Plant Process Area (Fisher)

PR—Power Regulator (Rosemount)

PSAP—Page Selector and Alarm Panel (ABB)

PSM—Power Supply Module (Moore)

PSR—Power Supply Rack (Moore)

PSU—Process Sequencer Unit (Westinghouse)

PTM—Process Termination Module (GSE Systems)

PW—Personal Workstation (Foxboro)

PW-C—Personal Workstation for Configuration (Foxboro)

PW-FB—Personal Workstation for Field Bus interface (Foxboro)

PW-HTG—Personal Workstation for Hydrostatic Tank Gauge (Foxboro)

PW-NB—Personal Workstation for NodeBus control systems (Foxboro)

PW-SSI—Personal Workstation for Single Station Interface (Foxboro)

QAH—High-speed Analog input card (Westinghouse)

QAM—Auto/Man station I/O card (Westinghouse)

QAO—Analog Output card (Westinghouse)

QAV—Low-level Analog input card (Westinghouse)

QAW—High-level Analog input card (Westinghouse)

QBO—Solid-state digital output card (Westinghouse)

QCI—Contact Input card (Westinghouse)

QDI—Digital Input card (Westinghouse)

QLC—Local Communication card (Westinghouse)

QLI—Loop Interface card (Westinghouse)

QRT—RTD analog input card (Westinghouse)

QSE—Sequence-of -Events input card (Westinghouse)

QTO—Sealed contact output card (Westinghouse)

RBL—Rosemount Basic Language (Rosemount)

RDB—Relational DataBase (Bailey)

RDP—Remote Display Protocol (ABB)

RFM—Remote Fieldbus Module (Foxboro)

RIC—Rack-mounted Industrial Computer (Moore)

RL-Bus—Proprietary communication in Centum-XL (JYC)

RMCD—Reserve Multifunction Controller Director (Honeywell)

RMP—Recipe Management Package (Moore)

RMPCT—Robust Multivariable Predict Control Technology (Honeywell)

RMS—Recipe Management Station (Moore)

RMTA—Relay Marshaled Termination Assembly (Moore)

RNI—RS-3 Network Interface (FRSD), Rack-mounted Network Interface (Moore)

ROC—Remote Operation Controller (Fisher)

RPQNA—Rosemount PeerWay Q-bus Network Adapter (FRSD)

RPU—Remote Processing Unit (L&N)

RS-3—Rosemount System Three (FRSD)

RTC—Remote Technical Center (Westinghouse)

RTM—Resistance Temperature Module (Moore)

RTP—Real-Time Processor (L&N)

RTX—Real-Time executive (Foxboro)

SABL—Sequence And Batch Language (GSE Systems)

SAM—Standard Analog Module (Moore)

SCI—Supervisory Computer Interface (Rosemount)

SCM—Satellite Control Module (Moore)

SDI—Satellite Discrete Input (Moore)

SDM—Standard Discrete Module (Moore)

SEBOL—SEquence and Batch-Oriented Language, (JYC)

SIM—Serial Interface Module (Westinghouse); System Integrity Module (ABB)

SIU—Station Interface Unit (Westinghouse); Serial Interface Unit (Fisher)

SLC—Single Loop Controller (Moore)

SLDC—Single Loop Digital Controller (Moore)

SODG—Screen-Oriented Display Generator software (Bailey)

SOPL—Sequence-Oriented Procedural Language (Honeywell)

SPCP—Statistical Process Control Package (Foxboro)

SPE—Structured Project Engineering (FRSD)

SRU—System Resource Unit (Rosemount)

SSI—Single Station microcontroller Interface (Foxboro)

SST—Small System Technology (Westinghouse)

STI—Smart Transmitter Interface (FRSD)

SV-Net—A MAP-based data highway, Centum-XL (JYC)

TCL—Taylor Control Language (ABB)

TCPC—Triple-redundant Critical Process Controller (Honeywell)

TCU—Total Control Unit (Westinghouse)

TDC—Total Distributed Control (Honeywell)

TDM—Time Division Multiplexing (Westinghouse)

TGIF—Trend Group In Force; in Operator Station (L&N)

TIWAY—Texas Instruments data highWAY (TI, used on GSE Systems)

TLDC—Triple Loop Digital Controller (Moore)

TLL—Taylor Ladder Logic (ABB)

TPB—Total Plant Batch (Honeywell)

TPH—Total Plant History (Honeywell)

TPO—Time Proportioning Output (Fisher)

TPS—Total Plant Solution (Honeywell)

TRIO—Taylor Remote Input/Output (ABB)

TU—Termination Unit (Bailey)

UAC—Uninterrupted Automatic Control backup system (Honeywell)

UCAL—User defined CALculations (ABB)

UCN—Universal Control Network (Honeywell)

UIOB—Universal I/O Bus (Westinghouse)

UOC—Unit Operations Controller (Fisher)

UOM—Unit of Measure (L&N)

UPLCI—Universal PLC Interface (Westinghouse)

US—Universal Station (Honeywell)

VAT—Voltage Adjusting Type control (L&N)

VCIA—VME-based Communications Interface Assembly (FRSD)

VERBAL—English text programming language (Westinghouse)

VIM—Voltage Input Module (Moore)

VXI—VAX computer Interface (Westinghouse)

WDPF—Westinghouse Distributed Processing Family (Westinghouse)

WP—Workstation Processor (Foxboro)

WS—WorkStation (L&N)

XDC—X-Windows Display Center (F&P)

XL-Net—Software to operate on multiple platforms, m XL (JYC)

XTC—Transmitter/Controller, Moore "Smart" Transmitter (Moore)

Index